# The
# Freezing Preservation
## of Foods

*Fourth Edition Augmented and Completely Rewritten*

---

### In Four Volumes

### VOLUME FOUR

### Freezing of Precooked
### and Prepared Foods

## other AVI books on food refrigeration and freezing

# The
# Freezing Preservation
## of Foods

---

In Four Volumes

### Volume Four—Freezing of Precooked and Prepared Foods

*Edited by*  DONALD K. TRESSLER, Ph.D.,

*Editor-in-Chief, Avi Publishing Co., Formerly Scientific Director, Quartermaster Food and Container Institute*

WALLACE B. VAN ARSDEL, B.S.,

*Assistant Director Emeritus, Western Regional Research Laboratory, U.S. Department of Agriculture*

*and*  MICHAEL J. COPLEY, Ph.D.,

*Director, Western Regional Research Laboratory, U.S. Department of Agriculture*

Fourth Edition Augmented and
Completely Rewritten

WESTPORT, CONNECTICUT

THE AVI PUBLISHING COMPANY, INC.

1968

# Contributors to Volume Four

W. S. ARBUCKLE, is Professor, Department of Dairy Science, University of Maryland, College Park, Md.

GEORGE G. COOK, is Professor and Chairman, Food Technology Department, State University of New York, Agricultural and Technical College, Farmingdale, N.Y.

MARY J. FANELLI, formerly Research Microbiologist, Campbell Institute for Food Research, Camden, N.J.

MILLARD F. GUNDERSON, (retired), was Director of Microbiological Research, Campbell Institute for Food Research, Camden, N.J.

MARJORIE HEID, is Research Food Technologist, Western Utilization Research and Development Division, Agricultural Research Service, U.S. Dept. Agr., Albany, Calif.

SAMUEL MARTIN, is Vice President, E. W. Williams Publications and Editor, Quick Frozen Foods, New York, N.Y.

HUGH H. MOTTERN, is Research Chemist, Food Products Investigations, Engineering and Development Laboratory, Southern Utilization Research and Development Division, Agricultural Research Service, U.S. Dept. Agr., New Orleans, La.

HELEN HANSON PALMER, is Head, Product Stability Investigations, Poultry Laboratory, Western Utilization Research and Development Division, Agricultural Research Service, U.S. Dept. Agr., Albany, Calif.

JAMES W. PENCE, is Chief, Cereals Laboratory, Western Utilization Research and Development Division, Agricultural Research Service, U.S. Dept. Agr., Albany, Calif.

ARTHUR C. PETERSON, is Division Head, Microbiological Research, Campbell Institute for Food Research, Camden, N.J.

THOMAS J. SCHOCH, is Professor of Food and Nutrition, New York State College of Home Economics, Cornell University, Ithaca, N.Y.

DONALD K. TRESSLER, is a consultant and President, Avi Publishing Co., Westport, Conn.

JASPER GUY WOODROOF, is Distinguished Alumni Professor of Food Science, University of Georgia, Experiment, Ga.

# Preface

This is the fourth and final volume of *The Freezing Preservation of Foods*. It is concerned with the freezing of precooked and prepared foods. The number of these foods now frozen commercially is very large, exceeding 300, and if the modifications such as different flavors are counted the number may be multiplied by ten.

The quantity of many of the items frozen is great. For example, French-fried potatoes have recently taken the lead in quantity frozen and not only is the no. 1 frozen vegetable, but the leader of all foods frozen (with the exception of ice cream which is not commonly listed with other frozen foods).

Not only is the quantity of precooked foods frozen increasing year after year but the variety frozen increases steadily. There was once a time when no one thought of freezing puff pastry, pizza pies, and hors d'oeuvres, yet today they are very popular. The freezing of King crab was of minor importance a decade ago; today it is one of the important Alaskan industries.

The first chapter of this volume opens with a review of the development of the industry starting with the development of frozen cooked lobster meat, crab, and winter squash. The rise of the industry is traced product by product; then the latest available statistics are presented. The second chapter is concerned with the chemical, enzymatic, and microbiological problems of preparation for freezing, freezing, storage, and reheating precooked foods. This is followed by a report on surveys made to determine what precooked foods are wanted by homemakers. The fourth chapter is concerned with the suitability of available packaging materials and packages as containers for frozen precooked foods.

In each of the next 18 chapters, formulas found best for freezing of a given class of food products are presented. The procedures used in making the products are outlined and the methods of freezing commonly employed are indicated.

These chapters are followed by a presentation of the problems of selecting foods for inclusion in meals on a tray such as those served by the airlines. Reheating and serving meals on a tray are also discussed. Then, there is a chapter on the storage of frozen precooked foods and means of increasing storage life. This is followed by a chapter on the handling and use of precooked frozen foods. Finally, the use of all kinds of precooked frozen foods in restaurants, hotels, institutions, diners, and other public eating places is considered, and suggestions for improving service offered.

Special thanks are due to Quick Frozen Foods, Food Engineering, Food Technology, and the National Association of Frozen Food Packers for the permission to reproduce production statistics and other data.


The authors are also indebted to the following for illustrative material.

Air Products and Chemicals, Inc., New York, N.Y.
American Institute of Baking, Chicago, Ill.
Andes Candies, Chicago, Ill.
Armour and Co., Chicago, Ill.
Bumble Bee Seafoods, Inc., Astoria, Ore.
Bureau of Commercial Fisheries, Fish and Wildlife Service, U.S. Dept. Interior, Washington, D.C.
Chemetron Corp., New York, N.Y.
Colborne Manufacturing Co., Chicago, Ill.
Cornell School of Hotel Administration, Ithaca, N.Y.
John H. Dulany and Son, Inc., Fruitland, Md.
Ekco Containers, Inc., Wheeling, Ill.
Excelsior Industrial Corp., Fairview, N.J.
Food Machinery and Chemical Corp., San Jose, Calif.
Frick Company, Waynesboro, Pa.
General Electric Co., Louisville, Ky.
J. W. Greer Div., Joy Manufacturing Co., Wilmington, Mass.
Green Giant Co., Le Sueur, Minn.
F. H. Langsenkamp Co., Indianapolis, Ind.
Liquid Carbonic Div., General Dynamics Corp., Chicago, Ill.
Magnuson Engineers, Inc., San Jose, Calif.
Manton-Gaulin Manufacturing Co., Everett, Mass.
National Dairy Council, Chicago, Ill.
National Fisherman, Seattle, Wash.
New York State College of Agriculture, Cornell University, Ithaca, N.Y.
Quick Frozen Foods, New York, N.Y.
Raytheon Co., Lexington, Mass.
REF Dynamics Corp., Mineola, N.Y.
Sam Stein Associates, Inc., Sandusky, Ohio
San Joaquin Valley Turkey Growers Assoc., Modesto, Calif.
J. R. Simplot Co., Caldwell, Idaho
John E. Smith's Sons Co., Buffalo, N.Y.
U.S. Testing Co., Hoboken, N.J.
Urschel Laboratories, Inc., Valparaiso, Ind.
Vahlsing, Inc., Robbinsville, N.J.

Wakefield Seafoods, Inc., Wakefield, Alaska
Western Utilization Research and Development Div., U.S. Dept. Agriculture, Albany, Calif.
York Corp., York, Pa.

DONALD K. TRESSLER
WALLACE B. VAN ARSDEL
MICHAEL J. COPLEY
*January 1968*

# Contents

## CHAPTER 1

# The Rise of Prepared and Precooked Frozen Foods

Sam Martin

## INTRODUCTION

Prepared frozen foods—those products which have been either cooked or converted into a processed or convenience item—are the giant product categories of the industry. So vast has this frozen food segment become, that for purposes of statistical grouping, French-fried potatoes and the family of kindred products, potato puffs, rissole potatoes, hash browns, and other variants which quite obviously are prepared and precooked foods are usually included with regular vegetables. Products such as breaded shrimp, fish sticks and fish portions have been classed as seafoods.

This placement may be necessary statistically, but by definition they must properly be regarded as prepared and precooked frozen foods. In this context they represent the largest single grouping of the frozen food industry both in poundage and in dollar value. The product categories broadly included in the reckoning of frozen prepared foods (see Tables 1 and 2) include, in addition to processed frozen potatoes, breaded shrimp, fish sticks, and fish portions, other products such as dinners, bakery foods, nationality foods, prepared vegetables, entrées, meat pies, fruit pies, cream pies, seafood specialties, soups, breaded and precooked poultry, as well as a broad miscellaneous category involving hors d'oeuvres, snacks, candy, hush puppies, frozen raw fruit preserves, sauces, crepes suzette, vegetable creams, synthetic meats, and a considerable variety of other items.

The total production and imports of all frozen products in the United States in 1966 was 12,568 million pounds. About 18.7% of that total, or 2,354 million pounds, was prepared foods. Sales value of these products was $6,245 million, of which $1,502 million (Table 3) was prepared foods (24.5%). By contrast, in 1950, total prepared foods production, including potatoes, was not over 70 million pounds out of a total of 1,949 million pounds of all frozen foods, and had a sales value of probably not over $30 million out of a total industry sales of $500 million or six per cent of the gross volume.

The feasibility of frozen prepared foods was evaluated seriously right from the beginning. The "father of frozen foods," Clarence Birdseye, in his Gloucester, Mass., laboratories experimented on a wide range of prepared products including bread, rolls, cakes, pies, and other bakery foods; fried

Sam Martin is Vice President, E. W. Williams Publications and Editor, *Quick Frozen Foods*, New York, New York.

Table 1

Production Of Major Precooked and Prepared Frozen Foods
in Poundage 1953–1965

(All Figures in Millions)

| Product | 1953 | 1954 | 1955 | 1956 | 1957 | 1958 | 1959 | 1960 | 1961 | 1962 | 1963 | 1964 | 1965 |
|---|---|---|---|---|---|---|---|---|---|---|---|---|---|
| Meat Pies | — | — | 150 | 188 | 175 | 150 | 158 | 160 | 158 | 161 | 167 | 195 | 199 |
| Breaded shrimp | — | — | 25 | 36 | 43 | 38 | 44 | 39 | 46 | 45 | 75 | 91 | 97 |
| Fish sticks | 7.5 | 50 | 66 | 53 | 52 | 60 | 60 | 62 | 70 | 72 | 79 | 74 | 82 |
| Dinners | — | — | 24 | 38 | 54 | 78 | 112 | 137 | 165 | 185 | 250 | 330 | 396 |
| Fruit pies | — | — | 44 | 62 | 102 | 125 | 162 | 214 | 246 | 271 | 312 | 320 | 313 |
| Nationality | — | 17 | 28 | 39 | 52 | 65 | 88 | 89 | 100 | 116 | 128 | 147 | 169 |
| Entrées | — | — | — | 12 | 48 | 62 | 78 | 86 | 95 | 117 | 152 | 213 | 239 |
| Baked goods | — | — | — | 25 | 28 | 31 | 39 | 59 | 77 | 108 | 146 | 229 | 286 |
| Soups | — | — | 23 | 30 | 35 | 34 | 28 | 30 | 32 | 34 | 35 | 34.5 | 32 |
| Prepared vegetables | — | — | — | — | — | — | — | 5 | 15 | 54 | 76 | 150 | 187 |
| Cream pies | — | — | — | — | — | — | — | — | — | — | — | 64 | 85 |
| Potato products | 71 | 85 | 129 | 190 | 247 | 262 | 371 | 555 | 579 | 761 | 862 | 1,118 | 1,219 |
| Fish portions | — | — | — | — | — | 48 | 37 | 48 | 60 | 79 | 95 | 106 | 138 |

Sources: U.S. Dept. of Agr., Fish and Wildlife Service and *Quick Frozen Foods*.

Table 2

Value of Major Frozen Prepared Foods at Retail (1951–1965 Inclusive)

(All Figures in Millions)

| Products | 1951 | 1952 | 1953 | 1954 | 1955 | 1956 | 1957 | 1958 | 1959 | 1960 | 1961 | 1962 | 1963 | 1964 | 1965 | 1966 |
|---|---|---|---|---|---|---|---|---|---|---|---|---|---|---|---|---|
| Meat pies | 7.5 | 30 | 45 | 60 | 75 | 95 | 92 | 78 | 81 | 82 | 80 | 83 | 86 | 99 | 104 | 113 |
| Breaded shrimp | — | 15 | 15.5 | 15.5 | 30 | 39 | 47 | 47 | 48 | 36 | 37 | 42 | 65 | 91 | 110 | 135 |
| Fish sticks | — | — | 5.5 | 38 | 46 | 37 | 37 | 42 | 42 | 44 | 47 | 43 | 51 | 51 | 66 | 58 |
| Dinners | — | — | 7 | 15 | 24 | 37 | 55 | 88 | 100 | 128 | 151 | 173 | 215 | 280 | 336 | 376 |
| Fruit pies | — | — | — | 10 | 18 | 25 | 41 | 48 | 60 | 79 | 90 | 100 | 114 | 115 | 112 | 115 |
| Nationality | — | — | — | 16.4 | 26 | 36 | 48 | 60 | 72 | 80 | 89 | 100 | 110 | 117 | 146 | 175 |
| Entrées | — | — | — | — | — | 5 | 20 | 26 | 33 | 42 | 46 | 61 | 92 | 129 | 145 | 167 |
| Baked goods | — | — | — | 10 | 11 | 17 | 20 | 22 | 27 | 44 | 57 | 80 | 113 | 170 | 213 | 226 |
| Soups | — | — | — | — | — | 12 | 14 | 14 | 12.5 | 14 | 14.7 | 16 | 16.4 | 18 | 15 | 14 |
| Prepared vegetables | — | — | — | — | — | — | — | — | — | 4 | 59 | 35 | 50 | 98 | 116 | 127 |
| Cream pies | — | — | — | — | — | — | — | — | — | — | — | 14 | 26 | 39 | 45 | 48 |
| Potato products | — | — | — | — | 42 | 61 | 72 | 77 | 105 | 150 | 155 | 167 | 178.5 | 282 | 283 | — |
| Fish portions | — | — | — | — | — | — | — | — | — | 235 | 27 | 35 | 46 | 60 | 84.4 | — |

Source: *Quick Frozen Foods.*

Table 3

1965 Estimated Retail Value and Poundage of Specialty (Prepared) Frozen Foods

(All figures in Millions)

| Category | Lb. | Dollars |
|---|---|---|
| Platters[1] | 396 | 336 |
| Bakery | 268 | 202 |
| Nationality foods | 147 | 131 |
| Prepared vegetables[1] | 187 | 116 |
| Entrées (including pouches) | 219 | 115 |
| Meat pies[1] | 199 | 104 |
| Fruit pies | 240 | 93 |
| Seafood specialties | 52 | 39 |
| Cream pies | 63 | 34 |
| Soups[1] | 32 | 15 |
| Breaded and precooked poultry | 23 | 11 |
| Miscellaneous | 84 | 39 |
| Totals | 1,910 | 1,235 |

Source: *Quick Frozen Foods*, Dec. 1966.
[1] Institutional value included.

and broiled poultry as well as more exotic poultry dishes; various pre-cooked meats and meat dishes; precooked fish, shellfish as well as many fish and shellfish soups, chowders, stews; many precooked vegetables and fruits; in fact, the entire gamut and range of prepared foods. In this research he was assisted by Donald K. Tressler, Clifford F. Evers, Bertha E. Nettleton, Lucy Kimball, James Powers, Stuart MacDonald, Karl B. Norton, and Gerald A. Fitzgerald.

Because of the early state of development of the freezing industry, the primitive state of distribution, the scarcity of suitable holding facilities at that time, and the economic severity of the depression, all this basic work resulted in nothing more than several patents, some technical papers, and stacks of laboratory notes.

As time went by, the Western Utilization Research and Development Division of the U.S. Dept. of Agr., at Albany, Calif., did experimental freezing of chicken à la king, cream sauce, cheese fondue, cream of celery soup, Cape Cod clam chowder, and lamb stew (with and without vegetables). Various universities independently conducted research projects on the formulation and freezing of a variety of prepared items, including many unusual items.

One of the first prepared products of any consequence was chicken à la king, marketed by Birdseye Frosted Foods and later emulated by several other firms. Why only this product should have found favor is difficult to say. Among factors in its favor was that it retained its character extremely well under freezing, had a long storage life, could be produced to sell at a reasonable price, could be packaged compactly, and would have been difficult for the consumer to prepare without special effort at home.

Most early prepared foods packers were restaurants freezing some specialty of the house for the take-out trade. The Villa Moderne, a Chicago restaurant, froze corn beef hash, brown beef stew, chicken à la king, chop suey, chili con carne, Welsh rarebit, spaghetti with meat balls, spaghetti with barbecue sauce; a pineapple-cream cheese, and watercress salad; shrimp gumbo, cream of tomato soup, onion soup, and baked Alaska. The Louisiane, a New Orleans restaurant, under the brand name of New Orleans Foods, shipped gourmet frozen foods packed in dry ice by air to various customers including such products as shrimp remoulade, gumbo a la Louisiane, redfish, court bouillon, cheese salad, and crepes suzette.

The farfetched selling methods of The Louisiane indicated the primitive and unrealistic state of frozen foods sales and distribution. No small company could hope to do much, except locally. It was estimated that in 1942 a total of 500,000 lb. of prepared foods of all types was produced. This sharply climbed to an estimated 4 million pounds in 1943, as the effect of the wartime point system for food and the shortage of canned goods acted to encourage people to experiment with whatever prepared dishes were available.

This figure was almost cut in half in 1944, when the ignorance of proper freezing methods, poor holding facilities, and general consumer ignorance quickly soured the more audacious consumers on prepared foods.

Nevertheless packers persisted and by the end of 1945 there were 45 processors of prepared foods whose product lines included fruit pies, chili, hors d'oeuvres, barbecued beef, barbecued chicken, beef stew, and dinners and such major brand names as Birdseye and Swanson seriously entered the field.

Historically important was National Dairy Products which through its Breyers Ice Cream Division in Long Island City, N.Y., introduced a line of frozen Chinese foods for both the retail and institutional trade. This was the era when ice cream companies, because they had freezing, storage, and delivery equipment, thought they could easily enter the frozen food business. It proved to be a delusion. The fields were completely different, requiring different temperatures and radically opposed methods of marketing and distribution. Ice cream must be stored, delivered and sold at a temperature *below* 0°F. ($-18$°C.). It has *no* tolerance to temperature abuse. Once the product has begun to deteriorate, the changed character is instantly recognizable and irreversible. Ice cream does not have national distribution. It is produced and delivered locally, with the processor maintaining complete control of every phase of the operation. Supplying a holding freezer to retailers who handle their brands exclusively is still a common practice in ice cream.

National Dairies divested itself of frozen foods, selling it to the sales manager of the division, James Thomas, who for many years ran it as Golden Palace. He did much to create the nationality foods end of the prepared frozen foods industry.

The pioneering work of The Cease Commissary Service, Dunkirk, N.Y., in the frozen fruit pie, meat pot pie, and entrée field prior to 1945 has been almost forgotten. Cease Commissary, a food preparation center serving 22 feeding installations, found that freezing improved pie crusts. The Cease Commissary produced with great success frozen fruit pies and frozen meat pies for the industrial cafeterias, restaurants, clubs, and hospitals it served. It also produced frozen platters with beef stew, roasts, and chops along with vegetables.

Late in 1945, some of the large department stores in New York began to carry in their food departments Maxon's French-fried potatoes, marketed by Maxon Food Systems, New York, a large caterer. These are believed to be the very first frozen potato products ever sold in the United States and were then regarded as an utter novelty with no sales staying power.

Tremendous impetus was given frozen food specialties when the Office of Price Administration gradually removed price controls from most such products, beginning May 15, 1946. The reason given was that "these foods are not significant in the cost of living." Before the year had ended, the number of packers of cooked and prepared frozen foods had jumped from 45 to 96 and the flood was on.

The range of products was extraordinary, including such diverse items as frankfurters and sauerkraut, chicken and vegetable dinner, lobster Newburg, salmon creole dinner, meat balls with sauce, filet mignon in mushroom sauce, chicken patties, chopped liver, corn beef hash, canapés, oyster stew, clam chowder, chicken gumbo soup, fish fillets in exotic wine sauces, baked goods of every type, ravioli, kosher entrées for two, chicken enchiladas, borscht, pigs knuckles, and spaghetti.

The initial reception was gratifying but then came the moment of truth. Dozens of new packers had frozen anything that would freeze without any scientific experimentation to ascertain proper methods for freezing, without any regard for quality, without any notion of proper packaging, pricing, product size, or marketing.

The result was a near disaster. As gradually fresh and canned foods were removed from OPA jurisdiction, the consumers stayed away from frozen prepared foods in droves. What was worse, they conferred the sins of the children upon the heads of the fathers, and many of the frozen fish and vegetable companies which had been maintaining good quality standards found themselves seriously hurt.

Frozen prepared food production, which had climbed from an estimated 40 million pounds in 1946, tobogganed to *five* million pounds by the end of 1947, a fantastic loss of 87½% in a single year!

Retailers eliminated prepared foods from their cabinets. Some retailers disposed of their cabinets and stopped handling frozen foods. Distributors imposed a ban upon specialty items. The entire industry found itself set back three years almost overnight.

Certainly not all of this can be blamed upon the prepared foods packers. The meteoric rise of frozen sales during the war, largely due to the shortage of many canned and fresh products, had been for the large part an artificial boom. The industry had done little to hold the good will of the public during this period of great expansion. Nevertheless, the prepared foods packers provided the straw that broke the camel's back.

Not everything was completely negative. While prepared foods products had boomed briefly, there had been no single product or group of products which had emerged as a volume seller. History would record, however, that during this brief period many of the best sellers of the future were born.

There had been only one packer of French-fried potatoes during 1945. By the middle of 1946 there were nine and their number continued to increase. French fries were destined to become the first big specialty number in the frozen foods industry.

The groundwork on meat pies and fruit pies was laid during this period. Time was to pass before either grew to anything like the present proportions, but it was a beginning.

Frozen entrées or main courses had been the most numerous of the new products marketed. They had suffered the worst fall and took the longest to revive. But today, entrées have become one of the best selling categories of frozen foods.

Certain nationality foods—Chinese, Italian, Mexican, and Jewish—were also introduced during this stage of frozen food development. They are today one of the most promising fields; Hawaiian and German dishes also show excellent promise.

The prepared frozen foods industry is really not one industry at all—it is a score of industries and therefore it requires a score of histories. The major facets must be dealt with on an individual basis as follows:

## POTATOES

French-fried potatoes spearheaded the renewal of prepared frozen foods popularity after the debacle of 1946. Early sales were primarily retail and every year found more and more packers processing the item until by the end of 1951 there were 28, including the finest names in the frozen food and potato business. The product's early gradual rate of growth may be attributed entirely to lack of any type of advertising and promotion. Viewed objectively, the product was a "natural."

French fries were popular in restaurants everywhere; they were so much trouble to prepare that they were not commonly served in the home. The potato, as a vegetable, had long been a basic part of the American diet. Almost all potatoes used were purchased fresh by the pound, and had to be washed, peeled, cut, and cooked, and then mashed. They were a lot of trouble.

Most other types of vegetables had done well in frozen form, but the idea of cut white potatoes in frozen food packages just didn't seem to make sense. In addition, there are special problems encountered in freezing potato slices as many processors found out to their sorrow.

French fries are potatoes in their most popular form and with all work done except the final browning, which, with the frozen product, was usually accomplished by heating in the oven, rather than deep-fat frying. They have no competition in either the fresh or canned form. They are in every sense a true convenience product.

The success of French fries bred many other potato specialties, including pancakes, mashed, hashed brown, whipped, patties, puffs, cottage fries, au gratin, preformed "baked" potatoes, and many others.

At first the primary sale of French-fried potatoes was at retail, but as labor costs continued to rise, mass feeders realized it was no longer practical to buy fresh potatoes and spend hours peeling, forming, and then deep-fat frying them. They had no control over quality of fresh potatoes or any way to predict the amount of waste in cutting. Prices could vary as much as 200% over the period of a year. There was no method of reliably estimating needs.

In the restaurant as well as in the home, mashed potatoes were the most common type served, not because it was preferred, but because it was the easiest and cheapest way to prepare and serve that vegetable. Restaurants that always had French fries on the menu found that they enjoyed a commercial advantage over their competitors. Potatoes frozen for the institutional trade were usually oil-blanched with the idea that, unlike the home, they would be finished in deep fat. This lowered production costs and made for a better reconstituted product. The oil blanching reduced the amount of oil absorbed during the final fry-off.

To cater to regional preferences and to lend more variety to French-fried potatoes, Coney Island style or crinkle-cut French fries were introduced, as were shoestring potatoes (long, thin French fries). Whereas the feeding establishment usually had to discard the wasted part of the potato in making

French fries (as much as 40%), the processor could use it for puffs, patties, hash browns, or any number of other products and actually make almost as efficient use of the potato as though it were being used for mashed. This held down costs.

Along about 1962, it was reported that the per capita consumption of potatoes that had been declining steadily for 50 years had reversed itself due to the widespread use of frozen potatoes. During 1966, the pack of frozen potatoes reached nearly 1½ billion pounds of edible weight and the end of the rapid advance seemed nowhere in sight (Tables 26 and 27).

## DINNERS

There is a great deal of confusion about what is meant by "dinners," so a definition is in order. A dinner is a frozen main course with two or more side dishes, packed on an aluminum tray with three or more compartments. If it has no side dish or only one side dish, it is a "main course" or an "entrée." There is one company that puts out a very successful meat loaf with mashed potatoes on an aluminum tray. This product is considered an *entrée* because it does not have *two* side dishes and because the tray has only one compartment. The company itself agrees with this definition.

The most commonly seen type of dinner is packed on an aluminum tray with three compartments, usually with an entrée and two vegetables. Dinners with a fourth compartment (which may contain a third vegetable, a sauce, or a dessert) have made great inroads. Similar dinners with five compartments which have a soup and a dessert in addition to the main course and two vegetables are enjoying favor.

In late 1945 and in 1946, the Maxon line of frozen dinners achieved a brief but great popularity. So many varieties were frozen that retail stores carried a menu which was changed every few weeks. There was a different price for every dinner and prices ranged up to several dollars apiece. The dinners were of very good quality and initially sold briskly because they required fewer ration points than nonfrozen products and because frozen foods were taken off rationing before fresh and canned foods. Imitators entered the field almost immediately, and unfortunately did not always offer good quality.

When rationing was lifted, the high-priced Maxon dinners were doomed. Nevertheless, a few regional packers turned out random frozen dinners, so the product category never completely disappeared.

C. A. Swanson and Sons, Omaha, the nation's largest freezer of poultry, which additionally had access to major beef supplies, decided to see what could be done to revive the frozen food dinner in the tray, utilizing their advantageous situation.

Since many persons were eating their meals in front of television sets, Swanson called its meals "TV" dinners, and are the only company that may legally do so. Their dinners were launched with much publicity and promotion, including the offer of a silver dollar to all who returned the label (one dollar was the average retail price). After a few false starts and some price readjustments, the product caught on. Retailers found that the turnover justified the space platters occupied in the cabinets.

What transpired was a chain reaction. In 1945, there were three packers of frozen platters. In 1952, the year before Swanson entered the field, there were nine. Before 1953 ended, the number had grown to 19, and climbed to 29 in 1954.

Today, while there was probably more than 50 firms packing dinners, three major companies (the Campbell Soup Co., Morton Frozen Foods and Banquet Canning Co.) do most of the business.

At no time since 1953 have frozen dinners failed to gain annually in sales. During 1966 it was estimated that the consumer paid $376 million for frozen dinners, by far the largest expenditure for any prepared frozen foods category, greater than that for *all* frozen potato products.

The frozen dinner field, despite the number of entrants, is primarily a business for giants. It is extremely difficult to mechanize frozen dinner production, with the result that no lines are fully automated. A high degree of technology is required just to make certain that all components heat at the same time. While this offered problems enough when there were only three components, now that there are sometimes four or five, the difficulty of having a main course, two vegetables, soup, and dessert to heat all at the same time, has defied all but a few companies.

<h3 style="text-align:center">MEAT PIES</h3>

Frozen meat pies had been made in the United States as early as 1945 by Cease Commissary Service, but did not become popular. Meat pies were not well known in the United States at that time. They had been a staple part of the diet in England, but not in America. A few restaurants, like Horn and Hardart, featured such products on their menu, but elsewhere meat pies were not common.

It is important to define the difference between a meat pie and a pot pie. A *meat pie* has a complete crust on all sides like a fruit pie. A pot pie has a *top* crust only. Though both names are used interchangeably, only one major company and a few minor ones actually market a pot pie; most of those sold are meat pies.

The Swanson Co., Omaha, was responsible for the popularization of the meat pie. They saw the product as an excellent way to utilize poultry, which they raised and processed in quantity. They employed the promotional device of returning half dollars for the initial purchase to the house-wife in a 1950 drive and immediately secured volume. Two years later, that volume had mounted to $30 million divided among numerous processors and eventually would go to $113 million in 1966.

The average meat pie was eight ounces in weight and sold for prices ranging from 19 to 39¢. The pie was suitable for a main course and with a salad could make a meal. It was particularly handy for a child's lunch. While the ingredients of the pie were precooked, the crust was raw and was baked by the user. Like the fruit pie, this resulted in a freshly-baked flavor and the freezing enhanced the flakiness of the crust of the meat pie as surely as it did that of the fruit pie.

The best-selling meat pies have been chicken, beef, and turkey in that order. Tuna pies have enjoyed a fair sale, but most other varieties, such as vegetable, lamb, chili, pork, and lobster have never succeeded in attaining wide popularity.

The gravy formulation in these products has always been excellent, so the consumer receives a very tasty main course for a cost that scarcely warranted home preparation. The very low price level soon resulted in cuts in the quantity of meat. From a high point of $95 million in sales in 1956, a decline set in for meat pies, which did not achieve that figure again until 1964 when sales climbed to $99 million.

The recent comeback may be attributed to the introduction of larger meat pies, weighing from 10 to 16 oz., and selling for prices ranging from 59 to 79¢. These contain a reasonable quantity of meat and are an adequate main course for an adult. As more of the major companies swung to the larger, higher-priced size, sales definitely began climbing once again and the market became segmented into the standard 8-oz. pies and the larger ones.

### FRUIT PIES

During the first few years after 1945 that frozen fruit pies were marketed, consumers were skeptical of the product. They thought of freezing merely as a preservation method, but did not understand the inherent advantages that went along with it.

The average commercial fresh pie in the retail store could hold up for as long as a week before it became inedible. This seemed perfectly satisfactory. Why take a frozen pie which when frozen *prebaked* proved soggy and inferior to fresh? A raw frozen pie had the inconvenient aspect of requiring 45 min. for baking time and 30 to 45 min. until it was cool enough to eat. A fresh pie, bought in a store, could be cut and served instantly. With frozen fruit pie the deciding factor proved to be quality, not convenience, because of the following:

(1) every frozen pie was a fresh-baked pie and a fresh-baked pie always has a flavor edge over a commercial baker's pie; (2) the crust was flaky and tasty; (3) there is no preservative in a frozen pie because freezing is a method of preservation; (4) there is no excessive pectin or gelatin in a frozen pie to keep it rigid in transport; none is needed; (5) a frozen pie could be stored for future use for long periods with virtually no deterioration. This is not possible with a fresh pie which has to be eaten as soon as possible and deteriorates every hour it is kept.

Commercially frozen pies were far superior to fresh from the processing standpoint. Production could be kept flowing at an even pace with the packer selling out of his warehouse and no longer required to guess at probable sales, which was necessary in the case of fresh pies.

National distribution, impossible with fresh pies which must be locally delivered, sometimes on a daily basis, is quite practical with frozen pies. A processor no longer needs his own delivery facilities. He can sell frozen pies to those who have distribution organization and save that cost.

Stale pies, which ran anywhere from 5 to 25% of the total production in fresh pie bakeries, were actually eliminated by a swing to freezing.

Pies could be frozen at the season when certain fruits were plentiful in quantities adequate to take care of the trade until the next season. Seasonal favorites became a thing of the past.

Similarly, certain varieties like coconut custard and lemon meringue, which could not be made in the summer because they spoiled too fast (ironically the very season of the year when the consumer preferred that type of pie), now could be marketed throughout the year.

Despite these advantages, frozen fruit pies were slow in taking hold because the distributors and the retailers insisted that only small 5- and 11-oz. pies were acceptable because of cabinet limitations. A survey published in *Quick Frozen Foods* for October 1956, changed the thinking of the industry. It showed that those companies who also marketed a larger 8-in., 24-oz. pie outsold those who made only the small pies at a ratio of five to one. As a result, the emphasis shifted to the larger pie. Sales which had gradually climbed to $25 million in 1956 shot to $41 million in 1957, and eventually reached $115 million in 1964.

Many years of intense competition saw the weight of the 8-in. fruit pie reduced to 20-oz. from 24-oz. with a noticeable drop in quality. Sales began to level off in 1964 and actually dropped in 1965. However, the development of a new institutional-size pie, 10-in. in diameter, weighing up to 48 oz., began to attract public fancy. Aware of this, most packers began to put out all pies in heavier weights, selling them for commensurately more money and thereby began to regain lost ground. Today, the production and scale of frozen fruit pies is again increasing.

## CREAM PIES

The true cream pie, usually made with whipped cream and a sweet base, such as peach, strawberry, blueberry, raspberry, lemon, pineapple, butterscotch, or nesselrode, was a rarity sold by bakeries with refrigerated display cases and generally bought as a special treat. People would have enjoyed eating them in the summertime, but few were made then, because of perishability. They kept better in the colder months, but were not as popular because they had to be eaten cold.

Early attempts to freeze cream pies ran into technical and legal problems. True cream pies had a tendency to weep and separate upon thawing. Since the pies were thawed and eaten without baking, they were prone to high bacterial counts possessing as they did a milk base which is a particularly good bacterial culture medium. States began to pass legislation against the importation of true frozen cream pies.

For a while it appeared that the entire concept of frozen cream pies would have to be abandoned. Then it was decided to attempt to market a frozen pie made with a synthetic cream from a vegetable base. Synthetic creams had proved the foundation of the frozen whip topping business and the rate of bacterial growth in that medium was relatively low.

Experimental work resulted in very acceptable frozen "cream" pies made from a synthetic product and the public began to show interest. True volume developed in 1962 when automated operations enabled cream pies of 8-in. size and 14-oz. in weight to be produced with such efficiency that prices of three-for-one dollar became common.

Able to purchase an entire cream pie for less than the cost of a single slice in a restaurant, the consumer response was dramatic, and by 1966 frozen cream pie volume had risen to $48 million. Nevertheless, the industry position is insecure because it has established itself entirely on a price basis, and is finding it difficult to shift to a higher-quality, higher-priced pie without endangering the sales momentum already attained.

## BREADED SHRIMP

Frozen shrimp in the shell and fantail shrimp have been important frozen food products since the earliest days. Processors of frozen shrimp were numerous in the forties, but breaded shrimp was a relatively late arrival. In 1949, only a single packer claimed to be freezing breaded shrimp, but in 1950 there were 20 companies freezing this product.

The one man freezing breaded shrimp in the United States in 1949 and probably the first to do so was William Mullis of Thunderbolt, Ga., who felt that shrimp would become a widespread favorite as a main course item if it were easy to prepare. Under the brand name of Trade Winds he began marketing his product in 1949 with a capital investment of only $5,000.

Within a year he had 250 people working for him and distribution in 32 states. The item started in gourmet shops and quickly spread from there. Mullis also advised frying the shrimp while still in frozen state, and this was largely instrumental in its quick acceptance.

Breaded fantail shrimp (the outer shell peeled off, but the tail left intact) was an early favorite. Regions outside the coasts had never eaten very much shrimp, but the same people who would not buy regular shrimp seemed to be willing to try breaded shrimp.

The earliest year production figures are available for breaded shrimp is 1952, and that year about 17 million pounds were packed. Four years later, in 1956, the pack had doubled to 36 million pounds. The pack reached 105 million pounds in 1966 and was still climbing.

Since the breading averaged about 50% of the weight of the product, it tended to lower the price which encouraged more people to try it. Esthetically, many appeared to enjoy shrimp better if they could not see its normal pink and white color.

Breading also made for abuses. Frequently it hid low-grade or unattractive shrimp. Sometimes the breading ratio rose as high as 70%. In an attempt to remedy this, voluntary standards for shrimp inspection were established in September 1960. These standards set the maximum quantity of breading permissible at 50%, but established no differences in grading for shrimp with lesser breading. Therefore, while it eliminated the worst abuses, it still set a ceiling on quality (which is an unfortunate side effect of many government standards). At present, new standards have been presented that will permit listing of the fact that a product is lightly breaded and establishing the maximum breading a product may have and be so designated.

Shrimp of all types have been selling beyond the ability of the industry to keep pace with demand. The United States imports from more than 60 different nations, far more shrimp than it produces. The high price of shrimp tends to shunt more product into breaded form as one means of reducing the final price.

Actually, more than two thirds of the total production of all frozen shrimp is used by the mass-feeding trade. It would appear that the public would eat much more at home were it not for the nuisance of preparation in a deep-fat fryer.

### FISH STICKS

All the other frozen prepared food products which have made such a great success, such as the dinners, meat pies, fruit pies, cream pies, breaded shrimp, and French-fried potatoes had merely been adaptations of existing dishes to the freezing process. Fish sticks are a singular exception since they were *invented* by the freezing industry, never having existed previous to their introduction by an ingenious frozen food processor.

The inventor of fish sticks was Rudy Wagner, owner of Redi Foods, New York. For years Rudy Wagner made that claim on his packages and it has never been disputed.

Mr. Wagner conceived the idea of fish sticks in 1949 to satisfy the demands of an Albany, N.Y., distributor for a frozen fish strip that could be fried by roadside stands for sandwiches.

The distributor had experimented with slicing strips lengthwise from fish fillets, but that proved an unprofitable procedure. Mr. Wagner then got the idea of sawing strips off a frozen fillet block. He has preserved for posterity the first saw he used for that purpose. The strips were breaded and fried to see if they would hold together in precooked form. They did.

The initial strips were quite long, running about six to a pound. For two years, these proved a profitable, fast-turnover number at New York roadside stands.

In 1951, Mr. Wagner decided to go into a retail pack. He prepared smaller sticks from haddock, which were roughly about the size of those today, but thinner, running 15 sticks to the 11-oz. plastic basket (the standard commercial sticks first ran 10 to a 10-oz. package and later 10 to an 8-oz. package) and retailing for about 32¢. The first name given them was not fish sticks but "Fish Frys."

The credit for popularizing the product and even the term "fish sticks" belongs to Birdseye. That organization spent many thousands of dollars on research to determine what size, species of fish, and degree of frying would produce the best product. Late in 1952 they went into production. Their product was precooked.

Other companies were on the market within a matter of months. The end of 1953 found 12 processors of fish sticks and 1954 closed with 64 processors of that product!

The sharp competition of so many labels resulted in an unwise decision to reduce the size of the fish sticks from one ounce to four-fifths of an ounce each. This resulted in a lower price but also in a higher ratio of breading to fish. Midway through 1956 sales slumped drastically from their peak of 65 million pounds.

The industry then realized that it needed product standards if it was to retain the confidence of the consumer and survive. Arranging for voluntary standards proved to be a tough battle, not only among themselves but with the government agencies which would have been more receptive to mandatory inspection such as was required of meat firms in interstate commerce. Nevertheless, fish stick standards were finally promulgated in August 1956, and the first firm to avail themselves of the service was Gorton's of Gloucester. Eventually most companies added inspection.

Though Rudy Wagner's fish sticks had been raw, the type that really caught on with the consumer was the precooked fish stick that required only heating. About ten per cent of the fish sticks frozen are still raw breaded, and it is a fact that it takes less time to cook a raw breaded fish stick than it does to heat a precooked fish stick, and the raw fish stick is better because it retains more moisture. Nevertheless, the consumer has been completely sold on the word "precooked."

Fish sticks have steadily increased in popularity and in 1966 some 81 million pounds of the product were frozen (Figs. 1 and 2).

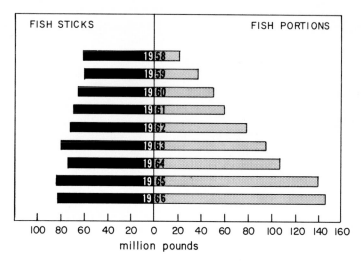

Courtesy of Bureau of Commercial Fisheries, Fish and Wildlife Service

Fig. 1.  Production of fish sticks and portions.

### FISH PORTIONS

Though fish sticks proved very popular in schools as part of the lunch program, they did very poorly with the institutional trade. Finally it was realized that the size was not right for drive-ins and restaurants. The industry then began to make fish portions, which are cut from the same fish blocks as sticks, only in a rectangular shape in sizes from 2 to 6 oz. each, and breaded. Though fish portions enjoyed a good retail acceptance after their gradual introduction in the early fifties, they have received a more enthusiastic acceptance by drive-ins, restaurants, diners, and other mass feeding establishments, and by 1962 poundage had passed fish sticks. In 1966, production was at an all-time record of 146,637,000 lb. (Fig. 2 and Table 34).

The fish portions are used as entrées, either 1 or 2 to the plate. They are

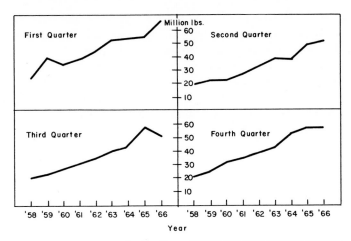

Courtesy of Bureau of Commercial Fisheries, Fish and Wildlife Service

Fig. 2.   Consumption of fish sticks and portions.

also suitable for fish sandwiches, the purpose for which such products were initially frozen.

## NATIONALITY FOODS

### Italian

Spaghetti and meat balls was one of the very first prepared products frozen, several companies marketing it in 1942, but a major reason why it never was too successful is that spaghetti tends to be mushy and pasty after freezing. The first important Italian frozen food firm was the Roman Ravioli Co., S. Hackensack, N.J., organized in August 1947 by Joseph and Cyrus Settineri. Their big product was ravioli, but they followed soon afterwards with pizza, and may have been the first in America to introduce that product in frozen form.

Among other more popular Italian frozen foods today are lasagne, manicotti, egg plant parmigiana, tomato and meat sauces, and cavetelli. Strangely enough, macaroni and cheese, fundamentally an Italian dish, quickly became the darling of some of the larger frozen food companies and became so popular that it is not considered as part of the Italian frozen food line by the industry.

Pizza has long since supplanted ravioli as the frontrunner in Italian foods. No figures are collected for the production or sales of Italian foods, but estimates were that $100 million was spent by the consumer on Italian-style frozen foods in 1966, and of that amount $75 million was for pizza alone. Pizza itself has become a sub-category, there being a great variety of sizes, shapes, and varieties. Every size from hors d'oeuvres to round pizzas a foot in diameter may be purchased. Cheese pizza is the most popular variety, followed by sausage pizza. Cheese pizza completely overshadows sausage pizza on the east and west coasts, but in the midwest sausage pizza is the major seller. It appears that the midwest thinks of pizza in terms of a main course whereas the east regards it primarily as a snack. There are also pepperoni, pepper, anchovy, hamburger, and chicken pizza, to name only a few varieties.

Certain regions of the country, specifically Milwaukee and New Orleans, prefer a thick-crust doughy pizza. This style has been growing more popular and it appears that eventually both thin and thick crust pizza will be found everywhere.

### Chinese

While it has previously been established that Chinese foods were introduced during World War II, they did not become nationally important until a young man named Jeno Paulucci, who had borrowed $200,000 from the Minnesota Iron Range Resources and Rehabilitation Commission in 1951 to expand a beansprout business he had started, decided that he could utilize more of that vegetable if he established a line of Chinese foods marketed under the Chun King label. Other Chinese frozen food companies also proved imaginative. Temple Frosted Foods in Brooklyn, N.Y., introduced the first Chinese dinner on a tray, the first Chinese soups, and probably the first egg rolls in frozen form. Most Chinese food companies were content to remain regional, but Jeno Paulucci of Chun King gambled great sums of money on fine packaging and promotion to go nationwide.

While his company packed the complete range of Chinese products, the spearhead of his line was a variety of frozen Chinese dinners on a tray. By 1966, he was virtually the only major company, having absorbed a number of outstanding frozen Chinese food firms in the United States and Canada.

The products which proved so popular included beef chop suey, chicken chow mein, shrimp chow mein, egg rolls, egg foo young, fried rice, spareribs, and a variety of dinners containing an assortment of the foregoing dishes.

An important segment of Chinese foods in which Chun King did little was that of soups. Chinese soups are a popular item in the frozen food cabinet, particularly egg drop, won ton, and tomato egg drop, and smaller companies have managed to do extremely well with them.

Since Chun King is the major factor in Chinese foods, and since they have never separated their frozen and nonfrozen products, sales of frozen Chinese foods can only be estimated, but were believed to be about $30 million in 1966, with Chun King accounting for $25 million of the total.

## Jewish Foods

The idea of freezing Jewish-style foods grew out of the whole-sale dairy business of Hy Epstein and Mac Levine who had been selling blintzes fresh in several frozen food stores they maintained in 1945. Frozen food distributors who supplied them with low-temperature products prevailed upon them to freeze blintzes for general sale. The year was 1946 and there was still a shortage of many foods. Distributors could sell anything they could get. This situation would change drastically in about a year, but during the interim the Milady brand was created and showed enough promise to encourage the two partners to stay in the frozen food business.

Heart and soul of the Jewish frozen foods business is the greater New York area with its population of over two million Jews. Unlike the Italians, who initially had little to do with frozen products derived from their old-world cookery, the Jews supported their own ethnic products. It is a well established fact that the Jews, despite the fact that they make up only about 3% of the population of the United States were largely responsible for the success of all types of nationality foods in the early stages, Italian and Chinese as well as Jewish, and that they purchase such products far out of proportion to their numbers.

Soon other items were added to the Jewish line: knishes, pancakes fried from raw potatoes, pirogen (potato dumplings), borscht, stuffed derma, and chopped liver (both chicken and beef). Despite a great deal of activity, specialized Jewish dishes have actually been declining in recent years. The major growth in this area has come from *kosher* dinners and meals, supplied in frozen form to airlines, hospitals, schools, hotels, and other institutions. Such dinners are not necessarily a nationality dish at all, but may be standard beef, chicken, turkey, meat loaf items, differentiated only by the fact that they are prepared under rabbinical supervision according to kosher ritual. Technically these might be termed religious foods, for superficially they are in no way distinguishable from any others. In this regard, it should be underscored that not all Jewish foods are kosher in a religious sense.

## Mexican

Spanish or Mexican foods were among the very earliest products to be frozen. Chili con carne appeared in the product line of a half-dozen companies between 1940 and 1945. Nevertheless, outside of the southwest, even canned chili was a modest seller, but scarcely a good item for national distribution. Furthermore, canned chili was sufficiently hot so that the uninitiated could scarcely tell whether it was good or bad; the milder frozen chili could be appreciated only by a connoisseur.

The initial company to truly popularize a broad spectrum of Mexican frozen foods was headquartered in San Antonio and appropriately known as Alamo Frosted Foods. Officers of the firm were H. E. Stumberg and Louis Stumberg. In addition to chili, which many packers had featured for some years, they also marketed such Mexican staples as tamales, enchiladas, Mexican rice, and later tortillas and tacos.

Early sales efforts in the opening year, 1945, were predominantly regional, but distribution gradually spread out to the west coast and the south. In 1949, the company name was changed to Patio Foods. The firm has never ceased to grow, until today it is probably the largest company specializing in Mexican frozen foods, though numerous other firms have entered the field.

Mexican frozen dinners have proved by far the most popular of all products marketed by such firms, particularly combination dinners containing 3 or 4 different foods on a foil compartmented tray, such as tamales, chili, refried beans, and tacos. Even where the main course may be some variety of enchilada, the side dishes may be refried beans, Mexican style corn (with peppers), and chili gravy.

Mexican style foods, particularly dinners, are now available in most parts of the nation, and the big dinner companies usually have at least one Mexican dinner to fill out their lines. Despite this, the bulk of frozen Mexican dinner sales continue to be made in the southwest and the west coast. True volume acceptance has not been achieved in many parts of the country, even though as early as 1955 strong promotional efforts were made in the greater New York City area.

No good statistics are available on the production of Mexican-style frozen foods and securing them has been complicated by the tendency of general frozen food companies also to market Mexican dinners. Informed estimates place frozen Mexican food sales between a low of $20 million and a high of $25 million annually, with the overwhelmingly greatest quantity purchased through the retail outlets.

## Others

Several major companies are attempting to create a demand for Hawaiian-style foods in frozen form. Such developments are recent and it is difficult to tell whether they will succeed. One of the larger companies involved in attempting to make a success of such products is the Chun King Corp. The procedure has been to take entrées like shrimp, pork, pepper steak, spareribs, chicken, and meatballs, and prepare them in sweet and sour sauce. A side dish has also been introduced called sweet potatoes Hawaiian, which is candied sweets with coconut.

German-style products have been tried from time to time, but none has caught on well enough to warrant a separate category. The German-style product with the greatest potential would appear to be sauerbraten. This well-known dish has been the basis of several frozen dinners and may spearhead experimentation with other German foods.

There are other ethnic dishes: French, Swedish, British, Russian, Japanese, to name some in frozen form. What has been happening is that, whereas 15 yr. ago nationality foods were predominantly produced by specialists, today there is scarcely a major firm with a broad line of dinners or entrées which does not process one or more. Beef stroganoff is produced by probably a half-dozen companies, yet not one processing specialist in Russian-style foods exists. The same is true of many styles of French foods. Actually, it is quite possible that the time will come when there will be no specialists in ethnic dishes as such.

Already the diffusion has made gathering of statistics very difficult. The best informed estimates placed total sales of all nationality foods in 1966 at $184 million and poundage at 203 million.

### ENTRÉES

An entrée is a main course, usually of meat, but it can also be macaroni and cheese or eggplant parmigiana. A main course with no more than one vegetable is still considered an entrée. However, if it has two or more, it becomes a dinner (See Chapter 11).

There is no true pioneer of the entrée. Such products have been produced and marketed ever since there was a frozen food industry. The amazing thing is the persistence with which early packers strove to sell beef stew, spaghetti and meat balls, Welsh rarebit, corn beef hash, and similar entrées, despite their very limited success.

For one brief year, when a processed meat was ration-point free but raw meat was subject to rationing, pseudo-entrées became the rage. A meat packer would dip his veal cutlet in wine sauce and have a point-free prepared entrée which meat-hungry Americans would pay exorbitant prices to buy. This marketing El Dorado lasted only about a year and then it was over.

The little man, freezing products in a store or in his garage, found the entrée the simplest thing to process. The cooking and sauce were adequate excuse to charge a good price and there were no standards of quality or value. The consumer had one great remedy for this—he did not have to buy them.

The first true volume success was not a meat product at all, it was macaroni and cheese, to be followed shortly afterward by macaroni and beef. Both of these products could be sold at very low prices and become volume products because their basic ingredient macaroni was so cheap, and because the cheese and meat used were primarily for flavoring.

If any one company can claim credit for popularizing the casserole type of entrée, it probably belongs to Stouffer's, a Cleveland restaurant chain, which as early as 1953 was freezing a variety of casseroles, desserts, and prepared vegetables to be sold through its outlets to the take-home trade.

They decided to make their first large-scale drive for national distribution with 20 products in 1956. They prepared such established standards as macaroni and cheese and macaroni and beef, but additionally they also packed roast beef hash, tuna noodle casserole, Swiss steak, lobster Newburg, salmon loaf, Welsh rarebit, sliced turkey breast, creamed chicken, escalloped chicken and noodles, and many similar products which were added or dropped from their lists as consumer acceptance dictated. Their standards of quality were high and they put a substantial sum of money into promotion. Gradually, their products and those of many other firms who followed the trend, began to gain cumulative, if not individual, volume.

The earliest boilable pouch products were entrées, and for a while it looked like they would prove the meccas of that phase of the industry. The first processor in a boilable plastic pouch was Luchow's, a New York restaurant, which, in 1956, packed meat balls with herb sauce cream, salisbury steak with mushroom sauce, and beef goulash with mushroom sauce.

Other companies entered the pouch field with entrées and at first it was a contest between foil bags, promoted primarily by aluminum and poly / Mylar pouches. The foil bags helped create a new line of entrées, meat slices in gravy, which came into existence in 1957. A number of sliced meats—beef, chicken, turkey, and ham—with appropriate gravies, were packed in foil bags which could be heated in two cycles on a toaster. These could adequately serve as a quick main course, but their popularity was sustained by their usefulness in making a *hot sandwich*. Two slices of bread, with the contents of a bag of meat slices and gravy poured over them made a quick hot sandwich in minutes. Such products in boilable plastic pouches today continue to sell for primarily this reason.

The most dramatic growth for frozen entrées now appears to be taking shape in the mass-feeding field. Not only rising cost, but the shortage of qualified chefs, cooks, and even scullery help, is leaving feeding establishments no alternative but to shift into frozen foods. Major restaurant chains, among them Schrafft's, Bickford's, Stouffer's, and Howard Johnson's, prepare up to 70% of their foods in central commissaries, freeze them and ship them to their individual restaurants for reconstitution. Kitchen help has been drastically reduced by this practice (See Chapter 26).

The ownership of production facilities has led a substantial number of mass feeders to begin selling to other restaurants. They have an advantage over the processor who is promoting a line of entrées for the mass-feeding trade, because they can show evidence that the products have been tested and work "in the field" i.e., in their own establishments.

One of the most successful ways of marketing frozen entrées to universities, hospitals, restaurants, and hotels has been to freeze 1 to 2 doz. servings in a large foil tray which can be inserted in the steam table and then discarded when empty. Another has been to take stews, Newburgs, à la kings, and rarebits and freeze them in large blocks which will fit into existing trays and can be reheated or quickly readied with the use of radiant quartz ovens.

One reason why a conversion to frozen entrées by the institutions has been slow is that standardization is impossible. A gourmet restaurant requires something far better than a university cafeteria. Portion sizes vary greatly from high school lunches to industrial feeding establishments. A hospital may require food prepared in a specified manner and a Jewish old-folks home will need strictly kosher meals. This is the problem which is slowing down acceptance. Frozen food processors now realize that they must become caterers and pack to order. They cannot standardize sizes and quality and move into mass production, and hope for general acceptance.

During 1966, it was estimated that 278 million pounds of entrées of all types were packed and sold for approximately $167 million. Of that portion, $40 million was sold to the mass-feeding trade and the rate of acceleration in that market was swift.

### BAKERY GOODS

As early as 1945, frozen baked goods of various types were common in the frozen food cabinets, along with other specialty products, but consumers did not see any special purpose in them and sales were anything but brisk.

## Waffles

The first product of this nature to gain volume, and actually it may be called "baked goods" only by courtesy, was the prebaked frozen waffle. A frozen waffle batter was produced by Frostmart Frozen Food Center, Peoria, Ill., in 1946, but was self-limiting since it required the housewife to own a waffle iron. One year later, Kwik-kold Foods, Howard Beach, N.Y., put up prebaked waffles in their present form. By 1948 there were five packers but growth was slow.

However, the waffle industry had a great natural "gimmick" which it began to exploit properly for the first time in 1950. That "gimmick" was the fact that frozen waffles could be prepared by insertion into the ordinary home toaster.

Millions of families owned toasters, and their use for the preparation of waffles turned that item into a smash hit as a convenience product. No longer was there any necessity to mix batter, to buy a special waffle iron, and to clean the iron after use. Waffles, for the first time, could become a swiftly prepared breakfast dish, making a highly desirable addition to breakfast variety.

Waffles caught on. In 1951, the number of processors leaped from 6 to 23. It increased to 30 the following year. That was the high-water mark as far as numbers were concerned, but sales continued to grow.

By 1952, waffles were the third best-selling specialty on the lists of frozen food distributors, topped only by French-fried potatoes and breaded shrimp.

Frozen waffles became an excellent drawing card, luring housewives to the cabinet. Retailers decided to package the product under their own label in order to sell them at low prices, usually 10¢ for a package of six. Since waffles were very easy to make and the ingredients very cheap in price, it was not long before most major retail chains had their own brand. To compete, the major brand, Downyflake, was forced to curtail seriously its consumer promotion and even go into private label manufacture. The result was that sales of waffles have for many years now leveled off at a plateau and are no longer regarded as a really important item.

Despite this, waffles, because of wide appeal, low retail price, and compact packaging, paved the way for the introduction of other baked goods into the frozen food cabinet in greater quantities than ever before.

The true builder of the broad line of basic frozen baked goods was Charles Lubin, a Chicago baker who supplied food stores in the greater Chicago area with daily deliveries of fresh cakes. He gained so fine a reputation for certain products, particularly his cream cheese cake, that companies in other cities asked that he franchise them his trade name of Kitchens of Sara Lee and give them his formulas.

Requests continued to come from outside of the Chicago area for his cakes. To satisfy them, he decided to try freezing and distributing his sweet goods through conventional frozen food distributors. Fortunately for Charles Lubin, his recipes for cakes called for very great quantities of high-grade butter. Butter freezes extraordinarily well. Therefore his cakes not only retained their fresh-baked quality, but he also found that his pound cake, coffee cake, and chocolate cake seemed to taste better in frozen form.

Though his packaging was oversized, outshaped, and awkward, and his cakes were generally regarded as high-priced for commercial products, his sales climbed from $400,000 in 1951 to $5 million in 1956, when his firm was sold to Consolidated Foods, Chicago. The most effective testimonial to the positive advantages of frozen baked goods over fresh was supplied by Charles Lubin himself in 1965. At that time Sara Lee was still delivering *fresh* cakes to outlets within a 300-mile radius of Chicago to the amount of $10 million annually. He stunned the business world by announcing that he was discontinuing all fresh cake and substituting frozen.

When asked for a reason, he maintained that purchasers a thousand miles away were getting fresher cake than people in Chicago. Within minutes after a cake is baked it begins to stale. A cake stales three times as fast dropping from 70° to 20°F. (21° to −7°C.), as it does at temperatures above that. Dropping a cake swiftly through the fast-staling zone by freezing assures the consumer a far superior product. Frequently a "fresh" cake may literally take days to sell, obviously not improving during that period. Because important production and distribution economies result from freezing as well as elimination of loss from staling, it is possible to sell a frozen cake cheaper than a comparable fresh cake. Simply stated, the consumer gets a better cake at a lower price in frozen form than she can in fresh. Therein rests the reason for the growing popularity of the frozen product.

The supermarkets have discovered a strong economic reason, peculiar to their operation, for promoting frozen baked goods. Shopping today tends to be increasingly on a once-a-week basis. Whereas the consumer can usually buy a week's supply of most foods, this is not practical with baked goods. Therefore, the tendency has been to purchase one day's needs of baked goods during the shopping trip and to buy the remainder from small food stores and bakery shops throughout the week as needed. Thereby the supermarket lost the bulk of the baked goods business through default. The one hope the supermarkets have of salvaging some of that volume is through offering a large selection of frozen baked goods so that those consumers with freezer space can stock up with a week's supply during the shopping trip.

One major retail chain, the Jewel Tea Co. of Chicago, has its own plant in which it freezes 150 different baked goods products and has a separate department in each of its stores for these goods. Increasingly, large additional cabinets are being set aside for frozen baked goods, sometimes in the fresh bakery foods department.

One sure way in which frozen bakery foods have obtained quality superiority is by selling their products in raw dough form. A substantial success has been accomplished by marketing puff pastry fruit turnovers in ready-to-bake products as introduced by Pepperidge Farm. The crispy, flaky texture of such foods when baked from the frozen product far surpasses that of most similar turnovers which can be bought commercially. Raw bread dough is marketed widely, and though it appears to be the height of inconvenience, requiring 5 to 7 hr. for thawing, setting, and baking, a government survey taken in 1965 showed that the product was 10% cheaper than fresh bread, frequently of superior quality and always possessing a better flavor and aroma.

The frozen bakery foods phase of the business is destined to become a major industry. Kitchens of Sara Lee publicly announced that they had attained a volume of over $80 million in 1966. Total sales of such products, exclusive of fruit and cream pies, were estimated to be valued at $226 million in 1966 with poundage 304 million for that year.

### PREPARED VEGETABLES

Some form of prepared vegetables has always been present in the frozen food industry. From the earliest beginnings of prepared foods, there have been items like winter squash (one of the first), egg plant parmigiana, potatoes au gratin, spinach and corn soufflé. Chinese vegetables, lima bean casseroles, baked beans, and various others. Birdseye Frosted Foods started freezing winter squash in the thirties.

Seabrook Farms purchased Luchow's frozen boilable pouch line in 1956 and had begun evaluating other products that could be marketed in that manner. Because they were the world's largest single frozen vegetable processing plant, their experiments revolved around vegetables. Early in 1958, they began test-marketing a group of vegetable products in boilable pouches that included asparagus cuts and tips hollandaise style, creole succotash, baby lima beans in cheese sauce, creamed spinach, potatoes and peas in cream sauce, delmonico potatoes, and chopped broccoli au gratin.

The first major volume in prepared vegetables was accomplished by Birdseye, White Plains, N.Y., when it introduced flavored vegetable combinations in 1961. These products were not packed in boilable pouches, but in standard overwrapped cartons. The vegetables were flavored with liquid spices and the consumer was either asked to add butter, or appropriate sauces were included in pouches packed with the vegetables. Products included French-style green beans with toasted almonds, green peas with sautéed mushrooms, Fordhook lima beans with cheese sauce, green peas and pearl onions, mixed vegetables with onion sauce, green peas with cream sauce, Fordhook lima beans with tomatoes, corn and peas with tomatoes, French-style green beans with sautéed mushrooms, and green peas and celery. Consumers were offered the total price back if they tried three different products. The product flavor was truly outstanding and volume came to the prepared foods industry.

The very next year, 1962, Green Giant picked up the boilable pouch idea for vegetables, but instead of packing a different sauce for each vegetable they froze them all in butter sauce. Their famous name, the universal preference for butter as a flavoring, and millions of dollars in promotional advertising, combined to capture much of the market. The standard vegetables—peas, string beans, cut corn, lima beans, and broccoli—packed in a boilable pouch with butter sauce greatly expanded the sales of frozen vegetables (see also Chapter 4, Vol. III).

Retailers have heavily moved into private label of prepared vegetables and processors are branching out into single serving while institutional packs are being aggressively marketed. Prepared vegetables have become a substantial, growing and worthwhile part of the frozen food scene.

## SOUPS

The week of February 22, 1954, the Campbell Soup Co., Camden, N.J., largest processor of canned soups in the world, introduced frozen soups in Philadelphia, Wilmington, Camden, and Trenton. The varieties were green pea with ham, chicken and vegetable, oyster stew, and cream of shrimp. The products were packed in 10½ oz. cans. Prices were substantially higher than hot-pack soups, but nevertheless the soups caught on. Soon there was national distribution and more varieties were added, most notably potato soup.

Because canned soups were required to be heat-sterilized, they were in effect cooked twice and those varieties with the more delicate flavors, particularly fish and seafood soups, as well as potato soup, were an inferior product in hot-pack. Frozen soups did not have to be heat sterilized and the superiority of flavor of the seafood soups was instantaneously evident.

There had been frozen soups almost since the beginning of the industry, particularly fish chowder, clam stew, oyster stew, won ton soup, and egg drop soup, and everyone was confident that sooner or later soups would become an important category. During 1955 and 1956, it appeared that the great day had arrived. Campbell's distribution and sales soared. The other soup giants, H. J. Heinz and Crosse & Blackwell, began freezing soups and it seemed to have become an exciting part of the frozen food industry.

While there had been a score of small producers before, now most of them dropped by the wayside. So did Heinz and Crosse & Blackwell. Only Campbell forged ahead until by 1958 it had 80% of the market and held it.

Unfortunately frozen soups have maintained themselves on a plateau ever since. The lack of competition has probably resulted in complacency on the part of the major industry factor, the Campbell Soup Co., for there has been very little promotion. Frozen soups have sustained themselves solely on the basis of their quality, but against the pressure of new products, they cannot grow until some attention is paid to them.

Sales of frozen soups were estimated at $14 million in 1966 and have been slipping for several years. The only exceptions were the Chinese soups which continued to grow and increase their share of the business.

## THE FUTURE

The future for the prepared frozen foods industry is virtually limitless. None of the major categories covered in the preceding review has come close to realizing their potential and there are new areas opening up.

Among them:

### Egg Products

Grade A homogenized eggs for making instant omelettes have been very successful institutionally and will shortly be appearing in retail containers. Frozen omelettes, including Western, cheese, and ham, are already finding favor with institutions.

### Synthetic Milk Products

Synthetic whipped cream made from vegetable oils; synthetic cream for coffee and other products that normally utilized light sweet cream; and synthetic sour cream are all making inroads. If an adequate source of sweet vegetable oils can be developed, it is quite conceivable that frozen synthetic milk may arrive before frozen retail concentrated cow's milk. It is scientifically possible to make such a product in an acceptable form with known methods.

### Synthetic Meats

Spun soybean protein is currently in use to make frozen imitation meats which look and taste like chicken, turkey, beef, lamb, pork, and other meat products. For special diets, vegetarians, in combination with other foods (sausage and waffles), "meat flavored" soups, and for those who acquire a preference for their flavor, such products have a future.

### Pancake Batter

This is a truly convenience item in frozen form, packed in milk cartons, sold frozen, and stored in the refrigerator. The batter is poured on the griddle as needed. It will greatly enlarge the frozen breakfast market.

There are many others and, in all truth, the actual scope of tomorrow's frozen prepared foods industry cannot be adequately visualized. Products will arise and grow to great popularity to fill needs which cannot be anticipated in the context of current conditions. Growth may proceed as quickly institutionally as at consumer level. The time is almost here when 25 to 50% of all perishable food may be sold in frozen form.

An estimate of prepared frozen food volume by the year 1976 was made by E.I. du Pont de Nemours & Company in 1967 by feeding all available past data on frozen foods into a computer. Utilizing a series of double exponential equations which roughly represented an "S" curve (new industries start off slow, accelerate, then level out) it was estimated that prepared frozen foods would grow 355% from $1.5 billion to $6.8 billion in 1976.

### BIBLIOGRAPHY

Anon.  1944A. College Inn chili dinner. Quick Frozen Foods *6*, No. 9, 29.

Anon.  1944B. Creamed chicken, one of line. Quick Frozen Foods *6*, No. 9, 30.

Anon.  1944C. New cooked apple sauce. Quick Frozen Foods *6*, No. 12, 32.

Anon.  1944D. Purees and precooked foods developed. Quick Frozen Foods *7*, No. 5, 44.

Anon.  1945A. Quick freezing to solve airline menu problems. Quick Frozen Foods *7*, No. 6, 33.

Anon.  1945B. Frozen pie crust developed. Quick Frozen Foods *7*, No. 12, 66.

Anon.  1945C. Commissary develops frozen pies and meats. Quick Frozen Foods *8*, No. 2, 57, 80.

Anon.  1950. A new item to the fore—fantail shrimp. Quick Frozen Foods *12*, No. 7, 127.

Anon.  1955. $80 million frozen pot pie sales predicted for 1955; 33⅓% climb from last year. Quick Frozen Foods *18*, No. 4, 167–170.

Anon.  1956A. Frozen soups could achieve major volume; most packers report big gains. Quick Frozen Foods *8*, No. 7, 361–371.

Anon.  1956B. Prepared foods pack placed at 534 million pounds by USDA. Quick Frozen Foods *18*, No. 8, 107–109.

Anon.  1956C. Prepared foods up 47% in 1955, 35% increase seen for 1956. Quick Frozen Foods *18*, No. 10, 180.

Anon.  1956D. Eight-inch frozen fruit pie best-selling size with 58% of responding packers. Quick Frozen Foods *19*, No. 3, 127–129, 132, 133.

Anon.  1956E. Entrees pace restaurants' bid for domination in frozen cooked and prepared foods. Quick Frozen Foods *19*, No. 4, 105–108, 112.

Anon.  1957A. How convenient are "convenience foods"? Quick Frozen Foods *19*, No. 6, 351–352, 476.

Anon.  1957B. Stream of FF business should flow from untapped luncheon market. Quick Frozen Foods *19*, No. 9, 45, 53–54.

Anon.  1957C. Facts behind the dynamic policies which saved the fish stick industry. Quick Frozen Foods *19*, No. 10, 67.

Anon.  1957D. Price wars in frozen fruit pie industry threaten quality and growth. Quick Frozen Foods *19*, No. 10, 171–173.

Anon.  1957E. 20% Prepared frozen food institutional. Quick Frozen Foods *19*, No. 13, 133–135.

Anon.  1957F. French fries sales climb 1,800% in ten years with 40% going to institutional markets. Quick Frozen Foods *20*, No. 3, 97–101; No. 4, 99–102.

Anon.  1959A. Boiling-in-bag—The new revolution. Quick Frozen Foods *21*, No. 8, 237–246.

Anon.  1959B. Majority of fruit pies excellent quality despite fierce price cabinet struggle. Quick Frozen Foods *21*, No. 8, 252–254.

Anon.   1960A.  Prepared frozen meals delivered hot from vending machines a reality. Quick Frozen Foods 22, No. 11, 113–114.

Anon.   1960B.  Why frozen bakery products. Quick Frozen Foods 23, No. 5, 72, 87–88, 93, 101.

Anon.   1963.  Frozen bread dough challenges prebaked and fresh varieties. Quick Frozen Foods 26, No. 2, 71–74; No. 3, 147–150.

Anon.   1964A.  Protein-controlled simulated meat concept opens unlimited frozen potential. Quick Frozen Foods 26, No. 6, 79–82.

Anon.   1964B.  Pizza packers find tight freezer space will stretch for profitable large size. Quick Frozen Foods 26, No. 10, 75–80.

Anon.   1964C.  Frozen fruit, cream pies—A consumer survey. Quick Frozen Foods 26, No. 8, 83–86.

Cook, G. G., and Martin, S.   1966.  Frozen bakery goods shopping list items; kept in home freezer at all times. Quick Frozen Foods 29, No. 4, 101–107, 413–416.

Martin, S.   1957.  The prepared foods story, history of the frozen cooked and prepared foods industry. Quick Frozen Foods 19, No. 11, 115–116, 126–135.

McIntyre, D. L.   1965.  Liquid Nitrogen quality claim in the freezing of baked goods. Quick Frozen Foods 28, No. 11, 110–112, 159, 160.

Pouchulo, D.   1967.  Computer estimates of frozen food growth in the next 10 years, 1966 to 1976. Quick Frozen Foods 30, No. 4, 151–158.

Tressler, D. K., and Evers, C. F.   1957.  The Freezing Preservation of Foods, 3rd Edition, Vol. 2. Freezing of Precooked and Prepared Foods. Avi Publishing Co., Westport, Conn.

Williams, E. W.   1945.  What is the future for cooked foods? Quick Frozen Foods 7, No. 12, 43.

Williams, E. W.   1963.  The biography of an industry. Quick Frozen Foods 26, No. 1, 149–310.

## CHAPTER 2

# Special Problems Encountered in Preparing, Freezing, Storing, Transporting, and Marketing Frozen Precooked and Prepared Foods

Donald K. Tressler

## PART 1
## Chemical and Physical Problems

### INTRODUCTION

Volumes 2 and 3 are devoted largely to the consideration of problems encountered in preparing, packaging, freezing, storing, transporting, and marketing raw foods. Much of the material included in these chapters applies not only to raw foods but also to prepared and precooked frozen foods. The authors assume that the reader is familiar with the contents of Volumes 2 and 3 and will not attempt to repeat or review the material presented in these volumes.

The reader is referred also to certain other chapters which follow in this volume, particularly Chapter 4 on Packaging, Chapter 24 on Storage, and Chapter 25 on Handling and Use.

In order to present an adequate resumé of all of the many problems confronting the freezer of precooked and prepared foods, this chapter is divided into three sections. The first is a general consideration of the chemical and physical changes encountered during cooling, freezing, storage, and reheating of many precooked foods. The second part, written by a specialist in starch chemistry, is concerned solely with the problems encountered during freezing and thawing of pasted starches. The third section is of special importance since it answers a great number of questions concerning the microbiology of precooked frozen foods and indicates clearly the necessity for rapid cooling of the cooked foods, the importance of the use of nearly sterile ingredients, and the maintenance of sanitary packing plants.

### SPECIAL PROBLEMS

In June 1956, the 1955–1956 Committee on Frozen Foods of the Institute of Food Technologists prepared an "Outline of Research Problems on Frozen Foods." This outline included the following research problems on prepared frozen foods:

Donald K. Tressler is a consultant and President, Avi Publishing Company, Westport, Conn.

(A) Processing Technology
  (1) Determine effects of preparation, freezing, handling, and storage on quality, flavor, and tenderness thresholds of the ready-to-serve product in terms of consumer acceptability.
  (2) Deep fat frying
    (a) Build more stability into the fat used in frying.
    (b) Improve the retention of quality in fat absorbed during frying prior to freezing.
  (3) Develop methods of precooking fish sticks, fish bits, chicken parts, shrimp, etc., without using butter.
  (4) Sauces, spices, and baked products
    (a) Evaluate starches and / or flours for white sauces in precooked frozen foods.
      (a-1) For consistency before freezing and after defrosting; and
      (a-2) For interference of thickening agent with flavor components.
    (b) Develop improved and large-scale methods of freezing and defrosting bakery products, especially cakes and pies.
    (c) Determine the effect of freezing on the flavor level of food products containing spices.
    (d) Formulate batters and doughs to improve the quality of product reaching the consumer.
    (e) Develop improved formulations for balanced flavor and built-in stability from time of seasoning and assembly to moment of preparation by the homemaker.
  (5) Packaging and labeling
    (a) Develop more commercial packaging with superior retention of quality.
    (b) Show the similarity of large-scale preparation and home cookery in order that label statements may be made in "homey" language.
  (6) General
    (a) Evaluate meats, precooked meats, seafoods, and poultry:
      (a-1) For flavor characteristics and precursors to enhance flavor; and
      (a-2) For factors causing rancidity, dryness, toughness, etc.
    (b) Develop information on nutritional composition.
    (c) Distinguish between the bacteriology of prepared and other frozen foods to show that under good conditions of plant sanitation, prepared frozen foods are without cause for public concern."

Although this list was drawn up 11 years ago, most of the problems have been only partially solved.

## WHICH FOODS MAY GIVE TROUBLE?

In view of the long list of precooked foods on the market, one might assume that practically all foods result in satisfactory products if carefully cooked, rapidly frozen, and then held at a low temperature until used. This is a long way from the truth, since many precooked foods are greatly changed by freezing, subsequent storage, and reheating for use.

Cooked foods may be classified into four categories (Tressler 1953):

(a) Those which may be frozen, stored, and thawed without marked change; for example, applesauce, winter squash, various pies, bread, rolls, cookies, most cakes, and clear soups.

(b) Those which are greatly changed by freezing, storage, and reheating, but which by certain changes either in the method of cooking or in the recipe, may be so modified as to be well suited for freezing. Creamed chicken and turkey, poultry pies, most sauces and gravies, and cream soups fall in this category.

(c) There are also many precooked products which, when freshly prepared, are excellent but which deteriorate relatively rapidly at ordinary storage temperatures, and consequently have a short storage life and so must be held at unusually low temperatures [e.g., $-20°F.$ ($-29°C.$) or lower], if they are to be stored for long periods. Turkey dishes, fatty fish, and shellfish are examples of such products.

(d) Those which are greatly changed by freezing and reheating and which are difficult or impossible to improve. Custards, cooked egg whites, and vegetable salads belong to this class of products.

In the listing of problems which are encountered in freezing, storing, and handling precooked frozen foods, mention should be made of bacteriological and food spoilage problems which may give trouble unless precooked foods are chilled immediately after preparation, frozen rapidly, held at temperatures well below freezing, and then rapidly reheated without permitting slow thawing. Detailed consideration of these bacteriological problems is given further on in this chapter (see Part 3).

### PROBLEMS ENCOUNTERED IN FREEZING

Some of the changes occurring when prepared foods are frozen, definitely may be attributed to physical phenomena (e.g., separation of emulsions), others partly to physical and partly to chemical changes (e.g., wilting of lettuce, celery, and other unheated vegetables), and still others may be caused by chemical actions.

## Physical

When French dressing is frozen, the oil and aqueous phases separate. Freezing causes the water to crystallize as ice, and when the dressing thaws, it does not again emulsify the oil. The "breaking" of many other dressings, sauces, and emulsions, affected by freezing and thawing, is wholly or largely caused by a similar physical phenomenon.

When ice cream, sherbets, and ices are stored for several months they usually become grainy because the ice crystals increase in size. Fluctuating temperatures and relatively high storage temperatures accelerate crystal growth.

Sucrose hydrates often crystallize in cold processed frozen fruit spreads during storage. These crystalline deposits cause deterioration in the appearance and the texture of the spreads. They first appear as white, mold-like, spherulitic formations at the surface of the product, slowly increase in size during storage, and eventually involve the entire mass of the product (Brekke and Talburt 1950). Some of the sucrose in these products can be replaced by corn syrup or by invert sugar, but if too much dextrose is used, dextrose hydrate appears as white, bead-like deposits throughout the mass during storage. Samples packed in paper cups were found by Brekke and Talburt to be affected by sucrose hydrate crystallization, whereas samples packed in hermetically sealed jars or cans were not, if they had not been seeded with crystals of the hydrate. According to Brekke and Talburt, the appearance of sucrose hydrate crystals was slowest at $-30°F.$ ($-34°C.$) successively faster at $+10°F.$ ($-12°C.$), $0°F.$ ($-18°C.$) and fastest at $-10°F.$ ($-23°C.$) storage. Fruit spreads with 30% of the sucrose requirements replaced by invert sugar showed only a very slight growth of sucrose hydrate crystals.

## Physical and Chemical

Most changes occurring when cooked foods are frozen result because of a combination of chemical and physical actions. The coagulation, or curdling, of custards is in part caused by the crystallization of water as ice and partly by the continuing denaturation of the egg proteins.

When frozen and thawed, many gravies and sauces (e.g., white sauce) curdle. This occurs for much the same reason as the coagulation of many types of custards. The crystallization of water causes retrogradation of the starch solution. The wider the temperature fluctuations and the higher the storage temperature, the greater the liquid separation from frozen sauces, other conditions being the same. This indicates clearly an important advantage of uniformly low temperatures for storage of frozen sauces and gravies.

Freezing and thawing wilts most vegetables and fruit tissues. Since greens must be crisp to be satisfactory for use in tossed and other vegetable salads, these salads are not satisfactorily preserved by freezing. Freezing wilts vegetables because of the crystallization of water which reduces the turgidity of the cells.

Wheat flour is not a wholly satisfactory stabilizer for gravies and white sauces (see p. 315). If, however, it is used in combination with gelatin or some other colloid, the coagulation may be retarded for considerable storage periods, and perhaps prevented altogether. White sauces and gravies in which the wheat flour is largely or wholly replaced by waxy maize or waxy rice flour are relatively stable. Hanson, Campbell, and Lineweaver (1951) carried out a comprehensive study of the development of a curdled appearance and liquid separation in white sauces and gravies subjected to freezing and frozen storage (see also Chapter 14, pp. 315–318). They concluded that the use of amylopectin starches and flour minimizes these defects but, since amylopectin starches, in contrast with some waxy cereal flours, have a long paste character, only certain flours appear suitable for use in sauces and gravies. Based on tests with the samples of waxy cereal flour available, waxy rice flour appears to be superior to waxy corn flour and waxy sorghum flour. But, if the appearance and liquid separation are important only in the heated sauces and gravies, then the waxy corn and rice flours are essentially interchangeable (see further details in Chapter 14).

The loss of gas from batters during freezing and thawing is in part caused by the separation of ice and the resultant concentration of the carbon dioxide in the remaining liquid phase, which eventually becomes so high that it will not stay in solution; and partly on account of the reaction of the carbonate of the soda and the acid in the more concentrated aqueous solution produced because of the separation of water as nearly pure ice. Further, it is probable that some denaturation of proteins occurs with resultant coagulation, thus permitting escape of carbon dioxide.

Yeast doughs also deteriorate in quality, if stored for long. The yeast cells gradually lose their viability; consequently, the longer the doughs are stored the more slowly the dough will rise after it is thawed and warmed. Further, during storage, some carbon dioxide is lost because of the separation and growth of ice crystals. This causes loss of gas for the same reasons given in the preceding paragraph for loss of carbon dioxide during freezing and storage of batters (except for the statement concerning reaction of the baking powder ingredients).

Changes in proteins, with resultant toughening or coagulation, occur in many foods. These changes are particularly noticeable in foods composed principally of proteins. Raw egg white is not markedly affected by freezing and thawing. However, freezing makes the cooked product tough and rubbery. Davis, Hanson, and Lineweaver (1952) have concluded that the damage to cooked egg white by freezing is caused by the mechanical effects of the ice crystals formed. They explain the phenomenon as follows:

"During freezing, the water in the elastic gel of the cooked egg white (denatured protein) migrates to increase the size of crystals wherever nuclei are present. As the crystals grow, they penetrate the gel and separate the structure, thus releasing a part of the elastic tension. The migration of the water from within the gel structure, plus the force exerted by the growth of ice crystals and the release of elastic tension by mechanical cleavage, cause the gel structure to contract. That this contraction is largely irreversible is demonstrated by the liquid-filled spaces remaining after thawing. The structure remaining is naturally tougher, since it contains a considerably higher proportion of protein than the original gel. Thus if a gel before freezing contains 12% solids and if a 55% liquid separation occurs during freezing, as occurred in many experiments, then the remaining gel would contain upward to 27% solids. The actual remaining solids will be somewhat lower than 27% because the liquid will contain part of the soluble solids."

### Chemical

Many chemical actions occur during freezing and storage of cooked foods; few of these are well understood. Lobster, crab, and shrimp gradually toughen during long-continued storage, probably because of continuing denaturation of proteins. The higher the temperature at which the frozen shellfish are held, the more rapidly these products toughen. Lobster meat also often changes from a red color to a yellow one (Dyer and Horne 1953). The change in color is believed to be due to oxidation.

Morrison (1956) studied the changes occurring in frozen cooked crab meat and reported that the meat of crabs which had been steamed for 40 min. (including 15 min. at 15 lb. steam pressure) contained active $l$-malic dehydrogenase, an enzyme which is capable of producing oxalacetic acid, which nonenzymatically decarboxylates, causing a loss of carbon dioxide. This conclusion is surprising in view of the long cooking given the crabs. A slight increase in pH was also noted. Morrison does not indicate if these changes are responsible for the toughening which usually occurs during long storage of precooked crab meat.

Oxidation and resultant rancidity are chemical changes which are likely to occur during the freezing and subsequent storage of certain fatty foods. Turkey fat is particularly subject to oxidative rancidity. This has been a factor limiting the use of turkey in precooked frozen foods. In the case of creamed turkey, rancidity may be detected immediately after the product has been prepared, and increases during frozen storage (Lineweaver, Anderson, and Hanson 1952). During preparation and storage of frozen creamed turkey, rancidity development may be greatly retarded when small amounts of edible antioxidant are present during cooking of the turkey. These workers have shown the importance of adding the antioxidant during the cooking rather than after the cooking has been completed.

Many frozen food research workers have assumed that the fats of cooked meat, in particular pork, turn rancid more rapidly than the fat of the uncooked product. Such is not the case; Watts and Peng (1947) compared the rancidification of raw and cooked pork and reached the following conclusions:

- "(1) The rate of rancidification of raw ground pork increased rapidly with decreasing pH of meat within the pH range of 6.5 to 4.8. The pH had no effect on rancidification of precooked ground pork. Except at the upper limits of normal pH range of fresh pork, the precooked kept better than the raw.

"(2) Certain salts (sodium chloride, sodium nitrate, sodium acetate, magnesium chloride, and potassium nitrate) had a marked accelerating effect on rancidity development in raw ground pork in freezing storage, but not on precooked ground pork. Other salts (potassium chloride and magnesium chloride) had no effect.

"(3) The effects of acids and salts on rancidity development in raw pork are believed to be due to the activity of a fat peroxidizing enzyme, possibly hemoglobin. Decomposition of the hemoglobin, with a resulting discoloration of the meat, accompanied rancidification."

Cooking, of course, causes inactivation of the peroxidizing enzyme or enzymes, and consequently rancidification occurs more slowly in the precooked product. Watts and Peng's results are summarized in Tables 4 and 5.

Table 4

Degree of Rancidification of Frozen Raw and Cooked Pork after
Storage for 4.5 Months at 0° to +5°F. (−18° to −15°C.)

| Lactic Acid Added % | pH of Raw Meat | Peroxide Number After Storage | |
|---|---|---|---|
| | | Raw | Cooked |
| None | 6.5 | 2.0 | 3.3 |
| 0.031 | 6.4 | 1.6 | 3.7 |
| 0.103 | 6.1 | 5.9 | 2.9 |
| 0.206 | 5.6 | 16.9 | 3.6 |
| 0.617 | 4.8 | 25.2 | 4.7 |

Source: Watts and Peng (1947).

Table 5

Effect of Various Salts on Rancidity Development in Frozen Raw
and Cooked Ground Pork

| Salt Added | pH of Raw Meat[1] | Peroxide Number After 10 Months' Storage | |
|---|---|---|---|
| | | Raw | Cooked |
| None | 6.3 | 5.5 | 2.6 |
| 1.5% sodium chloride | 6.3 | 15.2 | 2.4 |
| 1.0% sodium nitrate | 6.3 | 13.7 | 2.3 |
| 1.25% potassium nitrate | 6.3 | 12.3 | — |

Source: Watts and Peng (1947).
[1] pH of cooked samples 0.1 to 0.2 higher than raw.

During frozen storage, cooked ham, cured shoulder (picnic ham), Canadian bacon, and wieners usually lose their red color, and turn brown and then gray or dull green, and change in flavor.

These changes occur relatively quickly in the case of sliced meats and slowly in larger pieces. They may be greatly retarded by incorporating sodium ascorbate in the product, or by using the phosphate cure instead of the usual cure containing potassium nitrate and nitrite. Watts (1954) has indicated that the fading and discoloration of cured meats is due to the oxidation of nitric oxide myochromogen (which is formed by the heat denaturation of nitric oxide myoglobin). The oxidation products consist of (1) the ferric pigment, metmyoglobin, which is brown in color, and if the reaction proceeds far enough, (2) the green or faded decomposition products of the porphyrin ring.

Ascorbic acid is the only antioxidant that has shown any great promise in the protection of meat color (Bauernfeind 1953). In the presence of nitrite, ascorbic acid accelerates methemoglobin reduction at all temperatures (Lugg 1950). It protects cured meat surfaces from fading when exposed to air.

IMPORTANCE OF LOW STORAGE TEMPERATURE

Many investigators have indicated the advantages of low temperatures (e.g., 0°F.; −18°C., or even lower) when storing frozen precooked foods in retaining their original qualities if they are to be held for more than a week or two (Diehl and Berry 1933; Tressler and Evers 1936; Woodroof and Atkinson 1945; Woodroof 1946; Hutchings and Evers 1946A and B; Gleim and Fenton 1949; Hanson, Campbell, and Lineweaver 1951). In general, it can be said that precooked frozen fruits retain their quality during long-continued cold storage better than those frozen without cooking (see Table

23, p. 183). In the case of frozen vegetables, most of them retain their quality best during storage if they have been blanched just long enough to inactivate the enzymes, catalase, and peroxidase, but not completely cooked (see Table 23, p. 183). In the case of both frozen precooked fruits and precooked vegetables, their storage life is greatly extended by storing at low temperatures.

The rate of all chemical reactions which are the cause of deterioration of precooked frozen foods during cold storage is reduced by lowering the storage temperature. In general, it can be said that the following storage periods are roughly equivalent (see also pp. 524).

|               | °F. | °C. |
|---------------|-----|-----|
| 3 months at   | 15  | −10 |
| 6 months at   | 10  | −12 |
| 9 months at   | 5   | −15 |
| 12 months at  | 0   | −18 |
| 24 months at  | −10 | −23 |
| 36 months at  | −20 | −29 |

However, it must be kept in mind that various factors influence the rate of deterioration other than temperature. Of these, the type of packaging employed is of great importance (see Chapter 4, this volume and Chapter 12, Volume 2). Another factor is the frequency and latitude of temperature fluctuations. At lower temperatures, the rate of the deterioration of most precooked frozen foods is approximately the same at a given uniformly maintained temperature, and at the same mean temperature under fluctuating conditions, provided the maximum temperature is not so high that the product softens or partially thaws.

However, it must be remembered that widely fluctuating temperatures will cause the crystal size to grow during storage. This is particularly objectionable in ice cream, sherbets, ices, and also in sauces and gravies and other emulsions and colloids which may break or separate because of the changes in colloidal structure (see also pp. 44 and 314).

Also, it is important to note that certain products, which have a high soluble solids content, partially thaw at 15°F. (−10°C.) and consequently must not be allowed to warm to this temperature. Strawberry and other shortcakes, various ice cream toppings, many ice creams, sherbets, and ices belong in this class.

### OFF - FLAVORS CAUSED BY
### INSECTICIDES, FUNGICIDES, AND HERBICIDES

Much work has been carried out during the past decade to determine which insecticides, fungicides, and herbicides adversely affect the flavor of vegetables and fruits (Arthey and Adam 1964; Birdsall Weckel and Chapman 1957; Crang and Clarke 1961; Hening, Davis, and Robinson 1954; Murphy *et al.* 1961; Stitt and Evanston 1949; Tichenor *et al.* 1959). This work has shown that off-flavors in strawberries may under certain conditions be caused by a number of chemicals including aldrin, sulfur, Captan (Orthocide), Zineb (zinc ethylene bisdithiocarbamate), Thiram, Nabam (Dithane D14), Dichloran (Allisan, and metaisosystox). Peaches may take on off-flavors if sprayed with Lindane. Raspberries may be affected by Griseofulvin.

Potatoes, carrots, lima beans and peas may take on an off-flavor from Lindane. Pumpkin may be affected by dieldrin. Beets are sometimes given off-flavors by endrin.

Herbicides used in controlling weeds are not likely to give the crops grown on treated soils detectable off-flavors (Arthey and Adam 1964).

In general, sulfur and sulfur containing sprays and dusts (e.g., the thiocarbamates: ferbam, ziran, Thiram, Nabam, and Zineb) should be used cautiously on many crops. Some processors, have reported off-flavors in strawberries sprayed with Captan. Lindane has been known to cause off-flavors in potatoes and other root crops. These chemicals should not be applied to fruits and vegetables just prior to harvest if the products are to be used in foods to be frozen.

### CHANGES OCCURRING DURING REHEATING

#### Palatability and Nutritive Value

Some authors report that reheating of precooked frozen vegetables in a double boiler usually resulted in a product having greater palatability than those obtained by other methods (heating in Maxon oven, household range oven, in a polyethylene bag in boiling water, or in a dielectric oven).

Table 6

Mean Ascorbic Acid Retentions in Frozen Cooked Vegetables
Reheated by Several Methods

| Reheating Method | Mean Ascorbic Acid Retention % | | |
|---|---|---|---|
| | Cut Green Beans | Swiss Chard | Broccoli |
| Maxon oven | 71 | 66 | 91 |
| Household oven | 75 | 64 | 74 |
| Double boiler | 59 | 79 | 79 |
| Boiling water | 76 | — | 82 |
| Dielectric oven | 67 | 85 | 85 |

Source: Causey and Fenton (1951).

Causey and Fenton's observations on retention of ascorbic acid in frozen cooked green beans, Swiss chard, and broccoli are shown in Table 6. These results indicate only moderate losses of the vitamin during thawing and re-heating.

## CHANGES IN BAKED GOODS AND SANDWICHES

If properly packaged, most types of bread, rolls, cake, cookies, and pies can be frozen, stored, and thawed without marked change. After thawing, most custard pies "weep," and, without a marked change in formula, are not very satisfactory. Some types of bread change in texture and become rather crumbly.

Proper packaging is of very great importance for baked goods to be frozen. Packaging should be moisture-vapor-proof, not only to prevent the products from drying out in storage, but also to prevent condensation from wetting the surface of the cold product when it is brought out of storage for thawing on humid days. If much condensation occurs, the product will become soggy or the icing will become sticky, and this is likely to be highly objectionable, especially in the case of cookies. For further information concerning packaging of precooked foods and baked goods, see Chapter 4.

If one side of a sandwich or a loaf of sliced bread is much colder than the other, moisture will migrate from the warmer toward the colder side (Chapter 5, p. 130). Care must therefore be taken to avoid such a condition during freezing and thawing.

### BIBLIOGRAPHY

## Part 1.  Chemical and Physical Changes

Anon.  1965. New freeze-thaw stable potato starch. Food Technol. *19*, No. 12, 44.

Arthey, V. D., and Adam, W. B.  1964. Off-flavor of frozen foods through plant insecticides. Quick Frozen Foods *26*, No. 7, 125–126, 169–172; No. 8, 62, 66, 70, 74; No. 9, 46–47; No. 10, 43–44.

Barackman, R. A., and Klis, J. B.  1962. Eliminates blackening of cooked potato products. Food Processing *23*, No. 7, 76–77.

Bauernfeind, J. C.  1953. The use of ascorbic acid in processing foods. Advances in Food Research *4*, 359–431. Academic Press, New York.

Beveridge, E.  1956. Recent research in freezing. What's New in Home Economics *20*, No. 5, 26–27, 66–68.

Birdsall, J. J., Weckel, K. G., and Chapman, R. K.  1957. Effects of chlorinated hydrocarbon insecticides on flavors of vegetables. J. Agr. Food Chem. *5*, 523–526.

Brekke, J. E., and Talburt, W. F.  1950. Prevention of sucrose hydrate formation in cold processed frozen fruit spreads. Food Technol. *4*, 383–386.

Causey, K., and Fenton, F.  1951. Effect of reheating on palatability, nutritive value, and bacterial count of frozen cooked foods. I. Vegetables. J. Am. Dietet. Assoc. 27, 390–395. II. Meat dishes. *Ibid.* 27, 491–495.

Crang, A., and Clarke, G. M. 1961. Effect of some fungicides on the flavor of fruits and syrups. J. Sci. Food Agr. *12*, 227–234.

Davis, J. G., Hanson, H. L., and Lineweaver, H 1952. Characterization of the effect of freezing on cooked egg white. Food Research *17*, 393–401.

Diehl, H. C., and Berry, J. A. 1933. Relation of scalding practice and storage temperature to quality retention of frozen pack peas. Proc. Am. Soc. Hort. Sci. *30*, 496–500.

Dugan, L. R., Jr., Kraybill, H. R., Ireland, L., and Vibrans, F. C. 1950. Butylated hydroxyanisole as an antioxidant for fats and foods made with fat. Food Technol. *4*, 457–460.

Dyer, W. J., and Horne, D. C. 1953. Yellow discoloration in frozen lobster meat. Fisheries Research Board Can., Atlantic Fisheries Expt. Sta. Circ. New Series *2*.

Fenton, F. 1946. Unknown factors upset precooked foods quality control. Food Freezing *1*, 163–165.

Fenton, F. 1947. Frozen cooked foods. Refrig. Eng. *53*, 107–111.

Fenton, F. 1949. Experiments with precooked and ready-to-cook frozen foods. Electrical Women's Round Table, Inc. Workshop for Electrical Living Manual *1949*, 11–16.

Fenton, F., and Darfler, J. 1946. Foods from the freezer-precooked or prepared. Cornell Bull. for Homemakers *692*.

Fitzgerald, G. A. 1947. How to control the quality of frozen cooked foods. Food Inds. *19*, 623–625, 730, 732, 734.

Gleim, E., and Fenton, F. 1949. Effect of 0°F. and 15°F. storage on the quality of frozen cooked foods. Food Technol. *3*, 187–192.

Hanson, H. L., Campbell, A., and Lineweaver, H. 1951. Preparation of stable frozen sauces and gravies. Food Technol. *5*, 432–440.

Hanson, H. L., Nishita, K. D., and Lineweaver, H. 1953. Preparation of stable frozen puddings. Food Technol. *7*, 462–465.

Hanson, H. L., Winegarden, H. M., Horton, M. B., and Lineweaver, H 1950. Preparation and storage of frozen cooked poultry and vegetables. Food Technol. *4*, 430–434.

Heerdt, M., Jr., and Dassow, J. A. 1952. Freezing and cold storage of Pacific Northwest fish and shellfish. Part II. King crab. U.S. Fish and Wildlife Service, Com. Fisheries Rev. *14*, No. 12A, 29–35.

Hening, J. C., Davis, A. C., and Robinson, W. B. 1954. Flavor and color evaluation of canning crops grown on soil treated with insecticides. Food Technol. *8*, 227–229.

Hutchings, B. L., and Evers, C. F. 1946A. Research and quality control of precooked frozen foods. Refrig. Eng. *51*, No. 1, 27–29, 61, 78, 82.

Hutchings, B. L., and Evers, C. F. 1946B. Problems in the production of precooked frozen foods. Food Technol. *1*, 421–426.

Joslyn, M. A., and Diehl, H. C. 1952. Physiological aspects of low-temperature preservation of plant products. Ann. Rev. Plant Physiol. *3*, 149–170.

Klose, A. A., Mecchi, E. P., and Hanson, H. L. 1952. Use of antioxidants in the frozen storage of turkeys. Food Technol. *6*, 308–311.

Lineweaver, H:, Anderson, J. D., and Hanson, H L. 1952. Effect of antioxidant on rancidity development in frozen creamed turkey. Food Technol. *6*, 1–4.

Longrée, K. 1950. Quality problems in cooked, frozen potatoes. Food Technol. *4*, 98–104.

Lugg, J. W. H.   1950. Note on the effects of nitrate and nitrite upon ascorbic acid in acid solution. Med. J. Malaya 5, No. 2, 140–145.

Morrison, G. S.   1956. An investigation of the chemistry of factors affecting changes in the texture of frozen blue crab meat. Unpublished data.

Morse, R. E.   1955. How phosphates can benefit meats. Food Eng. 27, No. 10, 84–86.

Murphy, E. F., Briant, A. M., Doods, M. L., Fagerson, I. S., Kirkpatrick, M. E., and Wiley, R. C.   1961. Effect of insecticides and fungicides on the flavor quality of fruits and vegetables. J. Agr. Food Chem. 9, 214–223.

Nicholas, J. E., Ruth, D., and Swanson, M. E.   1947. Crystallization behavior in the freezing of fresh fruit pies. Frozen Food Industry 3, No. 7, 8–9, 31–34.

Olson, G., Nicholas, J. E., and Ruth, D.   1948. Factors in the crispness of the lower crust of some frozen fruit pies. Quick Frozen Foods 11, No. 1, 67–69.

Overman, A.   1947. Antioxidant effect of soybean flour in frozen pastry. Food Research 12, 365–371.

Stitt, L. L., and Evanston, J.   1949. Phytotoxicity and off-quality of vegetables grown in soil treated with insecticides. J. Econ. Entomol. 42, 614–617.

Tappel, A. L.   1954. Expanding uses of antioxidants. Food Eng. 26, No. 6, 73–75, 133–134.

Tichenor, D. A., Rodriguez, J. G., and Chaplin, C. E.   1959. The effect of certain pesticides on the flavor of frozen strawberries. Food Technol. 13, 587–590.

Tressler, D. K.   1953. What's new in frozen foods? J. Am. Dietet. Assoc. 29, 230–233.

Tressler, D. K., and Evers, C. F.   1936. The Freezing Preservation of Fruits, Fruit Juices, and Vegetables. Avi Publishing Co., New York.

Watts, B. M.   1954. Oxidative rancidity and discoloration in meat. In Advances in Food Research 5, 1–52. Academic Press, New York.

Watts, B. M., and Lehmann, B. T.   1952. Ascorbic acid and meat color. Food Technol. 6, 194–196.

Watts, B. M., and Peng, D.   1947. Rancidity development in raw versus precooked frozen pork sausage. J. Home Econ. 39, 88–92.

Woodroof, J. G.   1946. Problems in freezing cooked foods. Quick Frozen Foods 8, No. 9, 90–91.

Woodroof, J. G., and Atkinson, I. S.   1945. Freezing cooked foods. Food Inds. 17, 1041–1042, 1136–1138, 1179–1180, 1264, 1266.

Young, F. E., Jones, F. T., and Lewis, H. J.   1951. Prevention of the growth of sucrose hydrates in sucrose syrups. Food Research 16, 20–29.

Thomas J. Schoch

*PART 2*

# Effects of Freezing and Cold Storage on Pasted Starches

## INTRODUCTION

Uncooked or ungelatinized starches are not affected in any discernible way by freezing in the presence of water or by prolonged cold storage. While the cell structure of uncooked starchy vegetables (e.g., fresh legumes, corn-on-the-cob, potatoes) may undergo considerable mechanical damage by improper freezing, the starch granules themselves remain intact and unchanged. However, if the granules have been gelatinized[1] by cooking in the presence of water, the resulting pasted starch becomes susceptible to various changes in physical character on long refrigeration or during freezing. Typical instances where the starch is in a pasted state include bread and other baked goods, cooked starchy cereals and vegetables, and the wide variety of prepared foods where flour or refined starch is added as a thickening or stabilizing agent (e.g., cream soups, white sauces, toppings, pie fillings, baby foods).

The undesirable physical changes which occur during the freezing of pasted starch systems include the following: (a) increase in opacity of the product; (b) development of a coarse grainy structure and pulpy "mouthfeel"; (c) excessive increase in consistency and even congelation; and (d) the loss of water-holding capacity. As examples, the crumb structure of bread becomes hard and coarse (staling), starch thickened sauces may set up to rigid gels, and frozen pie-fillings may show the syneresis of a watery phase on thawing.

## THEORY OF STARCH INSTABILITY

The above physical changes are all attributable to associative hydrogen-bonding between starch molecules, whereby the pasted starch progressively becomes more desolvated or insoluble, and simultaneously loses its ability to hold water. In order to understand the effects of cold storage and freezing on starchy systems, it is necessary to consider certain pertinent aspects of the physicochemical behavior of starch molecules. Most common starches

---

Thomas J. Schoch is Senior Chemist and Research Group Leader, Moffett Technical Center, Corn Products Co., Argo, Ill.

[1] The starch granule is considered as pasted or gelatinized when it has been heated in the presence of water to a temperature sufficient to initiate swelling and to cause extinction of the characteristic birefringence cross when viewed under the polarizing microscope.

(e.g., corn, sorghum, wheat, rice, potato, tapioca) contain two types of polysaccharides. The minor component (termed the linear fraction or "amylose") is an extended chain molecule of some 500–2000 glucose units in length. The major component (the branched fraction or "amylopectin") is a highly branched or tree-like molecule with some hundreds of linear branches, each of which is 20–30 glucose units in length.

The linear-chain molecules show a strong tendency to associate with one another through hydrogen-bonding between hydroxyl groups; this phenomenon has been termed "retrogradation" and becomes apparent in either of two ways (Fig. 3):

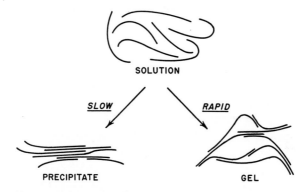

SOLUTION

SLOW          RAPID

PRECIPITATE          GEL

Fig. 3.   Mechanisms of retrogradation of the linear starch fraction. Dilute solutions slowly deposit an insoluble precipitate (left). Concentrated solutions rapidly set up to rigid gels (right).

(1) In dilute starch systems, the linear molecules slowly align themselves in parallel fashion to give insoluble bundles or "micelles," which cause opacity and eventual precipitation.

(2) In more concentrated systems (e.g., a cooked five per cent cornstarch paste), the linear molecules rapidly associate in random fashion to give the reticulated network of a gel. Thus cooked starchy foods develop firmness or gel characteristics on cooling and particularly on refrigeration, as exemplified by boiled potatoes, cooked oatmeal, and the old-fashioned type of molded cornstarch pudding.

Since the branched starch molecules are relatively globular in shape, and since they contain only short linear branches, they do not undergo the pronounced retrogradation of the linear molecules. However, these short linear branches are still capable of some degree of inter- and intra-molecular association through hydrogen-bonding. This probably involves a folding-up of the extended branches, and the slow progressive development of associative bonding both within and between branched molecules (Fig. 4). Actually, the mechanism of association of branched molecules is identical in principle with retrogradation of linear molecules; the only difference lies in the strength of the bonding. Thus a strongly retrograded gel or insoluble precipitate of linear molecules can be liquefied or redissolved only by heating to super-temperatures of 284°–302°F. (140°–150°C.). In contrast, an associated system of branched molecules can be readily dissociated merely by warming to 122°–140°F. (50°–60°C.). Both types of association occur in bread (Schoch and French 1947; Schoch 1965). The elastic gel structure of normal fresh bread (i.e., not "softened" with monoglyceride) is attributed to an associated network of linear molecules of the wheat starch, developed during baking and cooling of the loaf. The subsequent hardening or staling of the crumb structure is due to the gradual association of branched molecules; this may be readily reversed simply by reheating or toasting the bread.

In contrast with starch molecules, the polysaccharide glycogen has extremely high physical stability. This substance is present in certain shellfish (oysters, scallops), in animal liver, and in golden sweet corn. It is a highly branched glucose polymer with an average branch length of 9–11 glucose units. Hence its structure is tight and "bushy," as compared with the loose tree-like molecules of the branched starch fraction. Because its branches are too short to associate, glycogen shows no evidence of retrogradation or insolubilization. Solutions of relatively high concentration may be maintained indefinitely in cold storage, or may be subjected to repeated freezing and thawing, without any evidence of opacity or precipitation.

## PHYSICAL EFFECTS OF STARCH INSTABILITY

The physical changes in starchy foods during freezing or cold-storage are due both to retrogradation of linear molecules and (to a lesser extent) association of branched molecules. The normal cereal starches (corn, sorghum, wheat, rice) show a high degree of linear retrogradation, and hence foods containing these pasted starches are most prone to form gels, to develop opacity, and to show decreased water-holding capacity. Unmodified root and tuber starches (particularly tapioca and potato) have a lower content of linear fraction, and are less susceptible to retrogradative changes. However, these latter starches swell excessively when cooked in water, to give cohesive and somewhat slimy pastes; hence they are not generally acceptable as thickeners in American food products. Specific genetic varieties of certain cereals contain only branched starch substance, and hence the retrogradation of linear molecules is absent. These are the so-called "waxy" or amylopectin starches, commercially derived from waxy maize (or waxy corn), waxy sorghum, and to a very limited extent from waxy rice. Pastes from these waxy starches are likewise cohesive in character, and hence the unmodified starches are not generally used in foods, despite their relatively good physical stability toward freezing.

One undesirable aspect of the association of starch molecules is the increase in viscosity or even congelation of the product. Thus starch-thickened sauces may lose their smooth creamy consistency during freezing, and become lumpy or curdled in texture. In many cases, reheating will not fully restore the original appearance of the product. Another objectionable effect is the development of opacity. For example, the starch-thickened sauce in fruit-pie fillings should be transparent, to enhance the color and brightness of the fruit. Freezing or prolonged cold storage may cause insolubilization of the starch, thus imparting a dull opaque appearance to the filling.

Perhaps the most objectionable effect is the loss of water-holding capacity of the pasted starch. As the linear and branched molecules associate and contract, water molecules previously held within the system are literally squeezed out, becoming evident as the syneresis of a watery phase (Fig. 4).

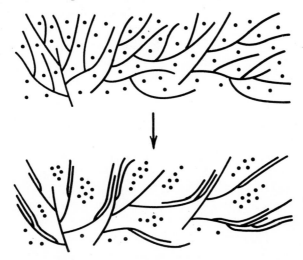

Fig. 4. Associative bonding within and between branched starch molecules. Freezing causes the starch paste (top) to lose its hydration capacity for water molecules (indicated as small black circles) with consequent sponge formation and syneresis of watery fluid (bottom).

For example, if a cooked cornstarch paste of five to seven per cent concentration is frozen and then thawed, the resulting structure is that of a microsponge. If this spongy mass is squeezed, most of the water can be pressed out, devoid of any soluble starch. Thus the starch molecules have associated to such an extent that the hydration capacity of the paste has been lost. An interesting practical application of this effect is the production of a dry starch sponge for use as a surgical packing material (MacMasters and Hoagland 1952). A cornstarch paste is frozen, thawed, and water pressed out, and the sponge then dried and granulated. The product has been recommended for packing cavities in surgery to avoid adhesions during healing. Subsequently, the associated starch is slowly liquefied and digested by normal amylases in the body fluids, and thus the packing is eventually absorbed.

When seepage or syneresis of water occurs on thawing a frozen food, simple recooking will frequently reconstitute a homogeneous paste, since the branched molecules thereby dissociate and expand to reabsorb the separated water. However, the aesthetic appearance of syneresis in the thawed paste is highly objectionable, suggesting to the housewife that the food has "curdled" or perhaps even been subject to microbiological spoilage. Another unpleasant effect is encountered with frozen fruit pies, where the unbaked pie shell is filled with the fruit in a starch-thickened sauce, and the pie then frozen. If syneresis occurs during thawing, the bottom crust will become soggy during subsequent baking. Also, this separated water may boil out through the steam vents in the top crust during baking, thus ruining the appearance of the pie.

The physical changes which occur in pasted starch during prolonged cold storage at 39°F. (4°C.) seem to parallel the changes caused by freezing and thawing. The only difference is the extent and rapidity of these changes; thus one cycle of freezing and thawing may cause as much damage to the hydration capacity of the pasted starch as several weeks of cold storage at 39°F. (4°C.). The worst possible circumstance is very slow freezing, since the gradual formation of large ice crystals causes a progressive increase of the starch concentration in the still-unfrozen portions of the paste, thus promoting associative bonding. Extremely poor practices have been encountered in the commercial freezing of unbaked cherry pies, where the pies were packed in corrugated-board shipping cartons and the latter piled closely together in the freezing chamber. With inadequate circulation of cold air, pies in the inner cartons may require several days to become fully frozen. Hence the thawed fillings were dull and opaque in appearance, the texture was grainy, and the crusts were sopping wet with separated water. No starch paste will withstand this maltreatment. Fast freezing is essential, and it is likewise important that the pie be kept in a fully frozen state until it is finally placed in the oven for baking. Even when properly frozen, a common hazard is that the starch-thickened food may become wholly or partly thawed by accident, and then refrozen. For example, the distributor of frozen fruit pies may deliver his products to a retail supermarket on a hot summer day. There may be a delay in placing the cartons in freeze-storage, and consequently some thawing and refreezing may occur. The housewife may purchase these refrozen pies, place them in the hot trunk-compartment of her car while she does other shopping, and finally refreeze the partly thawed pies in her own home freezer pending use. Even the most stable starchy food will break down under such conditions of repeated freezing and thawing.

Pasted starches appear to be completely stable when quickly frozen and then maintained in a deep-frozen state. In this connection, an early method of starch fractionation involved the quick-freezing of thin layers of potato starch paste followed by rapid thawing and filtration (Baldwin 1930). Under these circumstances, the linear molecules did not retrograde but remained dissolved in the aqueous filtrate. Similarly, recent studies on the quick-freezing of various pasted starches with liquid nitrogen showed no development of a curdled appearance or sponge-like structure on thawing (Albrecht *et al.* 1960). Studies on frozen bread are likewise pertinent.[2] While the rate of staling of bread is maximum around 27°F. (−3°C.), it is substantially retarded at +5°F. (−15°C.) and completely inhibited by quick-freezing and prolonged storage at −31°F. (−35°C.) (Katz 1928; Cathcart 1941). In these instances, water is presumably removed so rapidly from the pasted starch system in the form of fine ice crystals that the starch molecules literally have no time to associate. The common practice of storing bread in the refrigerator may be excellent for flavor maintenance and prevention of mold, but it accelerates staling. With bread as with other starchy foods, not only should the product be quickly frozen to a low temperature, but thawing should likewise be rapid. Slow thawing may be almost as detrimental to the texture and consistency as slow freezing.

### FACTORS INFLUENCING STARCH INSTABILITY

The following general considerations are pertinent to pasted starch systems which are frozen or which are maintained under prolonged refrigeration:

(1) The higher the starch concentration, the more rapid is the associative bonding. This is simply due to the closer proximity of molecules, and hence the greater probability of intermolecular combination.

(2) Associative bonding increases as the temperature of the pasted starch is lowered toward the freezing point. This may be ascribed to slowing of kinetic motion in the high-polymeric starch molecules, thereby favoring association.

(3) The longer the pasted starch is held in a near-frozen state, the greater is the association. However, no change occurs while in a "deep-frozen" state, e.g., at −13°F.(−25°C.).

(4) Thoroughly cooked starch pastes (i.e., cooked at an active boil) are

---

[2] For excellent reviews of the role of starch in bread-staling, see Geddes and Bice (1946) and Bice and Geddes (1953).

less prone to undergo physical changes than under-cooked starch, probably because of the better initial hydration and dispersion of the starch molecules.

(5) The higher the acidity of the system (i.e., down to pH 3), the greater is the tendency of the starch to associate or retrograde. The reason is obscure, but may perhaps be due to increased hydrogen-bonding activity at low pH.

(6) The presence of sugar usually hinders association of the starch molecules, probably by interposing mechanical obstructions between the parallel alignment of linear starch chains. However, higher concentrations of sugar may interfere with optimum cooking of the starch, by sequestering water and hence limiting the hydration of the starch. Such cooked starch-sugar systems may therefore show increased tendencies to associate. In such cases, a common practice is to withhold all or part of the sugar until after the starch has been thoroughly cooked in the water medium.

(7) Similarly, the introduction of chemical derivative groups (esters or ethers) into the starch molecules prevents association between linear chains and linear segments of branched molecules.

### FREEZE – RESISTANT STARCH MODIFICATIONS

The starch manufacturers have long been engaged in research activities to develop starch thickeners which will not be subject to such physical changes as syneresis or congelation during freezing or prolonged cold storage, but which will reconstitute to homogeneous pastes on thawing. While this might be readily accomplished in an industrial nonfood starch by etherifying with hydroxyethyl or carboxymethyl groups, such modifications are quite unacceptable in a food product. Hence the development of cold- and freeze-stable starches has taken the following direction. Base starches are those which have minimum association tendencies, particularly waxy maize and waxy sorghum starches, and to a lesser extent tapioca starch. While these unmodified starches have good paste clarity and show fairly good freeze resistance, they give cooked pastes of an undesirable stringy cohesive character, due to excessive swelling of the starch granules. Also, cooked pastes break down and lose viscosity under mechanical agitation, autoclaving, or acid conditions. To correct these deficiencies, the ungelatinized granular starches are chemically cross-bonded in alkaline medium with such agents as epichlorohydrin (Konigsberg 1950), phosphorus oxychloride (Felton and Schopmeyer 1943), or sodium trimetaphosphate (Kerr and Cleveland 1957). The introduction of trace amounts of ester or ether cross-linkages (i.e., less than 1 part per 1,000, based on starch weight) between the starch molecules stabilizes the granule against excessive swelling. Hence such cross-linked starches give heavy-bodied noncohesive pastes, are much less prone to thin out during autoclaving or under acid conditions, and in addition retain the high paste clarity of the parent starches (Kite *et al.* 1963). The presence of these trace cross-linkages does not impair the digestibility of the starch, and these products are generally recognized as food-acceptable in the United States. However, cross-bonding substantially reduces the cold storage and freeze stability of the starch (Fig. 5). Hence it

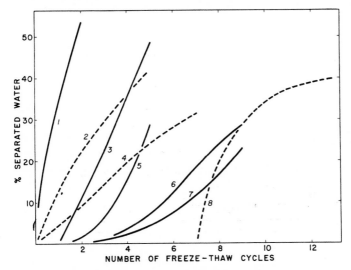

Fig. 5. Comparative freeze-thaw stabilities of various modified starches. (1) unmodified normal sorghum starch, (2) cross-bonded waxy sorghum starch, (3) unmodified waxy sorghum starch at pH 3, (4) cross-bonded waxy sorghum starch with additional acetate esterification, (5) waxy sorghum starch at pH 6, (6) cross-bonded waxy sorghum starch with additional ionic phosphate esterification, (7) unmodified waxy sorghum starch with ionic phosphate esterification, (8) waxy rice flour.

is necessary to superimpose a second modification on the cross-bonded starch, to introduce either acetate ester groups (Wurzburg 1960) or ionized phosphate ester groups (Kerr and Cleveland 1959). The introduction of a few such ester groups interferes with side-by-side alignment of linear chains and linear segments of branched molecules. Hence the freeze resistance of the pasted starch can be improved to the desired degree, without loss of paste clarity, thickening power, acid resistance, or water-holding capacity. The introduction of either phosphate or acetate groups at effective levels is also acceptable from the standpoint of U.S. food regulations.

## Tests for Freeze Resistance

The writer and his associates[3] have studied various practical tests for evaluating the cold storage stability and freeze resistance of various food starches. The criterion chosen was the rate of syneresis of water from the pasted starch, since this represents the most objectionable feature of instability. In preliminary studies, cooked five per cent starch pastes were maintained in the refrigerator at 39°F. (4°C.) for long periods of time, and the pastes centrifuged at intervals of a week to determine the progressive release of free water. Results of these stability tests showed good correlation with practical observations on both cold storage stability and freeze resistance of starch-thickened foods. However, the more stable starches might require as much as 3–4 months to show syneresis, far too long for practical test purposes. Hence a technique of repeated freeze-thaw cycles was finally adopted, and results therefrom have agreed well with prolonged cold storage tests and with practical evaluation on frozen starch-thickened foods.

Since this freeze-thaw test has not previously been published, some details may be appropriate. Depending on ultimate intended use, the test may be run in distilled water at pH 6.0, or in citric acid solution at pH 3.5, or in 37° Brix sucrose solution (either neutral or acidified). An appropriate amount (500–1,000 ml.) of five per cent starch paste in the desired medium is cooked for 30 min. in a boiling waterbath with moderate mechanical agitation, and the paste then cooled to room temperature. Several drops of three per cent phenyl mercuric acetate solution in formamide is added to inhibit any microbiological activity during long runs. In addition, approximately 100 mg. of precipitated silver iodide is stirred into the paste to act as nuclei to prevent supercooling during freezing. The paste is transferred to 50-ml. graduated centrifuge tubes, the latter placed overnight in a stirred 50% glycol bath maintained at +18°F. (−8°C.) and finally placed in a 86°F. (30°C.) waterbath for 1.5 hr. to thaw and equilibrate. Two of the tubes are centrifuged for 15 min. at 900× gravity, and the amount of any separated water determined. If this is less than 1 ml., all of the tubes are returned to the freezing bath for a second cycle. If more than 1 ml. of watery phase separates on centrifuging, the two centrifuged samples are discarded, and the remainder of the tubes returned to the freezing bath. Successive freeze-thaw cycles are run (discarding the centrifuged samples whenever the separated water exceeds 1 ml.), until ultimate equilibrium has been reached or until all the tubes have been used. The percentage of separated water is plotted against the number of freeze-thaw cycles. In general, one such freeze-thaw cycle is approximately equivalent to three weeks' cold storage at 39°F. (4°C.) In a practical sense, pastes may be considered

[3] The writer acknowledges with thanks the inclusion of previously unpublished material obtained by Dr. F. E. Kite and Mr. Jonas Montvila.

as stable until the separated water exceeds five to ten per cent. As a more rigorous variation of this procedure, the tubes may be frozen in a still-air freezer at $+18°F.$ ( $-8°C.$); the slower freezing time accentuates instability of the starch.

### Examples of Freeze-Resistant Starches

The relative freeze-thaw stabilities of various commercial and laboratory-prepared starches are shown in Fig. 5. Two different patterns of instability have been observed: (a) a slow progressive syneresis of water with each successive freeze-thaw cycle, and (b) no separation of water for a number of cycles, followed by rapid deterioration. Results on the various starches may be summarized as follows:

(1) Normal unmodified sorghum starch shows a high degree of instability, with more than 30% water separation after a single freeze-thaw cycle. This is typical of the normal cereal starches containing a linear fraction (e.g., corn, wheat, rice), and the extreme instability may be attributed largely to retrogradation of linear molecules.

(2) Unmodified waxy sorghum starch shows good stability, withstanding three freeze-thaw cycles before marked syneresis occurs. Waxy maize starch (not shown) is virtually identical.

(3) However, waxy rice flour anomalously shows very high stability, with no water separation until after seven cycles. This unusual behavior of waxy rice was originally discovered by Helen Hanson and co-workers (Hanson *et al.* 1953; Davis *et al.* 1955), who recommended the flour as a thickener for frozen white sauces and the like. The refined starch (laboratory-prepared) shows even higher stability, with no syneresis until after 20 cycles (Schoch 1967). Limited amounts of waxy rice flour are marketed in the United States, and commercial waxy rice starch has occasionally been available in Western Europe.

(4) The stability of waxy sorghum starch decreases substantially at pH 3, and this effect of acidity is generally true of other starches studied.

(5) Waxy sorghum starch cross-bonded with 0.06% trimetaphosphate (calculated on dry-starch basis) shows considerable loss of stability. The reason is not known. Since the cross-bonded granules swell to a lesser degree during cooking, it is possible that the starch substance within the granule is in a less dispersed and more concentrated state, and hence more subject to molecular association.

(6) The introduction of either phosphate or acetyl ester groups into the cross-bonded waxy sorghum or waxy maize starch greatly improves the freeze resistance. While an absolute comparison is not possible, it appears that the ionic phosphate group may be somewhat more effective than acetate in promoting stability. If freezing causes contraction and asso-

ciation of the branched molecules, the mutual ionic repulsion between phosphate sites may assist molecular dilation and hydration on thawing.

### INSTANCES OF DESIRABLE ASSOCIATION BY COLD STORAGE OR FREEZING

The associative changes which occur in pasted starches during cold storage or freezing are usually detrimental to the character of the food. However, several isolated instances may be cited where desirable results are achieved by retrogradation. For example, the gel strength of the old-fashioned cooked cornstarch pudding was increased by refrigeration, so that it could be cast and unmolded from a decorative form. Similarly, it is frequently recommended that boiled potatoes intended for potato salad be chilled for several hours, to increase the firmness by retrogradation. A somewhat similar procedure is employed in one method for manufacturing dehydrated mashed potatoes, whereby the potatoes are given a preliminary low-temperature cook to partially swell the starch granules, then cooled on a belt conveyor, and finally given a high-temperature cook (Sullivan et al. 1961). The retrogradation which occurs during the intermediate cooling period rigidifies the partially swollen granules, so that excessive swelling and consequent rupture of cell walls do not occur during the secondary cooking. Hence, after final dehydration, the product reconstitutes to a more fluffy and less cohesive texture.

The so-called "harusame" or "spring-rain" noodles of the Far East provide the best example of deliberate retrogradation to achieve certain desired results (Yamamura and Kono 1966). This product is a fine soup noodle, quite transparent in either dry or cooked form; hence a mass of parallel strands have apparently evoked the poetical comparison with the thin transparent appearance of a springtime rain shower. The writer has observed the manufacture of these noodles from potato starch and from white sweet potato starch in Hong Kong and in Japan. Approximately 3–6% of the total starch is first cooked in the requisite amount of water to give a thin paste; the remainder of the starch is then added to give a heavy slurry of 40–45% solids concentration. This suspension of ungelatinized granular starch in pasted starch has a peculiar dilatant flow similar to "silly putty." It is allowed to flow by gravity through a perforated screen to give thin strands which fall into a vat of vigorously boiling water. The strands are cooked for perhaps 15–30 sec., then rinsed with cold water, and arranged in "hanks" on bamboo-slatted trays. The latter are placed in a refrigerated room, either near the freezing point, or else actually frozen at +5°F. (−15°C.). Finally the trays are moved out into the open air, and the noodles sun-dried. Reputedly, the original harusame noodles were made centuries ago in North China from semi-refined mung bean starch. This was presumably a "cottage-industry" type of operation, whereby the noodles were cooked indoors during the wintertime, then moved outdoors to freeze (and perhaps to freeze-dry).

For use, the harusame noodles are soaked for a short time in cold water to hydrate and soften the strands. These are then picked up with chopsticks, immersed for a few seconds in boiling broth, and served in various clear soups with boiled slices of fish, chicken, vegetables, etc. The freeze treatment or cold storage accomplishes several useful purposes. First, any solubilized starch between the individual strands is retrograded to an insoluble state, and hence cannot act as an adhesive to stick the dried noodles together to a solid mass. Second, sufficient retrogradation occurs within the noodles to permit them to survive the short immersion in boiling broth. If the noodles were simply dried at ambient temperature without the freeze treatment, they would disintegrate immediately in boiling broth. So it appears that retrogradation was known and practiced centuries ago in the art of harusame manufacture. It is possible that similar techniques would be useful in modifying the cooking characteristics of occidental foods.

## BIBLIOGRAPHY

Albrecht, J. J., Nelson, A. I., and Steinberg, M. P.  1960. Characteristics of corn starch and starch derivatives as affected by freezing, storage and thawing. I. Simple systems. Food Technol. *14*, 57–63.

Baldwin, M. E.  1930. Separation and properties of the two main components of potato starch. J. Am. Chem. Soc. *52*, 2907–2919.

Bice, C. W., and Geddes, W. F.  1953. The role of starch in bread staling. *In* Starch and Its Derivatives, edited by J. A. Radley, 3rd Edition, Vol. 2, 202–242. Chapman and Hall Ltd., London.

Cathcart, W. H.  1941. Further studies on the retardation of the staling of bread by freezing. Cereal Chem. *18*, 771–777.

Davis, J. G., Anderson, J. H., and Hanson, H. L.  1955. Starchy cereal thickening agents for canned food products. Food Technol. *9*, 13–17.

Felton, G. E., and Schopmeyer, H. H.  1943. Thick-bodied starch and method of making. U.S. Pat. 2,328,537. Sept. 7.

Geddes, W. F., and. Bice, C. W.  1946. The role of starch in bread staling. U.S. Quartermaster Corps Rept. QMC *17*–10.

Hanson, H. L., Nishita, K. D., and Lineweaver, H.  1953. Preparation of stable frozen puddings. Food Technol. *7*, 462–465.

Katz, J. R.  1928. Gelatinization and retrogradation of starch in relation to the problem of bread staling. *In* Comprehensive Survey of Starch Chemistry, edited by R. P. Walton, 100–117 Chemical Catalog Co., New York.

Kerr, R. W., and Cleveland, F. C.  1957. Process for the preparation of distarch phosphate and the resulting product. U.S. Pat. 2,801,242. July 30.

Kerr, R. W., and Cleveland, F. C.  1959. Orthophosphate esters of starch. U.S. Pat. 2,884,413. Apr. 28.

Kite, F. E., Maywald, E. C., and Schoch, T. J.  1963. Functional properties of food starches (in German). Die Stärke *15*, 131–138.

Konigsberg, M. 1950. Ungelatinized starch ethers from polyfunctional etherifying agents. U.S. Pat. 2,500,950. Mar. 21.

MacMasters, M. M., and Hoagland, V. E. 1952. Preparation of starch sponge. U.S. Pat. 2,597,011. May 20.

Schoch, T. J. 1965. Starch in bakery products. Bakers Dig. 39, No. 2, 48–52, 54–57.

Schoch, T. J. 1967. Properties and uses of rice starch. In Starch: Chemistry and Technology, edited by R. L. Whistler and E. F. Paschall, Vol. 2, 79–86. Academic Press, New York.

Schoch, T. J., and French, D. 1947. Studies on bread staling. I. The role of starch. Cereal Chem. 24, 231–249.

Sullivan, J. F., Cording, J. and Willard, M. J., Jr. 1961. Process of producing dehydrated mashed potatoes. U.S. Pat. 3,012,897. December 12.

Wurzburg, O. B. 1960. Preparation of starch derivatives. U.S. Pat. 2,935,510. May 3.

Yamamura, E., and Kono, T. 1966. Studies on frozen starch noodles ("harusame"). I. Physical and chemical characteristics of the marketed product (in Japanese). J. Food Sci. and Technol. (Tokyo) 13, 322–328.

A. C. Peterson
M. J. Fanelli
and M. F. Gunderson

## PART 3
# Microbiological Problems

### INTRODUCTION

Like all other frozen foods, precooked frozen foods are preserved by freezing storage at temperatures below the minimum for microbial growth or action. Precooked frozen foods differ from other frozen foods in several important respects. All of the precooked frozen foods have received heat treatments in their processing which have materially and significantly modified the microbial flora of the ingredients and hence of the final product itself. But, generally there is no terminal sterilization. More significantly, these foods may be eaten without further heat treatment or may receive heat treatments which range from warming to pasteurizing effects.

### THE STATE OF THE ART

For the purposes of this discussion, all precooked and prefabricated (prepared) frozen foods which are not simply a commodity type of food will be considered. These foods range from raw or partially cooked doughs, rolls, breads, breaded seafoods, boil-in-the-bag uncooked vegetables with fabricated sauces, to prepared dinners, entrées and some boil-in-the-bag entrée items which only require warming, to some cakes and cream pies which need only to be defrosted. Some precooked foods are completely cooked during processing, for example, some frozen soups. Other foods are mixtures of raw fabricated components and completely cooked ones like the meat pot pies and frozen dinners which may require more than warming or pasteurizing heat treatment by the consumer to cook the raw portion.

In all of these precooked and prefabricated foods, the potential lurks even if only very vaguely, for food-borne infections or intoxications. This threat remains vaguely potential, however, only with the continuous, conscientious knowledgeable efforts by the processor. The efforts by the processor must begin with ingredients of excellent quality, especially microbiologically, carefully processed under conditions of excellent sanitation

A. C. Peterson is Division Head, Microbiological Research, Campbell Institute for Food Research, Camden, N.J.

M. J. Fanelli was Research Microbiologist, Campbell Institute for Food Research, Camden, N.J. Present address: Department of Epidemology and Preventative Medicine, University of California, Davis, Calif.

M. F. Gunderson was Director of Microbiological Research, Campbell Institute of Food Research, Camden, N.J., and is now retired.

and temperature control. They proceed through proper packaging and ex-
peditious freezing to 0°F. ( −18°C.) or below and storage under the same
condition. The story does not end there, however, because these foods
should be warehoused, transported, distributed, retailed, and even stored
by the consumer without having been thawed and having been preferen-
tially maintained at 0°F. ( −18°C.) or lower. Such temperatures are necessary to maintain the original quality of the product as produced by the
processor.

Frozen food processors have long realized that the freezing process cannot sterilize, pasteurize, or improve the microbiological quality of the product (Gunderson and Peterson 1964). They have likewise recognized that
adverse temperature effects on product quality due to thawing cannot be
reversed by refreezing (Peterson et al. 1963A, Peterson et al. 1963B, 1964).
These facts need to be emphasized to all concerned with frozen foods, and
especially to the consumer.

Precooking a food before freezing does not necessarily render it free from
pathogenic microorganisms. In those foods which do not receive terminal
sterilizing heat treatment, there is, as mentioned, a recognized potential
hazard of contamination with microbial pathogens and their growth or
toxin production in the food (a fortunately not materialized hazard). This
serious health hazard is least likely to develop during processing. It could
occur as a result of thawing at some point in the distribution chain (Geister
and Maack 1967), but would most likely occur as a result of mishandling
by the consumer (Dack 1956; Anon. 1960). The frozen food industry's educational program, concerning the care and protection which frozen foods
require, has been directed through the distribution chain, but processors
should recognize their responsibility to disseminate further and amplify this
information at the retailing and consumer levels.

A subcommittee on Milk and Food Protection of the Committee on Environmental Health Problems (PHS) observed that "technological changes
are occurring so rapidly in the food field that their public health implications are not receiving proper attention by either government or industry"
(Lewis 1962). Similar views were expressed by an international committee
which recommended microbiological standards for frozen foods, particularly for those precooked (Thatcher 1963). The concern for microbiological
health problems associated with precooked frozen foods has been well
summarized in a report of The Food Protection Subcommittee of the National Academy of Sciences (1964) as follows: "because of the great
amount of food produced in a short time in such processing operations and
because of the rapid and widespread distribution of food products, a very
large population is at risk in the event of a malfunction or error in the food
process." This latter fact, that large populations may be endangered, is the

crux of the entire matter of the public health aspects of precooked frozen foods (Peterson and Gunderson 1965).

For these reasons, considerable efforts have been made by various agencies, especially those charged with responsibilities for public health, to establish legal microbiological standards for precooked frozen foods. Such standards would be less stringent only than those for market milk, with which a frequent but fallacious parallel is drawn (Weiser 1957). The problem of microbiological standards for precooked frozen foods, however, is even more complex than the problem for fresh frozen foods, which was discussed previously in Chapter 13 of Volume 2. Without again delving deeply into the problem, the implications of such standards are most important and extend far beyond the selection of any particular numerical microbial index. These include especially, the actual or tacit assumption of responsibility by the processor for his product from the time of manufacture to actual consumption by the purchaser. This would be true even when the processor no longer has actual control of his product during its passage through many hands in the distribution chain, and even when the processor usually does not even have legal ownership of the food. Even the presence on the package of a reliable thawing indicator which effectively integrates the effect of exposure to various times at thawing temperatures as a true picture of quality changes in the product cannot resolve the larger issue. Excellent analyses of the problem of microbial standards for food have been given by Rayman et al. (1955); Dack (1956); Dack et al. (1960); Thatcher (1955, 1963); Abrahamson et al. (1959); Brandly (1960); Anon. (1960, 1961); Slocum (1961); Ingram (1961); and Shiffman and Kronick (1963). Elliott and Michener (1961) have provided a comprehensive review of the status of microbiological standards and handling codes for frozen foods.

One of the first reviews of the factors affecting quality of precooked frozen foods was provided by a symposium in 1955 sponsored by the U.S. Quartermaster Food and Container Institute. A more comprehensive review of the problems of precooked frozen foods and their microbiology is provided in the proceedings of a conference sponsored by the U.S. Department of Agriculture in 1960 (see Elliott and Michener 1960; also Fig. 43, Chapter 13, Volume 2).

### MICROBIOLOGICAL EXAMINATION OF PRECOOKED FOODS

The problems of microbiological analysis of precooked frozen foods are many. Perhaps most serious of these are the nonhomogeneity of samples from a given production run and even of parts of the same sample. The problem of obtaining replication of counts within the same laboratory as well as between different laboratories is much more severe than for milk (Donnelly *et al.* 1960; Messinger 1963).

Zaborowski *et al.* (1958), Fanelli and Ayres (1959), Hartman and Huntsberger (1961), and Lewis *et al.* (1964) have studied the applicability of various microbiological assay techniques to the examination of precooked frozen foods. The most useful and authoritative compilation of procedures is given in the second edition of *Recommended Methods for the Microbiological Examination of Foods* (APHA 1966).

### Total Aerobic Count

Most prominent in discussions of the microbiology of frozen foods, especially precooked ones, is the value of the total aerobic count. This determination and its significance were discussed in Chapter 13 of Volume 2. Microbiologists are generally agreed, however, that most foods involved in food poisoning and food-borne infections were those with large microbial populations (Hobbs 1953). Dack *et al.* (1960) observed that the total count was not a reflection of either the acceptability or the safety of frozen pot pies. They reported that the total count was a good measure of sanitation, however. These workers noted that the total count was a summation of many kinds of contamination and the time and temperature at which the ingredients were held.

Proctor and Phillips (1947, 1948) in one of the first surveys of precooked frozen foods reported that of over 100 types of such foods available in New England markets in 1947 and 1948, "The viable bacterial populations varied widely, some foods having plate counts of 50,000 per gram and a few having plate counts in excess of 1,000,000 per gram." These workers found that pastry products exhibited the lowest bacterial populations and creamed fish products, the highest. Data by Gunderson (1956), as shown in Table 7, early illustrated that frozen pot pies packed under good commercial practice should have low bacterial counts. Litsky *et al.* (1957) reported that over 70% of commercially prepared frozen beef, poultry, and tuna pies surveyed had total aerobic counts under 50,000 bacteria per gram. These data were substantiated by Kereluk and Gunderson (1959A) who reported that 83% of 188 samples of commercially produced meat pie samples had total aerobic counts less than 50,000 organisms per gram. They found that 12 of 56 chicken pot pies had total aerobic counts in excess of 100,000 bacteria per gram. Only one of 48 turkey pot pies had a total count in excess of 100,000 bacteria per gram. Two of 46 beef pot pies had total aerobic counts in excess of 100,000 bacteria per gram, and all 36 of the tuna pot pies had total counts less than 100,000 bacteria per gram. This latter result was probably a reflection of the use of canned tuna in the preparation of the tuna pies.

Of 117 samples of precooked frozen foods examined by Ross and Thatch-

Table 7

Total Plate Counts on Frozen Chicken Pies

| Time | Production Line (Week of January 6 to January 13, 1956) | | | | | |
|---|---|---|---|---|---|---|
| | 1-6-56 | 1-9-56 | 1-10-56 | 1-11-56 | 1-12-56 | 1-13-56 |
| 7:00 A.M. | 1,500 | 7,000 | 23,000 | 1,400 | 14,000 | 2,300 |
| 8:00 A.M. | 5,500 | 4,000 | 16,000 | 3,800 | 4,000 | 11,000 |
| 9:00 A.M. | 3,400 | 6,500 | 21,000 | 9,500 | 9,200 | 6,900 |
| 10:00 A.M. | 13,000 | 7,200 | 6,200 | 12,000 | 16,000 | 5,100 |
| 11:00 A.M. | 21,000 | 12,000 | 20,000 | 4,600 | 5,200 | 1,300 |
| 12:00 P.M. | 4,100 | 11,000 | 11,000 | 8,800 | 3,500 | 2,600 |
| 1:00 P.M. | 18,000 | 9,000 | 17,000 | 13,000 | 3,900 | 2,200 |
| 2:00 P.M. | 15,000 | 3,200 | 11,000 | 9,700 | 7,500 | 29,000 |
| 3:00 P.M. | 19,000 | 25,000 | 2,900 | 2,100 | 120,000[1] | 19,000 |
| 4:00 P.M. | 12,000 | 27,000 | 13,000 | 1,400 | 4,500 | 19,000 |
| 5:00 P.M. | 3,600 | 22,000 | 5,500 | 11,000 | 25,000 | 3,500 |
| 6:00 P.M. | 3,000 | 16,000 | 200,000[1] | 11,000 | 54,000 | 6,600 |
| 7:00 P.M. | 2,200 | 33,000 | 17,000 | 3,200 | 65,000 | 4,200 |
| 8:00 P.M. | 2,900 | 8,600 | 11,000 | 24,000 | 13,000 | 18,000 |
| 9:00 P.M. | 2,100 | 6,900 | 7,200 | 20,000 | 63,000 | 6,600 |
| 10:00 P.M. | 2,700 | 6,300 | 8,400 | 41,000 | 23,000 | 30,000 |
| 11:00 P.M. | 5,700 | 3,200 | 5,800 | 11,000 | 1,200 | 16,000 |
| Daily Average | 7,900 | 12,000 | 23,000 | 11,000 | 25,000 | 11,000 |

Source. M. F. Gunderson, Department of Bacteriology, University of Nebraska College of Medicine, Omaha, Neb.
[1] Such counts are subject to rechecks and complete bacteriological studies.

Table 8

Percentage of the Total Number of Organisms,
Coliforms and Staphylococci per gram of Retail
Samples of Turkey Pies Below Specific Levels for
Each Brand and for all Brands

| Brand | Percentage of Samples with Total Numbers of Organisms per Gram of Sample below | | | | | | |
|---|---|---|---|---|---|---|---|
| | 1,000 | 5,000 | 10,000 | 50,000 | 100,000 | 500,000 | 1,000,000 |
| A | 4.17 | 12.50 | 29.17 | 54.17 | 70.83 | 83.33 | 100.00 |
| B | 29.17 | 79.17 | 87.50 | 100.00 | 100.00 | 100.00 | 100.00 |
| C | 58.33 | 91.67 | 100.00 | 100.00 | 100.00 | 100.00 | 100.00 |
| D | 100.00 | 100.00 | 100.00 | 100.00 | 100.00 | 100.00 | 100.00 |
| E | 25.00 | 75.00 | 91.67 | 100.00 | 100.00 | 100.00 | 100.00 |
| F | 0.00 | 12.50 | 45.83 | 91.67 | 95.83 | 95.83 | 95.83 |
| G | 8.33 | 16.67 | 16.67 | 16.67 | 25.00 | 37.50 | 41.67 |
| H | 12.50 | 62.50 | 79.17 | 100.00 | 100.00 | 100.00 | 100.00 |
| J | 25.00 | 75.00 | 95.83 | 100.00 | 100.00 | 100.00 | 100.00 |
| K | 0.00 | 58.33 | 79.17 | 95.83 | 100.00 | 100.00 | 100.00 |
| L | 91.67 | 95.83 | 95.83 | 100.00 | 100.00 | 100.00 | 100.00 |
| M | 0.00 | 37.50 | 45.83 | 66.67 | 79.17 | 83.33 | 87.50 |
| N | 95.83 | 100.00 | 100.00 | 100.00 | 100.00 | 100.00 | 100.00 |
| All Brands | 34.62 | 62.82 | 74.36 | 86.54 | 90.06 | 92.31 | 94.23 |

| | Percentage of Samples with Coliforms per Gram of Sample below | | | | | |
|---|---|---|---|---|---|---|
| | 10 | 50 | 100 | 500 | 1,000 | 5,000 |
| A | 54.17 | 66.67 | 70.83 | 83.33 | 87.50 | 87.50 |
| B | 100.00 | 100.00 | 100.00 | 100.00 | 100.00 | 100.00 |
| C | 95.83 | 95.83 | 100.00 | 100.00 | 100.00 | 100.00 |
| D | 95.83 | 95.83 | 100.00 | 100.00 | 100.00 | 100.00 |
| E | 100.00 | 100.00 | 100.00 | 100.00 | 100.00 | 100.00 |
| F | 75.00 | 79.17 | 83.33 | 95.83 | 95.83 | 95.83 |
| G | 45.83 | 62.50 | 66.67 | 83.33 | 83.33 | 100.00 |
| H | 100.00 | 100.00 | 100.00 | 100.00 | 100.00 | 100.00 |
| J | 95.83 | 100.00 | 100.00 | 100.00 | 100.00 | 100.00 |
| K | 91.67 | 100.00 | 100.00 | 100.00 | 100.00 | 100.00 |
| L | 100.00 | 100.00 | 100.00 | 100.00 | 100.00 | 100.00 |
| M | 79.17 | 87.50 | 87.50 | 100.00 | 100.00 | 100.00 |
| N | 100.00 | 100.00 | 100.00 | 100.00 | 100.00 | 100.00 |
| All Brands | 87.18 | 91.35 | 92.95 | 97.12 | 97.44 | 98.72 |

| | Percentage of Samples with Staphylococci per Gram of Sample below[1] | | | | | | |
|---|---|---|---|---|---|---|---|
| | 10 | 50 | 100 | 500 | 1,000 | 5,000 | 10,000 |
| A | 4.17 | 4.17 | 8.33 | 33.33 | 45.83 | 62.50 | 79.17 |
| B | 37.50 | 62.50 | 66.67 | 91.67 | 100.00 | 100.00 | 100.00 |
| C | 41.67 | 87.50 | 91.67 | 100.00 | 100.00 | 100.00 | 100.00 |
| D | 95.83 | 100.00 | 100.00 | 100.00 | 100.00 | 100.00 | 100.00 |
| E | 50.00 | 75.00 | 91.67 | 100.00 | 100.00 | 100.00 | 100.00 |
| F | 12.50 | 16.67 | 16.67 | 29.17 | 37.50 | 87.50 | 91.67 |
| G | 8.33 | 12.50 | 12.50 | 20.83 | 29.17 | 45.83 | 45.83 |
| H | 54.17 | 79.17 | 83.33 | 100.00 | 100.00 | 100.00 | 100.00 |
| J | 66.67 | 95.83 | 95.83 | 100.00 | 100.00 | 100.00 | 100.00 |
| K | 4.17 | 16.67 | 29.17 | 70.83 | 83.33 | 100.00 | 100.00 |
| L | 87.50 | 91.67 | 91.67 | 100.00 | 100.00 | 100.00 | 100.00 |
| M | 20.83 | 45.83 | 50.00 | 91.67 | 91.67 | 100.00 | 100.00 |
| N | 66.67 | 100.00 | 100.00 | 100.00 | 100.00 | 100.00 | 100.00 |
| All Brands | 42.63 | 60.58 | 64.42 | 79.81 | 83.65 | 91.87 | 93.59 |

Source: Gunderson and Peterson (1964).
[1] Each brand represents seven different sample series, of three pies each, obtained from seven different retail outlets for a total of 21 samples per brand.

Table 9

Bacterial Counts—Frozen Turkey Dinners

Production Line (Week of Jan. 5 to Jan. 12, 1956)

| Time | Component | 1-5-56 | 1-6-56 | 1-9-56 | 1-10-56 | 1-11-56 | 1-12-56 |
|------|-----------|--------|--------|--------|---------|---------|---------|
| 7:00 A.M. | Meat | 1,000 | 2,100 | 1,000 | 1,500 | 1,600 | 15,000 |
| | Gravy | 1,400 | 1,000 | 1,000 | 1,000 | 4,200 | 1,200 |
| | Dressing | 1,000 | 1,000 | 3,200 | 6,700 | 2,500 | 32,000 |
| | Peas | 4,200 | 55,000 | 12,000 | 15,000 | 2,700 | 23,000 |
| | Potatoes | 2,200 | 6,000 | 4,900 | 6,100 | 2,800 | 12,900 |
| 9:00 A.M. | Meat | 1,000 | 5,200 | 8,700 | 3,100 | 1,000 | 1,800 |
| | Gravy · | 1,000 | 1,000 | 1,000 | 1,000 | 1,000 | 1,000 |
| | Dressing | 1,000 | 3,300 | 1,400 | 7,100 | 1,900 | 4,600 |
| | Peas | 1,000 | 3,800 | 26,000 | 42,000 | 6,000 | 7,200 |
| | Potatoes | 2,100 | 2,700 | 15,000 | 3,300 | 2,300 | 3,400 |
| 1:00 P.M. | Meat | 10,000 | 1,300 | 2,800 | 1,900 | 1,100 | 2,200 |
| | Gravy | 1,700 | 1,000 | 1,200 | 1,300 | 1,000 | 1,000 |
| | Dressing | 2,500 | 4,400 | 6,900 | 9,100 | 1,400 | 24,000 |
| | Peas | 2,600 | 15,000 | 4,900 | 8,400 | 3,400 | 22,000 |
| | Potatoes | 3,700 | 11,000 | 3,400 | 8,300 | 2,600 | 33,000 |
| 3:00 P.M. | Meat | 1,000 | 1,500 | 3,600 | 3,300 | 1,200 | 26,000 |
| | Gravy | 1,000 | 1,300 | 1,000 | 1,000 | 1,000 | 36,000 |
| | Dressing | 2,400 | 4,300 | 4,800 | 4,400 | 3,200 | 27,200 |
| | Peas | 1,000 | 2,500 | 11,000 | 16,000 | 1,000 | 22,000 |
| | Potatoes | 1,000 | 7,100 | 5,200 | 8,400 | 3,500 | 27,000 |

Source: M. F. Gunderson, Department of Bacteriology, University of Nebraska College of Medicine, Omaha, Neb.

er (1958), three-fourths had total counts of less than 50,000 organisms per gram while the median count was 13,000 bacteria per gram. Frozen pot pies have been extensively investigated. For example, 75% of 95 samples of frozen pot pies produced in 5 different plants had total counts less than 50,000 organisms per gram, while 16% had counts in excess of 100,000 bacteria per gram. Similar data by Gunderson (1963) showed the total aerobic count of 60 frozen beef pie samples was between 1,000 and 13,000 bacteria per gram with an average of 3,000 bacteria per gram. Gunderson and Peterson (1964) published data on the bacterial counts of frozen precooked turkey meat pies. Their results, shown in Table 8, were part of the Delaware Valley Survey carried out by the National Association of Frozen Food Packers (Gunderson 1961). Thirty-seven per cent of all brands of turkey pies had total aerobic counts less than 1,000 organisms per gram. Of the samples examined, 64% were under 5,000; 87% were under 50,000 and 90% were under 100,000 bacteria per gram.

The total aerobic count of frozen prepared dinners in good commercial practice should be low as was demonstrated by Gunderson (1956) and shown in Table 9. Huber et al. (1958), in an examination of precooked frozen meals prepared for the military, found that 86% of the samples had total counts less than 50,000 organisms per gram. They concluded that a total count standard of less than 100,000 bacteria per gram should be easily met by any producer. These authors stressed the importance of sanitary supervision in the quality control program and the importance of starting with good quality raw materials to insure a finished product with a low bacterial count.

Macaroni and cheese frozen prepared dinners had counts ranging from 880 to 63,000 per gram. Line survey data for the same dinners illustrated that the cheddar cheese topping was the principal source of the total aerobic count, coliform, and Staphylococcus organisms found in the finished product (Gunderson 1963). Abrahamson et al. (1959) found 76% of 195 samples of precooked frozen foods to have total aerobic counts of less than 100,000 bacteria per gram. They reported that generally poultry products appeared to be of poorer microbiological quality than other precooked foods.

An extensive bacteriological survey of the frozen precooked food industry was carried out in 1958 and 1959 by the Food and Drug Administration (Shelton et al. 1961). They studied 81 products with over 3,000 samples, but did not include any frozen dinners. The products were classified into four groups based on the degree of cooking which the product might get in the home and on the amount of cooking received by the product during manufacture. Group I, comprised of finished products which do not receive additional heat treatment by the consumer, was bakery products. Of these, 84% had total aerobic counts of less than 100,000 bacteria per gram. Group II items were primarily main course items like meat knishes, and macaroni and cheese which are cooked early in their manufacture and only warmed by the consumer. Seventy-five per cent of Group II products had less than 100,000 bacteria per gram, but 11% contained more than 1,000,000 bacteria per gram. Group III products were cooked late in the processing, but again only required warming by the consumer and included such items as chop suey, creamed chicken, fish cakes, and oyster stew. Of these, 83% had total aerobic plate counts less than 100,000 bacteria per gram while 8% had total counts in excess of 1,000,000 bacteria per gram. Group IV products were those which required cooking by the consumer and included such items as pot pies, pizza, raw breaded shrimp, and spinach loaf. Of the products in this group, 58% contained less than 100,000 bacteria per gram. The authors concluded that the total aerobic plate count and the coliform count varied with the product and production processes. It was noted that these counts served as rough guides to plant sanitation.

Machala (1961) reported that about 70% of 192 assorted samples of frozen precooked pot pies, dinners, seafoods, and entrée items had total aerobic counts less than 100,000 bacteria per gram. He pointed out that, in examining precooked frozen foods such as pizza pie, high total counts should be expected because of the cheese topping which incorporates starter culture microorganisms in the manufacture of the cheese. Such foods cannot be included in the group to which restrictive total count bacterial standards might apply. The frozen food industry undertook a comprehensive microbiological survey of its products, particularly of frozen pot pies and precooked frozen dinners in 1959 and 1960. From those results, the National Association of Frozen Food Packers concluded that such products should have total aerobic bacterial counts of less than 100,000 bacteria per gram (Gunderson 1961).

Larkin *et al.* (1956) reported that the total count of samples of precooked fish sticks examined never exceeded 3,000 bacteria per gram. Subsequent examination of 78 samples of frozen fish sticks showed that 95% had total aerobic counts of less than 100,000 bacteria per gram (Nickerson *et al.* 1962).

Proctor and Phillips (1947, 1948) reported that 85% of the frozen precooked fishery products examined had total plate counts exceeding $10^4$ bacteria per gram. Total aerobic counts running into the millions of bacteria per gram were observed by Gunderson *et al.* (1954) on breaded shrimp. Similar results were reported by Kachikian *et al.* (1959). The breading process was implicated as a major source of microbes on breaded shrimp (Kern 1957). Thus, it can be seen that frozen breaded shrimp have been an exception to the low microbial populations usually experienced elsewhere in the frozen prepared foods industry. At present, total counts on raw breaded shrimp are usually in excess of 100,000 bacteria per gram and commonly range up to several millions of organisms per gram (Silverman *et al.* 1961; Carroll *et al.* 1966; and Surkiewicz *et al.* 1967). The high counts commonly found on these breaded shrimp illustrate the difficulty which a processor of prepared frozen foods encounters in producing low total count products when the raw ingredient is of poor microbiological quality (Green 1949). Verma *et al.* (1964) found that 100 of 102 samples of precooked frozen dessert type foods (primarily cakes and pies) had total aerobic plate counts less than 100,000 bacteria per gram. The other two samples had less than 200,000 bacteria per gram. Similar results were obtained by Surkiewicz (1966) in a study of cream pies and their production where a majority of the samples had aerobic plate counts less than 25,000 bacteria per gram.

Gunderson (1962) and Kuehn and Gunderson (1962, 1963) found a definite psychrophilic fungal flora present on frozen pastries and on frozen chicken pot pies. The fungal flora was usually characteristic of the product.

In summary, it can be said that for many prepared and precooked frozen foods, the processor should be able to provide products with low total microbial counts. Each product type must be considered, however, with consideration given to the microbiological quality of the available ingredients and the extent of the heat treatment which the product receives during processing. High total counts are to be expected in some precooked foods which incorporate microbially inoculated foods like cheese in their manufacture. The total aerobic plate count can be useful in conjunction with other microbial indices as a measure of sanitation and care of handling of ingredients. Processors of precooked frozen foods must be aware of the fact that present concepts of the public health microbiology of these foods dictate not only that such foods be safe, but that they have been prepared under esthetically satisfactory conditions.

## Coliform Organisms

There has been an intense preoccupation by food sanitarians with the possibility of contamination or recontamination of precooked frozen foods with intestinal pathogens (Dack 1955). This has occurred because of the fact that some precooked frozen foods may be consumed without further heat treatment and others with something less than sterilizing heat treatment by the consumer. Accordingly, the coliform count was early used as a measure of sanitary control for frozen precooked foods. Again, analogies between water and milk provided the rationale for this application as previously discussed in Chapter 13 of Volume 2.

Data obtained by Proctor and Phillips (1947, 1948) on the coliform counts of various types of frozen precooked foods are shown in Table 10. The majority of samples had coliform counts that were less than 50 per gram. The highest coliform counts were obtained on samples of creamed

Table 10

Percentage Distribution of Coliform Plate Counts on Various Types of
Frozen Precooked Foods

| Product Type | Number of Samples | % of Samples Having Counts in Excess of | | |
|---|---|---|---|---|
| | | 50 per Gm. | 100 per Gm. | 200 per Gm. |
| Meat products | 57 | 10.5 | 3.5 | 0.0 |
| Stews | 53 | 22.6 | 5.7 | 1.9 |
| Fish products | 110 | 32.7 | 15.4 | 2.7 |
| Creamed meat and creamed poultry | 68 | 22.0 | 10.3 | 4.4 |
| Poultry products | 56 | 33.9 | 10.7 | 1.8 |
| Creamed fish | 38 | 39.5 | 26.3 | 10.5 |
| Vegetable products | 59 | 1.7 | 1.7 | 0.0 |
| Soups | 20 | 0.0 | 0.0 | 0.0 |
| Pastries | 14 | 0.0 | 0.0 | 0.0 |
| Miscellaneous | 27 | 1.1 | 0.0 | 0.0 |

Source: Proctor and Philips (1948).

fish products, creamed meats, creamed poultry, poultry and fish products. This pioneer survey early established the fact that the coliform count of precooked frozen foods should be low. A connection between low total counts, low enterococci counts and low coliform counts as representing good microbiological quality was suggested by Litsky *et al.* (1957). They found 75% of 131 samples of commercially prepared beef, poultry, and tuna pies to have coliform counts less than 50 organisms per gram. Similar results have been obtained by others (Larkin *et al.* 1955A; Canale-Parola and Ordal 1957; Hucker and David 1957; and Kereluk and Gunderson 1959A). Kereluk and Gunderson (1959B) reported that most of the coliform bacteria recovered from frozen meat pies were members of the genus *Aerobacter*. These workers reported that such organisms were present in 79 of 186 pot pie samples in numbers up to 12,000 coliforms per gram. The median coliform count was 10 organisms per gram, however. *Escherichia coli* was found in 54 of 117 specimens of precooked frozen foods in number up to 130,000 bacteria per gram by Ross and Thatcher (1958). Enterococci were found in 60 of the samples in numbers up to 60,000 per gram. Zaborowski *et al.* (1958) recovered coliforms and enterococci from 54 of 82 samples of frozen pot pies. However, in another survey, 90 of 105 samples of frozen pot pies were found to have less than 100 coliform organisms per gram (Dack *et al.* 1960). Data by Gunderson and Peterson (1964) on frozen turkey pies showed that 87% had less than 10 coliforms per gram and 93% less than 100 coliform bacteria per gram (Table 8 ).

*Escherichia coli* was isolated from 22 of 82 samples of frozen pot pies, from 22 of 53 samples of frozen dinners, from 12 of 23 samples of frozen macaroni and cheese entrées, and from 9 of 49 samples of cream pies (Hartman 1960). It was observed that the vegetable portions of the dinners contained a larger proportion of *E. coli* than did the meat portions. Some complicating inhibitory action due to the crusts of the pot pies was observed and *E. coli* were recovered from 41 of 61 samples of such pies when the crusts were omitted from the sample.

Eighty-six per cent of precooked frozen meals prepared for the military were found to have less than 10 coliforms per gram (Huber *et al.* 1958). About 70% of 192 samples of precooked frozen pot pies, frozen dinners, seafoods, and entree items were found to have less than 10 coliform organisms per gram (Machala 1961). Shelton *et al.* (1961) reported that the coliform content of a wide variety of precooked frozen foods varied with the production practice.

The coliform counts of 102 samples of precooked frozen desserts which were primarily cakes and pies were observed to vary from 0 to 275 per gram while 8% of the samples contained *Escherichia coli* (Verma *et al.* 1964). Surkiewicz (1966) in a study of 453 frozen cream pies and their production reported that the samples contained less than 50 coliforms per gram, with less than 3 *E. coli* per gram.

In a study of precooked fish sticks, the coliform counts were less than 20 per gram for most samples (Larkin *et al.* 1956). Similar results were reported by Nickerson *et al.* (1962) who found that the coliform counts of 78 samples of fish sticks ranged from 0 to 35 per gram. Coliform counts of breaded raw and of cooked shrimp were generally much higher running into the hundreds and thousands (Silverman *et al.* 1961; Carroll *et al.* 1966; and Surkiewicz *et al.* 1967). *Escherichia coli* was very frequently present on shrimp along with the enterococci. Liston (1965) noted that except for shellfish, seafoods have not been the source of public health problems in Western countries.

Thus it can be seen that coliform organisms are usually present in precooked frozen foods. The significance of their presence is subject to considerable debate. Coliform bacteria may be only a part of the natural microflora of the ingredients used in preparing the precooked food. Their presence does not necessarily indicate that the foods were inadequately cooked or that they were recontaminated after cooking during processing prior to freezing. Hartman (1960) stated, "Until nonfecal coliforms are shown to indicate contamination from a 'dangerous source' there is no reason to believe that these types of coliform bacteria, just because they form a colony on violet red bile agar should be considered any less desirable in pot pies than any other innocuous microorganism." When used in conjunction with other microbial indices the coliform count can be a useful tool in assessing sanitation and care in handling of the product.

As previously pointed out in Chapter 13 of Volume 2, there is considerable question as to whether or not the enterococci are of any greater significance than the coliform organisms in detecting contamination from warm blooded animal intestinal sources, especially that of man. The enterococci have been recommended as a more reliable indicator of the sanitary condition of precooked frozen foods because the coliform bacteria die out more rapidly during frozen storage than do the enterococci (Larkin *et al.* 1955B, C; Kereluk and Gunderson 1959C). Larkin *et al.* (1956) studied the incidence of fecal streptococci and coliform bacteria in frozen fish and shellfish products, most of which were precooked. Their results indicate a definite correlation between these types of bacteria (Table 11). They suggested that the breading procedures were responsible for the high incidence of fecal streptococci on some fish products. Enterococci have been implicated as cause of food poisoning and consequently, their presence in numbers in precooked frozen foods is undesirable apart from their possible role as indicators of contamination from intestinal sources. Hartman *et al.* (1965) have provided a concise summary of this aspect of food poisoning.

## Microbial Pathogens in Precooked Frozen Foods

Some workers have felt that precooked frozen foods should be free from viable pathogens because of the lack of terminal sterilizing heat treatments either in the processing plant or especially in the hands of the consumer. This should be the ultimate goal of all food processors. Unfortunately, it is an extremely difficult one to achieve, because some pathogens like Staphylococci are ubiquitous. An excellent and comprehensive review of the problem of food-borne diseases has been prepared by Galton and Steele (1961). Because pathogenic microorganisms survive freezing (Woodburn and Strong 1960) great stress has been placed on enumerating and identifying them in precooked frozen foods.

**Staphylococci.**—The presence of *Staphylococcus aureus* was observed in chicken salad even after extended frozen storage (Gunderson and Rose 1948). Buchbinder *et al.* (1949) reported the presence of food poisoning types of Staphylococci in chicken à la king. Similar results were observed by Proctor and Phillips (1947, 1948). Coagulase positive Staphylococci have been commonly found on frozen breaded shrimp (Gunderson *et al.* 1954; Silverman *et al.* 1961; Carroll *et al.* (1966); and Surkiewicz *et al.* 1967). Abrahamson *et al.* (1959) found no *S. aureus* in any of 195 samples of precooked frozen foods. A majority of precooked frozen meals prepared for the military were found to contain Staphylococci (Huber *et al.* 1958). It was concluded, however, that under good commercial practice the numbers of such organisms should be low. Survival of *S. aureus* in prestuffed frozen turkeys was reported by Rogers and Gunderson (1958B). Such fowl need complete thorough roasting to avoid the hazard of staphylococcal multiplication. Staphylococci were recovered from 73% of 188 pot pies examined by Kereluk and Gunderson (1959A). The median staphylococcal count was 120 organisms per gram. Coagulase positive staphylococci were found in 21 of 117 samples of precooked frozen dinners and pot pies in numbers ranging up to 70,000 bacteria per gram (Ross and Thatcher 1958). Data by Gunderson and Peterson (1964) on the bacterial counts of turkey pot pies (Table 8) showed that 46% of the samples contained less than 10 Staphylococci per gram; 66% had less than 100 and 81% of the samples had less than 500 Staphylococci per gram. Only 2 of 78 samples of frozen fish sticks were found to contain coagulase positive Staphylococci (Nickerson *et al.* 1962). Verma *et al.* (1964) found Staphylococci in 28 of 102 samples of precooked frozen desserts in numbers up to 100 per gram. No coagulase positive Staphylococci were found in a study of frozen cream pies (Surkiewicz 1966). Work by Bergdoll *et al.* (1967) has demonstrated that staphylococcal enterotoxin can be produced by coagulase negative Staphylococci. This development will lead to new appraisals of the total level of staphylococcal

Table 11

Comparison of MPN[1] Values for Coliform Bacteria and Fecal Streptococci in Frozen Fish Products

| Name and Type of Food | Coliform Bacteria | | | | | | Fecal Streptococci | |
|---|---|---|---|---|---|---|---|---|
| | MPN[1] per 100 Gm. Lactose Broth | | MPN[1] per 100 Gm. BGB[2] | | MPN[1] per 100 Gm. EMB[3] | | MPN[1] per 100 Gm. Ethyl Violet Broth | |
| | Blended | Shaken | Blended | Shaken | Blended | Shaken | Blended | Shaken |
| **Fish sticks brand** | | | | | | | | |
| 1 | 0 | 18 | 0 | 0 | 0 | 0 | 78 | 18 |
|  | 20 | 0 | 20 | 0 | 0 | 0 | 190 | 45 |
| 2 | 0 | 0 | 0 | 0 | 0 | 0 | 20 | 0 |
|  | 0 | 0 | 0 | 0 | 0 | 0 | 3,500 | 0 |
| 3 | 0 | 0 | 0 | 0 | 0 | 0 | 20 | 18 |
|  | 0 | 0 | 0 | 0 | 0 | 0 | 45 | 0 |
| 4 | 0 | 0 | 0 | 0 | 0 | 0 | 170 | 230 |
|  | 0 | 0 | 0 | 0 | 0 | 0 | 78 | 0 |
| 5 | 0 | 0 | 0 | 0 | 0 | 0 | 1,100 | 0 |
| 6 | 230 | 20 | 75 | 0 | 0 | 0 | 1,300 | 0 |
|  | 36 | 20 | 36 | 0 | 0 | 0 | 3,500 | 780 |
|  | 220 | 45 | 130 | 45 | 18 | 0 | 16,000 | 0 |
| 7 | 0 | 20 | 0 | 20 | 45 | 20 | 2,200 | 270 |
|  | 0 | 20 | 0 | 0 | 0 | 0 | 490 | 310 |
|  | 0 | 0 | 0 | 0 | 0 | 0 | 1,300 | 490 |
|  | 0 | 0 | 0 | 0 | 0 | 0 | 210 | 68 |
| 8 | 0 | 0 | 0 | 0 | 0 | 0 | 1,300 | 0 |
| 9 | 78 | 0 | 0 | 0 | 0 | 0 | 330 | 40 |
| 10 | 78 | 0 | 0 | 0 | 0 | 0 | 20 | 0 |
|  | 0 | 0 | 0 | 0 | 0 | 0 | 45 | 0 |
| **Scallops brand** | | | | | | | | |
| 4 | 78 | 0 | 0 | 0 | 0 | 0 | 40 | 0 |
|  | 0 | 0 | 0 | 0 | 0 | 0 | 0 | 0 |
|  | 0 | 0 | 0 | 0 | 0 | 0 | 0 | 0 |
| 5 | 40 | 20 | 0 | 20 | 0 | 0 | 950 | 20 |
|  | 20 | 0 | 0 | 0 | 0 | 0 | 20 | 0 |
|  | 0 | 0 | 0 | 0 | 0 | 0 | 140 | 20 |
| 7 | 20 | 0 | 0 | 0 | 0 | 0 | 45 | 0 |
|  | 20 | 20 | 0 | 0 | 0 | 0 | 790 | 270 |
|  | 0 | 0 | 0 | 0 | 0 | 0 | 2,400 | 40 |

| Sample | | | | | | | | |
|---|---|---|---|---|---|---|---|---|
| 10 | 130 | 20 | 130 | 20 | 78 | 0 | 2,400 | 790 |
| 11 | 45 | 0 | 0 | 0 | 0 | 0 | 490 | 78 |
| 12 | 330 | 170 | 130 | 00 | 0 | 0 | 1,700 | 0 |
| 13 | 18 | 0 | 0 | 0 | 0 | 0 | 310 | 230 |
| 14 | 0 | 0 | 0 | 0 | 0 | 0 | 0 | 0 |
| | 45 | 0 | 0 | 0 | 0 | 0 | 0 | 0 |
| | 0 | 78 | 0 | 20 | 0 | 20 | 330 | 140 |
| | 78 | 20 | 20 | 0 | 0 | 0 | 45 | 20 |
| **Shrimp croquettes brand** | | | | | | | | |
| 15 | 20 | 0 | 0 | 0 | 0 | 0 | 0 | 0 |
| | 45 | 0 | 45 | 0 | 20 | 0 | 40 | 0 |
| | 40 | 45 | 0 | 0 | 0 | 0 | 78 | 45 |
| **Shrimp brand** | | | | | | | | |
| 4 | 40 | 0 | 0 | 0 | 0 | 0 | 68 | 0 |
| 5 | 45 | 490 | 0 | 330 | 0 | 0 | 0 | 0 |
| | 68 | 0 | 68 | 0 | 40 | 0 | 61 | 0 |
| | 0 | 0 | 0 | 0 | 0 | 0 | 0 | 13 |
| | 0 | 0 | 0 | 0 | 0 | 0 | 0 | 0 |
| 16 | 1,300 | 130 | 1,300 | 45 | 18 | 45 | 24,000 | 16,000 |
| 17[4] | 1,100 | 490 | 1,100 | 330 | 40 | 0 | 16,000 | 16,000 |
| | 110 | 310 | 65 | 110 | 45 | 0 | 24,000 | 24,000 |
| 18[4] | 6,000 | 9,200 | 16,000 | 340 | 18 | 18 | 24,000 | 24,000 |
| **Haddock brand** | | | | | | | | |
| 19 | 40 | 0 | 0 | 0 | 0 | 0 | 0 | 0 |
| 4 | 20 | 0 | 0 | 0 | 0 | 0 | 140 | 0 |
| | 0 | 20 | 0 | 0 | 0 | 0 | 230 | 0 |
| 5 | 20 | 0 | 0 | 0 | 0 | 0 | 0 | 0 |
| 13 | 0 | 0 | 0 | 0 | 0 | 0 | 270 | 0 |
| | 20 | 0 | 0 | 0 | 0 | 0 | 230 | 20 |
| | 0 | 0 | 0 | 0 | 0 | 0 | 790 | 2,400 |
| **Fried clams brand** | | | | | | | | |
| 20 | 45 | 0 | 0 | 0 | 0 | 0 | 0 | 0 |
| | 0 | 0 | 0 | 0 | 0 | 0 | 20 | 0 |

Source: Larkin, Litsky and Fuller (1956).
[1] Most probable number.
[2] Green lactose bile.
[3] Eosine methylene blue.
[4] Raw.

Table 11 (continued)

| Name and Type of Food | Coliform Bacteria | | | | | | Fecal Streptococci | |
|---|---|---|---|---|---|---|---|---|
| | MPN[1] per 100 Gm. Lactose Broth | | MPN[1] per 100 Gm. BGB[2] | | MPN[1] per 100 Gm. EMB[3] | | MPN[1] per 100 Gm. Ethyl Violet Broth | |
| | Blended | Shaken | Blended | Shaken | Blended | Shaken | Blended | Shaken |
| Fried clams brand 21 | 490 | 0 | 0 | 0 | 0 | 0 | 0 | 0 |
| | 68 | 0 | 0 | 0 | 0 | 0 | 0 | 0 |
| Seafood dinner brand 5 | 140 | 0 | 78 | 0 | 0 | 0 | 130 | 37 |
| | 0 | 0 | 0 | 0 | 0 | 0 | 45 | 0 |
| | 78 | 0 | 0 | 0 | 0 | 0 | 20 | 20 |
| Ocean perch brand 11 | 18 | 0 | 0 | 0 | 0 | 0 | 40 | 68 |
| 14 | 330 | 230 | 330 | 45 | 20 | 0 | 3,500 | 170 |
| Crab cakes brand 5 | 45 | 0 | 0 | 0 | 0 | 0 | 20 | 0 |
| | 20 | 0 | 0 | 0 | 0 | 0 | 3,500 | 790 |
| Codfish cakes brand 5 | 40 | 0 | 0 | 0 | 0 | 0 | 0 | 20 |
| | 45 | 0 | 0 | 0 | 0 | 0 | 0 | 0 |
| | 230 | 0 | 45 | 0 | 0 | 0 | 45 | 68 |
| 22 | 0 | 0 | 0 | 0 | 0 | 0 | 24,000 | 110 |
| | 45 | 20 | 0 | 0 | 0 | 0 | 220 | 93 |
| 23 | 0 | 0 | 0 | 0 | 0 | 0 | 0 | 20 |
| Lobster brand 19 | 40 | 700 | 40 | 700 | 40 | 700 | 16,000 | 700 |
| | 20 | 0 | 0 | 0 | 0 | 0 | 0 | 0 |
| Lobster croquettes brand 15 | 0 | 0 | 0 | 0 | 0 | 0 | 330 | 18 |
| | 45 | 0 | 20 | 0 | 20 | 0 | 700 | 0 |
| | 130 | 78 | 0 | 45 | 0 | 0 | 490 | 20 |

Source: Larkin, Litsky and Fuller (1956).
[1] Most probable number.
[2] Green lactose bile.
[3] Eosine methylene blue.
[4] Raw.

contamination of precooked frozen foods and result in increased effort to reduce the level of staphylococcal contamination.

From the data presented, it seems clear that the population of Staphylococci in frozen prepared foods should be low. Staphylococci may be difficult to eliminate entirely from such foods but their presence is an indication of contamination through handling by human hands.

Salmonella.—Proctor and Phillips (1948) observed that *Salmonella enteritidis* inoculated into precooked foods which were then stored at 0°F. ( — 18°C.) decreased markedly, but at least ten per cent of the organisms survived for six months (Fig. 6). Similar results were obtained with *S.*

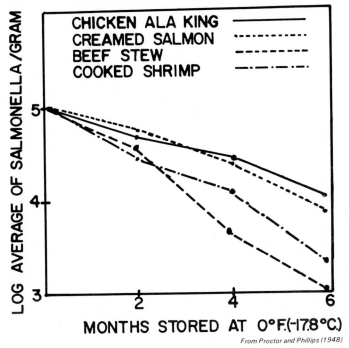

From Proctor and Phillips (1948)

Fig. 6. Survival of *Salmonella Enteritidis* in experimentally inoculated frozen precooked foods stored at 0°F. ( — 18°C.).

*aureus* and Streptococcus. They demonstrated that Salmonella could multiply in those foods after frozen storage if the foods were held at thawing temperatures of 86°F. (30°C.) to 98.6°F. (37°C.) for 6 to 8 hr. (Fig. 5). Survival of six strains of Salmonella inoculated into chicken chow mein, which was then frozen, and stored at —14°F. ( —23°C), extended to nine months (Gunderson and Rose 1948) as shown in Table 12. During early frozen storage, the death rate was essentially proportional to the number of viable or-

Table 12

Survival of Pure Cultures of Enteric Organisms in Chicken Chow Mein

| Organism | Bacterial Count per Gram (00,000 Omitted) after Storage at —14°F. (−26°C.) (Days) | | | | | | | | |
|---|---|---|---|---|---|---|---|---|---|
| | 0 | 2 | 5 | 9 | 14 | 28 | 50 | 92 | 270 |
| S. newington | 75.5 | 56.0 | 27.0 | 21.7 | 11.1 | 11.1 | 3.2 | 5.0 | 2.2 |
| S. typhimurium | 169.0 | 245.0 | 134.0 | 118.0 | 111.0 | 95.5 | 31.0 | 90.0 | 34.0 |
| S. typhi | 128.5 | 45.5 | 21.8 | 17.3 | 10.6 | 4.5 | 2.6 | 2.3 | 0.86 |
| S. gallinarum | 68.5 | 87.0 | 45.0 | 36.5 | 29.0 | 17.9 | 14.9 | 8.3 | 4.8 |
| S. anatum | 100.0 | 79.0 | 55.0 | 52.5 | 33.5 | 29.4 | 22.6 | 16.2 | 4.2 |
| S. paratyphi B | 230.0 | 205.0 | 118.0 | 93.0 | 92.0 | 42.8 | 24.3 | 38.8 | 19.0 |

Source: Gunderson and Rose (1948).

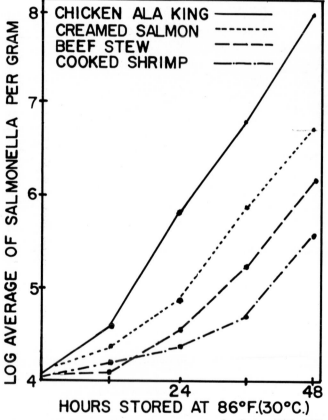

From Proctor and Phillips (1948)

Fig. 7.  Growth of *Salmonella Enteritidis* in experimentally inoculated frozen precooked foods at 86°F. (30°C.). After storage at 0°F. (−18°C.) for one week.

ganisms present, but was less rapid as storage progressed. Similarly, Salmo-nella organisms were shown to survive in the stuffing of prestuffed turkeys and to constitute a hazard unless the fowl were thoroughly cooked (Rogers and Gunderson (1958A). Wilson *et al.* (1961) have provided a concise sum-mary of the prevalence of Salmonella in meat and poultry products. While the studies cited indicate the possibility of survival of Salmonella organisms in artificial inoculation studies, a somewhat different perspective is ob-tained through the actual examination of frozen prepared foods.

The work of Litsky *et al.* (1957), Kereluk and Gunderson (1959A), and Machala (1961) indicated that they were unable to recover viable Salmo-nellae from commercially prepared frozen meat pies and a variety of frozen precooked foods. Arizona and Salmonella organisms were not recovered from any of 117 samples of precooked frozen foods examined by Ross and Thatcher (1958). Organisms belonging to the Bethesda-Ballerup group of paracolon organisms were present in 14 samples and from the Providence group in 2 samples. Nickerson *et al.* (1962) isolated a single presumptive Salmonella culture from one of 78 samples of precooked frozen fish sticks. Raj and Liston (1963) found no Salmonella or Shigella in any of 362 samples of frozen precooked seafoods examined.

Food sanitarians would be well advised to continue to stress the impor-tance of obtaining and using Salmonella-free ingredients for precooked fro-zen foods. Equally important is the prevention of recontamination of ingre-dients and finished product.

Clostridium.—The relatively widespread contamination of meats (Hall and Angelotti 1965) and poultry with *Clostridium perfringens* vegetative cells and spores (Strong *et al.* 1963), and the survival by that organism of extended freezing storage point out additional potential problems for pre-cooked frozen foods, especially for those packaged in gas impervious plastic films. Woodburn and Kim (1966) have shown that *Cl. perfringens* can be a problem when foods like prestuffed frozen turkeys are inadequately cooked. Hobbs (1953) and Despaul (1966) have provided excellent reviews of the *Cl. perfringens* food poisoning hazard. Foster and Sugiyama (1966) have provided a comprehensive review of the problem of botulism.

The work of Saleh and Ordal (1955) demonstrated an inhibitory effect of lactic acid bacteria on the growth of Clostridium organisms. They con-cluded that the growth of the lactic acid bacteria offered considerable pro-tection against the development of botulism toxin. This and the work of Perry *et al.* (1948) have provided valuable evidence as to why botulism has not been a problem to the frozen food industry. The probable action of pu-trefactive anaerobes in swelling the containers (Filz and Bennett 1965) be-fore the development of botulinum toxin is an important and probably lit-tle recognized aspect of the built in safety of frozen prepared foods.

While the possibilities for growth of *Clostridium botulinum* and toxin formation has heretofore been considered remote at temperatures below 50°F. (10°C.) (Saleh and Ordal 1955), several recent developments prompt caution in this regard. Growth of *Cl. botulinum* type E with toxin production has been reported at 38°F. (3°C.) (Schmidt *et al.* 1961.) Even more recently, Eklund *et al.* (1967) reported growth and toxin production by *Cl. botulinum* type B at 38°F. (3°C.). The use of oxygen impervious films for packaging precooked frozen foods is an area in which strict maintenance of 0°F. (−18°C.) temperatures for storage of the product is mandatory. The practice of holding precooked frozen foods packed in sealed plastic pouches in the refrigerated but thawed state for rapidity of reconstitution, must be avoided. Similarly, once these pouch packed precooked frozen foods have been thawed or heated, the food should be removed from the pouch, or the pouch opened if the food is to be stored refrigerated but not frozen.

**Bacillus cereus.**—Food poisoning due to *Bacillus cereus* is an evolving phenomenon. Hauge (1950) drew attention to this health hazard. Meyer (1953) has provided a concise review of the subject. The survival of spores of *B. cereus* after protracted exposure to 350°F. (176.7°C.) in turkey meat was reported by Tong *et al.* (1962). This great heat resistance makes this organism a real problem for food technologists. More will be heard in the future about this type of food poisoning.

**Viruses.**—A concise summary of viruses important to the health of man, which are disseminated through foods, has been provided by Becker (1966). Probably the most important of these is hepatitis virus which has sufficient heat resistance to survive pasteurization (Kachani 1965). Strawberries in frozen custard have been the source of hepatitis infection (U.S. Dept. Health, Education and Welfare 1965). Lemon (1964) has implicated foods, particularly milk and eggs, as sources of leukemia and lymphoma infections. Entero-viruses (polio viruses and Coxsackie viruses) artificially inoculated into commercially prepared foods have survived freezing and storage at −4°F. (−20°C.) for five months (Lynt Jr. 1966). Engley (1956) has provided a most comprehensive summary of knowledge of the survival of microorganisms especially in foods under freezing conditions. It is probable that, as knowledge of the extent of viruses in foods becomes available, viruses will be implicated in more food-borne infections.

**Mycotoxins.**—As yet, no frozen precooked foods have been implicated in the dissemination of diseases caused by fungi or their products. Work by Forgacs (1962) and by Newberne *et al.* (1964) pointed to the acute carcinogenicity and pathogenicity of mycotoxins. Improvements in assay techniques for detecting mycotoxins, isolating, identifying them, and demonstrating their toxicity (Verrett *et al.* 1964) point up the rapid developments and importance of this field. Food sanitarians would do well to keep informed of developments in this area of public health. The proceedings of a symposium edited by Wogan (1964) provide a very comprehensive review of the mycotoxins.

## Microbial Competition

The temperatures at which precooked frozen foods thaw are substantially below that at which water changes from a solid to a liquid. They may be as low as 15.2°F. (−9.3°C.) (Fanelli and Gunderson 1961). The presence of carbohydrates, especially refined sugars in quantity, starches, salts, gums, lipids and proteins in combination, act to depress the freezing point of precooked frozen foods. Modifications of the physical structure of foods, the creation of the colloidal state, affect the amount of available moisture for growth in the unfrozen state. It should be recalled that under these conditions, microorganisms most able to grow at low temperatures (psychrotrophs) may continue to grow during the freezing process and begin to grow again during the thawing process. At this time the psychrotrophs are usually the only microorganisms growing (Kereluk et al. 1960). The psychrotrophic microorganisms are saprophytic spoilage organisms for the most part, characteristic of the food itself or its ingredients. Microorganisms of public health significance involving food-borne infections and intoxications are not psychrotrophic (Burr and Elliott 1960). They are mesophiles which do not grow at refrigeration temperatures, with the exception of *Clostridium botulinum* type E.

Because of the inability of commercial processors to prepare sterile frozen foods and especially to ensure pathogen-free frozen prepared foods, Gunderson and Peterson (1964) pointed out that it is important to maintain a balance of the types of the natural saprophytic microflora of frozen precooked foods. It has been shown that during prolonged exposures to thawing temperatures, growth of the psychrotrophic saprophytic microorganisms inhibits the growth of pathogenic bacteria to a considerable degree. Saleh and Ordal (1955) observed that addition of lactic acid bacteria to chicken à la king inoculated with *Clostridium botulinum* spores prevented the development of toxin. Similar results were reported by others (Kautter et al. 1966; McCoy and Faber 1966). The growth of Staphylococci and of Salmonellae in thawed pot pies was inhibited by the natural saprophytic microflora present (Peterson et al. 1962; Dack and Lippitz 1962). Post-irradiation survival of S. aureus in seafoods was reported to pose a problem because the competing and spoilage microorganisms had been eliminated by the treatment (Slabyj et al. 1965). Other workers have demonstrated that organisms of public health significance do not grow well in situations where they are at a competitive disadvantage in obtaining their essential requirements (Oberhofer and Frazier 1961; Troller and Frazier 1963; Graves and Frazier 1963; Seminiano and Frazier 1966; Kao and Frazier 1966). An important "built in" aspect of the public health safety of frozen prepared foods is the action of the natural saprophytic, psychrotrophic microflora of these foods in destroying the organoleptic acceptability of these foods before the development of hazardous pathogenic microbial populations (Peterson et al. 1963A, 1963B, 1964).

It should be observed that this mechanism cannot protect the consumer against the presence of infectious pathogenic microorganisms which might be present in products which have never been thawed. Even legal standards using the usual microbial index counts will not guarantee freedom from this danger, however.

## SOURCES OF MICROBIAL CONTAMINATION

### Facilities

The production of precooked or prepared frozen foods is a maximum sanitation operation. It cannot be effectively implemented in the immediate proximity of a dirty operation like the killing and eviscerating of poultry or of the peeling of vegetables. Ventilation must be properly arranged so that air from highly contaminated areas is not circulated to maximum sanitation areas. Even aerosols set up by improperly functioning floor drains have been shown to be an important source of coliform bacteria. Separate locker rooms and washup facilities should be provided for personnel preparing precooked frozen foods. These areas should be apart from those of other workers.

### People

It is desirable to train all plant personnel in the concepts of sanitation and personal hygiene in order to insure sanitary conditions in the prepared foods areas. They must also be instilled with a sense of responsibility for the quality of the product. Clean uniforms, head covers, gloves, and the necessary essential hand tools provided by the processor are an excellent practical demonstration to the workers that the processor is interested in the personal appearance and hygiene of the workers. Workers who prepare precooked frozen foods need constant supervision and reminding of the necessity for washing the hands with germicidal soap before beginning work and before returning to work after every break. They need to be taught to keep their hands out of the ingredients and product unless handling is absolutely required. The hands of workers can be an important source of microbial contamination in the slicing, weighing, and placing of meats. Workers on these jobs need to wash their hands several times during the production shift. Workers must avoid resting pots, pans, tools, and other equipment on top of foods. Mechanics must wash their hands before working on equipment which contacts food. They must avoid resting the parts of such equipment on foods. Equipment contaminated by handling during repair or modification should be sanitized and rinsed before use. Workers must be made aware that stirring oars, ladles, thermometers, gage sticks, sanitary fittings, and gaskets cannot be allowed to rest on the floor or in their pockets between uses. They must be taught the importance of their part in keeping the foods uncontaminated.

The processor must realize that optimum results will be obtained with a stable well trained work force accustomed to performing the same tasks in an approved manner and who understand the principles of sanitation and personal hygiene. For this reason, it is very desirable to avoid transferring workers from other less fastidious operations to precooked frozen food production on a day to day basis, as production requirements vary, and labor force requirements might seemingly dictate.

## Equipment

There is a need for and an excellent opportunity for significant improvements in the microbiological aspects of the development of processing equipment. It should be designed with sanitary standards of the food and ease of cleaning in mind. Too often, equipment is adapted for use to a product or process for which it is neither suitable, sanitizable, or really economical. A meeting of minds between equipment design engineers and food sanitarians similar to that which has occurred in the dairy industry is needed for the entire food industry. (See also Volume 3, Chapter 15).

Particular attention must be directed to comminuters, colloid mills, homogenizers, plate coolers, pumps, slicers, dicers, and filling machines in order to be sure that these are regularly disassembled, washed (brushed), sanitized, and rinsed (Dack et al. 1960). Many of these pieces are difficult and laborious to disassemble, and production and cleanup workers will attempt to clean them by water flushing them only. These pieces cannot be satisfactorily cleaned in this manner. Plants and equipment for precooked frozen food production must be better than just "eyeball clean." Quality control personnel must periodically establish that equipment is satisfactorily clean on the basis of microbiological examination based on swab samples and contact plates. If serious microbiological problems are encountered, a line survey involving the ingredients and product before and after each step of processing and of every piece of equipment contacting the food may be needed. Because of the viscous, adhering nature of many precooked foods, in-place cleaning has not been widely successful. Where possible, equipment and lines should be washed (brushed) and sanitized at the start of the production shift, at the lunch break, and at the end of the shift. It is important that all ingredients and containers should be removed during this process so that splashings cannot contaminate them. Dead end piping and thermometer wells need particular attention. These should be eliminated where possible and kept scrupulously clean where their presence is absolutely required. Equipment used in the precooked frozen food operation should *not* be shared with other operations, particularly raw food preparation. Equipment used in the precooked frozen food operations should be washed and sanitized in a separate location from that used for other washing operations.

### Ingredients

One of the most serious problems facing precooked frozen food processors is the obtaining of high-quality ingredients, especially those with low microbial content. As has been previously stated, frozen foods must be good from the beginning. It is impossible to prepare low bacterial count precooked and prepared frozen foods from high-count ingredients. Quality frozen precooked frozen foods cannot be prepared from high-count ingredients which have been "laundered" to reduce their microbial content or to conceal incipient spoilage. Particular attention should be directed to spices as a source of microbial contamination. All ingredients used should have microbiological limits and qualifications included in their production or purchasing specifications. Meat slicing and dicing operations and equipment can be an important source of microbial contamination (Dack 1956). Meats, in particular, should be refrigerated during the lunch break. Unused food materials should be properly dated, tagged, and refrigerated at the end of each shift and most of those to be held more than 12 hr. should be quick frozen. It should be pointed out that meats, gravies, sauces, and other cooked foods in bulk returned to refrigeration for holding after preparation, need prechilling with agitation in the case of liquids (Moragne *et al.* 1960). Gravies and sauces in large containers can require many hours to reach effective refrigeration temperatures even in a low temperature environment. Cooked ingredients should be refrigerated separately from raw ones and those rejected for high bacterial counts. Satisfactory gravies cannot be made from puréed, soured, high-count meats.

The time during which product remains in the room temperature range during processing and freezing should be as short as possible; therefore lengthy holding of ingredients and products on the production line during line breakdowns and long freezing times are to be avoided.

In a study of the cooking and boning of poultry meats, it was shown that the bacterial content of the meat was drastically reduced during cooking (Gunderson *et al.* 1954). Boning of cooked meats involves contact with the hands of workers and much equipment. It also involves prolonged holding at room temperatures which results in rapid increases in bacterial numbers in the boned meats. The workers' hands may not only be an important source of bacterial contamination but may inoculate the meat with pathogens. The equipment used, especially pans, knives, slicing and dicing machines, may become heavily contaminated early in the production shift. Unless the equipment is cleaned and sanitized periodically during the production day, the equipment will serve as a source of bacterial inoculation for other clean, low-count meats with which it comes in contact. One of the original investigations of frozen food ingredient quality demonstrated that the bacterial counts of boned diced poultry meats should be low, as shown in Table 13 (Gunderson 1956). An interesting comparison of bacterial

Table 13

Total Bacterial Counts Boned Diced Chicken Meat

Weekly average—two producers

| Week Ending | Plant A | Plant G |
|---|---|---|
| 7- 9-55 | 2,400 | 13,000 |
| 7-16-55 | 35,000 | 50,000 |
| 7-23-55 | 19,000 | 32,000 |
| 7-30-55 | 10,000 | 42,000 |
| 8- 5-55 | 57,000 | 50,000 |
| 8-12-55 | 50,000 | 57,000 |
| 8-19-55 | 38,000 | 51,000 |
| 8-26-55 | 52,000 | 26,000 |
| 9- 3-55 | 15,000 | 23,000 |
| 9-10-55 | 12,000 | 15,000 |
| 9-17-55 | 26,000 | 16,000 |
| 9-24-55 | 48,000 | 16,000 |
| 10- 1-55 | 7,300 | 12,000 |
| 10- 8-55 | 52,000 | 14,000 |
| 10-15-55 | 52,000 | 20,000 |
| 10-22-55 | 17,000 | 25,000 |
| 11- 5-55 | 14,000 | 9,000 |
| 11-12-55 | 14,000 | 27,000 |
| 11-19-55 | 9,000 | 11,000 |
| 11-26-55 | 20,000 | 14,000 |
| 12- 3-55 | 6,700 | 16,000 |
| 12-10-55 | 21,000 | 9,000 |
| 12-17-55 | 4,900 | 13,000 |

Source: M. F. Gunderson, Department of Bacteriology, University of Nebraska College of Medicine, Omaha, Neb.

counts of cooked diced chicken meats in 1964 by Gunderson and Peterson (1964) shows that the original concept of low microbial populations in these meats was being maintained (Table 14).

Table 14

A Summary of Bacterial Counts on Weekly Basis on Cooked,
Diced, Frozen Chicken Meat

| Week No. | Total Count (SPC)/Gram | | | Coliforms Count/Gram | | | No. of Samples |
|---|---|---|---|---|---|---|---|
| | High | Low | Average | High | Low | Average | |
| 1 | 110,000 | 18,000 | 57,000 | — | — | — | 6 |
| 2 | 43,000 | 4,600 | 19,000 | 50 | 0[1] | 5 | 15 |
| 3 | 28,000 | 6,700 | 17,000 | 30 | 0 | 10 | 4 |
| 4 | 30,000 | 4,700 | 13,000 | 20 | — | 2 | 8 |
| 5 | 44,000 | 7,200 | 16,000 | 10 | 0 | 2 | 8 |
| 6 | 17,000 | 2,700 | 11,000 | 60 | 0 | 24 | 7 |
| 7 | 41,000 | 4,600 | 16,000 | 600 | 0 | 120 | 12 |
| 8 | 52,000 | 8,800 | 29,000 | 80 | 50 | 65 | 4 |
| 9 | 94,000 | 9,900 | 35,000 | 400 | 0 | 100 | 20 |
| 10 | 59,000 | 9,200 | 26,000 | 90 | 0 | 17 | 16 |
| 11 | 76,000 | 6,900 | 31,000 | 160 | 0 | 25 | 15 |
| 12 | 47,000 | 1,000 | 16,000 | 100 | 0 | 18 | 15 |
| 13 | 100,000 | 2,900 | 17,000 | 20 | 0 | 4 | 37 |
| 14 | 89,000 | 3,000 | 12,000 | 100 | 0 | 8 | 56 |
| 15 | 120,000 | 3,700 | 31,000 | 90 | 0 | 9 | 24 |
| 16 | 17,000 | 11,000 | 13,000 | 0 | 0 | 0 | 4 |
| 17 | 11,000 | 2,300 | 7,800 | 60 | 0 | 15 | 14 |
| 18 | 61,000 | 1,000 | 13,000 | 40 | 0 | 2 | 23 |
| 19 | 53,000 | 1,200 | 16,000 | 900 | 0 | 73 | 20 |
| 20 | 28,000 | 500 | 11,000 | 230 | 0 | 39 | 24 |
| 21 | 18,000 | 600 | 4,800 | 30 | 0 | 10 | 7 |
| Overall average | | | 20,000 | | | 30 | |

Source: Gunderson and Peterson (1964).
[1] (0) indicates no growth at 0.1 dilution.

## Effect of Processing

Fabricating procedures are the most serious source of microbial contamination for precooked and prepared frozen foods. Seafoods provide an excellent example of this fact. Ninety per cent of the bacterial load on fish fillets was observed to be picked up from the filet cutting board (Tretsven 1965). Similarly, utensils were reported as a major source of contamination of shellfish (Miller and Greenberg 1962). Bernarde (1958) found that the breading operation was a major source of bacteria on frozen fishery products. The effect of processing on bacterial content and on bacteria of public health significance in precooked frozen seafoods has been reviewed by Liston (1965).

Shelton et al. (1961) reported that the finding of coagulase positive Staphylococci in precooked frozen foods is usually related to extensive handling by the workers. They noted that a number of poor plant practices were reflected in high bacterial counts in the finished product. Raj and Liston (1963) observed that the initial cutting operation caused a tenfold increase in the counts of seafoods. The battering and breading operations further increased the contamination of the product with coliforms, enterococci, Staphylococci, hemolytic Streptococci, and anaerobes. The precooking process reduced the heat sensitive portion of the bacterial flora. The total count, coliform count, and streptococcal counts were reduced; the entero-cocci, Staphylococci, and anaerobes were only slightly affected.

Blanching and precooking procedures are usually responsible for sharp reductions in the microbial content of prepared and precooked foods. Sterility is usually not achieved, however. Subsequent handling contributes to an increase in the microbial counts of these foods. Logan *et al.* (1951) compared the microbial counts of hot-filled and cold-filled chicken à la king. They found that cold-filled product had a somewhat higher bacterial count than did hot-filled product. This was ascribed to post-heating contamination during handling and filling prior to freezing. Hot-filling followed by quick freezing at 0°F. ($-18$°C.) produced a nearly sterile product. This was not the situation when cold-filling was employed although the counts were

Table 15

Effect of Delay in Freezing, Time of Frozen Storage, and Elapsed Time During Defrosting on Increase in Aerobic Plate Counts of Precooked Frozen Creamed Chicken Inoculated with *Staphylococcus Aureus* [1]

| Time of Frozen Storage at —30°F. (—34°C.) | Ratio of Final to Initial Aerobic Plate Counts for Samples Defrosted and Held at 77°F. (25°C.) | | | |
| | Control[2] | 6 Hr. | 11 Hr. | 18 Hr. |
| --- | --- | --- | --- | --- |
| | Samples Placed in Freezer Immediately After Preparation | | | |
| 2 days | 1.2 | 1.3 | — | 66.0 |
| 14 days | 1.1 | 1.3 | — | 19.0 |
| 28 days | 1.2 | 1.0 | — | 1.0 |
| 3 months | 1.2 | 1.3 | 1.2 | — |
| 6 months | 1.4 | 1.1 | 1.7 | — |
| 12 months | 1.2 | 1.1 | 24.0[3] | — |
| | Samples Held at 77°F. (25°C.) for 2 Hr. After Preparation Before Placing in Freezer | | | |
| 2 days | 4.1 | 16 | — | 66 |
| 14 days | 2.5 | 4 | — | 420 |
| 28 days | 4.9 | 3 | — | 12 |
| 3 months | 3.6 | 10 | 13 | — |
| 6 months | 3.2 | 3 | 15 | — |
| 12 months | 2.8 | 3 | 175[3] | — |
| | Samples Held at 77°F. (25°C.) for 5 Hr. After Preparation Before Placing in Freezer | | | |
| 2 days | 32 | 66 | — | 66 |
| 14 days | 29 | 52 | — | 607 |
| 28 days | 35 | 42 | — | 231 |
| 3 months | 56 | 59 | 110 | — |
| 6 months | 26 | 48 | 202 | — |
| 12 months | 31 | 28 | 1035[3] | — |

Source: Straka and Combs (1952).
[1] Initial count 370,000 per ml. based on the average of two containers.
[2] Defrosted immediately in warm running water.
[3] Room temperture went up to 86°F. (30°C.).

low. Fitzgerald (1947A, B) pointed out the great importance of reducing the time to a minimum in which a food is allowed to remain in the bacterial incubation danger zone of 50°F. (10°C.) to 130°F. (54°C.) regardless of whether a product is cooled before or after packaging. Straka and Combes (1952) clearly demonstrated the significance of proper temperature control during processing and the necessity for rapid freezing without delay as soon as processing and packaging have been completed (Table 15). Their results showed how rapidly bacteria can multiply in the favorable environment of a precooked food at room temperatures. Working with creamed chicken and creamed turkey artificially inoculated with *S. aureus*, they concluded that precooked foods should not be held more than two hours before freezing. Obold and Hutchings (1947) had previously reached similar conclusions based on other frozen foods. The development of even small populations of saprophytic bacteria in precooked foods can lead to organoleptic impairment of the product (Peterson and Gunderson, 1960A and 1960B and Felstehausen *et al.* 1963). Angelotti *et al.* (1959, 1960) have provided a comprehensive study of the growth of Salmonellae and Staphylococci in foods which illustrates that the danger zone for multiplication of these pathogens is between 40°F. (4°C.) and 120°F. (49°C).

It can be seen that management has a most important role in recognizing the scope of the problem, in providing the necessary tools and supervision and in providing the necessary checks to be sure that the products are being produced under conditions of care and good sanitation. Likewise, conscientious precooked frozen food processors will be fully aware of the microbiological condition of their products.

### Freezing and Thawing

The detailed effects of the freezing process and of the thawing process on microbial survival and of extended storage in the frozen state on microbial survival were considered previously in Chapter 13 of Volume 2.

Blast freezing was found to reduce the total numbers of microorganisms in chicken pot pies. The fecal Streptococci, Staphylococci, coliforms, and yeasts and molds were sharply affected, but not the anaerobes (Fanelli and Ayres 1959).

Logan *et al.* (1951) studied the effect of storing frozen chicken à la king for a 15-day period in which the temperature to which the food was exposed was cycled from 20°F. (−7°C.) to 30°F. (−1°C.) and back to 20°F. (−7°C.) in a five-day cycle. After three cycles, the product was returned to 0°F. (−18°C.) for five days and then examined. Temperature cycling was not found to have any appreciable effect on the acceptability of the product. Product which had been cold filled had a significant decrease in bacterial count as a result of this treatment. Hot-filled product showed essentially no change in microbial content because its count was already very low. Thawing of packages of chicken à la king at 40°F. (4°C.) for three days produced a slight increase in bacterial content which was reduced on refreezing. Hucker and David (1957) reported that alternate freezing and thawing did not increase the total microflora of chicken pies unless growth was initiated in the thawed state. They observed no growth at 36°F. (2°C.), 45°F. (7°C.) and at 65°F. (18°C.) in 48 hr. Growth of bacteria was observed after 10 hr. at 70°F. (21°C.) and 90°F. (32°C.). Cyclic freezing and thawing was observed to cause a decrease in the numbers of bacteria of public health significance in seafoods (Raj and Liston 1961A). Fluctuating temperatures have been shown to be responsible for moisture migration in frozen foods to localized areas in the food (Peterson 1962; Gunderson 1962). This migration resulted in sufficient available water for mold growth even during short periods of exposure to high temperatures in which the product did not thaw completely.

Work by Peterson *et al.* (1963A, 1963B, 1964) has demonstrated that precooked frozen foods can be thawed and refrozen with safety. This process cannot be recommended to consumers, however. Thawing, particularly with protracted holding in the thawed state, invariably leads to quality losses which are not reversed by refreezing.

### RECONSTITUTION—HEATING

Hussemann (1951) studied the effect of thawing frozen chicken à la king, beef stew, and creamed seafood in a household refrigerator at 43°F. (6°C.) and then heating to 181°F. (83°C.) This was followed by refrigeration for 48 hr. at 43°F. (6°C.) and reheating to 185°F. (85°C.). Continued multiplication of bacteria under those conditions of refrigeration was observed in most cases. Cooking was observed to reduce the numbers of all kinds of microorganisms, but it failed to completely eliminate any type originally present (Table 16). Causey and Fenton (1951A, B) studied the effect of reheating on the bacterial populations of various meat dishes including creamed chicken and rice, chicken paprika and gravy, spaghetti and meatballs, and ham patties. The initial counts were less than 2,000 bacteria per gram and were very low after heating to 185°F. (85°C.). They reported that frozen broccoli with an initial total aerobic count of 55,000 bacteria per gram and frozen green beans with 40,000 organisms per gram had 5 and 10 bacteria per gram respectively after heating to 185°F. (85°C.).

Castellani *et al.* (1953) demonstrated that in the early phases of roasting frozen stuffed poultry, bacterial multiplication occurred. The center of the stuffing must reach 165°F. (73.9°C.) in order to kill food-borne microbial pathogens and provide a margin of safety. Time required to reach that temperature varied with the initial temperature of the bird, stuffing and

Table 16

Average Values for Bacteria per Gram in Frozen Precooked Foods
Subsequent to Kitchen Handling

| Condition of Product | Total Bacterial Count (Tryptone Glucose Extract Agar) Count/Gm.[2] | Micrococci Count (7.5 % NaCl Phenol Red Mannitol Agar) Count/Gm.[2] |
|---|---|---|
| Chicken à la king[1] | | |
| Thawing in refrigerator at 43°F. (6°C.) | 2,310,100 | 213,100 |
| Heating at 185°F. (85°C.) | 341,000 | 3,100 |
| Household refrigeration for 48 hr. following heating | 815,000 | 10,000 |
| Reheating to 185°F. (85°C.) after household refrigeration for 48 hr., following first heating | 497,000 | 1,100 |
| Beef stew[3] | | |
| Thawing in refrigerator at 43°F. (6°C.) | 4,400 | 3,700 |
| Heating to 185°F. (85°C.) | 100 | 57 |
| Household refrigeration for 48 hr. following heating | 250 | 191 |
| Reheating to 185°F. (85°C.) after household refrigeration for 48 hr., following first heating | 40 | 5 |
| Creamed sea food[3] | | |
| Thawing in refrigerator at 43°F. (6°C.) | 3,400 | 1,400 |
| Heating to 185°F. (85°C.) | 720 | 200 |
| Household refrigeration for 48 hr., following heating | 430 | 160 |
| Reheating to 185°F. (85°C.) after household refrigeration for 48 hr., following first heating | 330 | 70 |

Source: Hussemann (1951).
[1] Samples taken from eleven packages.
[2] Each figure represents, on an average, counts of 73 plates.
[3] Samples taken from 14 packages.

size of the bird, and oven temperature.

Work by Canale-Parola and Ordal (1957) demonstrated that nonspore forming bacteria were completely killed or reduced to less than one per cent of the original numbers when meat pies were baked according to the manufacturers directions. Spore forming bacteria survived, however. Ross and Thatcher (1958) showed that there was a reduction in population of 57.5 to 100% of the total aerobic count on baking of precooked frozen foods. Similarly, Kereluk and Gunderson (1961) reported that most of the microorganisms present in frozen pot pies were eliminated by baking as directed. Sterility was not achieved, however.

## PERSPECTIVES

Precooked and prepared frozen foods represent a special category of convenience foods which are protected from microbial damage by storage at freezing temperatures. In general, they are prepared from ingredients which are superior in microbiological quality to those available to the homemakers. The precooked and prepared foods are also generally superior in microbiological quality to those which can be prepared by the home-maker. Nevertheless, precooked and prepared frozen foods are perishable and need the same consideration as other foods once they are removed from their protective environment.

## BIBLIOGRAPHY

Abrahamson, A. E., Buchbinder, L., Guenkel, J., and Heller, M. A. 1959. A study of frozen precooked foods: their sanitary quality and microbiological standards for control. Assoc. Food Drug Officials, U.S. Quart. Bull. 23, No. 2, 63–72.

American Public Health Association. 1966. Recommended Methods for the Examination of Foods. 2nd Edition. American Public Health Assoc., New York.

Angelotti, R., Foter, M. J., and Lewis, K. H. 1960. Time-temperature effects on Salmonellae and Staphylococci in foods. II. Behavior at warm holding temperatures. Thermal death-time studies. Tech. Rept. F60-5. The Robert A. Taft Sanitary Engineering Center, U.S. Public Health Service, Cincinnati, Ohio.

Angelotti, R. Wilson, E., Foter, M. J., and Lewis, K. H. 1959. Time-temperature effects on Salmonellae and Staphylococci in foods. I. Behavior in broth cultures and refrigerated foods. Tech. Rept. F59-2. The Robert A. Taft Sanitary Engineering Center, U.S. Public Health Service, Cincinnati, Ohio.

Anon. 1960. Conference report. Microbiological standards for foods. Public Health Rept. 75, 815–822. Public Health Service, U.S. Dept. Health, Education, and Welfare.

Anon. 1961. Industry—AFDOUS team works on frozen food handling code. Western Edition, Canner and Packer 130, No. 3, 31.

Becker, M. E. 1966. Water-borne and Food-borne viruses. J. Milk and Food Technol. 29, 243–245.

Bergdoll, M. S., Weiss, K. F., and Nuster, M. J. 1967. Production of Staphylococcal enterotoxin by a coagulase negative microorganism. A-68 (abstract) Proc. Am. Soc. Microbiol. 67th Ann. Meeting.

Bernarde, M. A. 1958. Breading contributes to the microbial populations of frozen breaded fishery products. Comm. Fisheries Rev. 20, 6–10.

Brandly, P. J. 1960. Consideration concerning microbiological standards for frozen food quality. In Conference on Frozen Food Quality, U.S. Dept. Agr. 79–80, U.S. Dept. Agr., ARS 74-21, Albany, Calif.

Buchbinder, L., Loughlin. V., Walter, M., and Dangler, G. 1949. A survey of frozen precooked foods with special reference to chicken à la king. J. Milk and Food Technol. 12, 209–213, 231.

Burr, H. K., and Elliott, R. P. 1960. Quality and safety in frozen foods. J. Am. Med. Assoc. 174, 1178–1180.

Canale-Parola, E., and Ordal, Z. J. 1957. A survey of the bacteriological quality of frozen poultry pies. Food Technol. 11, 578–582.

Carroll, B. J., Love, T. D., Ward, B. Q., and Waters, M. E. 1966. Microbial analysis of frozen raw breaded shrimp. Fishery Industrial Res. 3, No. 3, 5–11; Dept. of Interior, Fish and Wildlife Service, Bureau of Comm. Fisheries.

Castellani, A. G., Clarke, R. R., Gibson, M. L., and Meisser, D. F.   1953. Roasting time and temperature required to kill food poisoning microorganisms introduced experimentally into stuffing in turkeys. Food Research 18, 134–138.

Causey, K., and Fenton, F.   1951A. Effect of reheating on palatability, nutritive value and bacterial count of frozen precooked foods. I. Vegetables. J. Am. Dietet. Assoc. 27, 390–395.

Causey, K., and Fenton, F.   1951B. Effect of reheating on palatibility, nutritive value and bacterial count of frozen precooked foods. II. Meat dishes. J. Am. Dietet. Assoc. 27, 494–495.

Conference on Frozen Food Quality.   1960. U.S. Dept. of Agr., ARS-74-21, Albany, Calif.

Dack, G. M.   1955. The significance of enteric bacilli in foods. Am. J. Public Health 45, 1151–1156.

Dack, G. M.   1956. Evaluation of microbiological standards for foods. Food Technol. 10, 507–509.

Dack, G. M., and Lippitz, G.   1962. Fate of Staphylococci and enteric microorganisms introduced into a slurry of frozen pot pies. Appl. Microbiol. 10, 472–479.

Dack, G. M., Wheaton, M. M. N, and Schuler, M. N.   1960. Public health significance of microorganisms in frozen pot pies. Quick Frozen Foods 22, 44–45.

Despaul, J. E.   1966. The gangrene organism—a food poisoning agent. J. Am. Dietet. Assoc. 49, 185–190.

Donnelly, C. B., Harris, E. K., Black. L. A., and Lewis, K. H.   1960. Statistical analysis of standard plate counts of milk samples split with state laboratories. J. Milk Food Technol. 23, 315–319.

Eklund, M. W., Wieler, D. I., and Poysky, F. T.   1967. Outgrowth and toxin production of nonproteolytic Type B. Clostridium botulinum at 3.3° to 5.6°C. J. Bacteriol. 93, 1461–62.

Elliott, R. P., and Michener, H. D.   1960. Review of the microbiology of frozen foods. In Conference on Frozen Food Quality 40–61. U.S. Dept. Agr., Agr. Research Service ARS-74-21.

Elliott, R. P., and Michener, H. D.   1961. Microbiological process report. Microbiological standards and handling codes for chilled and frozen foods. (A review), Appl. Microbiol. 9, 452–468.

Elliott, R. P., and Straka, R. P.   1964. Rate of microbial deterioration of chicken meat at 35.6°F. (2°C.) after freezing and thawing. Poultry Sci. 43, No. 1, 81–86.

Engley, F. B., Jr.   1956. The persistence (survival) of microorganisms: IV. In food. Texas Rept. Biology and Medicine 14, 313–361.

Fanelli, M. J., and Ayres, J. C.   1959. Methods of detection and effect of freezing on the microflora of chicken pies. Food Technol. 13, 294–300.

Fanelli, M. J., and Gunderson, M. F.   1961. Defrosting of prepared frozen foods. 1. Defrost temperatures of frozen fruit pies, frozen meat pies and frozen soups. Food Technol. 15, 419–422.

Felstehausen, V. C., Strong, D. H., and Torrie, J. H.   1963. The influence of selected bacteria upon the flavor of a precooked frozen poultry product. Food Technol. 17, No. 5, 146–148.

Filz, W. F., and Bennett, R. W.   1965. Private communication. North Pacific Canners and Packers, Inc., Portland, Oregon.

Fitzgerald, G. A.   1947A. Are frozen foods a public health problem? Am. J. Public Health 37, 695–701.

Fitzgerald, G. A.   1947B. How to control the quality of frozen cooked foods. Food Inds. (May) 19, No. 5, 623–734.

Forgacs, J. 1962. Mycotoxicoses: The neglected diseases. Feedstuffs 34, No. 18, May 5, 124–134.

Foster, E. M., and Sugiyama, H. 1966. Latest developments in research on botulism. J. Milk Food Technol. 29, 342–347.

Galton, M. M., and Steele, J. H. 1961. Laboratory and epidemiological aspects of food-borne diseases. J. Milk Food Technol. 24, No. 4, 104–114.

Geister, R. S., and Maack, A. C. 1967. Sanitation in meat and poultry processing plants. J. Milk Food Technol. 30, No. 3, 67–70.

Graves, R. R., and Frazier, W. C. 1963. Food microorganisms influencing the growth of Staphylococcus aureus. Appl. Microbiol. 11, 513–516.

Green, M. 1949. Bacteriology of shrimp. III. Quantitative studies on frozen shrimp. Food Research 14, 384–394.

Guadagni, D. G., and Nimmo, C. C. 1957. The time-temperature tolerance of frozen foods. III. Effectiveness of vacuum, oxygen removal and mild heat in controlling browning in frozen peaches. Food Technol. 11, 43–47.

Gunderson, M. F. 1955. Need for sanitation standards in production and processing. In Precooked Frozen Foods—A symposium Quartermaster Food and Container Institute for Armed Forces. 52–55, Chicago, Ill.

Gunderson, M. F. 1956. Private communication. Dept. of Bacteriology. Univ. of Nebraska College of Medicine, Omaha, Nebraska.

Gunderson, M. F. 1961. Frozen food industry gives initial results of bacterial survey. Quick Frozen Foods 23, No. 6, 31–33.

Gunderson, M. F. 1962. Mold problem in frozen foods. In Proc. Low Temperature Microbiol. Symp., Campbell Soup Co., Camden, N.J. 1961, 299–312.

Gunderson, M. F. 1963. Food microbiological problems from the standpoint of industry. In Microbiological Quality of Foods. L. W. Slanetz, C. O. Chichester, A. R. Gaufin, and Z. J. Ordal (Editors). 205–222. Academic Press, New York.

Gunderson, M. F., and Peterson, A. C. 1964. A consideration of the microbiology of frozen foods. Assoc. of Food and Drug Officials of the U.S. 28, No. 1, 47–61.

Gunderson, M. F., and Rose, K. D. 1948. Survival of bacteria in a precooked fresh-frozen food. Food Research 13, 254–263.

Gunderson, M. F., McFadden, H. W., and Kyle, T. S. 1954. The Bacteriology of Commercial Poultry Processing. Burgess Pub. Co., Minneapolis, Minn.

Hall, H. E., and Angelotti, R. 1965. Clostridium perfringens in meat and meat products. Appl. Microbiol. 13, 352–357.

Hanson, H. C., and Fletcher, L. R. 1958. Time-temperature tolerance of frozen foods. XII. Turkey dinners and turkey pies. Food Technol. 12, No. 1, 40–43.

Hartman, P. A. 1960. Further studies on the selectivity of violet red bile agar. J. Milk Food Technol. 23, No. 2, 45–48.

Hartman, P. A., and Huntsberger, C. V. 1961. Influence of subtle differences in plating procedures on bacterial counts of prepared frozen foods. Appl. Microbiol. 9, No. 1, 32–38.

Hartman, P. A., Reinbold, G. W., and Saraswat, D. S. 1965. Indicator organisms—a review. II. The role of enterococci in food poisoning. J. Milk Food Technol. 28, No. 11, 344–550.

Hauge, S. 1950. Matforgiftninger Fremkalt av Bacillus cereus. (In Danish) Nord. Hyg. Tidskr. 31, 189.

Hobbs, B. C. 1953. The intensity of bacterial contamination in relation to food poisoning with special reference to Clostridium welchii. Intern. Cong. Microbiol., 6th (Rome) 3, 288–289.

Huber, D. A., Zaborowski, H., and Rayman, M. M. 1958. Studies on the micro-biological quality of precooked frozen meals. Food Technol. *12*, 190–194.

Hucker, G. J., and David, E. R. 1957. The effect of alternate freezing and thawing on the total flora of frozen chicken pies. Food Technol. *11*, 354–356.

Hussemann, D. L. 1951. Effect of cooking on the bacteriologic flora of selected frozen precooked foods. J. Am. Dietet. Assoc. *27*, 855–858.

Ingram, M. 1961. Microbiological standards for foods. Food Technol. *15*, No. 2, 4–12, 16.

Kachani, Z. F. 1965. Propagation and properties of hepatitis virus. Nature *208*, 605–606.

Kachikian, R., Fellers, C. R., and Litsky, W. R. 1959. A bacterial survey of commercial frozen breaded shrimp. J. Milk Food Technol. *22*, 310–312.

Kao, C. T., and Frazier, W. C. 1966. Effect of lactic acid bacteria on growth of *Staphylococcus aureus*. Appl. Microbiol. *14*, 251–255.

Kautter, D. A., Harmon, S. M., Lynt, R. K. Jr., and Lilly, T., Jr., 1966. Antagonistic effect on *Clostridium botulinum* type E by organisms resembling it. Appl. Microbiol. *14*, 616–622.

Kereluk, K., and Gunderson, M. F. 1959A. Studies on the bacteriological quality of frozen meat pies. I. Bacteriological survey of some commercially frozen meat pies. Appl. Microbiol. *7*, 320–323.

Kereluk, K., and Gunderson, M. F. 1959B. Studies on the bacteriological quality of frozen meat pies. II. A comparison of the methods for the enumeration of coliforms. J. Milk Food Technol. *22*, 176–178.

Kereluk, K., and Gunderson, M. F. 1959C. Studies on the bacteriological quality of frozen meat pies. IV. Longevity studies on the coliform bacteria and enterococci at low temperature. Appl. Microbiol. *7*, 327–328.

Kereluk, K., and Gunderson, M. F. 1961. Survival of bacteria in artifically contaminated frozen meat pies after baking. Appl. Microbiol. *9*, No. 1, 6–10.

Kereluk, K., Peterson, A. C., and Gunderson, M. F. 1960. Effect of different temperatures on various bacteria isolated from frozen meat pies. J. Food Sci. *26*, No. 1, 21–25.

Kern, J. 1957. Bacterial studies of frozen raw breaded shrimp. Technical Note No. 41, Comm. Fisheries Rev. *19*, 11–14.

Kuehn, H. H., and Gunderson, M. F. 1962. Psychrophilic and mesophilic fungi in fruit-filled pastries. Appl. Microbiol. *10*, 354–358.

Kuehn, H. H., and Gunderson, M. F. 1963. Psychrophilic and mesophilic fungi in frozen food products. Appl. Microbiol. *11*, 352–356.

Larkin, E. P., Litsky, W., and Fuller, J. E. 1955A. Fecal Streptococci in frozen foods. I. A bacteriological survey of some commercially frozen foods. Appl. Microbiol. *3*, 98–101.

Larkin, E. P., Litsky, W., and Fuller, J. E. 1955B. Fecal Streptococci in frozen foods. II. Effect of freezing storage on *Escherichia coli* and some fecal Streptococci inoculated onto green beans. Appl. Microbiol. *3*, 102–104.

Larkin, E. P. Litsky, W., and Fuller, J. E. 1955C. Fecal Streptococci in frozen foods. III. Effect of freezing storage on *Escherichia coli*, *Streptococcus faecalis* and *Streptococcus liquefaciens* inoculated orange concentrate. Appl. Microbiol. *3*, No. 2, 104–106.

Larkin, E. P., Litsky, W., and Fuller, J. E. 1956. Incidence of fecal Streptococci and coliform bacteria in frozen fish products. Am. J. Public Health *46*, 464–468.

Lemon, H. M. 1964. Food-borne viruses and malignant hemopoietic diseases. Bacteriol. Rev. *28*, 490–492.

Lewis, K. H.   1962. Problems of food protection in relation to environmental health. Assoc. Food Drug Officials U.S. *26*, No. 4, 166–178.

Lewis, K. H., Angelotti, R., Hall, H. E., Crisley, F. D., Galton, M. M., and Boring, J. R. III.   1964. Examination of foods for enteropathogenic and indicator bacteria. U.S. Public Health Serv., PHS Pub. *1142*, 123.

Liston, J.   1965. Sanitation in seafood production and distribution. J. Milk Food Technol. *28*, 152–158.

Litsky, W., Fagerson, I. S., and Fellers, C. R.   1957. A bacteriological survey of commercially frozen beef, poultry, and tuna pies. J. Milk Food Technol. *20*, 216–219.

Logan, P. P., Harp, C. H., and Dove, W. F.   1951. Keeping quality of precooked frozen chicken 'a la king—a bacteriological evaluation of hot and cold packs. Food Technol. *5*, 193–198.

Lynt. Jr., R. K.   1966. Survival and recovery of enterovirus from foods. Appl. Microbiol. *14*, 218–222.

Machala, W. E.   1961. A bacteriological investigation of frozen foods in the Oklahoma City area. J. Milk Food Technol. *24*, 323–327.

McCoy, D. W., and Faber, J. E.   1966. Influence of food microorganisms on staphylococcal growth and enteroxin production in meat. Appl. Microbiol. *14*, 372–377.

Messinger, H. B.   1963. Statistical analysis of standard plate counts of a food sample split among laboratories. J. Milk Food Technol. *26*, 328–331.

Meyer, K. F.   1953. Food poisoning, New Engl. J. Med. *29*, 843.

Miller, L. R., and Greenberg, A. E.   1962. Bacteriological testing of utensils for quality control in an oyster shucking plant. J. Milk Food Technol. *25*, 183–184.

Moragne, L., Longree, K., and White, J. C.   1960. The effect of some selected factors on the cooling of food under refrigeration. J. Milk Food Technol. *23*, 142–150.

National Academy of Sciences-National Research Council 1964.   An evaluation of public health hazards from microbiological contamination of foods. A Report of the Food Protection Committee of the Food and Nutrition Board, Publication *1195*.

Newberne, P. M., Wogan, G. N., Carlton, W. W., and Abdel Kader, M. M.   1964. Histopathogenic lessons in ducklings caused by *Aspergillus flavus* cultures, culture extracts and crystalling aflatoxins. Toxicol. Appl. Pharmacol. *6*, 542–556.

Nickerson, J. T. R., Silverman, G. J., Solberg, M., Duncan, D. W., and Joselow, M. M.   1962. Microbial analysis of commercial frozen fish sticks. J. Milk Food Technol. *25*, 45–47.

Oberhofer, T. R., and Frazier, W. C.   1961. Competition of *Staphylococcus aureus* with other organisms. J. Milk Food Technol. *24*, 172–175.

Obold, W. L., and Hutchings, B. L.   1947. Sanitation technique in the frozen food industry. Food Technol. *1*, 561–564.

Perry, H., Townsend, C. T., Andersen, A. A., and Berry, J. A.   1948. Studies on *Clostridium botulinum* in frozen pack vegetables. Food Technol. *2*, 180–190.

Peterson, A. C.   1962. An ecological study of frozen foods. *In* Proc. Low Temperature Microbiol Symp., Campbell Soup Co., *1961*, 157–195, Camden, N.J.

Peterson, A. C., Black, J. J., and Gunderson, M. F.   1962. Staphylococcus in competition. I. Growth of naturally occuring mixed populations in precooked frozen foods during defrost. Appl. Microbiol. *10*, 23–30.

Peterson, A. C., Fanelli, M. J., and Gunderson, M. F. 1963. The limits of edibility of defrosted chicken pies. *In* Microbiological Quality of Foods. Slanetz, L. W., Chichester, C. O , Gaufin, A. R., and Ordal, Z. J. (Editors) Academic Press, New York.

Peterson, A. C., Fanelli, M. J., and Gunderson, M. F. 1964. The limits of edibility. II. Defrost of frozen prepared turkey dinners and macaroni and cheese dinners. Am. J. Public Health. *54*, 649–659.

Peterson, A. C. and Gunderson, M. F. 1960A. The role of psychrophilic bacteria in frozen food spoilage. Food Technol. *14*, 413–417.

Peterson, A. C., and Gunderson, M. F. 1960B. Some characteristics of proteolytic enzymes from *Pseudomonas fluorescens*. Appl. Microbiol. *8*, 98–104.

Peterson, A. C., and Gunderson, M. F. 1965. Two sides of the coin. The food industry today and tomorrow. New York State Milk and Food· Sanitarians Annual Report, 45–70.

Peterson, A. C., Karlson, K. E., and Gunderson, M. F. 1963. Effects of time and temperature on food quality. Cornell Hotel Restaurant Admin. Quart. *4*, No. 1, 25–36.

Proctor, B. E., and Phillips, A. W., Jr. 1947. Microbiological aspects of frozen precooked foods. Refrig. Eng. *53*, 30–33, 68.

Proctor, B. E., and Phillips, A. W. Jr. 1948. Frozen precooked foods. Am. J. Public Health. *38*, 44–49.

Raj, H., and Liston, J. 1961A. Survival of bacteria of public health significance in frozen sea foods. Food Technol. *15*, 429–434.

Raj, H., and Liston, J. 1961B. The detection and enumeration of fecal indicator organisms in frozen seafoods. I. *Escherichia coli*. Appl. Microbiol. *9*, 171–174.

Raj, H., and Liston, J. 1963. Effect of processing on public health bacteria in frozen seafoods. Food Technol. *17*, No. 10, 83–89.

Raj, H., Wiebe, W. J., and Liston, J. 1961C. The detection and enumeration of fecal indicator organisms in frozen seafoods. II. Enterococci. Appl. Microbiol. *9*, 295–303.

Rayman, M. M., Huber, D. A., and Zaborowski, H. 1955. Current microbiological standards of quality for precooked frozen foods and their basis. *In* Precooked frozen foods—a symposium. pp. 55–67. U.S. Quartermaster Food and Container Inst., Chicago, Ill.

Rogers, R. E., and Gunderson, M. F. 1958A. Roasting of frozen stuffed turkeys. I. Survival of *Salmonella pullorum* in inoculated stuffing. Food Research *23*, 87–95.

Rogers, R. E., and Gunderson, M. F. 1958B. Roasting of frozen stuffed turkeys. II. Survival of *Micrococcus pyogenes var. aureus* in inoculated stuffing. Food Research *23*, 96–102.

Ross, D. A., and Thatcher, F. S. 1958. Bacteriological content of marketed precooked frozen foods in relation to public health. Food Technol. *12*, 269–371.

Saleh, M. A. and Ordal, Z. J. 1955. Studies on the growth and toxin production of *Clostridium botulinum* in a precooked frozen food. II. Inhibition by lactic acid bacteria. Food Research *20*, 340–350.

Schmidt, C. F., Lechowich, R. V., and Folinazzo, J. F. 1961. Growth and toxin production by type E. *Clostridium botulinum* below 40°F. (4.4°C.) J. Food Sci. *26*, 626–630.

Seminiano, E. N., and Frazier, W. C. 1966. Effect of Pseudomonads and Achromobacteraceae on growth of *Staphylococcus aureus*. J. Milk Food Technol. *29*, 161–164.

Shelton, L. R. Jr., Leininger, H. V., Surkiewicz, B. F., Baer, E. F., Elliott, R. P., Hyndman, J. B., and Kramer, N. 1961. A bacteriological survey of the frozen precooked food industry. U.S. Dept. of Health, Education and Welfare. Food and Drug Administration.

Shepard, A. D. 1960. Relative stabilities of various frozen foods. *In* Conference on Frozen Food Quality, U.S. Dept. Agr., ARS 74–21, 18–23, Albany California.

Shiffman, M. A., and Kronick, D. 1963. The development of microbiological standards for foods. J. Milk Food Technol. *26*, 110–113.

Silverman, G. J., Nickerson, J. T. R., Duncan, D. W., Davis, N. S., Schachter, J. S., and Joselow, M. M. 1961. Microbial analysis of frozen, raw, and cooked shrimp. I. General results. Food Technol. *15*, 455–458.

Slabyj, B. M., Dollar, A. M., and Liston, J. 1965. Post-irradiation survival of *Staphylococcus aureus* in seafoods. J. Food Sci. *30*, 344–350.

Slocum, G. G. 1961. The status of bacteriological standards for frozen foods. J. Milk Food Technol. *24*, 345–346.

Straka, R. P., and Combes, F. M. 1952. Survival and multiplication of *Micrococcus pyogenes var. aureua* in creamed chicken under various holding, storage and defrosting conditions. Food Research *17*, 448–455.

Strong, D. H., Canada, J. C., and Griffiths, B. B. 1963. Incidence of *Clostridium perfringens* in American foods. Appl. Microbiol. *11*, No. 1, 43–44.

Surkiewicz, B. F. 1966. Bacteriological survey of the frozen prepared foods industry. I. Frozen cream-type pies. Appl. Microbiol. *14*, No. 1, 21–26.

Surkiewicz, B. F., Hyndman, J. B., and Yancy, M. V. 1967. Bacteriological survey of the frozen prepared foods industry. II. Frozen breaded raw shrimp. Appl. Microbiol. *15*, No. 1, 1–9.

Thatcher, F. S. 1955. Microbiological standards for foods: their function and limitations. J. Applied Microbiol. *18*, 450–461.

Thatcher, F. S. 1963. The microbiology of specific frozen foods in relation to public health: Report of an international committee. J. Applied Bacteriol. *26*, 266–285.

Tong, J. L., Engle, H. M., Cullyford, J. S., Shrimp, D. J., and Love, C. E. 1962. Investigation of an outbreak of food poisoning traced to turkey meat. Am. J. Pub. Health. *52*, 976–990.

Tretsven, W. J. 1965. Bacteriological survey of filleting processes in the Pacific northwest. IV. Bacterial counts of fish fillets and equipment. J. Milk Food Technol. *28*, No. 9, 287–291.

Troller, J. A., and Frazier, W. C. 1963. Repression of *Staphylococcus aureus* by food bacteria. II. Cause of inhibition. Appl. Microbiol. *11*, 163–165.

United States Department of Agriculture. 1960. Conference on Frozen Food Quality. *ARS-74-21*, Albany, Calif.

United States Dept. Health, Education, and Welfare. 1965. Hepatitis Surveillance Rept. *24*.

United States Quartermaster Food and Container Institute. 1955. Precooked frozen foods. A symposium. Bollman, M., and Peterson, M. S. (Editors). Quartermaster Research and Development Command, U.S. Army Quartermaster Corps. Advisory Board on Quartermaster Research and Development Committee on Foods. National Academy of Sciences-National Research Council Washington.

Verma, N. N. S., Foltz, V. D., and Mickelsen, R. 1964. Sanitary status of some precooked, frozen, dessert-type foods. J. Milk Food Technol. *27*, 359–362.

Verrett, M. J., Marliac, J. P., and McLaughlin, J., Jr. 1964. Use of the chicken embryo on the assay of aflatoxin toxicity. J. Assoc. Offic. Agr. Chem. 47, 1003–1006.

Weiser, H. H. 1957. Bacteriology of precooked frozen foods. J. Milk Food Technol. 20, No. 2, 33–35.

Wilson, E., Paffenbarger, R. S., Jr., Fotor, M. J., and Lewis, K. H. 1961. Prevalence of Salmonellae in meat and poultry products. J. Infect. Diseases. 109, 166–171.

Wogan, G. N. (Editor). 1964. Mycotoxins in Foodstuffs. Proceedings of a symposium held at Mass. Inst. Technol., March 18, 1964. M.I.T. Press, Mass. Inst. of Technol., Cambridge, Mass.

Woodburn, M., and Kim, C. H. 1966. Survival of Clostridium perfringens during baking and holding of turkey stuffing. Appl. Microbiol. 14, 914–920.

Woodburn, J. M., and Strong, D. H 1960. Survival of Salmonella typhimurium, Staphylococcus aureus, and Streptococcus faecalis frozen in simplified food substrates. Appl. Microbiol. 8, 109.

Zaborowski, H , Huber, D. A., and Rayman, M. M. 1958. Evaluation of microbiological methods used for the examination of precooked frozen foods. Appl. Microbiol. 6, 97–104.

## CHAPTER 3

George G. Cook

# Consumer Surveys of the Acceptability of Precooked and Prepared Frozen Foods[1]

## INTRODUCTION—THE IMPORTANCE OF CONSUMER SURVEYS

Some frozen food packers attempted to process and sell frozen prepared foods in the thirties. Most of these ventures failed primarily because the consumer was not ready and conditions were not favorable! The economic situation did not lend itself to such progressive ideas. It seems likely that had effective consumer surveys been run on representative groups of the population at that time, the results would have induced extreme caution. To introduce a new item into the market was *very* expensive, much more so to introduce a revolutionary new idea—prepared foods.

Today, the climate is vastly different. Zero storage in consumer homes greatly exceeds that of all zero warehouses in the United States (Anon. 1967B). There is a large work force of married couples and single people who would rather buy prepared foods than to spend the time preparing them; there are also the elderly who are financially able and willing to pay for foods with built-in conveniences that are time-saving. Thus there is a very strong demand for many types of precooked and prepackaged frozen foods. Today, it is even more expensive to introduce a new food item onto the market. It is indeed an expensive proposition to search for new products, new ideas, market test, and finally move into production, gambling on the public to buy in sufficient quantity to make the whole undertaking profitable. Thus the key to this puzzle is in the hands of the consumer. We must find out what she really needs and wants, and how much she is willing to pay. All of this requires careful analysis, being mindful of the psychological demands and influences. For example: in questioning the housewives as to which ice cream they purchased for their children, their responses indicated they bought the best grades (Anon. 1965B). However, when they indicated the prices they paid it was discovered that they actually bought the cheapest grades. Before questioning them as to reasons for their choice of an ice cream for their children, we were of the belief that quality would receive priority but were surprised to find that they wanted an ice cream to "satisfy this hunger and to fill them up." Such information certainly is of great importance to a manufacturer of ice cream as are many

---

George G. Cook is Professor and Chairman, Food Technology Department, State University of New York, Agricultural and Technical College, Farmingdale, N.Y.

[1] Carried out at the Agricultural and Technical College of the State University of New York.

other aspects which can be discovered through carefully planned consumer surveys.

PRELIMINARY FINDINGS

For several years, the students (Fig. 8) in the Food Technology Program at the State University Agricultural and Technical College at Farmingdale, N.Y., have been making such surveys. Since the population in this area is ever changing, with almost all areas of the United States represented, it has proved to be an almost ideal location for these surveys. The students have surveyed house to house in Farmingdale, Bethpage, Plainedge, Levittown, North Massapequa, and as far north as Huntington. The last seven or eight surveys have been analyzed and published in *Quick Frozen Foods* (Anon, 1963A, B; 1964A, B; 1965A; 1966A; Cook and Martin 1966). Prior to these surveys, which will be discussed later in this chapter, the students discovered many valuable points which in general should prove of interest. Several of these findings in brief are:

Fig. 8.  Prof. George G. Cook and students of the Food Technology Department, State University of New York, Agricultural and Technical College, Farmingdale, N.Y., who made the consumer surveys.

(1) The housewife finds directions on the frozen food packages quite unreliable.

(2) She needs and wants to know what size pot to use, covered or uncovered, amount of water to use, exact amount of salt to use, whether to cook on high, medium, or low heat and for how long.

(3) She is interested in practical and interesting ways of cooking (given on the packaged poultry and lesser known cuts of meat).

(4) She is becoming more conscious of the importance of good nutrition for her family, thus welcomes good information when considering the use of precooked or prepackaged frozen foods.

(5) She could be interested in practical, reliable, and economically sound menu suggestions on the package.

(6) She is displeased with the unreliable information regarding the number of servings on many packages of precooked frozen foods. It would appear that many food processors should re-examine what they have on their packages relative to this.

(7) An attractive package showing how the food should look when properly prepared is preferred to the film window displaying a very unappetizing frozen food item.

(8) The consumer looks for time-saving and convenience items at reasonable cost, but she wants and expects consistent quality and is willing and able to pay for it.

(9) She is very unhappy about deceptive marketing practices such as jumbo pound packages, low calorie foods (lower than what?), exaggerated numbers of servings, half truths regarding the length of time required to actually prepare and serve a given food item.

These and other items have shown up time and again in different consumer surveys.

Consumer frozen food surveys were started at the college as a result of an intensive study of marketing methods, market trends, and per capita (consumption) figures dealing with changing eating habits of our population. The students concluded, and rightly so, that the consumer held the key to the success of any given food item.

The first one of the series that was developed was "Who Eats Frozen Dinners?" (Anon. 1963A). However, the survey questionnaire used by the students to make approximately 1,000 family consumer interviews was headed, "Frozen Dinner Survey Questionnaire." The survey was made by students contacting housewives in a house-to-house survey that required three half-day field trips for each student. After completing the survey the students totaled the answers for each question and drew up summary conclusions. The questionnaire and summary conclusions were published in *Quick Frozen Foods*. This procedure has been followed with each succeeding survey. It has been a fine experience of real practical value for the students who took part and to the frozen food industry as reflected by many favorable responses. It is hoped that there will be positive values to the consumer through the industry's recognition of some points made in the summary conclusions from each consumer survey. Thus, if the survey is well done, the student, the industry, and the consumer may all profit from these enterprises. If the survey functions as a communication link between the consumer and the industry, then it's more likely that both will profit—the consumer by getting food items that she likes the way she likes and those in industry who can satisfy her demands will have greater assurance of financial success.

## VALUE OF PERSONAL INTERVIEWS

The personal interview is time-consuming, and consequently expensive. Much care should be used in formulating the questions. The housewife must be made to understand that the interviewer is not there to sell anything. The first and last questions need to be very carefully phrased. The questionnaire should remain in the hands of the interviewer and he or she should very carefully clarify any questions not made clear when initially asked. Student interviewers were urged to be respectful, courteous, and to thank the person interviewed for her time, opinion, and suggestions. Since there are some who are fearful of strangers, we have found that a fair percentage of those asked to participate by answering certain questions will answer in the negative to avoid further contact.

## FROZEN DINNER SURVEY QUESTIONNAIRE: WHO EATS FROZEN DINNERS?

In this, the first survey, 12 questions were asked of approximately 1,000 consumers in and around the State University at Farmingdale, Long Island (Anon. 1963A). All of the questions when summarized produced some very interesting and informative responses, some of greater significance than others. From these findings, the reader may see other values than those presented.

The following is a type of summarization of the findings. Interpretations are given at some points for clarification. The reader can thus draw his own conclusions. In answer to the first question, "Who eats frozen dinners?," we found:

| | |
|---|---|
| Entire family | 49 |
| Children under 12 years | 22 |
| Couples | 7 |
| Teenagers | 5 |
| Never buy them | 18 |

"How many frozen dinners are purchased on the average shopping trip?" The findings are significant: an average of 4 dinners per trip were purchased by those interviewed. Some purchased 10 and 12 at a time—72% of those purchasing bought from 3 to 12 dinners per shopping trip. "What dinner varieties were purchased and per cent of each?"

| Variety | % | Variety | % |
|---|---|---|---|
| Shrimp dinners | 4 | Chicken | 60 |
| Chinese dinners | 2 | Turkey | 40 |
| Meat loaf dinners | 3 | Beef | 32 |
| Pork dinners | 3 | Fish dinners | 15 |
| Scallops | 3 | Ham dinners | 7 |

"At what times are dinners served?" Here we found 86% served at dinner, 26% at lunch (none for breakfast), or for snacks. (Some people served them at both meals, thus the percentage will not add up to 100%.)

"What other foods and drinks do you serve with the frozen dinners?"

| | % | | % |
|---|---|---|---|
| Served bread or rolls | 61 | Served deserts | 36 |
| Served coffee | 59 | Served soup | 25 |
| Served milk | 55 | Served tea | 24 |
| Served salads | 43 | Served fruit cups | 10 |

Thus, it can be seen that very few served frozen dinners without some side dish or drink.

To the question, "What new varieties of dinners would you like to see?," 90% had no suggestions. Suggestions made: Italian dinners, beef stew, Brook trout, and dinners with more than one meat. Fifty-five per cent liked the idea of having dinners with soup and dessert included. Thirty-nine per cent did not approve of this innovation. Two per cent favored dinners with only a dessert added. One per cent had no answers. When asked to suggest improvements in existing dinners, the following ideas were given:

| | % |
|---|---|
| Suggested bigger portions | 28 |
| Suggested different vegetables | 11 |
| Suggested butter flavor | 6 |
| Suggested different potatoes | 35 |
| Were satisfied | 49 |

It is quite possible that teenagers do not accept the dinners because of the small servings.

When asked "What other vegetables they would like to see in the dinners?," we found the following:

| | % | | % |
|---|---|---|---|
| Green beans | 23 | Cauliflower | 6 |
| Broccoli | 13 | Asparagus | 6 |
| Corn | 13 | Beets | 3 |
| Spinach | 13 | Turnips | 3 |
| Greens | 10 | Red cabbage | 3 |

Questions on the packaging of dinners met with general satisfaction by 89%. Easier opening of the foil corners was suggested; the placement of the heating directions on the side of the package instead of the bottom was requested.

In response to the question, "What prompted you to purchase the dinner?," we obtained this information:

| | % | | % |
|---|---|---|---|
| TV commercials | 40 | Radio | 7 |
| Store displays | 24 | Friends, relatives | 6 |
| Newspapers | 14 | Magazines | 2 |

### FROZEN MEAT PIES SURVEY

Meat pies have precooked meat, vegetables, and gravy frozen in an unbaked pie crust—sometimes top and bottom—sometimes only top crust (a pot pie). The pie is then baked in the home and served directly. Volume of these pies has declined, thus an effort was made to determine the cause and possible solution by surveying consumers. Twelve questions were asked with subdivisions to these questions for more details and clarification (Anon. 1963B).

The following is a brief summarization of key questions and areas of great interest. Extensive explanations are not made since interests vary.

"Who eats meat pies in your family?" The facts were compiled:

| | % |
|---|---|
| Wife | 73 |
| Husband | 60 |
| Children 12 years and younger | 50 |
| Teenagers | 39 |
| Other adults | 5 |
| Pets | 1 |

*Note:* Thirty-nine per cent of the teenagers eat meat pies compared with 4.8% who eat frozen dinners—a very significant fact.

The distribution of their use is good but somehow the consumer must be motivated to buy more and to use them more frequently. A surprise was the per cent used for pets. But why not—many want the best for their pets!

"How frequently do you use frozen meat pies?" We found that:

|  | % |
|---|---|
| 3 or more per week | 5 |
| 2 per week | 5 |
| 1 per week | 26 |
| At least 1 per month | ·23 |
| Less than 1 per month | 40 |

"When are meat pies served, which meal?"

|  | % |
|---|---|
| For dinner | 57 |
| For lunch | 35 |
| For snacks | 15 |

This totals over 100% because some people may serve pies at each meal.

"Are these pies adequate?" Sixty per cent answered "Yes," 18% answered "No," with 22% expressing "No opinion."

"What size meat pie is preferred?" Sixty-seven per cent preferred the small pie, 15% favored the large,—14 oz. and larger; 18% expressed no choice.

"Are you satisfied with quality?" The conclusions are significant since this is of such importance:

|  | % |  | % |
|---|---|---|---|
| Excellent | 10 | Fair | 13 |
| Very good | 26 | Poor | 4 |
| Good | 35 | No opinion | 12 |

"Are meat pies a good value?" The consumer should have a good idea on this one. Seventy-two per cent answered "Yes," 12% answered "No," with 16% expressing "No opinion."

"Which type of meat pie do you prefer?" The summarization showed:

|  | % |
|---|---|
| Preferred chicken | 77 |
| Preferred beef | 47 |
| Preferred tuna | 10 |
| Preferred other potpies | 1 |

*Note:* Many had multiple interests due to different family member tastes.

"What started consumer buying frozen meat pies?"

|                                           | %  |
|-------------------------------------------|----|
| Emergency, quick meal convenience         | 23 |
| Store sales and displays                  | 17 |
| TV spots and newspaper advertisements     | 15 |
| Curiosity and impulse                     | 11 |
| Family, friends, and relatives            | 9  |
| No reply                                  | 25 |

"Do you like the idea of family-sized frozen meat pies?"

|            | %  |
|------------|----|
| Yes        | 37 |
| No         | 44 |
| Undecided  | 6  |
| No opinion | 13 |

*Note:* The possibilities of the larger frozen meat pies should be examined carefully.

It is always interesting to compare, and still more so to validate a point or position. This survey indicates that 56.9% of the families served frozen meat pies at dinners and 34.8% at lunch, while the *Seventeen* Magazine survey taken three years earlier had 54% at dinner and 38% at lunch.

There were a number of other factors that turned up in this survey. We have predicted some of the most obvious. The reader can surely draw other conclusions.

### FROZEN FRUIT, CREAM PIES SURVEY

Frozen fruit and cream pies sell volume-wise as well as all other bakery foods combined. How does the consumer feel about these products? What varieties does she like? When does she purchase them and who in the family eats them? The 16-question-consumer survey attempted to find the answers to these questions and other additional pertinent information (Anon. 1964A).

Who Eats Frozen Fruit—Cream Pies?

|               | %  |
|---------------|----|
| Mother        | 59 |
| Father        | 54 |
| Under 12      | 40 |
| Teenagers     | 40 |
| Grandparents  | 23 |
| Bachelor      | 15 |
| Couples       | 14 |
| Bachelor girl | 12 |

## Frozen Pie Varieties Purchased and % That Bought Them

| | % | | % |
|---|---|---|---|
| Apple | 81 | Pineapple | 19 |
| Cherry | 41 | Chiffon | 19 |
| Blueberry | 26 | Strawberry | 17 |
| Peach | 24 | Pecan | 8 |
| Mince | 21 | Custard | 8 |
| Lemon | 20 | Boysenberry | 4 |
| Coconut custard | 20 | | |

Apple pie proved to be an 82% variety favorite with cherry a strong second and blueberry third. The relationship percentages prove interesting and informative according to the survey of consumers. We found the price fair for these pies; 18% considered the price low and 14% considered the price high. These figures were based on 87% of consumers offering opinions. The remaining 13% had no opinion.

What size pie does the consumer actually prefer? Of those consumers who had opinions, 78% preferred 8-in. standard size pies, 11% favored the small size, and 11% favored the large frozen pie.

"At what meal are these pies eaten?" As expected 85% of the pies are eaten at the dinner meal; 36% eat pie between meals or for snacks with coffee; and 30% eat pie for lunch. The surprise was that 11% eat pie for breakfast. In the northwest it is a very common thing—perhaps it could be encouraged in the east.

It would be very interesting to see how sales of a given pie could be pushed upward by a careful study of consumer flavor acceptance, color preferences, and texture interest. At the college, we have found that pumpkin pie can be sold throughout the year if the consumer thoroughly likes the taste, color, texture, and is properly motivated through advertising or promotions.

When questioned on quality of flavor of frozen pies, we found:

| | % | | % |
|---|---|---|---|
| Good | 46 | Excellent | 12 |
| Very good | 22 | Poor | 1 |
| Fair | 12 | | |

This certainly speaks well of the overall flavor acceptance. Quality of crust produced this statistic: Good 42%; Very good 20%; Fair 18%; Excellent 9%; Poor 9%. Quality of fillings produced this information: Good 44%; Very good 20%; Fair 18%; Excellent 14%; Poor 3%.

The frozen pies are consumed more on some days than others:  Sundays 50%; Saturdays 28%; Mondays 24%; Tuesdays 15%; Wednesdays 15%. Thursday is a poor day with only 5% of the pies consumed.

When questioned regarding preferences of frozen, fresh, or home-baked, the consumers indicated 14% frozen, 19% fresh, 34% home-baked, and 31% gave no preference. Besides buying frozen, 58% buy fresh, and 51% also bake some of their own pies. Some indicated in fact that they baked quantities of pies and kept them in their freezer.

### FROZEN FISH SURVEY

Approximately 800 housewives were questioned in a door-to-door survey conducted by Food Technology freshmen at the State University Agricultural and Technical College at Farmingdale, Long Island, N.Y., in an endeavor to find out what induced the consumer to buy frozen fish (Anon. 1964B).

The following summarizations of the fish survey are perhaps of greatest importance though one must concede that one's interests will condition one to see different values in many of these conclusions.

To the question, "In what form are fish purchased?," the percentages were as follows:

|        | %  |        | %  |
|--------|----|--------|----|
| Fresh  | 76 | Frozen | 67 |
| Canned | 73 | Smoked | 15 |

What per cent of the consumers eat fish in one form only?

|        | %  |
|--------|----|
| Fresh  | 22 |
| Frozen | 10 |
| Canned | 3  |

A question sought out why consumers do not eat frozen fish. The summarization yields these facts:

|                   | %  |                    | %  |
|-------------------|----|--------------------|----|
| Prefer fresh fish | 46 | Won't try frozen fish | 8  |
| Frozen flavor poor | 23 | Fear fish are too old | 5  |
| Do own fishing    | 10 |                    |    |

It is of considerable importance to determine how often fillets are eaten by the average consumer. The findings pointed it up this way:

|                     | %  |                        | %  |
|---------------------|----|------------------------|----|
| Once per week       | 42 | More than once per month | 26 |
| More than once per week | 5  | Less than once per month | 6  |
| Once per month      | 21 |                        |    |

It is significant that frozen fillets are eaten 100% for dinner; 7% for lunch; and 2% for snacks—probably in a sandwich. It is also significant to determine who eats the frozen fillets. The findings:

|                    | %  |
|--------------------|----|
| Wife               | 94 |
| Husband            | 89 |
| Children under 12  | 55 |
| Teenagers          | 51 |
| Grandparents       | 2  |

Just why are frozen fillets used by the homemaker?

|                        | %  |
|------------------------|----|
| Convenience            | 55 |
| Flavor                 | 14 |
| No bones               | 10 |
| Immediate availability | 4  |
| Price favorable        | 17 |

Note that convenience, flavor, no bones, and availability are significant justification for using this type of fish. Of course, the block freezing of fillets slows their thawing. There appeared to be good interest in individually quick-frozen fillets because of the increased speed of thawing—it can be served more quickly.

Consumers purchased more frozen fish fillets (92%) than fish sticks (73%). Eighty-five per cent serve fish sticks at dinner, 28% at lunch, and 5% at snack time. Complaints made against frozen fish sticks were as follows:

|                                    | %  |
|------------------------------------|----|
| Do not like for various reasons    | 64 |
| Too much breading—not enough fish  | 9  |
| Not enough in package for family   | 8  |

In spite of these, however, on the positive side we found:

|                                 | %  |
|---------------------------------|----|
| Buy because of convenience      | 72 |
| Buy because of flavor           | 54 |
| Buy because of price            | 16 |
| Buy because of availability     | 9  |
| Buy because children like them  | 4  |
| Buy because of greater variety  | 1  |

"Who eats fish sticks?" The wife—75%, husband—79%, children under 12—65%, and teenagers—54%, while grandparents—2%, apparently do not favor this item.

"Who eats fish portions?" Here we have an even stronger acceptance among the adults:

| | % |
|---|---|
| Husband | 86 |
| Wife | 83 |
| Children under 12 | 42 |
| Teenagers | 40 |
| Grandparents | 3 |

The objections to frozen fish portions were as follows:

| | % |
|---|---|
| Do not like taste | 30 |
| Never tried them | 17 |
| No particular reason | 8 |
| Never noticed them in store | 4 |
| Prefer other varieties | 3 |
| They have no taste | 3 |
| Do not like breading | 2 |

Flavor and convenience topped the reasons why the consumer buys fish portions. Of those consumers who were asked which they preferred, portions or sticks, we found 53% preferred the former and 40.3% the latter, while 6.5% had no preference.

Certainly the information given above could influence what some packers, distributors, or retailers plan to do to increase frozen fish sales.

### PREPARED VEGETABLE SURVEY

A group of 18 students at the State University Agricultural and Technical College at Farmingdale, N.Y., interviewed some 600 housewives in the area adjacent to the College on Long Island. These housewives represent upper middle to lower middle income groups and consisted primarily of young families from widely divergent localities within the United States (Anon. 1966A).

The selection of this product was felt to be timely and had many potentialities. A portion of the questionnaire is included in order to indicate the thoroughness of the survey study. All questions were verbally presented and the responses recorded by the student interviewers. The sum total of the responses for each question was then determined by the students as a part of their work.

In response to the question, "Which type of package of prepared vegetables do you purchase?" we obtained these percentage figures:

|  | % |
|---|---|
| Boilable pouch | 96 |
| Regular box | 78 |
| Aluminum tray | 18 |

Percentages of purchases of pouch vegetables in butter sauce?

| | % | | % |
|---|---|---|---|
| Peas | 49 | Sliced carrots | 9 |
| Corn | 40 | Baby carrots | 9 |
| Spinach | 34 | Lima beans | 8 |
| Broccoli | 25 | Mushrooms | 4 |
| Stringbeans | 21 | Mexicorn | 3 |
| Mixed vegetables | 16 | Brussels sprouts | 1 |
| Cauliflower | 16 | Asparagus | 1 |
| Italian green beans | 16 | | |

What prepared vegetables are purchased in sauces other than butter?

| | % |
|---|---|
| Chopped spinach in cream sauce | 18 |
| Peas in onion sauce | 14 |
| Broccoli au gratin | 12 |
| Asparagus with Hollandaise sauce | 10 |
| Potatoes and peas in cream sauce | 9 |
| Baby lima beans in cheese sauce | 7 |
| Buttered parsley potatoes | 6 |
| Corn and lima beans in tomato sauce | 5 |
| Smothered onions | 4 |
| Mixed vegetables with tomatoes | 4 |
| Green beans with tomato sauce | |
| Creole succotash | 3 |
| Zucchini in tomato sauce | 3 |
| Creamed onions | 1 |
| Cauliflower in cheese | 1 |
| Cauliflower in cream sauce | 1 |

It was significant to find that the consumer preferred pouched vegetables
because of convenience 66%, quality 33%, and nutritional advantage 1%.
Her reaction to the price factor yielded this information:   price just right

56%, too high 42%, and too low 1%. It was most encouraging that the consumer rated quality of prepared vegetables as:

|           | %  |      | %  |
|-----------|----|------|----|
| Excellent | 18 | Fair | 7  |
| Very good | 39 | Poor | 2  |
| Good      | 33 |      |    |

This summarization came from questioning the housewife as to why she purchased prepared vegetables:

|                    | %  |
|--------------------|----|
| Convenience        | 46 |
| Quality and flavor | 21 |
| No special reasons | 16 |
| Reasonable price   | 7  |
| Variety            | 6  |
| Nutrition          | 3  |
| Promotion          | 1  |
| Do not know        | 1  |

*Note:* With so many women joining our work force in the United States, we see 46% purchasing because of convenience as a very modest figure.

From the survey results, we found 46% favoring single pouched vegetables with 53% against. Here again convenience would account for a significant portion of the affirmative answers. Since price is not a major issue, the single portion pouch would permit each member of the family to have his choice of vegetable. This has not been obtainable and practical to date.

In order to stimulate sales of pouched vegetables, one should be mindful that some housewives dislike them for these reasons: difficult to handle 69%, high-priced 19%, and of poor quality 11%. Top consideration should be given to resolving the first and last objections. The many advantages, including catering to individual tastes, could justify the price. Fifty-four per cent of those interviewed preferred the pouches to boxes or trays for prepared vegetables, while 26% found no difference.

To the question, would the consumer buy larger pouches for larger families, the response was 55% "Yes," and 45% "No." This is a very important question and together with that of the individual serving we have an apparently strong mandate to offer the consumer a diversity of sizes of the very same products. In the earlier history of the frozen food industry both approaches were attempted. The large packages of vegetables up to 16 oz.

were once sold, and in 1959 single-serving pouches were placed on the market. Food "Plans" across the United States have sold quantities of vegetables for larger families in two and one-half pound cartons. These are normally sold as institutional packs.

When asked what product lines other than vegetables would be of interest to them in pouches, the consumers responded thus:

|  | % |  | % |
|---|---|---|---|
| Meat slices | 53 | Entrées | 33 |
| Seafoods | 49 | Fruits (for thawing) | 28 |
| Desserts | 44 | Baby foods | 20 |
| Soups | 38 |  |  |

Since the consumer has had experience with prepared vegetables in the pouch, the box, and the tray, she was asked if she would favor buying other items in these respective units. The response: 65% agreed regarding the pouch, 58% agreed regarding the box, and 52% agreed regarding the tray.

This survey provides us with a wealth of information which can point the way for further industrial development in frozen foods, in prepared vegetables, and other frozen product lines.

### Questions Asked in the Frozen Prepared Vegetable Survey

(1) Do you buy frozen vegetables for your family's meals? Yes____No____

(2) Do you purchase specially prepared vegetables in a boilable pouch? Regular box____or aluminum tray____? If you no longer use them, give reasons why not. 1._____2._____3._____

(3) If you buy prepared vegetables in a boilable pouch, which ones do you buy?
*In Butter Sauce:* Peas____Lima Beans____Corn____Mexicorn____Broccoli ____Baby Carrots____Mixed Vegetables____Cauliflower____Mushrooms____ Others:
*In Sauces Other Than Butter:* Chopped spinach with cream sauce____ Creole Succotash____Potatoes and peas with cream sauce____Peas in onion sauce____Smothered onions____Broccoli au gratin____Delmonico potatoes ____Baby lima beans in cheese sauce____Asparagus with Hollandaise sauce ____Buttered parsley potatoes ____Corn and lima beans in tomato sauce ____ Green beans with tomato sauce____Mixed vegetables with tomatoes____Zucchini in tomato sauce____Others:_____

(4) Which ones are your favorites? 1._____2._____3._____ 4._____

(5) If you buy prepared vegetables in a regular box or aluminum tray, which ones do you buy? Peas with pearl onions____French beans with almonds____ French beans with mushrooms____Baby lima beans with pimento ____Corn and peas with tomatoes____Broccoli with cream sauce____Corn, carrots, and pearl onions with cream sauce____Small onions with cream sauce____Peas with cream sauce ____Peas with celery____Peas and potatoes with cream sauce ____Peas and rice with mushrooms____Chopped spinach with cream

sauce____Onion rings____Potatoes au gratin____Spinach souffle____Corn souffle____Others: ____
(6) How do you feel about the price of these prepared vegetables? Too high ____ Just right____Too low____
(7) What do you think of the quality of these prepared vegetables? Excellent____ Very good____Good____Fair____Poor____
(8) What brands do you like?____ ____ ____
What brands do you dislike?____ ____ ____
(9) Which day of the week are you most likely to serve the prepared vegetables? M____T____W____Th____F____S____Su____No special day____
(10) Do you use more of these prepared vegetables in winter____spring____summer____fall____
(11) Why do you buy these prepared vegetables? 1.____2.____
.3. ____4.____Frequency of purchase?____

### FROZEN BAKED GOODS SURVEY

This, the most complex survey ever made by a group studying frozen foods, was completed recently by 15 food technology students interviewing 400 consumers at their homes on Long Island (Cook and Martin 1966). All of the questions were specifically concerned with frozen baked goods.

"Does your family use frozen baked goods?" was the first question asked. To this, 75% responded "Yes" and 24% responded in the negative.

To the question, "How frequently are frozen baked goods bought?," we obtained these answers:

| Frequency | % |
| --- | --- |
| Once a week | 45 |
| More than once a week | 8 |
| Three times a week | 3 |
| Irregular periods | 43 |

"How do frozen baked products compare with home baked?"

| Opinion | % |
| --- | --- |
| Better | 26 |
| Just the same | 40 |
| Not as good | 33 |

"How do frozen baked products compare with bakery made?"

| Opinion | % |
| --- | --- |
| Better | 22 |
| Just the same | 23 |
| Not as good | 32 |
| No answer | 13 |

From the last two tables above we may conclude that the bakery made products give just slightly more competition to frozen baked goods than do home baked products, "Just the same" percentages in each table are significant as is the "No answer" in the last table relative to this point.

But what does the housewife think about the *cost* of homebaked versus the *cost* of frozen baked? These were our findings:

| Opinion | % |
|---|---|
| Higher | 46 |
| Lower | 13 |
| About the same | 21 |
| Do not know | 15 |
| No answer | 2 |
| Total | 97 |

When asked the question, "What factors do you consider in the cost of home baking?," we obtained this information:

| Factors | % |
|---|---|
| Good materials | 58 |
| Own labor | 27 |
| Gas, electricity | 3 |
| Depreciation of equipment | 1 |
| Baking and cleanup time | 23 |

(This adds up to more than 100% due to multiple answers.)

The above data rather clearly indicate that the housewife does not consider all of the facts when she compares her costs against the purchase of a frozen baked item.

To the question, "What type of advertising started you buying frozen baked goods?," the following information was obtained:

| Media | % |
|---|---|
| Friends and acquaintances | 39 |
| Store food display | 34 |
| Television | 33 |
| Point of purchase | 18 |
| Newspaper ads | 18 |
| Radio | 8 |

(Multiple answers were given.)

The above points up the fact that word-of-mouth recommendations from friends and acquaintances is the most important advertising medium in the sale of frozen baked goods.

At the same time, it is interesting and important to know why some consumers do not buy frozen baked goods. Their reasons are as follows:

| Reasons | % |
|---|---|
| Prefer to bake own | 40 |
| More expensive to buy | 13 |
| Not interested in frozen | 12 |
| Little or no flavor or value | 9 |
| Not real or appealing | 8 |
| Stores mishandle these products | 6 |
| Too sweet | 2 |
| No particular reason | 6 |

"What improvements could be suggested for frozen baked goods?" was asked. Only two suggestions of possible significance were offered: The first was "lower price," which was requested by 8%, and the second was "larger sizes" requested by 6%. Less than 25% of those surveyed could think of any suggestions. We must conclude then that it is the packer who induces the consumer to buy and to develop her interest in his products. From another question it was found that consumers (12%) are interested in larger sized dessert cakes.

To the question, "Who would like to see frozen puddings on the market?," the response was thus:

| | % |
|---|---|
| Yes | 52 |
| No | 37 |
| Do not know | 9 |

The high percentage of affirmative answers plus the "do not know" responses certainly justifies some research in this area.

Twenty-three frozen baked goods products were rated by the consumers. The summary follows and warrants study by those producing these items that they may improve the rating and thereby increase sales.

| Baked Goods | Excellent | Good | Fair | Poor |
|---|---|---|---|---|
| | % | % | % | % |
| Waffles | 25 | 63 | 2 | 9 |
| Pancakes | 37 | 42 | 11 | 18 |
| Coffee cakes | 36 | 55 | 6 | 1 |
| Strudels | 37 | 51 | 8 | 2 |
| Danish cakes | 43 | 51 | 3 | 1 |
| Biscuits | 21 | 70 | 6 | 1 |
| Baked bread | 37 | 45 | 11 | 5 |
| Frozen dough | 35 | 45 | 6 | 12 |
| Doughnuts | 21 | 54 | 18 | 6 |
| Honey buns | 52 | 28 | 8 | 12 |
| Sweet muffins | 26 | 47 | 21 | 5 |
| Pound cake | 48 | 48 | 1 | 1 |
| Plain muffins | 10 | 55 | 25 | 10 |
| Cheese cake | 44 | 47 | 6 | 1 |
| Fruit turnovers | 32 | 62 | 3 | 1 |
| Frosted cake | 36 | 43 | 13 | 6 |
| Parfaits | 45 | 41 | 4 | 8 |
| Brownies | 32 | 50 | 14 | 3 |
| Cookies | 18 | 77 | 0 | 4 |
| Loaf cakes | 27 | 50 | 18 | 4 |
| Cream cake | 23 | 48 | 15 | 12 |
| Chocolate eclairs | 31 | 40 | 22 | 4 |
| Rolls | 18 | 77 | 2 | 2 |

It appears from this survey that frozen baked goods are on a firm foundation, moving well, and well accepted. Sound merchandising can move more frozen baked goods through dynamic new approaches. For example: Many housewives think that the cost of their home baked items is less than that of frozen baked goods. However, sales of frozen baked items could be stimulated if the facts were effectively presented. A case in point: A cake mix costs approximately 42 cents; one egg to be added costs 5 cents; one cup of milk costs 7 cents, bringing the cost of the cake to 54 cents. Icing materials will cost about 15 cents, bringing the cake cost to 69 cents. Still there are utility costs of mixing and baking, depreciation on equipment, and cleanup and putting equipment away. A comparable frozen cake can be purchased for approximately 79 cents. Surely no one would provide all of these extras, including the labor, for a mere 10 cents or even 20 cents, when home-baked quality and flavor can be matched or excelled by commercial processing. That industry is on its way to success when it conveys these facts to the consumer. The future for frozen baked goods looks bright indeed.

### CONCLUSIONS

It is evident that the Consumer Survey is a valuable teaching device. It stimulates students to know that the survey will be useful to the very industry into which many of them will be going. Thus they become a working part, can contribute to the industry, and will themselves learn a great deal. They find that they must sell themselves and their program even before questioning the housewife. If they do not make plausible presentations explaining their mission, the doors are often slammed in their faces. The manner of questioning and type of concluding question can create suspicion and doubt, even anger, on the part of the housewife. To state at the beginning of the interview that one is not selling a thing, but only there to get the housewife's opinion, usually flatters her into answering the questions; but if the last question starts off by asking, "Would you buy . . .?," she suspects this to be the "gimmick" that the whole series of questions were leading up to this one, asking her to buy something. This, they learn, must be avoided.

Following the actual survey work of contacting consumers at their homes, the students are each assigned one or more questions from the survey and are required to record the answers from all completed surveys. When they have recorded the answers from a questionnaire they place their initials in the left margin, indicating that they have completed that question. When all questions are initialed from all questionnaires, the student then totals his answers, recording individual specifics. With these facts before them the students are encouraged to evaluate their findings and to draw conclusions. Their limited background will naturally limit the scope of their conclusions. Here the instructor can point up certain aspects that tie in with their background knowledge or observations to make the survey more meaningful. The Consumer Survey thus is a valuable teaching device.

From our experience, the personal interview survey taken at the home is the best, most authentic information obtained from the consumer, with few distractions to harmfully influence her opinions and / or preferences. When the interviewer (the food technology student) feels responsible for the success of the survey, is basically interested in the results, and has some knowledge of the product, there is a much greater chance for a successful survey.

The cost to make such a survey of frozen food products is not prohibitive if great care is taken to prepare good, pertinent questions and the interviewers are properly prepared to do the questioning. Basic interest and knowledge of the product on the part of interviewers are vital, based on our experiences. Each of these surveys required approximately 162 hr. of house-to-house interviews, with approximately 54 hr. spent in totaling responses and summarizing. Of course, to critically collate results will take much study.

If these surveys provide information helpful to the frozen food industry it is hoped that they will likewise provide products more acceptable to the housewife. It is our firm conviction that such surveys can and should provide a new gain to both the industry and the consumer.

## BIBLIOGRAPHY

Anon.   1963A. Who eats frozen dinners? Quick Frozen Foods 25, No. 8, 86, 87, 89.
Anon.   1963B. What does the consumer think of frozen meat pies? Quick Frozen Foods 26, No. 4, 63–66.
Anon.   1964A. Frozen fruit, cream pies—a consumer survey. Quick Frozen Foods 26, No. 8, 83–86.
Anon.   1964B. Why consumers purchase fillets, sticks, portions. Quick Frozen Foods 27, No. 3, 80–83.
Anon.   1965A. Frozen chicken portions should stress quality, sanitation, before price. Quick Frozen Foods 27, No. 6, 97–99.
Anon.   1965B. Ice cream review consumer study. Ice Cream Review 49, No. 5, 17–20.
Anon.   1966A. Prepared vegetable survey-consumers want pouch size diversity; satisfied with available varieties. Quick Frozen Foods 28, No. 10, 43–49.
Anon.   1966B. 2500 new grocery products introduced yearly: "This Week" (11 Biennial Study), Advertising Age 37, No. 11, 26.
Anon.   1966C. Half of food buyers choose by price, not brand, says food commission. Advertising Age 37, No. 34, 2, 124.
Anon.   1967A. Green giant's news release on single serving frozen vegetable line. Green Giant Company.
Anon.   1967B. Zero warehouse capacity—home freezer sales at better than million per year. 1967 Frozen Food Fact Book (National Frozen Food Association, 55 West 43rd Street, New York City, N.Y.) 25, 57–58.
Cook, G. G., and Martin, S. 1966. Frozen bakery goods shopping list items; kept in home freezer at all times. Quick Frozen Foods 29, No. 5, 101–107, 413, 414, 416.

## CHAPTER 4

Donald K. Tressler

# The Packaging of Precooked and Prepared Frozen Foods

## INTRODUCTION

Although the basic principles of packaging of frozen foods have been presented in Chapter 12 of Volume 2, the problems encountered in packaging precooked and prepared foods are sufficiently different to necessitate a special chapter on the packaging of precooked foods in this volume. The following are a few of the special problems encountered in packaging precooked foods:

(1) Many of them are very fragile and cannot be sold if their appearance or texture has been damaged, e.g., cakes, puff pastry, and stuffed peppers. (2) Some of them are difficult to transfer to other utensils and therefore must be reheated in the container in which they were frozen, e.g., batters, doughs, pot pies, and pies. (3) In many cases, it is desirable to reheat and serve the product in the container in which it was frozen, e.g., pies, pot pies, shortcakes, complete meals, pizza pies, "thermidors," etc. (4) Many precooked foods are covered with a sauce or gravy and consequently the package must not only be watertight, water- and greaseproof, but in many instances must also be able to stand heating in a hot oven. Examples of such products are chicken and other pot pies, and meat stews. (5) Many precooked foods are usually filled hot; therefore, they must be packaged in containers which are waterproof even at high temperatures.

## RIGID ALUMINUM FOIL CONTAINERS

Of the requirements listed above, the rigid aluminum foil container probably comes closest to satisfying all of the demands which may be made on a package to be used for precooked frozen foods. As is evident from Fig. 9, this type of container is available in about every conceivable shape and size to meet the needs and requirements of the industry.

The thickness of aluminum used in rigid foil containers ranges from 0.0025 to 0.0125 in., the latter being in reality a light aluminum sheet (Marcoux 1956). The rigidity of the finished foil container depends not only on the physical design of the container, but also on the gage of the foil used and whether it is hard or soft temper.

The properties of rigid foil containers have been summarized by Carlile (1966), who points out that these containers can withstand very high and

---

Donald K. Tressler is a consultant and President of the Avi Publishing Company, Westport, Conn.

Courtesy of Ekco Containers, Inc.

Fig. 9.   Assortment of rigid aluminum foil containers of the types used in packaging frozen foods.

very low temperatures, far higher than commercial oven temperatures and much lower than those employed in commercial freezing operations. Aluminum foil has no odor and it provides an effective barrier against transfer of odors from adjacent products. Assuming that the foil used is free from pinholes, neither moisture nor moisture-vapor can pass through. Of course, proper seals or closures must be used. Aluminum foil is nontoxic even when pitted by saline solutions. It is insect resistant and has excellent heat conductivity; the latter property is important both during food freezing and also during reheating. Aluminum foil containers can be fabricated in light weights, often an advantage both in freezing foods and in reheating them.

Although foil is highly resistant to the weak organic acids found in many food products, it is attacked by strong mineral acids. Foil is less resistant to weak alkaline products, hence with such products it is desirable to use foil coated with a protective film of a polyvinyl plastic. Therefore, a packer, considering foil containers for a saline or slightly alkaline food, should conduct actual storage and handling tests prior to commercial adoption of the package.

Thermoplastic coatings have been devised (approved by the FDA) that can be used for coating aluminum foil for protection against strong food acids and alkaline foods which may corrode the aluminum.

Food in plastic coated foil containers may be reheated in a microwave oven without the objectionable arcing which occurs when frozen food is thawed and reheated in plain aluminum foil containers in this type of oven. These coatings are not damaged by oven heat because of their thermosetting properties.

Aluminum pie plates have been perfected in which a pie can be baked with a nicely browned bottom crust free from sogginess. This was accomplished by perforating the bottom of the pie plate with a few pinholes and by applying a black coating to the bottom which absorbs instead of reflects the radiant heat.

At a small cost, vivid decorative colors can be applied to the outside of an aluminum container. Careful preparation and proper printing of aluminum foil give a depth and luminosity to inks and also a dramatic printing effect. Color coatings have been devised that are acceptable to the U.S. Food and Drug Administration for inside application to aluminum foil containers.

### Methods of Manufacture

Foil is fabricated into rigid containers by two principal methods. All having central ridging or other special shape modifications are formed by the single stroke of a die into the metal. These containers are referred to as seamless, having no folds or joints. They have the characteristic corrugation or wrinkled sidewalls, which gives them considerable strength. This corrugation is sometimes controlled to produce a fluted effect. These containers have a slight shoulder offset, for additional rigidity and are finished at the rim in one of four ways. When a raw edge is grooved to add rigidity, it is referred to as trenched. That type rim and the semi-curl (which is a raw edge rolled downward to give a skirting effect) are today being superseded by the full-curl rim, which is tightly rolled and beaded, greatly increasing rigidity; and by the vertical flange rim, which is a combination flat flange and vertical projections, designed to receive and crimp over a flat cover. Practically all round and many rectangular foil containers are made by this seamless method in a variety of sizes and shapes.

The second method of manufacturing rigid foil containers is by folding. The foil is handled like paperboard and folded into a rectangular shape. These containers have folded seams at the corners, a flat, hemmed rim; there are no corrugations in the sidewalls. Obviously, folded containers are square or rectangular only. They are available in a variety of sizes and have the advantage of being somewhat easier to handle on high speed over-wrapping equipment. However, they lack the reinforcing effect of corrugations in the sidewalls and the rigidity that is added by the full curl rim of the seamless container. Like the seamless containers, the walls are tapered to permit nesting during shipment. Solid foil recessed covers are available for folded containers, as well as a variety of closure equipment.

The frozen food packer who plans to use rigid foil containers should choose between these two general types based on the specific packaging and marketing characteristics of his products.

### Equipment for Closing Foil Containers

The basic closure styles are: (1) aluminum foil hooding; (2) board or plastic covers in vertical flange containers; (3) snap-in lids of paper, foil, or

*Courtesy of the Marathon Corporation*

Fig. 10.   Pot-pie packaging machine is fully automatic.

plastic; and (4) plastic snap-on lids. In addition, shrinkable films, conventional overwraps, and bagging are used.

In recent years great strides have been made in the perfection of equipment for putting the container cover in place and crimping it securely in position. In the case of equipment for vertical flange containers to be fitted with a foil-board laminated cover, the basic principle is the use of a male and female two-part die. Automatic equipment (Fig. 10) will effect 120 closures a minute. Simple foot-press machines, which operate on the same principle, can make 10 or 12 closures per minute.

Hermetic closures are a recent development for rigid aluminum foil-containers. Vinyl interior coatings are applied both to the container and a foil-board cover. Heat and pressure seal the two vinyl surfaces together, forming a completely airtight, dustproof, leakproof seal.

## New Shapes

Attractively shaped aluminum containers are now available made of heavy-gage aluminum sheeting, ranging up to 0.01 in. or even more in thickness. These sturdy packages may have snap-in heavy-gage aluminum lids; easy opening, tear-off closures, or snap-on plastic lids, or even double-seamed can-type lids that are airtight.

### ALUMINUM FOIL LAMINATIONS

Containers made of aluminum foil, laminated to kraft or other paper, have a limited use in packaging certain frozen food products. A satisfactory container for frozen citrus and other juices and beverages is made by sandwiching several layers of kraft paper between a liner and an exterior of aluminum foil. The liner is coated with polyethylene as the barrier material, thus preventing the corrosion of the aluminum (Crane 1966).

### WIDE USE OF ALUMINUM FOIL AND ALUMINUM FOIL LAMINATED CONTAINERS

Aluminum foil containers are available in a wide assortment of shapes and sizes. They are used for packaging a large number of different precooked frozen food items. With the possible exception of the poly pouch (see Table 17), no other container is used in such great numbers. Some of nearly every precooked item on the market are packaged in foil. The manufacturers of foil packages are very ingenious; they have been successful in designing a package to fit almost every product commonly packed. Further, most of the packages are well suited for (1) freezing, and (2) reheating the product. Often the hot food is served in the same foil container in which it was packed.

## FLEXIBLE ALUMINUM FOIL

The properties of rigid aluminum foil have been considered on pp. 116–117; obviously the chemical properties of flexible aluminum foil are the same as those of the rigid product. However, its use in packaging precooked and prepared frozen foods is quite limited. A sheet of it is sometimes used to

Table 17

Frozen Vegetable Pack in Polyethylene Bags—1959–1964

| Product | 1959 | 1960 | 1961 | 1962 | 1963 | 1964 |
|---|---|---|---|---|---|---|
| Potato products | [1] | [1] | [1] | [1] | 43,898,186 | 103,769,533 |
| Green peas | 8,158,074 | 8,489,456 | 17,589,746 | 14,604,201 | 15,441,894 | 21,934,926 |
| Cut corn | 1,828,571 | 2,992,406 | 13,969,861 | 13,586,920 | 3,980,460 | 16,110,496 |
| Mixed vegetables | 2,275,629 | 6,573,817 | 12,348,808 | 13,878,548 | 14,699,466 | 15,597,743 |
| Green beans, regular | [1] | [1] | [1] | [1] | 9,259,682 | 10,336,526 |
| Black-eyed peas | [1] | [1] | [1] | [1] | 4,677,007 | 9,767,885 |
| Peas and carrots | 2,078,650 | 4,544,374 | 6,548,926 | 4,685,139 | 4,241,924 | 6,118,923 |
| Baby lima beans | 1,926,096 | 2,278,143 | 3,133,697 | 2,047,700 | 3,429,306 | 4,990,070 |
| Fordhook lima beans | [1] | [1] | [1] | [1] | [1] | 4,141,928 |
| Misc. vegetables | [1] | 193,164 | 982,106 | 4,700,762 | 5,540,390 | 7,813,768 |
| Incl. in other categories | 2,384,046 | 6,562,409 | 15,258,653 | 22,798,191 | 31,362,313 | 17,915,621 |
| Total | 18,651,066 | 31,633,769 | 69,733,653 | 76,301,461 | 136,530,628 | 218,497,419 |
| Percentage increase | [2] | 69.6% | 120.5% | 9.4% | 78.9% | 60.0% |
| Percentage of total vegetable pack in poly bags | 1.15% | 1.61% | 3.30% | 3.37% | 5.88% | 8.28% |

Source: National Association of Frozen Food Packers.
[1] Not reported separately.
[2] Negligible volume prior to 1959 not reported separately.

cover the top of a rigid foil container. This is satisfactory provided the entire food container is packaged in a carton.

Flexible foil does not possess the strength to be used by itself as a packaging material. When laminated to paperboard, it can be used to make excellent covers for rigid foil containers. Because of its grease- and moisture-proofness laminated with paperboard, it is generally used for this purpose. Laminations of foil and paper make very good pouches and are used by some packers for products to be reheated by the "boil-in-the-bag" method (Crane 1966).

## POUCHES AND PREFORMED BAGS

Unless packed in a protective carton, preformed bags have a rather limited use for packaging precooked foods. They are mostly used for baked goods which will withstand some rough handling. High density polyethylene performed bags have found an important use in packaging precooked products (entrées, vegetables, etc.) for institutions, hotels, and restaurants when the "boil-in-the-bag" procedure is to be used for reconstitution (reheating). For satisfactory use, a vacuum must be pulled and the bag sealed while the product is still under vacuum.

## Pouches

According to Cross *et al.* (1966), a pouch is "a flexible package configuration which can be formed continuously from a roll of material, filled, and heat-seal closed on automatic machinery."

Large quantities of both partially cooked vegetables in butter and cream sauces, and precooked entrées are packed in evacuated pouches usually made of high density polyethylene. The quality of these products is retained very well indeed for two reasons: (1) they are vacuum packed in a pouch; this prevents desiccation and retards oxidation; and (2) there is little loss of quality during reheating.

The pouch in a carton package is not costly because the pouches are made in the food packing plant at the time the food is packed. The Bartelt machine used in filling, evacuating, and sealing the bags occupies relatively little floor space and is substantially automatic. Anon. (1963A) has described the making and filling of the pouches by the Bartelt machine as follows:

"The 'Scotchpak' film feeds out into a series of rollers leading to pouch formation, after a worker controls the level of incoming vegetables on an overhead conveyor and inspects for discoloration and damaged products. A single spring-loaded roller keeps the film tension as even as possible during and between indexing stops of the machine. A break in the film makes this roller drop into a switch which stops the line."

"The film passes around a plow which folds it to form the front and back of the pouch. The machine first forms the bottom, then the side seal. A pressure crimper prevents the pouch from curling inward prior to forming the top seal. The feed roll stops the film as the continuous line of formed pouches passes a knife which cuts successively formed pouches apart. The static bond is broken by air releases, separating the front and back of each pouch and thus prepares it to receive the vegetables."

"As the machine is forming the pouches, the frozen vegetables drop from an overhead conveyor into the machine's large hopper. Vegetables from the hopper feed into measuring cups of the continuously rotating filler turret and then pass into each pouch through small tapered chutes."

"Filling is done at two stations. At the first, each pouch receives approximately one half of its full contents. Then the pouch moves along the line where a second filler turret discharges the final half of the contents."

"A timer interval valve operates a nozzle. This injects the butter sauce into each pouch. A vacuum draw snorkel then removes the air after which a flat seal bar puts on the top seal. The pouch then passes to a round heat-seal bar which the machine applies to the pouch to insure a good top seal."

"Each filled pouch drops from an indexing chain down a slide and goes into one of the individual cartoner conveyor pockets. A cam-operated arm pushes the pouch into the carton further along the line."

"The carton end is then closed. The closed carton then moves to heat-sealing equipment shown in Figs. 11 and 12, after which the cartons are conveyed into the freezer storage."

*Courtesy of Green Giant Co.*

Fig. 11. After passing hoses that force hot air against their sealing flaps, the cartons of boil-in-the-bag vegetables move between cooling bars that set the seal firmly eliminating dog ears and providing great strength.

*Courtesy of Green Giant Co.*

Fig. 12. After "hot-melt" sealing cartons of boil-in-bag frozen vegetables are conveyed to a freezer for storage.

## PAPERBOARD CARTONS AND OVERWRAPS

In the early days of the quick frozen food industry, the usual carton was made from either ordinary or cold waxed paperboard. The frozen food was protected from desiccation by a sheet of moistureproof cellophane or plastic liner and a heat-sealed lithographed waxed paper overwrap. When precooked frozen foods were introduced, they were usually packaged in this type of carton with or without the plastic sheet liner. Many frozen food packers have now shifted over to the use of polyethylene coated paperboard and have dispensed with both the overwrap and the liner, lithographing the carton itself.

Polyethylene coated paperboard is grease-resistant, and substantially moisture vapor proof. Foods do not stick to the inside of the carton nor does the polyethylene flake off into the food (Pilaro 1963). Since polyethylene is heat-sealable, the cartons may either be heat-sealed or they can be closed by conventional gluing equipment.

A number of packers of precooked frozen foods still use a plain paperboard (sulfite) carton overwrapped with lithographed paper, coated with one of the following: polyethylene; ordinary paraffin; paraffin modified either with ten per cent or less of a modifier (microcrystalline wax, butyl rubber, or polyethylene or other plastic, e.g., ethylene vinyl acetate copolymer), or a so-called hot-melt coating. A hot-melt coating is usually a formulation of paraffin containing more than ten per cent of modifiers. The modifiers used in hot-melt coatings may include those listed above and also ethyl cellulose, cyclized rubber, and butadiene copolymers. There are also some promising "hot-melts" that contain no paraffin, but consist only of resins. Hot-melt coatings are characterized by extremely strong seals and fair blocking resistance (Wolper 1966).

Since the details of the construction and modes of closing paperboard cartons have been considered in Chapter 12 of Volume 2, they will not be repeated here. However, it may be pointed out that because of the very great number of different precooked foods packed, and the wide variation in their shape and size, a large number of shapes and sizes of cartons is required.

## CANS

With a few exceptions, ordinary tin cans and composite cans (those with laminated bodies and metal ends) are not extensively used for packaging precooked and/or prepared foods. However, the company that packs more frozen soup than any other puts their product in tin cans. Further, nearly all fruit juice concentrates and fruit purées are packed and frozen in either tin cans or composite cans (e.g., Sefton cans). Melon balls in light syrup are also packed in Sefton cans.

One of the important innovations in composite cans is the rather general use of easy opening devices. One of these has a strip called a Mirastrip around one end of the can. When this is pulled, the entire end of the can comes off so that the contents can be emptied after only enough thawing to release the grip of the ice. Another is known as the T-Tab which, when pulled, pulls the end out of the can. The third is called Easy-O which also removes the can end.

## COMBINATION PACKAGES

Thus far in this chapter certain basic packaging materials have been considered including coated papers and boards, foil sheets, and laminated paper and foil sheets, bags and pouches, plastic pouches and bags, both metal and composite cans, and molded plastic and molded pulp containers. Few frozen food packages consist of only one of these items.

Some of the frozen precooked or prepared foods that are often packed in a "package" consisting of only a single component are the following: melon balls in either enamel-lined tin cans or in Sefton cans (a composite can); various fruit and "punch" concentrates in enamel-lined cans; whip toppings in molded plastic containers; bagels in plastic bags; bread dough in bags. Bags made of kraft paper laminated with polyethylene are often used for institutional packs of French-fried potatoes.

On the other hand, the great majority of the prepared and/or precooked foods are packed in a package having at least two components. Many foods are put first in a rigid foil container which in turn is placed in a paperboard container. In some instances the paperboard container is wrapped and sealed in a coated lithographed wrapper. The coating may be ordinary paraffin wax, a modified wax or polyethylene. Or, the carton may not be overwrapped but is made of coated lithographed sulfite paperboard.

As a rule the rigid aluminum foil container in which the food is placed for freezing is used by the housewife as the container in which the product is reheated, and also often as the "dish" in which the product is served. For example, a pot pie is put in a small aluminum foil pan, which in turn is placed in a lithographed carton. When the housewife prepares the pot pie for the table, she removes it from the carton, places it, still in the aluminum pan, in a hot oven, and when it is thoroughly reheated, she serves it without removing it from the neat little foil pan, in which it had been frozen.

Since the container in which the food is packaged is usually placed on the consumers' dining table, the rigid foil containers are neat and attractive. Indeed, some are so well constructed that they may be saved by the housewife and later used again as a cooking or serving utensil.

Pouches and bags containing food which is to be reheated by immersion in boiling water are almost invariably packaged in cartons; some of these are made of lithographed sulfite paperboard coated with polyethylene, and consequently need no additional barrier to prevent desiccation; others, which are not coated, require overwrapping with coated lithographed paper. Two of the reasons why the pouches and bags of this type are always packed in cartons are: (1) since they have been evacuated, they are not attractive in appearance because they are so wrinkled; and (2) if they are damaged in handling, they become leakers and the food cannot be reconstituted by the "boil-in-the-bag" procedure without loss.

A few frozen baked goods are attractively packaged in rigid aluminum foil pie or cake pans with a cover composed of a piece of coated lithographed paperboard held in place by crimping the foil container. Even if the foil pans are not placed in a carton, this type of packaging is satisfactory provided the aluminum foil is sufficiently heavy to withstand the rough treatment it may get during marketing.

### SHIPPING CONTAINERS

Corrugated fiberboard boxes are standard shipping containers for all frozen foods, including fresh, precooked, and prepared. Of the numerous types of products that fall into the latter classes, there are many in which the initial container is not solidly packed; this makes the product more fragile during handling. Likewise some products, like frozen fruit pies are easily damaged by shipping unless amply protected against breakage.

A special corrugated container for frozen pies, which is lightweight and expendable and offers savings in transportation and damage costs is shown in Fig. 13. This replaces the nonexpendable metal case with wood trays once used as shipping containers for frozen pies. A six-sided corrugated insert piece fits snugly around each of the pies, which are packed in six layers of two each. These inserts are high enough to give clearance for pies, and they support corrugated "shelf" inserts. As may be noted (see Fig. 13), printing on the box cautions to keep the top side up and to keep the contents frozen.

To guard against weakening of the box from condensation formed when warm air strikes its cold surfaces and from other exposure to moisture, the box and inserts are made of water-resistant V3C board, a type much used for military overseas shipments. For extra stability, the "shelf" inserts of the package have flanges that are folded down and wedged against the container walls. The package also has corrugated pads at top and bottom for added protection.

The reader is referred to Volume 2, Chapter 12 for more detailed information on the general subject of the packaging of frozen foods.

*Courtesy of Stone Container Corp.*

Fig. 13. Corrugated container for frozen pies. Frozen pies, which presented a special challenge in damage-free shipments, are now being packaged successfully in this special corrugated box.

## BIBLIOGRAPHY

Allen, N.   1966. Perspectives for films. Mod. Packaging *39*, 4A, 136–137.

Anon.   1955A. Pie-packaging machine is fully automatic. Food Eng. *27*, No. 12, 133.

Anon.   1955B. Marathon develops poly carton for use with cooked foods. Quick Frozen Foods *17*, No. 6, 95.

Anon.   1956A. "Boil-in-a-bag" process scores hit at retail, institutional level. Quick Frozen Foods *18*, No. 11, 58–59.

Anon.   1956B. Sticks that don't stick. Mod. Packaging *29*, No. 7, 190–191.

Anon.   1956C. Mechanized pies. Mod. Packaging *29*, No. 7, 214–217.

Anon.   1962. Versatility spearheads aluminum gains. Quick Frozen Foods *24*, No. 12, 82–83.

Anon.   1963A. Boilable bag breakthrough? Quick Frozen Foods *25*, No. 12, 53–54, 59.

Anon.   1963B. Poly-coated parchment pouch gets full-line treatment. Quick Frozen Foods *25*, No. 12, 70.

Anon.   1963C. Vegetables in wide packaging types. Quick Frozen Foods *25*, No. 12, 72, 74.

Anon.   1964A. Wax coatings stage comeback in partnership with plastic. Quick Frozen Foods *26*, No. 12, 53.

Anon.   1964B. Steel foil seeks penetration of prepared foods packaging. Quick Frozen Foods *26*, No. 12, 56.

Anon.   1964C. Edible transparent films for packaging. Quick Frozen Foods *26*, No. 12, 60.

Anon.   1964D. Cellophane-like plastic for frozen foods. Quick Frozen Foods *26*, No. 12, 61–62.

Anon.  1964E. Wrapperless cartons gain foothold. Quick Frozen Foods 26, No. 12, 70–71.

Anon.  1964F. 12-oz. cans gain with drinks. Quick Frozen Foods 26, No. 12, 72–73.

Anon.  1965A. Plastic lined corrugated container for bulk IQF frozen fruits. Quick Frozen Foods 27, No. 12, 47.

Anon.  1965B. Rigid linear poly trays seek share of industry. Quick Frozen Foods 27, No. 12, 50–51.

Anon.  1965C. The 30-pound bulk can-workhorse of industry. Quick Frozen Foods 27, No. 12, 53–54.

Anon.  1965D. Bright future for plastics. Quick Frozen Foods 27, No. 12, 64–65.

Anon.  1966A. Molded pulp plates for frozen pies withstand 450°F. baking temperature. Quick Frozen Foods 28, No. 12, 49.

Anon.  1966B. The shape of the future today in aluminum FF containers. Quick Frozen Foods 28, No. 12, 52–53.

Anon.  1966C. Boil-in-the-bag shaping product development. Quick Frozen Foods 28, No. 12, 60–61.

Anon.  1966D. Eight-ounce size alters packaging. Quick Frozen Foods 28, No. 12, 62–63.

Anon.  1966E. Reconstitution method packaging influence. Quick Frozen Foods 28, No. 12, 64–65.

Anon.  1966F. Properties of packaging films—How to identify packaging films. Mod. Packaging 39, No. 4A, 145–148.

Anon.  1967A. Double-boiler principle invoked by pot-topper aluminum tray. Quick Frozen Foods 29, No. 12, 50–51.

Anon.  1967B. Poly-lined bleached kraft bag form-fits over French fries. Quick Frozen Foods 29, No. 12, 53.

Anon.  1967C. Tear-Tab metal opener latest in modernization of Sefton. Quick Frozen Foods 29, No. 12, 55.

Anon.  1967D. Both product protection sealing adhesive provided by hot-melt carton coating. Quick Frozen Foods 29, No. 12, 57–58.

Anon.  1967E. Converting rapidly to wrapperless. Quick Frozen Foods 29, No. 12, 69–70.

Anon.  1967F. Easy open cans to conquer concentrates. Quick Frozen Foods 29, No. 12, 73.

Carlile, J.  1966. Rigid aluminum foil containers. Mod. Packaging 39, No. 4A, 348D–349.

Crane, D. R.  1966. Aluminum foil for packaging. Mod. Packaging 39, No. 4A, 162–166.

Cross, W. W., Wolper, P. K., and Boston, W. T.  1966. Pouches: form, fill, seal. Mod. Packaging 39, No. 4A, 246–248.

Delaney, J. F.  1966. Aluminum cans, boxes, drums, cylinders. Mod. Packaging 39, No. 4A, 342–344.

Dulmage, F. C.  1966. Saran. Mod. Packaging 39, No. 4A, 149.

Gardner, H. S., Edwards, D. G., and Smith, M. F.  1955. New developments in paperboard containers. Food Technol. 9, 31–33.

Gaulke, R. G.  1962. Dramatic foil container advances combine sense with imagination. Quick Frozen Foods 24, No. 12, 60–61.

Goldman, R. L.  1962. Checkpoints for practical FF package design. Quick Frozen Foods 24, No. 12, 72, 77.

Halbach, O  1966. Wraps and overwraps. Mod. Packaging 39, No. 4A, 240–242.

Lowry, J. C.    1966. Polyethylene. Mod. Packaging 39, No. 4A, 137–139.

Lowry, R. D.    1966. The growth of shrink packaging. Mod. Packaging 39, No. 4A, 256–261.

Marcoux, W.    1956.    Private communication.    Ekco-Alcoa Containers, Inc., Wheeling, Ill.

McCarthy, V. D.    1962. Plastic-coated paperboard broadens market for resins. Quick Frozen Foods 24, No. 12, 68–69.

Pilaro, J. F.    1963. Polyethylene-coated cartons. Quick Frozen Foods 25, No. 12, 64–65.

Reynolds, C. M.    1966. Cellulose acetate. Mod. Packaging 39, No. 4A, 139.

Robe, K.    1956. Dinner is in the bag. Food Processing 17, No. 2, 22, 35.

Sacharow, S.    1966. How to determine when a plastic film will perform the frozen food job. Quick Frozen Foods 28, No. 12, 55–56.

Shelor, E., and Woodroof, J. G.    1954.    Frozen food containers. Food Technol. 8, 490–497.

Sineath, H H.    1966. Cellophane. Mod. Packaging 39, No. 4A, 154–157.

Thompson, A. J.    1966. Polyester. Mod. Packaging 39, No. 4A, 142–143.

Van Sickle, R. W.    1966. Plastic containers. Mod. Packaging 39, No. 4A, 262–265.

Welshenbach, C. D.    1966. Corrugated shipping containers. Mod. Packaging 39, No. 4A, 689–692.

Wolfe, R. C.    1966. Silicone release coatings. Mod. Packaging 39, No. 4A, 86–86B.

Wolper, P. K.    1966. Coatings: types and uses. Mod. Packaging 39, No. 4A, 109, 111–113, 116–117.

Young, W. E.    1966. Vacuum and gas packaging. Mod. Packaging 39, No. 4A, 249–252.

## CHAPTER 5

# Sandwiches, Sandwich Fillings, Salads, Salad Dressings

Donald K. Tressler

*PART 1*

## Sandwiches, Canapés, Hors D'oeuvres, and Appetizers

### INTRODUCTION

Freezing is the only known way of keeping most kinds of sandwiches, canapés, and hors d'oeuvres fresh. One of the chief reasons for the remarkable retention of freshness is the fact that freezing retards staling of bread better than any other method of preservation (see p. 386). Properly packaged bread frozen rapidly and stored for a year at 0°F. ($-18$°C.) is as fresh as bread held at 70°F. (21°C.) for a single day. On the other hand, when exposed to a dry atmosphere, slices of many kinds of bread become dry and unpalatable in a very short time. This indicates the great importance of rapid preparation and the sealing of the sandwiches in moisture-vapor-proof sheetings or packages.

From the above it might be assumed that no problems are encountered in freezing sandwiches. However, the fillings of a number of kinds of sandwiches are undesirably changed by freezing and subsequent storage. For example, the white of hard-cooked eggs becomes tough and also develops an off-flavor. Because of their high sugar content, jellies and jams do not freeze completely even at 0°F. ($-18$°C.) and gradually soak into bread and discolor it. Sliced and minced ham, cured tongue, bologna, and Canadian bacon lose their color and flavor and become rancid in about three months. Lettuce and other crisp vegetables lose their crispness during freezing and subsequent thawing. Mayonnaise and other salad dressings may separate.

Further, freezing by rapid contact with a metal surface may not be desirable (Franklin 1953). If the sandwiches are frozen on a very cold metal surface, one face may become abnormally dry and the opposite face undesirably moist. The explanation offered by Franklin is that water vapor moves within the sandwich as a result of the two faces of the sandwich being at different temperatures. The water vapor moves by diffusion from the warmer face of the sandwich (higher vapor pressure) to the colder face (lower vapor pressure). A considerable accumulation of water vapor occurs on the colder face and forms ice crystals on this face of the sandwich. This accumulation of an excess of moisture on one face of the sandwich results

Donald K. Tressler is a consultant and President of the Avi Publishing Company, Westport, Conn.

in a soggy condition. Conversely, the maximum dryness occurs on the warmer face of the sandwich. If the sandwiches are stored with one face in contact with a cold surface, this "soggy-dry" condition gradually becomes worse.

Franklin also studied the effect of the freshness of the bread used on the quality of the sandwich after freezing, storage, and thawing. He concluded that sandwiches made from day-old bread had greater acceptability and were more uniformly moist and fresh appearing than those made from fresh bread. When sandwiches are frozen in contact with a cold metal surface, the soggy-dry effect is more noticeable in those made from fresh bread than in those prepared from day-old bread.

### QUALITY OF VARIOUS KINDS OF SANDWICHES
### AFTER FREEZING, STORAGE, AND THAWING

As has previously been indicated, some frozen sandwiches retain their good quality for several months, others do not. Franklin froze fresh white bread sandwiches using 20 kinds of filling, then thawed and tested the sandwiches after storage for periods varying in length from ten days to six months. In preparing the sandwiches, the bread was buttered liberally except that used for the turkey salad sandwiches, which was not buttered.

Table 18

Quality Ratings of Frozen Sandwiches Following Various Storage Periods at −5°F. (−20°C.)

| | Sandwich | 10 Days | 20 Days | 30 Days | 2 Months | 3 Months | 6 Months |
|---|---|---|---|---|---|---|---|
| 1 | Grape jelly | G+ | G+ | F | F | F | F |
| 2 | Strawberry jam | G | G | F | P | P | P |
| 3 | Peanut butter | E | E | E | E | E | E |
| 4 | Cream cheese | G | G | G | G+ | G | G+ |
| 5 | Cream cheese and nuts | E | G+ | G | G | G | G |
| 6 | Cream cheese and olives | E | G+ | G | G | G+ | G |
| 7 | Processed cheese | E | G+ | G+ | G+ | G+ | E |
| 8 | Sliced egg | P | P | P | P | P | P |
| 9 | Chopped egg | F | P | P | P | P | P |
| 10 | Egg yolk | G+ | G+ | G | G | G | P |
| 11 | Salmon | G+ | G+ | E | G | G | G+ |
| 12 | Sardine | G+ | G+ | G+ | E | G+ | G+ |
| 13 | Tuna fish | G+ | G+ | G | G | G+ | F+ |
| 14 | Turkey | G+ | G+ | G | G+ | G+ | G+ |
| 15 | Turkey salad | G+ | G+ | G | G+ | G | G+ |
| 16 | Jellied tongue | E | G+ | G | G | G | P |
| 17 | Minced ham and pickle | G+ | G+ | G | G | G+ | P |
| 18 | Sliced ham and mustard | G+ | G | G+ | G | G | P |
| 19 | Sliced lamb | E | G+ | G+ | G | G | P |
| 20 | Bologna | E | G+ | G+ | P | P | P |

Source: Franklin (1953).
E—Excellent; G—Good; F—Fair; P—Poor.

Each sandwich was heat-sealed in a pliofilm wrap and all were stored in eight-pound covered pails in a home freezer, operated at a temperature of −5°F. (−20°C.). The quality ratings given by Franklin are presented in Table 18.

Franklin's comments follow:

"Ratings of fair and poor were for the following reasons:

No. 1. Grape Jelly—After 20 days' storage, the jelly soaked into the bread, discoloring it although the flavor remained good.

No. 2. Strawberry Jam—Similar to No. 1.

Nos. 8 and 9. Sliced and Chopped Egg—The egg white was tough, rubbery, and inedible. After 20 days' storage, an undersirable flavor was evident.

No. 10. Egg Yolk—After six months' storage the characteristic flavor was lacking.

No. 13. Tuna Fish—Similar to No. 10.

No. 16. Jellied Tongue—Similar to No. 10 plus a peculiar "off-flavor."

No. 17. Minced Ham and Pickle—Rancid at six months' test.

No. 18. Sliced Ham and Mustard—Slightly rancid at the six months' test; also little ham flavor.

No. 19. Sliced Lamb—Similar to No. 10.

No. 20. Bologna—After one month's storage, gray in color with an offensive odor.

## Recommendations

Based on the above work and other experiments, Franklin offered the following recommendations for freezing sandwiches:

"(1) Fillings satisfactory for frozen sandwiches: up to six months —cream cheese with nuts or olives, processed cheese, peanut butter, salmon, sardine, and sliced turkey. Up to three months—egg yolk, minced ham and pickle, sliced ham and mustard, sliced lamb, tongue, and tuna fish. Up to one month—bologna. Up to two weeks—jam and jelly.

"(2) Hard-cooked egg white cannot be frozen; it becomes rubbery.

"(3) Mayonnaise tends to separate when frozen.

"(4) Crisp vegetables lose their crispness when frozen.

"(5) Day-old bread will result in more uniformly moist sandwiches than fresh bread.

"(6) Spread butter liberally to prevent fillings from soaking through the bread.

"(7) Package the sandwiches with crusts on, in groups of 6 to 8 rather than individually. Place an extra slice or crust of bread at each end of the group for protection against drying.

"(8) For storage up to two weeks, a carefully applied double wrap of standard kitchen type wax paper is satisfactory. Overwrap with ordinary paper to prevent handling damage to the wax paper.

"(9) For longer than two weeks of storage, use a moisture-vapor-proof wrap, e.g., aluminum foil, Cellophane, Pliofilm, or polyethylene. Overwrap with aluminum foil and Cellophane to prevent handling damage.

"(10) Do not freeze the package of sandwiches by placing it against the freezer wall as is done with many products. This can result in sandwiches that are not uniformly moist when thawed. Locate the package at least a few inches from the wall of the freezer with the edges of the sandwiches toward the wall.

"(11) Defrost the sandwiches in their sealed inner wrap at room temperature for four hours."

Shields (1949) recommends the following fillings for sandwiches to be frozen: cream cheese or well drained cottage cheese with orange marmalade or with chopped dates, figs, prunes, or other fruit; cream cheese and pickle relish; cream cheese with jelly (both inside slices spread with cheese, and jelly spread in between); cream cheese and chopped olives; peanut butter with jelly, or sweet pickle relish, or apple sauce; cheddar cheese; cheddar cheese and chopped olives or pimentos, or pickle relish; sliced meat; ground meat; miscellaneous meats such as sliced tongue, corned beef, or ground cooked liver seasoned with finely minced onion; sliced chicken or turkey; and fish—tuna, salmon, sardines, or flaked baked fish. Shields suggests thoroughly spreading the bread used in making these sandwiches with either soft butter or margarine to prevent the bread from becoming soggy as the fillings thaw.

Snavely (Anon. 1955B) has studied the packaging, freezing, and storage of some of the sandwiches commonly used in box lunches for crews and passengers on U.S. Air Force planes. The proportions of ingredients used in preparing these sandwiches are the following:

Bread (regular baker's bread) two ⅜-in. slices.
Roast beef (sliced about 12 slices to one inch) 2 oz.
Baked ham (sliced about 12 slices to one inch) 2 ¼ oz.
Roast turkey (sliced about ten slices·to one inch) 2 oz.
Bologna (sliced about ten slices to one inch) 2 oz.
Liverwurst (used as a spread) 2 oz.
Cheese (sliced about ten slices to one inch) 1.9 oz.
Whipped margarine (canned according to military specification) eight gm.

"The sandwiches were wrapped individually in aluminum foil (0.001-in. thick), using the butcher-type fold, and were grouped into a series of five sandwiches for the storage test study. Each series was dated and labeled for storage evaluation tests at 24 hr., one week, one month, and six months, and frozen, using the rack freezing method, then stored at 10°F. (−12°C.)"

The following conclusions were reached by Snavely:

"All of the sandwiches rated above the level of acceptability at the one-month evaluation period. The American cheese and baked ham, however, showed a significant decline after one month of storage.

"The six-month evaluation test indicated a definite decline in all samples with the exception of roast beef and liverwurst sandwiches, which were scored at a higher level than the initial test.

"Based upon this study, liverwurst, bologna[1], turkey, and roast beef are recommended as suitable for freezing. Ham and American cheese are not recommended.

"Frozen sandwiches should be defrosted in their sealed inner wrap. At a temperature of 70°F. (21°C.), 3 to 4 hr. will be required; at 80°F. (26°C.) or above, 2½ to 3 hr."

### PROPER PACKAGING IMPORTANT

In this "Termination Report" (Anon. 1955B) the conclusions presented below were reached in a comparison of the effectiveness of packaging of sandwiches in the following five sheetings:

Wax paper, light, commercially designed as a sandwich wrap.
Wax paper, heavy, Specification UU-P-134, for wrapping bread or other food uses.
Polyethylene-coated bleached Kraft paper.
Aluminum foil, 0.001-in. thick.
Moisture-proof Cellophane[2] 450 M.S.A.T. Coating No. 80.

"If sandwiches are to be kept four weeks or less, they can be adequately protected by any of the five packaging materials tested. If they are to be stored for longer periods, the use of aluminum foil or moisture-proof Cellophane is recommended. Aluminum foil is easy to handle, permits oven thawing, and does not require heat- or tape-sealing as does the Cellophane.

"The butcher or drug-style wraps are equally effective and the butcher type is recommended as superior only from the standpoint of greater utility in kitchen preparation."

Shields (1949) emphasizes the importance of wrapping sandwiches in moisture-vapor-proof sheetings. Waxed paper and lightweight aluminum foil are not satisfactory. Moisture-proof Cellophane and polyethylene, when properly heat-sealed, are excellent. Heavy aluminum foil is satisfactory if wrapped with an overlapped fold and with ends pressed in tight (see also Chapter 4).

Commercially, sandwiches are often packaged in folding cartons, which are overwrapped with a lithographed wrapper.

---

[1] Bologna sandwiches have a relatively short storage life.
[2] Required heat- or tape-sealing.

### SANDWICHES AND CANAPÉS FOR PARTIES

Several food packers specialize in the freezing of party sandwiches, canapés, and hors d'oeuvres. Four of these packers are located in the metropolitan New York area, others are located in California, Washington, D.C., and Connecticut.

Proper packaging is of even greater importance in the case of the small thin party sandwiches, canapés, and hors d'oeuvres. The prepared sandwiches are placed either on a cardboard which has been covered with moisture-proof Cellophane or some other moisture-proof sheeting, or in a shallow rectangular carton lined with a moisture-proof sheeting. Some packers put a paper doily on the cardboard or in the bottom of the tray-like carton in order to improve the appearance of the package. After the cardboard or tray-like carton has been filled with canapés, party-sandwiches, or hors d'oeuvres, it is overwrapped and heat-sealed with a transparent, moisture-vapor-proof sheeting. In some cases, two or more layers of canapés or sandwiches are placed in the shallow carton with a sheet of moisture-proof Cellophane, polyethylene, or similar sheeting between each two layers; the carton is then closed, and overwrapped with a moisture-vapor-proof sheeting which is then heat-sealed.

A great variety of fillings and toppings freeze well (see also p. 131); additional variety is gained by using different kinds of bread, by rolling, and by making ribbons or checkerboards. *Rolled sandwiches* are made by cutting with a very sharp knife the crusts from a loaf of unsliced white or whole wheat bread, then slicing thinly lengthwise. The surface is spread with creamed butter or margarine, then with tinted cream cheese or other filling. The long slice is rolled up firmly (as for a jelly roll), then, preferably after freezing, wrapped in moisture-proof sheeting, partly thawed, and thinly sliced into rolled sandwiches ready for packaging and refreezing. *Ribbon sandwiches* are made by evenly cutting the crust with a very sharp knife from unsliced loaves of white and whole wheat bread. The loaves are then sliced thinly lengthwise. First, a slice of white bread is spread with

### Ribbon Sandwiches

*Courtesy of Motor Products Corp.*

Fig. 14.   Cutting ribbon sandwiches.

plain or tinted cream cheese (or other filling which freezes well), then a slice of whole wheat bread is laid on it and spread with a constrasting cheese or filling. The alternation of white and whole wheat slices is continued until a loaf of the desired size is obtained. The loaf is wrapped in moisture-proof sheeting, frozen, partly thawed, then thinly sliced ready for packaging and refreezing (Fig. 14). In making *checkerboard sandwiches*, the first step is to prepare a four-layer ribbon loaf as described above. Then the ribbon loaf is cut into half-inch slices. These slices are spread with butter and filling, then four of the slices are stacked together with the dark strips on top of the light in checkerboard fashion. The stack of slices is pressed firmly together, wrapped in a moisture-vapor-proof sheeting, frozen, then partly thawed, and sliced crossways of the bread strip so that each slice is checkerboard in design (Fig. 15).

## Checkerboard Sandwiches

*Courtesy of Motor Products Corp.*

Fig. 15.   Cutting checkerboard
sandwiches.

### OPEN–FACED SANDWICHES OR CANAPÉS

Canapés are particularly attractive and appetizing, if made in circular, oval, diamond, crescent, star, and lady finger shapes. This is accomplished by spreading thinly sliced bread, first with butter, and then with a well-seasoned filling, after which it is cut into canapés with a cookie cutter.

Shields (1949) recommends the following fillings or spreads for open-faced sandwiches or canapés: (1) Olive and nut; (2) cream cheese (plain or tinted), blended with finely minced parsley, or finely chopped olives; (3) cheddar cheese spread, with an anchovy fillet on top; (4) cream cheese, edged with caviar or anchovy paste; (5) a mixture of either cream or soft cheddar cheese with chopped pimientos; (6) cream or drained and sieved cottage cheese, decorated with sliced stuffed olives, strips of pimiento or riced egg yolk.

Breads of all types freeze without great change, and, therefore, are well suited for use in making canapés. Although sandwich bread is more commonly used than any other kind, whole wheat, rye, Boston brown bread, and pumpernickel may all be used in preparing a great variety of canapés. If toasted bread or crackers or other crisp bakery products are used in making frozen canapés or appetizers, special care must be taken to thaw the products in a warm room before unwrapping the packages, as otherwise the mosture condensing on the appetizer will cause it to lose its crispness.

## FORMULAS FOR CANAPÉ SPREADS

The following spreads have been used on canapés which were frozen, tested after 3, 6, and 9 months' storage, and found to retain their flavor well. In using these products for making canapés, they are spread on previously buttered bread, which is then cut into attractive shapes, garnished if desired, packaged as indicated on p. 135, and frozen. The yields indicated are based on the assumption that four canapés will be cut from each slice of bread. If the canapés are smaller, a larger yield will be obtained.

### Crab Meat and Mushrooms

| | |
|---|---|
| Finely chopped crab meat | 1 lb. |
| Finely chopped cooked mushrooms | 8 oz. |
| Tabasco sauce | ½ oz. |
| Prepared horseradish | 2 oz. |
| Monosodium glutamate | 15 grains |
| | (1 gm.) |

The ingredients should be mixed thoroughly, and salted to taste. [3]

### Chicken and Mushrooms

| | |
|---|---|
| Finely ground cooked chicken | 1 lb. |
| Finely ground canned mushrooms | 4 oz. |
| Cayenne pepper | 7½ grains |
| | (½ gm.) |
| Sherry wine | ½ oz. |
| Monosodium glutamate | 22 grains |
| | (1.5 gm.) |

The ingredients are mixed thoroughly.
Yield—8 doz. canapés

### Liverwurst—Mushrooms

| | |
|---|---|
| Liverwurst | 4 oz. |
| Chili sauce | 1 oz. |
| Finely chopped cooked mushrooms | 3 oz. |
| Ground celery seed | 7½ grains |
| | (½ gm.) |
| Monosodium glutamate | 15 grains |
| | (1 gm.) |

---

[3] In this and all of the following formulas, sufficient salt should be added to be pleasing to the average person.

The ingredients should be mixed thoroughly, then, after spreading, the canapés should be garnished with parsley.

Yield—4 doz. canapés

### Sardines—Cheddar Cheese

| | |
|---|---|
| Drained mashed canned sardines (packed in oil) | 1 oz. |
| Cheddar cheese | 8 oz. |
| Prepared mustard | 4 oz. |
| Heavy cream (40%) | ½ oz. |
| Monosodium glutamate | 15 grains |
| | (1. gm.) |

The sardines are drained, then mashed with the other ingredients, and seasoned with Tabasco sauce.

Yield—6 doz. canapés.

After spreading, the canapés should be sprinkled with grated hard-cooked egg yolks. About one egg yolk should be used with each pound of spread. Canapés on which this spread is used should be heated before serving.

### Sardine—Cream Cheese

| | |
|---|---|
| Cream cheese | 1 lb. |
| Minced canned sardines (packed in oil) | 8 oz. |
| Monosodium glutamate | 30 grains |
| | (2 gm.) |

The ingredients are mixed together and flavored with capers. This spread should be used on whole wheat or rye bread.

Yield—10 doz. canapés.

### Liver Pâté—Egg White

| | |
|---|---|
| Liver pâté | 1 lb. |
| Egg whites, cooked and chopped | 4 |
| Worcestershire sauce | 24 grains |
| | (1.5 gm.) |
| Mayonnaise | 1½ oz. |

The ingredients should be thoroughly mixed.

Yield—9 doz. canapés.

### Savory Spread

| | |
|---|---|
| Softened butter | 15 oz. |
| Cream cheese | 15 oz. |
| Prepared mustard | ¾ oz. |
| Curry powder | ⅜ oz. |
| Worcestershire sauce | ⅛ oz. |
| Tabasco | ⅛ oz. |
| Prepared horseradish | ¼ oz. |
| Onion juice | ¼ oz. |

The butter, cheese, and other ingredients should be creamed together, taking care to mix thoroughly.

Yield—13 doz. canapés.

## Chicken—Ham—Cheese

| | |
|---|---|
| Cold, chopped cooked chicken | 1 lb. |
| Cold, chopped cooked ham | 1 lb. |
| Salt | $\frac{1}{4}$ oz. |
| Black pepper | 12 grains |
| | (approx. $\frac{1}{40}$ oz.) |
| Monosodium glutamate | $\frac{1}{12}$ oz. |

The ingredients should be mixed thoroughly. After spreading, the canapés should be sprinkled with grated cheddar cheese in the proportion of 2 oz. of cheese per pound of spread.
Yield—12 doz. canapés.

## Peanut Butter—Bacon

| | |
|---|---|
| Peanut butter | 10 lb. |
| Heavy cream (40%) | 1 qt. |

The peanut butter and heavy cream should be well blended together. After spreading the mixture on unbuttered bread, the canapés are sprinkled with chopped cooked crisp bacon, in the proportion of 1 lb. bacon for each 10 lb. of peanut butter.
Yield—21 doz. sandwiches, or 84 doz. canapés.

## Cream Cheese—Liver Pâté

| | |
|---|---|
| Cream cheese | 1 lb. |
| Liver pâté | 8 oz. |
| Worcestershire sauce | 24 grains |
| | (1.5 gm.) |
| Monosodium glutamate | 22 grains |
| | (1.5 gm.) |

The cream cheese, Worcestershire sauce, and pâté are creamed together. The canapés should be decorated with pimiento, using 2 oz. of pimiento to 12 oz. of spread.
Yield—10 doz. canapés.

## Anchovy Paste

| | |
|---|---|
| Anchovy paste | 1 lb. |
| Tomato catsup | 2 oz. |
| Worcestershire sauce | $\frac{1}{6}$ oz. |
| Mayonnaise | 4 oz. |
| Monosodium glutamate | 15 grains |
| | (1 gm.) |

The anchovy paste, catsup, and Worcestershire sauce are mixed together, then the mayonnaise is mixed in.
Yield—11 doz. canapés.

## Crab Meat

| | |
|---|---|
| Flaked crab meat | 1 lb. |
| Mayonnaise | 6 oz. |
| Chopped pickles or capers | 4 oz. |
| Monosodium glutamate | 22 grains |
| | (1.5 gm.) |

The crab meat is mixed with the mayonnaise, then the chopped pickles are added.
Yield—10 doz. canapés.

## Tuna

| | |
|---|---|
| Canned tuna, drained | 8 oz. |
| Mayonnaise | 4 oz. |

The fish is mashed with the mayonnaise; then spread on buttered bread and the canapés sprinkled with grated egg yolk.
Yield—5 doz. canapés.

## Deviled Ham

| | |
|---|---|
| Deviled ham (canned) | 1 lb. |
| Pepper relish, drained | 2 oz. |
| Mayonnaise | 2 oz. |
| Onion juice | 4 oz. |
| Monosodium glutamate | 22 grains (1.5 gm.) |

All ingredients are thoroughly mixed.
Yield—10 doz. canapés.

## Deviled Ham—Cheese

| | |
|---|---|
| Deviled ham (canned) | 1 lb. |
| Cream cheese | 1 lb. |
| Mayonnaise | 1 oz. |
| Monosodium glutamate | $\frac{1}{12}$ oz. |

The ingredients should be thoroughly mixed.
Yield—13 doz. canapés.

## Cream Cheese—Clams

| | |
|---|---|
| Cream cheese | 4 oz. |
| Minced, canned clams, drained | 4 oz. |
| Mayonnaise | $\frac{1}{4}$ oz. |
| Worcestershire sauce | 12 grains (.8 gm.) |
| Onion guice | $\frac{1}{2}$ oz. |
| Monosodium glutamate | 15 grains (1 gm.) |

All ingredients should be thoroughly mixed together.
Yield—4 doz. canapés.

## Cream Cheese—Pâté de Foies Gras

| | |
|---|---|
| Pâté de foies gras | 4 oz. |
| Cream cheese | 8 oz. |
| Mayonnaise | $\frac{1}{2}$ oz. |

The pâté de foies gras is mashed with the cream cheese, then the mayonnaise is added and the whole mixed thoroughly. This spread may be seasoned with lemon and onion.
Yield—5 doz. canapés.

### Anchovies and Roquefort Cheese

| | |
|---|---|
| Danish blue or Roquefort cheese | 1 lb. |
| Canned anchovies (packed in oil) | 4 oz. |
| Finely chopped parsley | 1 oz. |
| Crushed dill seeds | 3 grains |
| | (0.2 gm.) |
| Monosodium glutamate | 22 grains |
| | (1.5 gm.) |

The cheese, parsley, and anchovies (including oil) should be mashed together, the crushed dill seeds added, and the whole mixed thoroughly.
Yield—8 doz. canapés.

### Cream Cheese and Horseradish

| | |
|---|---|
| Cream cheese | 8 oz. |
| Prepared horseradish | 1 oz. |

The cream cheese and horseradish are mixed together and the mixture moistened and flavored to taste with mayonnaise.
Yield—4 doz. canapés.

### Deviled Ham and Olives

| | |
|---|---|
| Deviled ham (canned) | 1 lb. |
| Chopped green olives | 2 oz. |
| Chopped pickled onions | 2 oz. |
| Chopped fresh parsley | ½ oz. |
| Monosodium glutamate | 22 grains |
| | (1.5 gm.) |

The deviled ham, chopped olives, and chopped onions are mixed together, then the chopped parsley is added and thoroughly mixed in.
Yield—8 doz. canapés.

### Kippered Herring

1 lb. canned kippered herring mashed without draining, mixed with ½ oz. vinegar, and seasoned with a little Tabasco.
Yield—6 doz. canapés.

### Liverwurst and Bacon

| | |
|---|---|
| Liverwurst | 1 lb. |
| Crushed or crumbled cooked crisp bacon | 8 oz. |
| Monosodium glutamate | 22 grains |
| | (1.5 gm.) |

Should be mixed thoroughly and spread on rye bread.
Yield—10 doz. canapés.

Other tested canapés include the following:

### Caviar and Cream Cheese

This is made by spreading squares of buttered bread with caviar, and fluting edges with cream cheese.

## Herring

Prepared by placing strips of herring, either the pickled product or that canned in soured cream, on buttered oblong slices of white, rye, or pumpernickel bread, then sprinkling with grated egg yolks.

### PREPARING THE SPREADS

The first step in preparing the spreads is to grind, chop, or shred the basic ingredients, such as crab meat, chicken, anchovies, sardines, ham, tuna, herring, and bacon. If a smooth, homogenous paste is desired, the dry or fibrous ingredient or ingredients are first put through a meat grinder; then they are placed in a mixer (e.g., Hobart, Champion, Univex, or Leland) of the type used in the large restaurants for creaming mashed potatoes or for mixing meats; the other ingredients are added, and the product mixed until it is creamy. If there are no fibrous ingredients, the several components may be weighed or measured into the mixer bowl and then creamed together.

If the spread is of the type in which the individual components should be recognizable on the canapé, e.g., crab meat and pickles with mayonnaise, the ingredients are either lightly mashed or coarsely chopped or shredded, and then combined with the mayonnaise, monosodium glutamate, other seasonings, and any other ingredients, with a minimum of mixing. This can be done either by hand or in the mixer by operating it at low speed.

### PREPARING CANAPÉS FOR FREEZING

The canapés can be prepared by first cutting the crust from the exterior of loaves of sandwich or other bread, then slicing thinly. The thin slices are spread first with butter, then with tasty spreads, such as those whose formulas have been given (pp. 137 to 141). Then each slice is cut into four canapés (squares, triangles, or fingers), or they may be cut in various shapes with a cookie cutter, as described on p. 136. They are then placed in shallow cold-waxed, foil, or laminated foil and paperboard trays, ordinarily 24 to the tray. An assortment of six or more different canapés is usually put on each tray. If 12 different kinds are placed on each tray holding two dozen and the formulas used (such as those presented above) yield ten dozen canapés each, a total of 60 trays will be obtained. After packaging, as described under Hors d'oeuvres (p. 143), they are frozen as indicated on p. 144.

### HORS D'OEUVRES AND APPETIZERS

Although many hors d'oeuvres can be satisfactorily frozen and stored for a few months, a number of different types are markedly changed by freezing, a short storage period, and subsequent thawing. Egg whites toughen, become rubbery, and develop an unpleasant flavor. Therefore, ham and egg balls, poached eggs in aspic, hard cooked eggs on tomatoes with sauce, deviled eggs, stuffed eggs, mayonnaise eggs, and mashed eggs do not freeze satisfactorily. Freezing and thawing wilts celery, and consequently it loses its crispness; therefore, it is unwise to freeze filled celery. Raw tomatoes, tomato slices, and tomato cases become very watery and collapse when thawed; consequently, hors d'oeuvres having these as components cannot be expected to be satisfactory when frozen. Freezing and thawing wilts lettuce, carrot sticks, and radishes, so they should not be frozen for use for decoration of hors d'oeuvres. Skinned grapefruit sections become rather watery and "weep" on thawing, and so should not be used as a component of frozen hors d'oeuvres.

Certain frozen hors d'oeuvres, which are excellent if eaten within a month after freezing, may not retain their quality if stored for a longer period. These include those containing sausage, salami, smoked salmon, ham, and Canadian bacon.

However, many hors d'oeuvres can be frozen, stored for several months, and then thawed without notable change. Consequently, the list of hors d'oeuvres which can be frozen satisfactorily include the following and many others: Stuffed pecans and walnuts; stuffed olives, both green and ripe; pickled onions; tidbits (cooked shrimp, oysters, sautéed chicken livers, stuffed dates and pickled onions) in "blankets" (cooked bacon strips); sardine and bacon rolls; peanut butter and bacon rolls; anchovy pickles; cheese balls; marinated onions; French-fried shrimp; codfish balls on toothpicks; pickled beets and caviar; filled Edam cheese; filled puffed pastry; and various "cocktail dips" such as cream cheese spread, and blends of cream cheese with (1) anchovy paste, (2) shredded shrimp, (3) ground chicken or turkey, (4) mashed tuna, (5) shredded crab meat, (6) shredded or broken lobster meat, (7) shredded sardines, (8) chopped olives, (9) canned minced clams, (10) shredded salmon and (11) diced dried beef. Avocado dip, prepared by mashing the flesh of a soft ripe avocado and seasoning it with lemon juice, Worcestershire sauce, and salt, freezes very well.

### PACKAGING HORS D'OEUVRES

Hors d'oeuvres are so small that individual packaging is too laborious. For this reason they should be packed in shallow cold-waxed cartons lined with a moisture-proof sheeting. Two or more layers can be packed in each shallow carton using sheets of moisture-proof paper, Cellophane or plastic sheeting to cover each layer and prevent direct contact with the layer above. After the carton has been filled, it is closed and overwrapped with a lithographed wrapper, which is then heat-sealed.

## FREEZING SANDWICHES, CANAPÉS, AND HORS D'OEUVRES

Sandwiches and canapés should be frozen rapidly, otherwise the bread will become stale before they become solidly frozen. Once the temperature of these products reaches 0°F. (−18°C.), bread staling almost ceases (see p. 391, Chapter 18). In order to freeze them rapidly, they must be placed in relatively small packages (not shipping containers) in a freezer maintained at 0°F. (−18°C.), or preferably lower. The freezer should be designed for rapid heat transfer, e.g., an air-blast, plate, or liquid nitrogen freezer. In several plants, the overwrapped trays or packages are placed on racks which are wheeled into an air-blast freezer. The packages of sandwiches, canapés, or hors d'oeuvres should be put into fiberboard containers for shipment or storage *after* they have been quick frozen.

## THAWING—FOR USE

Since bread stales rapidly at temperatures between 25°F. (−3.5°C.) and 60°F. (15.5°C.) canapés and sandwiches should be rapidly thawed just before use, otherwise the bread may be stale before they are eaten. Probably the best way of thawing then is to remove the overwrapped trays, or packages, from the shipping containers, and place them before one or more electric fans in a warm room either on a rack or spread out on a table or counter. When this method is used, canapés, party sandwiches, and hors d'ouevres, on trays or in small packages, thaw rapidly. One hour is usually sufficient in front of a fan in a room maintained at 75°F. (15.5°C.) or above.

## BIBLIOGRAPHY

Allen, I. B. 1955. Ida Bailey Allen's Sandwich Book. Fawcett Publications, Greenwich, Conn.

Anon. 1947. Refrigerated and frozen sandwiches. Am. Inst. Baking Publ.

Anon. 1952A. Sandwiches in the freezer. U.S. Dept. Agr. Farm and Home Notes No. 733–52–4.

Anon. 1952B. Serve frozen sandwiches with tea over Atlantic. Quick Frozen Foods 14, No. 9, 131.

Anon. 1953. Frozen hors d'oeuvres, a growing favorite at parties. Quick Frozen Foods 15, No. 6, 100–103.

Anon. 1955A. Formulas for chicken spread and deviled chicken. Food Eng. 27, No. 8, 174.

Anon. 1955B. Freezing of sandwiches to prevent deterioration. Termination Rept., Experimental Cookery Division, QM. Food and Container Institute, Chicago, Ill.

Anon. 1955C. Frozen sandwich pointers. Unpublished information supplied by Am. Inst. Baking, Chicago, Ill.

Anon. 1965. Entire main course, sandwich menu of N.J. Feeder received frozen. Quick Frozen Foods 27, No. 10, 105–107.

Boutell, Z. 1952. The Home Freezer Book For Better Living. Viking Press, New York.

Carlson, C. J.   1955. Preparation of a smoked salmon caviar spread. U.S. Fish and Wildlife Service, Com. Fisheries Rev. *17*, No. 1, 13–15.

Farmilee, F. J.   1951. Sandwich storage at low temperatures. Brit. Baking Inds. Research Assoc. Bull. *24*.

Fenton, F.   1951. Foods from the freezer: precooked and prepared. Cornell Extens. Bull. *692* Rev.

Franklin, E. W.   1953. Frozen sandwiches (a paper presented on Nov. 26 before Subcommittee on Food Preservation of Nat'l. Research Council of Canada in Ottawa, Ont.).

Franklin, E. W., Snyder, E. S., Stillwell, E. C., Truscott, J. H. L., and Clarke, M. J. 1955. Frozen foods. Ontario Dept. Agr. Bull. *504* Rev.

Grimm, R. T.   1955. This filtering of frying oil assures better looking, tasting, lasting products. Food Eng. *27*, No. 6, 113.

Shields, R. V.   1949. Sandwiches in great array from your Deepfreeze home freezer. Notes from the Deepfreeze Pantry *3*, No. 2, 2–4.

Simpson, J. I.   1962. The Frozen Food Cookbook and Guide to Home Freezing. Avi Publishing Co., Westport, Conn.

PART 2

# Frozen Salad Dressings, Salads, and Sandwich Fillings

Hugh H. Mottern

## INTRODUCTION

Some convenience foods have gained wide acceptance not merely for their ease of serving, but also for their lower cost as compared with that incurred by the housewife who has to purchase a number of items to prepare a multi-ingredient recipe. Meat salads and meat salad sandwich fillings fall into this class.

Mayonnaise and salad dressings as ordinarily prepared break their emulsion when frozen. Hence, the admonition sometimes seen on mayonnaise labels "Protect from Freezing." Successful preparation of such frozen salad dressing products awaited the development of freeze-thaw stable dressings. Hanson, Campbell, and Lineweaver (1951), and Hanson and Lineweaver (1953) made an initial contribution in the direction of developing freeze-thaw stable salad dressings in their work on freeze stable frozen sauces and gravies. These were lower in oil content than salad dressings, containing only about 6% total fat compared with up to 65% for salad dressings. In their exhaustive study of the effects of a variety of conditions and ingredients such as emulsifiers, stabilizers, and thickening agents, they found that waxy rice flour gave the most satisfactory sauce. The reason for this is the high amylopectin content of the starch fraction. Solutions of starch tend to undergo retrogradation at temperatures near freezing in which part of the starch forms aggregates and finally an insoluble precipitate. This starch will go back into solution on reheating, but in the meantime the emulsion may have broken and droplets of oil will have separated and be apparent in the heated product. This may not be noticeable in a boil-in-bag or in an institutional product where the consumer does not see it immediately after thawing, but it spoils the appearance of salads and sandwich fillings that are not heated before serving.

## STABILIZATION OF HIGH-FAT SALAD DRESSINGS

Although use of waxy cereal flours is one solution for the problem of separation of oil in sauces, the stabilization of higher fat salad dressings necessitated further study and modification of ingredients. Hanson and

Hugh H. Mottern is Research Chemist, Food Products Investigations, Engineering and Development Laboratory, Southern Utilization Research and Development Division, Agricultural Research Service, U.S. Dept. of Agr., New Orleans, La.

Fletcher (1961) showed that the important factors influencing oil and water separation from salad dressings conforming to FDA standards of identity were: (1) characteristics of the oil; (2) identity of the thickening agent; (3) character of egg yolk and quantity used; (4) salt concentration; and (5) ratio of emulsion to starch paste. Much attention was given to the winterized character of the oil; the conclusion was that a highly winterized oil, or one which by nature showed little or no separation at 20°F. ($-7$°C.), was highly desirable. However, some salad dressings prepared from some oils when stored indefinitely at temperatures low enough to cause complete solidification of the oil show no separation on thawing. The possible explanation is offered that such oils are in an amorphous rather than a crystalline form. Hanson and Fletcher again found waxy rice flour superior to other thickening agents tested.

Partyka (1963) prepared a stable salad dressing by using hydrogenated fat or nonwinterized oil, strengthening the emulsion with additional egg yolk, and using a modified food starch such as "Col-Flo 67" or "Freezist." The significant property of such starches is that they are modified by phosphorating to render them freeze stable. By modifying a waxy starch in this way, a greater degree of freeze stability can be obtained than by modifying a starch high in amylose.

Although satisfactory results may be obtained in freezing solutions of natural starches high in branch-chained amylopectin (so-called waxy type starches) in some products such as low-fat content sauces, for higher fat content emulsions such as salad dessings, certain chemically modified starches are more desirable. Drastic changes in properties are effected with very little quantitative chemical modification. Amylopectin is cross-linked by means of phosphorus oxychloride, sodium trimetaphosphate, and epichlorohydrin. Those modified with phosphorus compounds are sometimes referred to in the trade as "phosphorated" and are labeled modified starches and given some trade name suggestive of their freeze-thaw stability such as "Freezist," "Cold-Flo," etc. Fawcett (1967) gives an excellent review of such modified starches.

Protecting mayonnaise from damage due to freezing is of minor importance in the moderate climate of the United States, where there are well organized food distribution facilities. The economics of protecting 100% of the product for what might happen to a fractional per cent of the production focuses emphasis on protection during handling. However, in colder climates such as Canada or in less well organized distributing facilities protection of mayonnaise from freezing may be difficult.

Production of mayonnaise-based frozen salads and frozen salad sandwich fillings would seem to fill a need in the sophisticated food economy of the United States. Not only should these be enthusiastically received by the housewife, but the institutional field should find a cost saving and superior bacteriological quality in such products prepared by food manufacturers under controlled conditions by trained personnel with adequate knowledge of the hazards involved. Since such products are consumed on thawing without cooking, it is necessary to prepare them under adequate sanitary conditions from raw materials of known freedom from contamination with significant microorganisms.

### PREPARATION OF FROZEN VEGETABLE SALADS

Starting with the vegetables used in such salads, it is necessary to treat the raw diced carrots, onions, celery, pepper, etc., to reduce the microbiological contamination to a low level. A practical working level might be less than 10 coliforms and not more than 50 yeasts and molds per gram. Vegetables such as peas and carrots that can withstand blanching may be treated for a minimum of two minutes with live steam. Other vegetables not blanched should be given a 5 to 10 min. treatment by immersion in 200 p.p.m. chlorine water both before and after dicing.

Nylon laundry bags are useful in immersing trimmed and diced vegetables in the 200 p.p.m. chlorine solution. The ratio of vegetables to chlorine solution should not be more than 1 to 2 by weight. The chlorine solution used to treat the vegetables should not be re-used, because the organic matter from the vegetables renders it ineffective after ten minutes exposure. Dicing to a size of $\frac{1}{4} \times \frac{1}{4} \times \frac{1}{8}$ in. gives a flat-sided particle with better texture than a $\frac{1}{4}$-in. cube. Dicing to a $\frac{1}{8}$-in. cube yields too much fine material.

Dicing is superior to a random cut which also yields excessive fines. Because of the low microorganism count required, frozen vegetables such as peas and carrots must be specially prepared before freezing. It is not practical to attempt to treat thawed vegetables with chlorine water because of leaching of solids and development of off-flavors from chlorine. Fresh vegetables do not pick up off-flavors from chlorine treatment. Green peppers seem to give more difficulty with high microorganism counts than other vegetables, even root vegetables. Apparently, extensive growth can take place in pepper pods without outward signs of its presence. Furthermore, this contamination does not seem to be reached and destroyed in all cases by chlorine treatment. Celery seems to give the least trouble. Onions respond well to treatment.

It is best to use fresh vegetables to avoid loss of texture from thawing and refreezing. Freezing of these items should be conducted in 10-lb. poly bags laid in trays so that the thickness is not more than 2 in. This facilitates quick thawing.

## Meat Ingredients for Salads

The quantity of meat ingredient in a frozen ham or chicken salad is regulated by the Meat Inspection Division (MID) of the U.S. Department of Agriculture. Also the packing of items containing ham and chicken must be under the supervision of an MID inspector, even though the meat used may have been inspected previously. MID regulations do not apply to tuna or salmon.

If frozen chicken and ham are used, close attention must be given to bacteriological standards for these items. Canned tuna and salmon may be easily contaminated from contact with equipment during their preparation in particulate form. Frozen shrimp, if used, should be cooked on the premises or else canned shrimp should be used. Shrimp varies greatly in flavor depending on source and type of handling. Selection should be made from brokers' samples to get a product of desirable flavor at minimum cost. Shrimp, tuna, and salmon should be prepared with counts of less than ten per gram for total; yeasts, molds, coliform, Staphylococci, and, of course, Salmonella must be zero.

One reason for emphasizing low counts in frozen sandwich fillings, especially as used in vending machines, is that the time the product is held within the machine before vending to the customer may be appreciable. A vendor may prepare salads for sandwich fillings the night before placing them in the machine. The finished sandwich is prepared by placing a scoop of the salad filling on a slice of bread, spreading, adding a top slice, and wrapping. These are stored in trays and placed in a walk-in refrigerator until the route loads are made up early the next morning. Bread is a fair insulating material, and it requires some time for a stack of sandwiches to cool from ambient temperature to that of the refrigerator. Using formed frozen sandwiches interleaved with wax paper, the sandwiches can be made up so as to gradually thaw during route delivery. One and one-half to 2 oz. may be used as the sandwich portion.

The salad dressing used with frozen sandwich fillings can be made at lower pH than that of home prepared products, so that the resultant sandwich filling has a low pH (*ca.* 4.5) to protect against bacteria of public health significance. This excessive acidity would be noticeable in a product served as a salad, and in this case the lower pH would not be advisable or advantageous.

A suggested recipe follows:

|                                                  | %     |
|--------------------------------------------------|-------|
| Freezable salad dressing                         | 33    |
| Meat (ham, chicken, or tuna)                     | 33    |
| Diced vegetables, celery, and green peppers      | 15    |
| Pickle relish, diced                             | 10    |
| Pimientos, diced                                 | 5     |
| Onions, diced                                    | 1     |
| Salt                                             | 1.5   |
| Starch (cold water soluble)                      | 1.5   |
|                                                  | 100.0 |

Spice, MSG, HVP, and lemon juice may also be included. The purpose of the starch added to the mix is to absorb the juices that tend to bleed out of the diced vegetables upon thawing. It should be mixed with the diced vegetables and pickle relish before adding the freezable dressing and meat portion.

### BIBLIOGRAPHY

Fawcett, P.   1967. Ingredient survey. Food Manuf. Jan. 16–17.

Hanson, H. L., Campbell, A., and Lineweaver, H.   1951. Preparation of stable frozen sauces and gravies. Food Technol. 5, 432–440.

Hanson, H. L., and Fletcher, L.   1961. Salad dressing stable to frozen storage. Food Technol. 15, 256–262.

Hanson, H. L., and Lineweaver, H.   1953. Stabilized creamed food products. U.S. Pat. 2,653,876, September 29.

Krett, O. J., and Gennuso, S. L.   1963. Salad dressing. U.S. Pat. 3,093,486, June 11.

Partyka, A.   1963. Salad dressing. U.S. Pat. 3,093,485, June 11.

## CHAPTER 6

Donald K. Tressler | # Soups, Chowders, and Stews

## INTRODUCTION

Soups are relatively new additions to the line of commercial precooked frozen foods. A decade ago, the quantity of frozen soup sold was negligible. A number of little known brands were on the market; none sold in quantity. When some of the leading packers of canned soup began to advertise frozen soups, the homemaker became aware of the availability of frozen soups of a quality and kind not available in the heat-processed product.

Many persons still ask "why freeze soup?" The answer is not hard to find. Some kinds of soup, e.g., tomato, can be subjected to the canning process without marked change in flavor or consistency. Certain others are undesirably changed by heat processing but not notably changed by freezing. Included in the latter class are oyster stew, clam chowder, fish chowder, onion soup, cream of shrimp, cream of corn, cream of potato, green split pea, snapper soup, crayfish bisque, bouillabaisse, and many others. In fact, the list of kinds of soups now offered on the market, which can be frozen without marked change, is very long.

Soups prepared from seafood are most popular. Oyster stew and clam chowder are both in demand.

In 1966, approximately 20 different American packers froze soup. This is a notable drop, since in 1955, 60 packers were freezing soup. The number of kinds of soup packed is still great, including the following: bean; beef vegetable; borsht; chicken; chicken broth; crayfish; clam chowder, both New England and Manhattan; fish chowder; gumbo; lentil; lobster; minestrone; mushroom; onion; oyster stew; green pea; potato; shrimp; and snapper. Packers of frozen soup are located in the following states: California, Connecticut, Delaware, Illinois, Kentucky, Louisiana, Maryland, New Jersey, New York, Pennsylvania, Rhode Island, and Texas.

A survey carried out by the senior author in 1956 (Tressler and Evers 1957) indicated that the soup packed for the retail trade was put into either 10. or 16-oz. containers, ordinarily in tin cans (see also p. 160) or Sealright cartons. Four packers used a waxed carton with a heat-sealed bag liner, and two others put the soup into Lily-Tulip cups. All of the packers using 10-oz. containers recommended diluting the frozen soup with an equal quanti-

Donald K. Tressler is a consultant and President of the Avi Publishing Co., Westport, Conn.

ty of water (or in some instances milk) during preparation for the table. On the other hand, most of those packing the soup in 16-oz. containers suggested reheating the frozen soup without dilution.

## PROBLEMS

Loss of, and change of flavor is often a problem in frozen soups flavored with onions and garlic. If the time allowed for boiling or simmering during preparation is kept to a minimum, less loss of flavor will occur. Filling in tin cans at temperatures close to the boiling point, so as to obtain a vacuum in the headspace, followed by rapid cooling, quick freezing, and storage and handling at 0°F. ( −18°C.) or below, all reduce flavor loss and change.

Curdling is sometimes a problem in cream soups. In soups containing milk and cream, it is important to use only the very freshest products. Ingredients with a low pH, e.g., tomatoes and other acid vegetables, should never be used in soups, chowders, etc. containing milk and cream unless the pH is adjusted with a little soda and / or buffered with sodium citrate or some other substance. In preparing soups, chowders, and stews, the milk and / or cream is added as the final ingredient and merely brought to the boil. If permitted to boil long, curdling and / or scorching may result. Oysters, clams, and other shellfish should not be kept at the boiling point very long or they may become tough.

Although many packers use wheat flour and / or cornstarch for thickening soups to be frozen, it should be noted that a smoother texture will be obtained in the reheated product if waxy rice or waxy maize flour or starch is used (see also pp. 46 and 315). Hanson, Campbell, and Lineweaver (1951) have clearly shown the advantages of the use of waxy cereal flours and starches for thickening all types of creamy products which are to be frozen. Ordinary flours and starches may be suitable for thickening cream soups if they are rapidly frozen, then held at a uniformly low temperature for only a short time before use. If the product is slowly frozen, or is subject to fluctuating temperatures, either during storage, or transportation and marketing, curdling or "separation" may occur during reheating. If, however, the homemaker vigorously stirs the product before it is removed from the range, the roughness of the cream may not be noticed unless it is examined closely.

## FORMULAS

As indicated by the long list of soups, chowders, stews, etc. frozen commercially, the kind of soups which can be successfully frozen and marketed is very great. It does not seem to be necessary in a general book on the technology of freezing preservation such as this, to give formulas for more than a few of the general types of soups which have been found to freeze satisfactorily.

**Oyster Stew**

| | Quantity | | |
|---|---|---|---|
| Ingredients | % | Lb. | Oz. |
| Fresh oyster meats, drained | 30.00 | 28 | 2 |
| Water, including oyster liquor | 58.35 | 55 | — |
| Milk, dry skim | 6.90 | 6 | 9.2 |
| Butter or margarine | 4.20 | 4 | — |
| Salt | 0.30 | — | 5.0 |
| Irish moss extract (SeaKem Type 3) | 0.10 | — | 1.5 |
| Monosodium glutamate | 0.10 | — | 1.5 |
| Paprika | 0.03 | — | .5 |
| Pepper, white | 0.02 | — | .3 |
| | 100.00 | 94 | 4.0 |

**Preparation of Base**

(1) Melt margarine in steam-jacketed kettle. (2) Mix milk powder and other dry ingredients; add to oleomargarine, stirring constantly until fat is well distributed. (3) Add water as needed; blend until mixture is homogeneous. (4) Add remainder of water; increase heat and continue stirring until it comes to a simmer. (5) Draw off and keep hot. To avoid fat separation and surface scum, milk should be homogenized at this point.

**Preparation of Oysters**

(1) Place shucked oyster meats on coarse screen and collect juice. (2) Remove any pieces of shell that may still adhere. (3) Heat oysters in their own liquor for about five minutes or until the edges begin to curl.

**Packing Procedure**

(1) Strain hot liquor into hot milk base. (2) Pack 8 to 12 oysters per serving (depending on size) volumetrically into containers and cover with milk base.

If packed into cartons or composite cartons, both the oysters and milk base should be cooled to about 55°F. (13°C.) before filling.

If an oyster stew concentrate is desired, use one half as much water in the milk base. Pack double the amount of oysters per package (3 to 3.5 oz.) plus 8.5 to 9 oz. of milk base and state in directions to add an equal quantity (1½ cups) of milk for reheating on top of stove.

Source: Fitzgerald (1956).

In packing oyster stew, it is of great importance to have the same quantity of oysters in each can of stew. According to Lawler (1955), this is accomplished in the following manner:

"Soup is filled into the Campbell-made lithographed cans by multi-spout rotating machines, operating on a volumetric principle. In filling oyster stew, the oysters are put into the cans first with the aid of a machine. The right quantity of tender oysters is deftly transferred from an open front stainless steel bin into the pockets of a rotating-disk dispenser. As each disk turns, the oysters drop from each pocket into a can on a conveyor below. Then the can goes to the liquid filler."

In following this system of packing oyster stew for freezing, only the hot seasoned milk is heated prior to filling; the contact of the hot milk on the oysters cooks them sufficiently.

**New England Clam Chowder**

**From Fresh Clams**

| | Quantity | | |
|---|---|---|---|
| **Ingredients** | % | Lb. | Oz. |
| Fresh soft clams, diced or ground quahogs | 31.00 | 31 | 5.0 |
| Potatoes, new, diced | 10.50 | 11 | — |
| Water, including clam liquor | 45.40 | 46 | 7.0 |
| Bacon or salt pork, diced | 3.80 | 4 | — |
| Onions, chopped | 3.80 | 4 | 8.0 |
| Salt | 0.40 | — | 4.0 |
| Pepper | 0.04 | — | .6 |
| Milk, dry skim | 3.17 | 3 | 4.0 |
| Flour, pastry type | 0.74 | — | 12.0 |
| Margarine | 0.95 | 1 | — |
| Monosodium glutamate | 0.10 | — | 1.7 |
| Irish moss extract (SeaKem, type 3) | 0.10 | — | 1.7 |
| | 100.00 | 102 | 12.0 |

**Preparation of Fresh Clams**

(1) Place clam meats on coarse screen and collect juice. (2) Remove any pieces of shell that may still adhere to the meats. (3) Separate tough from tender portions, discarding tough skin cover of siphon. (These may be tenderized by pressure cooking if desired.) (4) Open stomachs with small scissors, lay back, and remove black portions (livers) near siphon. (5) Grind or dice clams, as desired.

**Preparation of Chowder**

(1) Fry salt pork until crisp and pale brown and remove solid pieces. (2) Add chopped onions and sauté until almost tender and light golden brown color. Add margarine. (3) Mix flour, monosodium glutamate, Irish moss extract, salt and pepper, and sprinkle mixture gradually into cooking onions while constantly stirring. (4) When above dry ingredients are well absorbed, add dry milk gradually while stirring, adding a small amount of water, if necessary. (5) When milk appears to be well distributed, add clam liquor, gradually stirring until no lumps of milk remain. Add remainder of clam liquor. (6) Add potatoes and simmer until potatoes are about half done. (7) Add clams, remainder of water, and continue to simmer

until potatoes are just tender (about ten minutes). (8) Strain out solids and homogenize liquid. (9) Pack in ratio of six ounces of solids and six ounces of liquid per twelve-ounce pack. (This formula gives 70 twelve-ounce packages.)

If a clam chowder concentrate is desired, use only 65% of the stated amount of liquid in preparing the chowder, pack eight ounces of solids and four ounces of liquid in the container and give directions to add an equal quantity of whole milk (1½ cups) for reheating on top of range.

If the product is packed in cartons or composite cartons, both the liquid and the solids should be cooled to 55°F. (13°C.) before filling.

Source: Fitzgerald (1956).

## Clam Chowder
### From Canned Clams

| Ingredients | Quantity Oz. |
|---|---|
| Salt pork, ¼ in. cubes [1] | 8 |
| Butter | 3½ |
| Yellow leeks, diced | 8 |
| Celery, diced | 8 |
| Fresh onions, ¼ in. cubes | 16 |
| Salt | 1 |
| White pepper | |
| Sachet bag | |
| (1 medium bay leaf, ¾ tsp. thyme, and 3 cloves) | |
| Fish stock or water | 120 |
| Potatoes, diced | 32 |
| Powdered milk | 3½ |
| Instant potatoes | 3½ |
| Clams, chopped plus juice (No. 2 can) | 20 |

### Preparation of Chowder

(1) Sauté salt pork in butter until transparent. (2) Add leeks, celery, onions and sauté 5 min., stirring often. (3) Add salt, pepper, sachet bag, and fish stock. (4) Bring to a boil, reduce heat, and simmer 15 min. (5) Add potatoes and continue to simmer 8 more min. (6) Bring to a boil. Remove sachet bag. (7) Combine powdered milk and instant potato. (8) Slowly add clams and juice. (9) Add to soup and heat to 180°F. (82°C.), stirring constantly. (10) Cool to room temperature. (11) Pack 12 oz. into polyethylene bags (type used for "boil-in" bag). (12) Evacuate bag, then heat-seal.

Source: Sayles and MacLennan (1965).

---

[1] Soak salt pork overnight.

## Lobster Chowder

| Ingredients | Quantity Lb. | Oz. |
|---|---|---|
| Lobster meat, diced | 25 | — |
| Salt pork, diced | 6 | 4.0 |
| Celery, diced | 1 | 8.0 |
| Potatoes, diced | 25 | — |
| Carrots, diced | 6 | — |
| Onions, diced | 12 | 8.0 |
| Parsley, chopped | — | 2.0 |
| Chicken stock | 100 | — |
| Tomatoes | 31 | 4.0 |
| Rice, cooked | 4 | — |
| Poultry seasoning | — | .2 |
| Waxy maize or waxy rice flour | 1 | 8.0 |
| Milk | 50 | — |
| Butter | 1 | — |
| | 264 | 2.2 |

**Procedure**

(1) Fry salt pork. (2) Add diced vegetables. (3) Fry. (4) Add chicken stock, and poultry seasoning; simmer until vegetables are tender. (5) Add lobster meat, simmer 15 min. (6) Add tomatoes and cooked rice. (7) Using mixer, blend the waxy maize starch with the milk. (8) Add milk starch mixture to chowder, stirring constantly. (9) Beat in butter. This product should be used without dilution.

## Shrimp Bisque

| Ingredients | Quantity Oz. |
|---|---|
| Shrimp, cooked | 36 |
| Onions, chopped | 7 |
| Celery, coarsely chopped | 7 |
| Butter | 7 |
| Brandy, inexpensive | 2 |
| Water or fish stock | 136 |
| Salt | 1 |
| White pepper | 1/4 |
| Rice, cooked | 7 |
| Evaporated milk | 14 |
| Tabasco sauce | 1/3 |
| Modified starch[2] | 2 3/4 |
| Sherry | 4 |

**Procedure.**—Chop 2 of the shrimp. Dice 1/4 lb. of shrimp and reserve for garnish. Sauté onions and celery in butter until transparent but not brown.

Add shrimp and heat through. Add brandy and flame. Add water or fish stock, salt, pepper, and rice. Cover, bring to a boil, reduce heat, and simmer 15 min.

Purée through a fine food mill and bring to a boil. Slowly add evaporated milk and tabasco sauce to modified starch and stir until smooth. Add to stock; heat to 180°F. (82°C.), stirring constantly. Add sherry.

[2] Purity 69.

Package 12 oz. in each vacuum bag (12 in. $\times$ 8 in.). Add a few diced shrimp. Yield 10 bags. Blast freeze for 30 min.

**To Serve:** Heat pouch 6 min. in boiling water to cover. Serve in heated soup tureen. May be served with ½ tsp. brandy.

Source: Sayles and MacLennan (1965).

**Fish Chowder**

| Ingredients | Quantity Lb. | Oz. |
|---|---|---|
| Haddock fillets[3] or other skinless, boneless fish, cut into ½ in. cubes | 100 | — |
| Water | 75 | — |
| Salt pork, diced | 12 | 8 |
| Potatoes, peeled, thinly sliced | 100 | — |
| Onions, chopped | 10 | — |
| Milk | 5 | — |
| Butter | 1 | — |
| Salt | — | 3 |
| Paprika | — | 0.5 |

**Procedure.**—Simmer the fish 10 min. in half of the water. Slowly heat the diced salt pork in a steam-jacketed kettle for 15 min. Add the potatoes, onion and remainder of the water, cover kettle and cook for 10 min. Add the fish and simmer for 5 min. Melt the butter and homogenize it with the milk which has been warmed in a double boiler to 100°F. (38°C.). Add salt, paprika, and the homogenized milk to the cooked fish, potatoes, etc. Bring to a boil, cool, then package and freeze.

When reheated, this chowder should be diluted with half its weight of milk.

**Fish Stew** See also, Chapter 12.

| Ingredients | Quantity Lb. | Oz. |
|---|---|---|
| Salt pork, finely diced | 3 | 12.0 |
| Corn, frozen whole kernel | 7 | 8.0 |
| Tomatoes, canned | 40 | — |
| Green lima beans, frozen baby | 6 | 4.0 |
| Onion, finely diced | 5 | — |
| Potatoes, ¼ in. dice | 7 | 8.0 |
| Carrots, diced | 3 | 2.0 |
| Celery, diced | 5 | — |
| Green pepper, diced | — | 5.0 |
| Salt | — | 1.0 |
| Pepper, black | — | 0.5 |
| Thyme | — | 0.2 |
| Cod consommé | 20 | — |
| Waxy rice flour | — | 10.0 |
| Water, cold | 25 | — |
| Cod fillets, 1 in. cubes | 60 | — |
| Butter | — | 6.0 |
| Yield | 184 | 8.7 |

[3] After comminution, frozen blocks of fillets may be used.

Procedure.—Fry out salt pork in steam-jacketed kettle until golden brown. Add vegetables and water. Simmer 30 min. Run flour and water through colloid mill, then add to batch and blend well. Cook 5 to 8 min. to thicken.

To Serve.—This product may be thawed and used as a stew without dilution. Or it may be diluted with an equal volume of milk before use.

### French Onion Soup

| Ingredients | Quantity Oz. |
|---|---|
| Fresh onions, sliced | 32 |
| Butter | 4 |
| Water | 132 |
| Espagnole extract | |
| White pepper | |
| Dry white wine | 16 |
| Modified starch [4] | 1¾ |
| Croutons of French bread | |
| Parmesan or Swiss cheese | |

Procedure.—Sauté onions in butter in a deep sauce pan, stirring constantly, until onions are a golden brown.

Add water, Espagnole extract, salt, and pepper. Bring to a boil, reduce heat, and simmer for 5 min.

Slowly add white wine to starch; stir until smooth and add to soup. Heat to 180°F. (82°C.), stirring constantly.

Package 12 oz. in vacuum pouch. Evacuate bag, then heat-seal. Yield: 120 oz.

To Serve: Heat pouch 6 min. in boiling water to cover. Pour into hot soup tureen. Float croutons on top of soup and sprinkle 1 tsp. of parmesan or Swiss cheese on croutons. Place soup under salamander flame for 15 sec. to melt cheese; do not allow cheese to burn.

### Vichysoisse

| Ingredients | Quantity Lb. | Oz. |
|---|---|---|
| Potatoes, sliced | 100 | 0 |
| Onions, sliced | 15 | 0 |
| Leeks, sliced | 10 | 0 |
| Water | 104 | 0 |
| Chicken bouillon cubes, granulated | 2 | 8 |
| White pepper | — | 5 |
| Celery salt | | 1.75 |
| Cream, light | 40 | 0 |
| | 271 | 14.75 |

Procedure.—Slowly cook in steam-jacketed kettle until vegetables are done, then run batch through pulper or paddle-type finisher. Next, mix five gallons of light cream into the pulp. Fill into containers and freeze.

Use.—May be used without dilution.

Source: (Anon. 1956A).

---

[4] Purity 69 or equivalent.

## COMMERCIAL EQUIPMENT AND METHODS

The type of equipment and methods employed for making and freezing soup varies from plant to plant. Some of the important factors which should be considered in the selection of equipment are the following: (1) the kinds of soups, chowders, and stews to be made; (2) the scale on which operations are to be conducted; (3) the choice of container for the product; and (4) the methods of freezing to be used.

Most soup-making operations are conducted in a battery of stainless steel, steam-jacketed kettles. The number and size of these kettles will depend upon the quantity to be made, the number of different kinds of each, and the methods to be followed in making each soup.

If the soup is packed in cartons, a heat exchanger will be needed to cool the soup prior to packaging, and a pump will be required to move it from the kettles through the exchanger. Pumps will also be needed to transfer the product to the filling machines. The type of pump used will depend upon whether the soup contains solids (pieces of oysters, clams, vegetables, etc.) which will not pass through a small opening, or is a substantially homogenous fluid.

The type of filler and packaging equipment will depend on the kind and size of package used. If the soup is packed in small tin cans, the usual high speed equipment employed in filling and closing soup for heat processing should be used.

### Concentration

Although many of the smaller packers of frozen soup freeze a single-strength product, which does not require dilution before use, most of those operating on a large scale pack a product which is to be diluted by the homemaker with an equal volume of water or milk.

### Containers

Most of the larger packers of frozen soups pack their product in cans holding 10 or 10½ oz. (the 211 × 400 can is commonly used). Soups prepared from fish and shellfish (oyster stew, clam chowder, lobster bisque, fish chowder, and stew) require C-enamel cans. This enamel traps sulfur which otherwise would cause blackening of the can interior.

As has been previously indicated (p. 155), if the soup is cooled prior to packaging, paperboard cartons without liners may be used. Some soup packers use containers which nest (when empty), such as Lily-Tulip cups (Gale 1955). If the paperboard cartons have special linings (e.g., certain Sealright cartons), they may be filled with hot soup without danger of damage or leakage (Anon. 1952).

## FREEZING SOUP

The methods and equipment employed in various plants for freezing soup vary about as widely as does the equipment used in its manufacture.

The Campbell Soup Co. freezes 10-oz. cans of "condensed" soup (oyster stew, snapper soup, clam chowder, fish chowder, vegetable, green pea with ham, cream of potato, and cream of shrimp) in an alcohol brine in a Food Machinery and Chemical Corp. Continuous Round Shell Freezer (Fig. 16). Freezing operations have been described by Lawler (1955) as follows:

*Courtesy of Food Machinery and Chemical Corp.*

Fig. 16.    Immersion freezer used by Campbell Soup Co. for freezing soup in cans. Designed specially for Campbell Soup Co., the FMC immersion-type can freezer has a capacity of 400 cans per minute. It is a twin-shell machine in which picnic size (10-oz.) cans of soup are immersed in an alcohol refrigerant for a given period of time and then discharged completely frozen from the second unit. A reel and spiral assembly conveys the cans continuously from the feed end to the discharge valve. Cans are fed direct to the can carrying reel by a cup feed at the top of the first shell. Transfer from one shell to the other is made by a V-valve assembly located between the units.

"Can tracks on the freezer shell move the cans from one end of the freezer to the other. Two of these freezer units (Fig. 16) are located side by side, and operated in series in a U-circuit to double the distance of can travel in the refrigerant. As they discharge from the first section, the cans are transferred automatically by conveyor to the second section. Cans enter and leave the units through pockets in a rotary device which closes the opening against the escape of any significant volume of fumes.

"Circulated by a 100 hp. pump at a rate of 1,800 gal. per min., the below zero refrigerant from the chilling heat exchanger enters each freezer unit at the top through a distributor. Then it flows in both directions toward the ends of the freezer. This removes the heat so rapidly that the canned soup freezes in 30 min. or less, even though cans enter the freezer at a hot 190°F. (88°C.). It takes some 7,000 gal. of freezing fluid to fill the space between drum and shell in each freezer.

"It is significant that there is no precooling step ahead of the freezer. Calculations by a consulting refrigeration engineer proved that it is more economical to take all the B.t.u. out of the soup in the freezer. Besides, the cans do not pick up moisture, as they would in precooling, to dilute the freezing fluid. This means that the refrigerant doesn't have to be reconditioned as often.

"A special refrigerant was selected for the freezer. It has just the right viscosity, correct moisture absorption characteristics, and the desired heat conductivity.

"While loss of freezing fluid carried out of the freezer on can surfaces is not a major factor, the cans are passed through a revolving-brush machine to recover most of the adhering refrigerant.

"Heat which freezing fluid removes from the soup is extracted in a large York horizontal shell-and-tube heat exchanger with 300 tons of cooling capacity, located end-to-end with the first freezer section.

"All of the freezing and refrigerating equipment operates automatically after a pushbutton start. One man watches the instruments and signal lights, and is available in event of any malperformance in the system."

## BIBLIOGRAPHY

Anon.  1944. Sauces, soup bricks frozen. Quick Frozen Foods 6, No. 10, 37.
Anon.  1952. Turns ham stock into busy soup trade. Quick Frozen Foods 14, No. 12, 99–100.
Anon.  1954. Frozen oyster stew is catching on with consumers, packers report. Quick Frozen Foods 17, No. 5, 65, 122.
Anon.  1955. Lobster chowder formula. Food Eng. 27, No. 8, 170.
Anon.  1956A. Frozen vichysoisse. Food Eng. 28, No. 5, 186.
Anon.  1956B. Campbell test markets new frozen soup, old-fashioned vegetable with beef. Quick Frozen Foods 18, No. 12, 87.
Anon.  1956C. A big soup order. Food Eng. 28, No. 4, 182, 184.
Anon.  1956D. With educational program and quality standards frozen soups could achieve major volume; most packers report big gains. Quick Frozen Foods 18, No. 7, 361–362, 364, 366, 368–371.
Anon.  1964. Frozen soups and sauces for restaurants could be overlooked volume. Quick Frozen Foods 26, No. 11, 122–124.
Anon.  1967. Quick Frozen Foods 1967–1968 Directory of Frozen Food Processors. E. W. Williams Publications, New York.
Fitzgerald, G. A.  1956. Private communication. Donald K. Tressler Assoc., Westport, Conn.
Gale, A.  1955. Specialty seafood items—now precooked, frozen ready for heating. Fishing Gaz. 72, No. 10, 40–41.
Hanson, H. L., Campbell, A., and Lineweaver, H.  1951. Preparation of stable frozen sauces and gravies. Food Technol. 5, 432–440.
Kerr, R. G.  1950. Fish cookery for one hundred. U.S. Fish and Wildlife Service, Test Kitchen Series 1.
Lawler, F. K.  1955. Campbell streamlines freezing. Food Eng. 27, No. 6, 68–70, 241.
Sayles, C. I., and MacLennan, H. A.  1965. Ready foods. Cornell Hotel and Restaurant Quarterly Research Rept. 10.
Schaal, W.  1955. Campbell Soup Co.'s new frozen soups. Food Packer 36, No. 4, 21–22.

Tressler, D. K., and Evers, C. F. 1957. The Freezing Preservation of Foods. 3rd Edition, Vol. 2. Precooked and Prepared Foods. Avi Publishing Co., Westport, Conn.

Watts, B. M., Lewis, H , Gardner, E. A., and Wentworth, J. 1956. Progress in preservation studies on Southern oysters. Fishing Gaz. 73, No. 7, 42, 60–61.

## CHAPTER 7

Helen Hanson Palmer

# Prepared and Precooked
# Poultry Products

## INTRODUCTION

The rapid increase in variety and volume of prepared and precooked poultry products since 1940 is indicative of the facility with which poultry meat has been adapted to this form of marketing. The growth of the industry was primarily prompted by lack of reasonable profits on whole body birds. Production of new products was required for higher profits. Problems have been encountered in production and product stability, but their solution has led the industry from chicken à la king and pot pie to the gourmet poultry items on today's menu (Fig. 17). Prompt and comprehensive re-

Courtesy of Armour and Co.

Fig. 17.   Chicken paprikash with egg barleys.

search has provided the information needed for production of a large variety of poultry products with the flavor and texture stability required to meet modern marketing conditions and the demands of the consumer.

The information in this chapter includes basic principles needed in formulating, processing, and packaging prepared and precooked poultry products. Flavor and texture problems and microbiological hazards are discussed, and recommendations are made that will minimize these problems and lead to high-quality, stable products.

## CREAMED POULTRY AND À LA KING PRODUCTS

Chicken à la king was probably the first precooked frozen poultry prod-

Helen Hanson Palmer is Head, Product Stability Investigations, Poultry Laboratory, Western Utilization Research and Development Division, Agricultural Research Service, U.S. Dept. of Agr., Albany, Calif.

uct to appear on the retail market in the early forties, and it has remained popular to the present time. Formulas and directions for preparing 10- and 1,000-portion batches have recently been published by Cornell University, School of Hotel Administration (1965) and are reproduced in part in Table 19. The study includes certain estimates of the preparation time, cost of labor and packaging materials, and cost per portion. A basic formula for a 200- to 220-lb. batch of chicken à la king was published earlier (Tressler and Evers 1957).

Foods such as chicken à la king and creamed chicken retain an acceptable flavor for a year at 0°F. ($-18$°C.). Chicken meat itself is relatively stable; this inherent stability is maintained by using a suitable cooking method and retarding oxidative flavor changes by eliminating air from the package (Hanson et al. 1950). Simmering is the usual method of cooking the chicken for these products, particularly when older, less tender birds are used. Turkey meat is less stable than chicken (Mecchi et al. 1956A, B), and the cooking method used can retard or accelerate the development of off-flavors. Simmering is also recommended for turkeys, but even when turkeys are simmered, sufficient rancidity to be detected may develop occasionally. Roasting is not recommended for turkey meat to be frozen since it accelerates the development of fat rancidity. The addition of antioxidants to the water in which turkey is simmered retards rancidity development, since the fat liberated during such cooking is stable. Tests of this procedure were made primarily with a formulated antioxidant, Tenox II, containing butylated hydroxyanisole, propyl gallate, citric acid, and propylene glycol (Lineweaver et al. 1952). Limited tests using other antioxidants showed similar beneficial effects. The use of antioxidants has not been specifically approved for turkey products by the Food and Drug Administration, but their use in limited amounts has been approved for other foods.

Elimination of oxygen from the package is important in preserving the stability of all precooked frozen foods. In à la king and creamed products, air (oxygen) is largely excluded by the sauce which surrounds the meat. Rancidity is often a problem if the turkey fat is used in making a sauce or gravy. Some processors use chicken fat to replace the turkey fat to increase stability. The label must show this addition. Processors may also eliminate use of turkey skin, since it tends to develop off-flavors at an earlier date than chicken fat or skin.

The relative flavor and texture stability of vegetables used occasionally in à la king products influence quality of the whole product. Cooked peas frozen in a loose pack and held at 0°F. ($-18$°C.) develop off-flavors more rapidly than blanched frozen peas, but in the solid pack existing in à la king products, cooked peas have about the same stability as blanched peas stored without a sauce. (Hanson et al. 1950). Celery, carrots, peas, and pep-

Table 19

Chicken à la King

Formula and Method for Ten Portions

| Ingredients | Quantity | Measures |
|---|---|---|
| Formula | | |
| Chicken, cooked white and dark meat, 1 in. long, 1/2 in. wide, and 1/4 in. thick | 10 lb. (3 1/4–3 1/2 lb. each) | — |
| Chicken base | 2 oz. | — |
| Powdered milk | 3 1/2 oz. | — |
| Chicken stock, boiling | — | 2 1/2 qt. |
| Evaporated milk | 4 1/2 oz. | —. |
| Modified starch[1] | 4 1/2 oz. | — |
| Dry sherry | 3 3/4 oz. | — |
| Yellow food color | — | 20 drops |
| Lemon juice | — | 1 lemon |
| Green pepper, diced and cooked; Pimiento, diced | — | 1 tsp. |
| Mushrooms, cooked and sliced lengthwise | 1 oz. | — |
| Puff pastry, diamond shaped, 2 1/2 in. long, pre-heated | — | 20 |

Method

Add chicken base and powdered milk to broth.
Slowly add evaporated milk to modified starch.
Stir until smooth and add to broth. Heat to 180°F. (82°C.), stirring constantly.
Add the sherry, color and lemon juice.
Combine 4 1/2 oz. chicken with 8 1/2 oz. of sauce.
Package chicken and sauce in pouch (12 × 8 in.).
Add 1 tsp. of peppers and pimientos, and 1 tsp. mushrooms to each pouch, evenly distributed. Blast freeze 30 min.

*To Serve*

Heat pouch in boiling water to cover, 6 min. Pour over 2 diamond-shaped puff pastries. Garnish with watercress or sprigs or parsley.

Estimated Quantities and Cost for 1,000 Portions

| Ingredients | Quantity | Unit Price | Amount | |
|---|---|---|---|---|
| Chicken, raw | 1,030 lb. | $0.30 | $309.00 | |
| Sauce | 60 gal. | —. | 81.38 | |
| Pepper | 11 lb. | .22 | 2.42 | |
| Mushrooms | 50 lb. | .65 | 32.50 | |
| Fleurons | 2,100 | .02 | 42.00 | |
| Total estimated ingredient cost | | | | $467.30 |
| Total estimated wage cost | | | | 56.73 |
| Cost of Pouches—1,050 at $36.48 per M | | | | 38.30 |
| Total estimated cost per 1,000 portions | | | | $562.33 |

Estimated cost per portion—56.2 cents

Source: Cornell University, School of Hotel Administration.
[1] Purity 69.

pers deteriorate in either color or texture during slightly prolonged reheating on the steam table. Chinese water chestnuts are an exception in this regard, since they do not lose their crisp texture with prolonged heating.

Hard cooked eggs, occasionally used in creamed products may present a problem on freezing. Hard cooked egg yolk retains a satisfactory consistency on freezing, but cooked egg white separates into layers and becomes granular or rubbery under such conditions. The damage to the cooked white is due to protein dehydration and mechanical effects of the ice crystals formed during freezing (Davis et al. 1952). No consistently satisfactory method was found for solving this problem, but mixtures containing a yolk: white ratio from 40:60 to 80:20, diluted with 20% water and adjusted pH 6.0 to 7.0 before cooking, have a texture after freezing and thawing that is satisfactory for use.

Monosodium glutamate is often included for its effect on flavor in formulas for frozen poultry products. A limited consumer preference test showed that a group of 50 to 100 individuals preferred samples to which monosodium glutamate was added over those without glutamate (Hanson et al. 1960A). Glutamate has also been recommended as a flavor stabilizer. However, the addition of monosodium glutamate at 0.15 and 0.35% levels does not prevent or delay off-flavor development in turkey à la king during storage for nine months at 10°F. ( − 12°C.). (Hanson et al. 1960B).

Since creamed products are excellent substrates for the growth of microorganisms, constant care must be exercised by processors during their preparation and freezing. Foods which are subject to much handling, such as chicken à la king, are particularly vulnerable. For such foods the holding time should be kept to a minimum and should not exceed four hours in the temperature range in which growth of food poisoning organisms is most rapid, 50° to 88°F. (10° to 31°C.) (Bowmer 1965). Early studies indicated the hazards involved and the need for improvement in processing conditions for chicken à la king and other creamed poultry products (Proctor and Phillips 1947; Buchbinder et al. 1949). Straka and Combes (1952) showed that prefreezing delay and defrosting times of more than two hours allowed Micrococcus pyogenes var. albus to multiply several fold in creamed chicken. However, they showed that defrosting at 77°F. (25°C.) can be extended for a somewhat longer period without encountering excessive counts of microorganisms. Logan et al. (1951) showed that with careful, sanitary handling and speed, a wholesome product of high acceptability can be produced by both hot and cold pack methods. Tests on commercial packages of chicken à la king and other precooked frozen products showed that the heating recommendations provided to consumers are adequate to destroy infectious pathogens but, of course, not sporeforming bacteria (Ott et al. 1961). A pasteurization treatment for packaged cooked chicken products has been suggested as a means of significantly reducing the number of organisms without decreasing acceptability (Woodburn *et al.* 1962). Individual servings in polyester-polyethylene laminated bags were heated in an electronic range or by immersion in boiling water. Products were inoculated with approximately one million cells per gram of *Salmonella senftenberg, S. typhimurium,* or a food-poisoning strain of *Staphylococcus aureus.* Product temperature after two minutes in a microwave oven was above 194°F. (90°C.) and after ten minutes in boiling water was 176°F. (80°C.) Survival of added organisms was generally less than ten per gram. Products of this type are generally packaged in boilable pouches in cartons, in foil pouches, or in aluminum trays and blast or plate frozen (see Chapter 5).

### POULTRY DINNERS AND PIES

Chicken pies are the biggest selling frozen meat pie, and chicken dinners are the largest selling frozen dinners (Martin 1966). Sliced poultry meat and gravy is marketed separately or as a component of a dinner (Fig. 18). These products are relatively resistant to flavor changes under recommended conditions of commercial frozen storage. Their stability is mainly attributed to replacement of air in the container by the sauce or gravy that surrounds or covers the meat. Turkey dinners and turkey pies, prepared in the laboratory and under commercial conditions, have been studied to determine flavor stability at temperatures ranging from −30° to 20°F. (−34.4° to −6.6°C.) (Hanson and Fletcher 1958). Stale flavors and rancidity were detected in 1½ to 3 months in these products held at 20°F. (−6.6°C.). At 10°F. (−12°C.) mild stale flavors and occasional rancidity developed after 6 to 12 months at 10°F. (−12°C.) and below. The flavors of products stored at temperatures fluctuating from 0° to 20°F. (−18° to −6.6°C.) and from −10° to 10°F. (−23° to −12°C.) were not significantly different from

*Courtesy of Armour and Co.*

Fig. 18.   Roast turkey and gravy.

Table 20

Chicken Pot Pie

Formula and Method for Ten Portions

| Ingredients | Quantity | Measures |
|---|---|---|
| Formula | | |
| Chicken, cooked, white and dark meat, 1 × 1/2 × 1/4 in. | 8 lb. (3 1/4–3 1/2 lb. each) | — |
| Chicken base | 14 oz. | — |
| Chicken broth, boiling | — | 1 1/2 qt. |
| Milk, nonfat, dry | 3 oz. | — |
| Evaporated milk | 14 oz. | — |
| Modified starch[1] | — | 1 1/4 c. |
| Dry sherry | 2 oz. | — |
| Lemon juice | — | 2 tbsp. |
| Yellow food color | — | 20 drops |
| Carrots, cooked, 1 in. long and 1/4 in. wide | 1 3/4 oz. | — |
| Celery, cooked, cut crosswise, 1/4 in. thick | 1 3/4 oz. | — |
| Mushrooms, cooked and quartered | 1 3/4 oz. | — |
| Peas[2] | 2 oz. | — |
| Pearl onions[2] | — | 30–40 |
| Pie crust, 7 × 5 3/4 in. unbaked; 6 3/4 × 5 in. baked | — | 10 |

Method

Add chicken base to broth.
Slowly add the evaporated milk to the modified starch and stir until smooth. Add to broth. Heat to 180°F. (82°C.), stirring constantly. Add sherry, lemon juice, and color.
Package 2 3/4 oz. chicken, 1 1/2 tbsp. of carrots, and 1 tbsp. each of celery, mushrooms, and peas, in a pouch (12 × 8 in.). Add 3–4 pearl onions. Add 8 oz. sauce, evenly distributed. Blast freeze 30 min.

Pie Crust

Yield: 12 (5 oz. Pot Pies)  Temperature: 400° F. (204°C.)
Time: 8 min.

| Ingredients | Quantity | Measures | Method |
|---|---|---|---|
| Flour | 2 lb. | | Combine the flour and the salt. Rub the fat into the flour with both hands until of cornmeal consistency. Add evaporated milk, blend well, keeping kneading to a minimum. Refrigerate dough 2–3 hr. Prior to rolling crust, leave at room temperature approximately 10 min. (depending on type of fat). Roll crust 2/8 in. thick. For chicken pies, cut oblong shape, 7 × 5 3/4 in. Score (design) with a fork, brush with egg wash. Bake at 400°F. (204°C.) for 8 min. |
| Salt | | 1 tbsp. | |
| Lard | 14 oz. | | |
| Evaporated milk | 14 oz. | | |

Table 20 (continued)

To Serve

Heat pouch 6 min. in boiling water to cover. Heat prebaked pie crust. Empty pouch into dish, baste rim of dish with egg wash, and place pie crust on top. Return to microwave oven 10–15 sec. to seal crust.

Estimated Quantities and Cost for 1,000 Portions

| Ingredients | Quantity | Unit Price | Amount |
|---|---|---|---|
| Raw chicken | 880 lb. | $0.30 | $264.00 |
| Sauce | 62 gal. | — | 81.38 |
| Carrots | 18 lb. | .09 | 1.62 |
| Celery | 11 lb. | .15 | 1.65 |
| Mushrooms | 11 lb. | .65 | 7.15 |
| Pearl onions | 27 lb. | .55 | 14.85 |
| Peas | 18 lb. | .52/40 oz. | 3.64 |
| Seasoning | — | — | 2.00 |
| Evaporated milk | 12 gal. | 1.30 gal. | 15.60 |
| Flour | 150 lb. | 0.07 | 8.50 |
| Fat | 100 lb. | 0.20 | 20.00 |
| Eggs | 16 doz. | 0.50 | 8.00 |

Total estimated ingredient cost                                                        $428.39
Total estimated wage cost                                                               120.78
Cost of pouches          1,050 at 36.48 per M               $38.30
Saran wrap               1,000 ft. at 55¢ per C                5.50
Total estimated package cost                                                             43.80

Total estimated cost per 1,000 portions                                                $592.97
Estimated cost per portion 60 cents

Source: Cornell University, School of Hotel Administration.
[1] Purity 69.
[2] Use frozen peas and pearl onions.

those held at the mean temperatures of 10° and 0°F. ($-12°$ and $-18°$C.). Storage at 20°F. ($-6.6°$C.) should not exceed a few weeks, and storage at 10°F. ($-12°$C.) or lower should not exceed six months to avoid the occasional off-flavors that develop even at the lower temperatures.

Because chicken and turkey pies were among the first precooked frozen foods to be prepared on a commercial scale and because they are good media for bacterial growth, they were the subject of numerous bacteriological surveys. The handling required in boning of the cooked poultry also introduces a bacteriological hazard, particularly if the opportunity exists for growth of organisms in the product before freezing or after thawing. Early studies of frozen chicken and turkey pies indicated the need for improved technological and sanitary measures in preparation of the pies, revision of baking instructions, and formulation of pie crusts that would brown more slowly (Canale-Parola and Ordal 1957; Hucker and David 1957; Fanelli and Ayres 1959). However, a survey of chicken, turkey, beef, and tuna pies, including six brands of chicken pies and seven brands of turkey pies, showed that almost 60% of the pies had counts lower than 25,000 per gram (Litsky et al. 1957). These authors expected further reduction in counts in view of the trend toward high sanitary standards in modern packing procedures. A more recent study indicated that in chicken pot pies the growth of Staphylococci does not constitute a food poisoning hazard, since in the presence of the normal flora it was not possible to promote the growth of appreciable numbers of Staphylococci under any conditions of defrosting tested (Peterson et al. 1962).

Standards have been established for minimum meat content in frozen poultry dinners and pies, and these should be consulted for details (Anon. 1965A). The minimum cooked deboned poultry meat required for an 8-oz. pie is 14% or 1⅛ oz.; the minimum raw deboned poultry meat required is 25% or 2 oz. The minimum cooked deboned meat required in dinners, excluding the weight of appetizers, desserts, etc., is 18% or 2 oz., whichever is greater. A minimum of 45%, or 5 oz. per dinner, whichever is greater, of cooked poultry including bone and breading may be used in lieu of the minimum 18% or 2 oz. of cooked deboned poultry meat, and the cooked poultry including bone and breading shall not contain more than 30% breading.

The Cornell University School of Hotel Administration recent research report, "Ready Foods," includes a formula for 10-pie quantity of chicken pot pie with directions for preparation, freezing, reheating, and serving. The report also includes an estimate of quantities of ingredients needed for 1,000 portions, the time required for preparation, and cost of labor and packaging materials. The cost per portion was estimated to be 60 cents (Table 20).

Specifications have been published by the Department of Defense for a frozen turkey dinner menu containing 3 oz. turkey, 2 oz. each of dressing and gravy, 2½ oz. of mixed vegetables, and 3 oz. mashed sweet potatoes (Anon. 1964A). The materials and processing methods to be used, proportion of light and dark meat, directions for assembling of ingredients, microbiological, packaging, and labeling requirements are specified.

Poultry pies are generally packed in aluminum pie tins and placed in cartons for freezing by the usual methods (see Chapter 5). The meat and sauce portions of pot pies may be packaged in boilable pouches and combined with the crusts after reheating (see Table 20). Dinners are usually packed in aluminum trays with lids and blast or plate frozen. However, separate entrées are also frozen in boilable pouches.

### FROZEN STUFFED POULTRY

Frozen stuffed poultry has enjoyed continuing popularity since it was introduced on the market in the early 1950's. The primary problem in its production was the potential microbiological hazard associated with the stuffing. Careful control of processing and adequate instructions for roasting have successfully contended with this problem. The recommendations for roasting are based on heat treatments adequate to destroy food poisoning bacteria and at the same time produce a good quality cooked product.

Commercial poultry stuffing usually contains bread, shortening, chopped onions, chopped celery, and seasonings (Mountney 1966). Since it is an excellent medium for bacterial growth, it should be refrigerated or frozen at all times except during the actual processing operation. A temperature of 165°F. (73.9°C.) reached in the center of the stuffing· during the roasting period is sufficient to kill food poisoning microorganisms such as Streptococci (enterococci), Straphylococci, and Salmonellae in the turkey stuffing and to allow some margin of safety (Castellani *et al.* 1953; Webster and Esselen 1956; Rogers and Gunderson 1958A, B). The roasting process should be completed in one operation. Interruption of roasting introduces the possibility that the internal temperature will favor bacterial multiplication during the interruption. This may lead to spoilage or to such large numbers of bacteria that the final cook will not kill all of them. After cooking, birds may be allowed to remain at room temperature for 20 min. to take advantage of the rise of 5° to 10° F. (2.8° to 5.6°C.) that occurs in the center of the stuffing during this holding.

The growth of acid-producing microorganisms during defrosting of stuffed poultry is fast enough to prevent or inhibit the growth of spores of a putrefactive anaerobe of the genus Clostridium inoculated into poultry stuffing (Esselen and Levine 1954).

Laboratory tests have shown that recommended roasting treatments adequately destroy food poisoning organisms in frozen and thawed birds of various weights. Stuffed, ready-to-cook turkeys ranging in weight from 6 to 15 lb. (including stuffing) and Cornish Cross broad breasted chickens weighing 2½ lb. were roasted in open pans in a 325°F. (163°C.) oven (Esselen *et al.* 1956). Thawed birds were initially at 30° to 40°F. (−1° to 4° C.). The times required for roasting were 3¾ to 4 hr. for 6-lb. birds, 4½ to 5 hr. for 9–lb. birds, 5 to 5½ hr. for 12-lb. birds, and 5½ to 6 hr. for 15-lb. birds. Frozen turkeys initially at −5° to 5°F. (−20° to −15°C.) required 5 to 5½ hr., 6¼ to 6¾ hr., 7½ to 8 hr., and 8 to 8½ hr. at comparable weights. The thawed chickens required 2½ to 3 hr., the frozen ones, 3 to 3½ hr. All of these birds were considered to be of acceptable quality and had received more than sufficient heat to destroy potential food poisoning bacteria. In all cases cooking was fast enough so that the stuffing was in the temperature range of 50° to 120° F. (10° to 49°C.) (the zone most conducive to bacterial growth) less than 4 hr., the maximum permissible for safety. Birds weighing 12 to 15 lb. were removed from the oven when the stuffing temperature was 155°F. (68°C.); smaller birds were removed at 165°F. (74°C.). A temperature of 155°F. (68° C.) was considered adequate for the larger birds because the longer time required to cook them provided sufficient lethality. For larger turkeys (16–21 lb.) defrosted before roasting at 325°F. (163°C.), an adequate final temperature in the stuffing was reached when the thigh temperature reached 185°F. (85°C.) (Hoke and Kleve 1966).

Precautions to be observed in preparing stuffed poultry are included in the U.S. Dept. of Agr. Poultry Inspector's Handbook (Anon. 1964B).

These products are usually encased in a bag which is shrunk by heat and blast frozen.

### POULTRY ROLLS AND ROASTS

Over 200 million pounds of turkeys (ready-to-cook weight) were further processed in this country in 1964, and a major part was used for boneless rolls (Wilkinson and Dawson 1967). Six million pounds of institutional-size cooked turkey roasts and 30 million pounds of retail-size raw turkey roasts were produced in 1964 (Franklin 1965). In 1965, 34,800,000 of retail-size roasts were produced, with a dollar value of over 36 million (Anon. 1966).

The increasing demand for poultry rolls during the last ten years reflects the increasing demand for convenience products. Roasts prepared from de-boned birds have relatively low transportation costs and are convenient to handle, store, and use. They require less labor in the home or institution and shorter cooking time. They provide superior portion control, eliminate waste, and have the same potential for variety of uses as does the whole bird. They are available as light meat only, dark meat only, or a mixture of light and dark meat. For many of the newer roasts and rolls on the market, the pieces of meat which make up the roast have been pretreated before cooking so that after cooking uniform whole slices can be obtained which do not fall apart. The meat is treated with phosphates, and the surface cells of the meat pieces are abraded by various means. Most retail-size roasts weigh between 2 and 3 lb., institutional-size rolls are larger (Fig. 19).

The following specifications for labeling of poultry rolls have been published by the U.S. Dept. of Agr. (Anon. 1965A).

**Poultry rolls.**—(1) Binding agents, including but not limited to gelatin and wheat gluten, may be added in quantities not in excess of a total of 3% for cooked rolls and 2% for raw rolls, based on the total ingredients used in the preparation of the product, without affecting the name of the product. However, when such agents are added in excess of 3 or 2%, whichever is applicable, the common name of the agent or the term "Binders Added" shall be included in the name of the product; e.g., "Turkey Roll—Gelatin Added."

(2) With respect to heat-processed rolls, two per cent or less liquid based on the weight of the finished product without liquid may remain with or be returned to product labeled as "(Kind) Roll."

*Courtesy of San Joaquin Valley Turkey Growers' Assoc.*

Fig. 19.  Turkey Roasts, ready to serve.

(3) Heat-processed rolls which have more than two per cent liquid remaining with or returned to the product shall be labeled as "(Kind) Roll with Natural Juices." If any liquid other than natural cookout juices is added, the product must be labeled to indicate that fact; e.g., "Turkey Roll with Broth." Liquid shall not be returned or added to product within this subdivision (3) in excess of the amount normally cooked out during preparation.

Specifications have also been published by the armed forces for procurement of cooked, frozen, boneless turkey (Anon. 1954).

Proposed amendments to the regulations governing the grading and inspection of poultry and edible poultry products (Anon. 1965B) include the following description of Grade A quality poultry roast labeled with terms such as " Ready-to-Cook Roasts," "Rolls," "Bars," or "Logs."

(a) The deboned poultry meat used in the preparation of the product shall be from young poultry of A Quality with respect to fleshing and fat covering.

(b) All tendons, cartilage, large blood vessels, blood clots, and discolorations shall be trimmed from the meat.

(c) All pinfeathers, bruises, hair, discolorations, and blemishes shall be removed from the skin, and where necessary, excess fat shall be removed from the skin covering the crop area or other areas.

(d) Seventy-five per cent or more of the outer surface of the product shall be covered with skin, whether attached to the meat or used as a wrap. The skin shall not appreciably overlap at any point. Product packaged in an oven-ready pan or container need have only the entire exposed surface of the roast covered with skin. The combined weight of the skin and fat used to cover the outer surface and that used as a binder shall not exceed 15% of the total net weight of the product.

(e) The product shall be fabricated in such a manner that each slice remains substantially intact (does not separate into more than three parts) when sliced warm after cooking. This may be accomplished by use of large pieces of poultry or by use of approved binders.

(f) Seasoning or flavor enhancers, if used, shall be uniformly distributed.

(g) Product shall be fabricated or tied in such a manner that it will retain its shape after defrosting and cooking.

(h) Packaging shall be neat and attractive.
(i) Product shall be practically free of weepage after packaging and/or freezing, and, if frozen, shall have a bright, desirable color.

Methods of boning turkeys for the preparation of rolls have been described and illustrated by several authors (Joule and Forward 1959; Fry et al. 1964; Dawson 1964). The use of large birds with an eviscerated weight of 24 lb. or more is generally recommended in order to reduce labor costs and to obtain a meat yield of 60% or better. Such a bird should yield two 7- to 8-lb. rolls. Excess fat, the outer wing sections, tail, neck, and giblets are not used. The remainder of the bird is deboned, tendons are removed, and skin and meat divided into portions for two rolls. One method of forming rolls is to place skin in the lower half of a two-part cylindrical mold cut in half lengthwise. Meat is arranged on the skin, seasonings are added, followed by the remainder of the meat. The skin is folded over the meat, and the top half of the cylinder used to apply pressure while the roll is tied. Rolls may be wrapped in heat-shrinkable bags before chilling and freezing. Stretch-type bags are commonly used for packing hot rolls.

The internal temperature to which turkey roasts, rolls, bars, or logs should be cooked depends upon two considerations: (1) the heating required for destruction of pathogenic bacteria and; (2) the progressive loss in weight and juiciness that occurs with increasing heat treatment.

A number of variations in cooking methods have been tested to determine their effect on quality and yield of rolls of varying size and composition. The major effects of the variables tested were the expected progressive loss of weight and juiciness with increase in heat treatment (Augustine et al. 1962; Marquess et al. 1963; Fry et al. 1964; Bowers et al. 1965; Wilkinson and Dawson 1967). The last authors reported the most desirable juiciness in rolls roasted at 325°F. (163°C.) to an internal temperature of 160°F. (71°C.). Light meat roasts were more tender when cooked to 180°F. (82° C.), but became tougher and very dry when cooked to 190°F. (88°C.). Differences in tenderness and juiciness of roasts were less serious in dark than in light meat roasts.

The following cooking requirements for poultry rolls are specified by the U.S. Dept. of Agr. (Anon. 1965A):

" When poultry rolls are heat processed in any manner, cured and smoked, poultry rolls shall reach an internal temperature of at least 155°F. (68°C.) prior to being removed from the cooking media, and all other poultry rolls shall reach an internal temperature of at least 160°F. (71°C.), prior to being removed from the cooking media."

The temperature requirements are based on evidence that pathogenic bacteria are destroyed in poultry rolls heated to those temperatures. Rolls used for tests at Michigan State University were approximately 12 in. in length, 5 in. in diameter, and weighed 9 lb. The tests demonstrated that selected species of Salmonellae, Staphylococci, and Streptococci inoculated into commerically-prepared turkey rolls are destroyed when the rolls are cooked in an oven set at 225°F. (107°C.) to an internal temperature of 160° F. (71°C.) (Wilkinson *et al.* 1965). The internal temperature of the rolls increased several degrees after rolls were removed from the oven even when the rolls were immediately submerged in ice water.

Prevention of contamination after cooking, rapid chilling and freezing are required to insure safety and quality of cooked rolls. Dawson (1964) recommends that cooked rolls be ice-chilled and frozen in packages with low permeability characteristics. Rolls are usually frozen in an air blast (see Chapter 5, Vol. 1). Since flavor changes during frozen storage occur more rapidly in cooked than in uncooked rolls, storage at 0°F. ( −18°C.) or lower is recommended.

### FROZEN FRIED CHICKEN

Twenty-one million pounds of breaded and precooked poultry were produced in 1964 for the retail market and 22 million pounds for the institutional market (Franklin 1965). Frozen fried chicken is the most popular poultry product of this type. However, because the shape of the cooked chicken pieces prevents a "solid pack" and permits exposure of large surface areas of the chicken to the atmosphere within the package, oxidative changes take place relatively rapidly, making fried chicken one of the least stable of frozen prepared poultry products. The fairly rapid rate of off-flavor development dictates the need to store this product at low temperatures even for relatively short times.

The stability studies conducted on frozen fried chicken include determination of the rates and kinds of flavor changes that occur in products stored for periods of two weeks to one year at temperatures ranging from −10° to 20°F. ( −23° to −6.6°C.) (Hanson *et al.* 1959). The flavor stability was approximately the same for two commercial lots and one lot prepared in the laboratory. The first flavor change was loss of the "freshly cooked" chicken flavor in about two months at 0°F. ( −18°C.) Staleness developed in about four months, and rancid flavors in about nine months at 0°F. ( −18°C.). At 10°F. ( −12°C.) off-flavors developed more rapidly: staleness in about two months and rancidity in about six months. Peroxide development tended to parallel off-flavor development as storage times and temperatures were increased. Adverse flavor changes and increases in peroxide values occur in the meat as well as in the skin and coating, indicating that flavor instability is not a problem of the skin layer only (Hanson *et al.* 1959; Carlin *et al.* 1959). The latter authors found for 15 weeks' storage at 0°F. ( −18°C.) that flavor changes occurred to approximately the same extent whether precooked broilers were packaged in Cryovac bags, polyethylene bags, or aluminum freezer foil. Commercially fried chicken removed from the retail package and hermetically sealed in cans in nitrogen showed little or no rancid flavor development during frozen storage (Hanson et al. 1959). The slight staleness that develops under this condition is probably not sufficient to be detected by most consumers. Inert gas packing to preserve flavor in precooked frozen products is not used to any extent, but it may well be a practical method of preventing rancidity in high-cost food with an otherwise limited storage life.

The tendency of batter coatings to peel or loosen from cooked poultry is accentuated in precooked frozen products. Failure of the coating to adhere after reheating results in a nonuniform appearance and complicates serving and handling. The peeling tendency of coatings on frozen fried chicken can be almost eliminated by cooking the poultry before application of the batter (Hanson and Fletcher 1963). Ordinary batter coatings generally form a loose fitting cover on the meat, because the coating sets before the cooking shrinkage occurs. Shrinkage of the pieces by a partial cook before application of the coating results in a form-fitting cover which resists peeling and has less tendency to stick to the container in which it is frozen. Variations in formula of the coating influence adhesive quality, thickness, appearance, and consistency, but no variation is as effective as preshrinking to reduce the peeling tendency. Thickness increases with the solids-water ratio in the batter and the number of coating layers applied. Peeling tendency increases with increasing thickness of the coating. Waxy cereal thickening agents produce more elastic coatings than those from common cereals, and inclusion of waxy or common cornstarch improves adhesive qualities more than other cereals tested. Egg yolk content of the coating influences color but has little effect on adhesion. Mixtures of thickening agents were suggested as a means of obtaining the various attributes desired.

Recommendations for producing fried poultry products are contained in the U.S. Dept. of Agr. Poultry Inspector's Handbook (Anon. 1964B).

### CHICKEN SALAD AND OTHER PRECOOKED POULTRY PRODUCTS

The amount of handling involved in preparing chicken salad gives ample opportunity for bacterial contamination. Since chicken salad is frequently served in warm weather, bacterial growth may occur fairly rapidly if the food is left unrefrigerated very long. Chicken salad has often been implicated in food poisoning outbreaks and has been the subject of microbiological investigations to determine conditions necessary for its safe handling (Lewis et al. 1953; Winter et al. 1953). The time required for cooling from room to refrigerator temperature is the most critical factor. Approximately three hours are required for chicken salad four inches deep in a shallow pan to reach refrigerator temperature (41°F.; 5°C.) when moved from room temperature or to reach room temperature when moved from the refrigerator. A 10-lb. bowl of salad required 6 hr., and a 30-lb. can of salad required more than 24 hr. Chicken salad kept below 50°F. (10°C.) showed little or no increase in bacterial count after 72 hr. The value of cooling the salad rapidly in shallow pans is obvious. There was also no appreciable increase in standard plate counts or Salmonella counts in shallow pans of chicken salad held alternately 6 hr. at 80°F. (26.7°C.) and 18 hr. at 41°F. (5°C.) during a three-day holding period.

A number of other precooked frozen chicken, turkey, and goose meat products have been proposed or prepared on a limited commercial scale. These include chicken cooked with various barbecue sauces or spices, boneless or stuffed baked chicken breast, stuffed boneless turkey leg, barbecued meat, chicken and turkey loaves, creamed and roasted goose, patties, burgers, fillets, sausages, and frozen smoked turkey (Strandine 1963; Kovac and Morse 1955; Bean and Hanson 1962; Baker *et al.* 1966) (Figs. 20, 21, 22).

Courtesy of New York State College of Agriculture at Cornell University

Fig. 20. Chicken salami.

Courtesy of New York State College of Agriculture at Cornell University

Fig. 21. "Bake and serve" chicken loaf.

Courtesy of New York State College of Agriculture at Cornell University

Fig. 22. Chicken hash.

Specifications have been established by the U.S. Dept. of Agr. for amounts of meat required in various poultry meat products with skin and fat not in excess of natural proportions (Anon. 1965A). Products containing fillers or binders are to be named "Patties." Specifications for other items which contain poultry meat are given in Table 21.

Table 21

Other Frozen Products Containing Poultry Meat

| | Min. % Cooked Poultry Meat of Kind Indicated | |
|---|---|---|
| Product Name[1] | Deboned | Including Bone |
| (Kind) ravioli | 2 | — |
| (Kind) soup | 2 | — |
| Chop suey with (kind) | 2 | — |
| (Kind) chop suey | 4 | — |
| (Kind) chow mein without noodles | 4 | — |
| (Kind) tamales | 6 | — |
| Noodles or dumplings with (kind)[2] | 6 | — |
| (Kind) stew | 12 | — |
| (Kind) fricassee of wings | — | 40 |
| (Kind) noodles or dumplings[2] | 15 | 30 |
| Creamed (kind) | 20 | — |
| (Kind) cacciatore | 20 | 40 |
| (Kind) fricassee | 20 | 40 |
| (Kind) à-la-king | 20 | — |
| Sliced (kind) with gravy | 35 | — |
| Minced (kind) barbecue | 40 | — |

[1] The product name may contain other appropriate descriptive terms such as "noodle"; e.g., "chicken noodle soup."
[2] Product also includes rice or similar starches.

Terminology has been established by the U.S. Dept. of Agr. governing the labeling of poultry products differing in their proportions of light and dark meat (Anon. 1965A). If a product contains light and dark meat in other than natural proportions, a qualifying statement of composition is usually required. The terminology, given in Table 22, has been specified

Table 22

Labeling Terminology

| Terminology | % Light Meat | % Dark Meat |
|---|---|---|
| Natural proportions | 50–65 | 50–35 |
| Light or white meat | 100 | 0 |
| Dark meat | 0 | 100 |
| Light and dark meat | 51–65 | 49–35 |
| Dark and light meat | 35–49 | 65–51 |
| Mostly white meat | 66 or more | 34 or less |
| Mostly dark meat | 34 or less | 66 or more |

for the light and dark meat combinations indicated. If the cooked, cooled poultry meat to be used in poultry products does not have 34% solids, excluding salt, the percentage of poultry meat required in the food must be increased in proportion to the deficiency.

## BIBLIOGRAPHY

Anon. 1954. Turkey, boneless, frozen (cooked). Military Specification *MIL-T-35006*, Sept. 14.
Anon. 1964A. Meal, precooked, frozen. Military Specification *MIL-M-13966C*, Dec. 30.
Anon. 1964B. Poultry Inspector's Handbook, U.S. Dept. Agr., Agr. Marketing Service, Poultry Division, Inspection Branch.
Anon. 1965A. Regulations governing the inspection of poultry and poultry products. Poultry Division, Agr. Marketing Service, U.S. Dept. Agr., Jan. 1.
Anon. 1965B. Proposed Amendments. Federal Register May 7. (7CFR, Part 70).
Anon. 1966. Turkey roasts, Rock Cornish hens gain; 1965 frozen poultry pack plateaus. Quick Frozen Foods 29, No. 4, 79–80.
Augustine, G. M., Carlin, A. F., and Marquess, C. G. 1962. Quality of whole turkey and turkey rolls. J. Am. Dietet. Assoc. 41, 443–447.
Baker, R. C., Darrah, L. B., and Darfler, J. M. 1966. The use of fowl for convenience items. Poultry Sci. 45, 1017–1025.
Bean, M. L., and Hanson, H. L. 1962. Utilization of geese. 2. Precooked frozen foods. Poultry Sci. 41, 243–249.
Bowers, J. R., Goertz, G. E., and Fry, J. L. 1965. Effect of cooking method and skewers on quality of turkey roll. Poultry Sci. 44, 789–793.
Bowmer, E. J. 1965. Salmonellae in food.—A review. J. Milk Food Technol. 28, 74–86.
Buchbinder, L., Loughlin, V., Walter, M., and Dangler, G. 1949. A survey of frozen precooked foods with special reference to chicken à la king. J. Milk Food Technol. 12, 209–213, 231.
Canale-Parola, E., and Ordal, Z. J. 1957. A survey of the bacteriological quality of frozen poultry pies. Food Technol. 11, 578–582.
Carlin, A. F., Pangborn, R. M., Cotterill, O. J., and Homeyer, P. G. 1959. Effect of pretreatment and type of packaging material on quality of frozen fried chicken. Food Technol. 13, 557–560.
Castellani, A. G., Clarke, R. R., Gibson, M. I., and Meisner, D. F. 1953. Roasting time and temperature required to kill food poisoning microorganisms introduced experimentally into stuffing in turkeys. Food Research 18, 131–138.
Cornell University, School of Hotel Administration. 1965. Ready foods. The Cornell Hotel and Restaurant Administration Quarterly 6, No. 2, 21–43.
Davis, J. G., Hanson, H. L., and Lineweaver, H. 1952. Characterization of the effect of freezing on cooked egg white. Food Research 17, 393–401.
Dawson, L. E. 1964. Quality in turkey rolls. Turkey World 39, No. 7, 42, 44.
Esselen, W. B., Jr., and Levine, A. S. 1954. Bacteriological investigations of frozen stuffed poultry. J. Milk Food Technol. 17, 245–250, 255.
Esselen, W. B., Jr., Levine, A. S., and Brushway, M. 1956. Adequate roasting procedures for frozen stuffed poultry. J. Am. Dietet. Assoc. 32, 1162–1166.
Fanelli, M. J., and Ayres, J. C. 1959. Methods of detection and effect of freezing on the microflora of chicken pies. Food Technol. 13, 294–300.

Franklin, H. F. 1965. What the American consumer uses per capita in frozen foods. Quick Frozen Foods 28, No. 5, 36–41.

Fry, J. L., Goertz, G. E., Taylor, M. H., and Hooper, A. S. 1964. A comparison of cooking methods for boneless turkey rolls and bars. Poultry Sci. 43, 1572–1577.

Hanson, H. L., Brushway, M. J., and Lineweaver, H. 1960A. Monosodium glutamate studies. I. Factors affecting detection of and preference for added glutamate in foods. Food Technol. 14, 320–327.

Hanson, H. L., Brushway, M. J., and Lineweaver, H. 1960B. Monosodium glutamate studies. II. Evaluation of a possible stabilizing effect of glutamate in frozen foods and of the stability of glutamate to commercial canning process. Food Technol. 14, 328–332.

Hanson, H. L., and Fletcher, L. R. 1958. Time-temperature tolerance of frozen foods. XII. Turkey dinners and turkey pies. Food Technol. 12, 40–43.

Hanson, H. L., and Fletcher, L. R. 1963. Adhesion of coatings on frozen fried chicken. Food Technol. 17, 115–118.

Hanson, H. L., Fletcher, L. R., and Lineweaver, H. 1959. Time-temperature tolerance of frozen foods. XVII. Frozen fried chicken. Food Technol. 13, 221–224.

Hanson, H. L., Winegarden, H. M., Horton, M. B., and Lineweaver, H. 1950. Preparation and storage of frozen cooked poultry and vegetables. Food Technol. 4, 430–434.

Hoke, I. M., and Kleve, M. K. 1966. Heat penetration, quality, and yield of turkeys roasted to different internal thigh temperatures. J. Home Econ. 58, 381–384.

Hucker, G. J., and David, E. R. 1957. The effect of alternate freezing and thawing on the total flora of frozen chicken pies. Food Technol. 11, 354–356.

Joule, T. and Forward, J. F. 1959. How to bone a turkey. Turkey World 34, No. 4, 18–21.

Kovac, G. M., and Morse, R. E. 1955. They turned by-products into profitable co-products. Food Eng. 27, No. 11, 72–73.

Lewis, M. N., Weiser, H. H., and Winter, A. R. 1953. Bacterial growth in chicken salad. J. Am. Dietet. Assoc. 29, 1094–1099.

Lineweaver, H., Anderson, J. D., and Hanson, H. L. 1952. Effect of antioxidant on rancidity development in frozen creamed turkey. Food Technol. 6, 1–4.

Litsky, W., Fagerson, I. S., and Fellers, C. R. 1957. A bacteriological survey of commercially frozen beef, poultry, and tuna pies. J. Milk Food Technol. 20, 216–219.

Logan, P. P., Harp, C. H., and Dove, W. F. 1951. Keeping quality of precooked frozen chicken à la king—A bacteriological evaluation of hot and cold packs. Food Technol. 5, 193–198.

Marquess, C. G., Carlin, A. F., and Augustine, G. M. 1963. Factors affecting the quality of roasted turkey rolls. Food Technol. 17, 1582–1587.

Martin, S. 1966. Why one factor will force up frozen food prices next year. Quick Frozen Foods 29, No. 2, 39–42, 148.

Mecchi, E. P., Pool, M. F., Behman, G. A., Hamachi, M., and Klose, A. A. 1956A. The role of tocopherol content in the comparative stability of chicken and turkey fat. Poultry Sci. 35, 1238–1246.

Mecchi, E. P., Pool, M. F., Nonaka, M., Klose, A. A., Marsden, S. J., and Lillie, R. J. 1956B. Further studies on tocopherol content and stability of carcass fat of chickens and turkeys. Poultry Sci. 35, 1246–1251.

Mountney, G. J. 1966. Poultry Products Technology. Avi Publishing Co., Westport, Conn.

Ott, T. M., El-Bisi, H. M., and Esselen, W. B. 1961. Thermal destruction of *Streptococcus faecalis* in prepared frozen foods. J. Food Sci. *26*, 1–10.

Peterson, A. C., Black, J. J., and Gunderson, M. F. 1962. Staphylococci in competition. I. Growth of naturally occuring mixed population in precooked frozen foods during defrost. Appl. Microbiol. *10*, 16–22.

Proctor, B. E., and Phillips, A. W., Jr. 1947. Microbiological aspects of frozen precooked foods. Refrig. Eng. *53*, 30–33, 68.

Rogers, R. E., and Gunderson, M. F. 1958A. Roasting of frozen stuffed turkeys. I. Survival of *Salmonella pullorum* in inoculated stuffing. Food Research *23*, 87–95.

Rogers, R. E., and Gunderson, M. F. 1958B. Roasting of frozen stuffed turkeys. II. Survival of *Micrococcus pyogenes* var. *aureus* in inoculated stuffing. Food Research *23*, 96–102.

Straka, R. P., and Combes, F. M. 1952. Survival and multiplication of *Micrococcus pyogenes* var. *aureus* in creamed chicken under various holding, storage and defrosting conditions. Food Research *17*, 448–455.

Strandine, E. J. 1963. Poultry production and processing. *In* Food Processing Operations, Vol. 2, J. L. Heid, and M. A. Joslyn (Editors). Avi Publishing Co., Westport, Conn.

Tressler, D. K., and Evers, C. F. 1957. The Freezing Preservation of Foods, 3rd Edition, Vol. 2. Avi Publishing Co., Westport, Conn.

Webster, R. C., and Esselen, W. B., Jr. 1956. Thermal resistance of food poisoning organisms in poultry stuffing. J. Milk Food Technol. *19*, No. 8, 209–212.

Wilkinson, R. J., Mallman, W. L., Dawson, L. E., Irmiter, T. F., and Davidson, J. A. 1965. Effective heat processing for destruction of pathogenic bacteria in turkey rolls. Poultry Sci. *44*, 131, 136.

Wilkinson, R. J., and Dawson, L. E. 1967. Tenderness and juiciness of turkey roasts cooked to different temperatures. Poultry Sci. *46*, 15–18.

Winter, A. R., Weiser, H. H., and Lewis, M. 1953. The control of bacteria in chicken salad. II. Salmonella. Appl. Microbiol. *1*, No. 6, 278–281.

Woodburn, M., Bennion, M., and Vail, G. E. 1962. Destruction of Salmonellae and Staphylococci in precooked poultry products by heat treatment before freezing. Food Technol. *16*, No. 6, 98–100.

## CHAPTER 8

Donald K. Tressler

# Prepared and Precooked
# Fruit Products

## INTRODUCTION

A great variety of prepared and precooked fruit products are frozen. The list includes not only pies (covered in Chapter 19), sherbets and ices (Chapter 20), baby foods (Chapter 15), but cobblers, fritters, jellies and spreads, pectinized purées, pie fillings, shortcakes, relishes, toppings or sundae sauces, Velva Fruit, confections, sauces, and various specialty items such as baked apples. Freezing retains the color and flavor of many prepared and precooked fruits far better than does canning. Even strawberry shortcake can be preserved satisfactorily by freezing (see p. 452).

Woodroof and Atkinson (1945) carried out a study of the desirability of eight fruits which were cooked in one of three ways and held in freezing storage for a year. They concluded that apples, blueberries, blackberries, cherries, and raspberries were excellent when cooked by immersion in boiling 50% sugar syrup for 15 sec. Apples also were excellent when steamed in a closed container for 90 sec. When these fruits were steamed in an open vessel, considerable flavor was lost and they became more watery. The loss of flavor by steaming in an open vessel was caused both by leaching and the distilling off of the flavors.

Plums, pears, and soft-flesh (Elberta type) freestone peaches were less desirable as preheated products, except when prepared as a purée or a solid pack. Woodroof and Atkinson also found that unpeeled plums were delicious when heated enough to produce sufficient juice to cover the halves (see Table 23).

Woodroof and Atkinson concluded that not only certain fruits may be preheated before freezing, but that apples, blueberries, raspberries, blackberries, and plums are superior when so treated, provided proper methods of heating and suitable packages are used. Preheated fruits should be solid packed, without bubbles or air spaces, in rigid, leakproof moisture-proof containers.

## APPLES

**Apples, Peeled Whole**

Esselen, Fellers, and McConnell (1949) report that peeled whole apples have been found to make a tasty and colorful salad or dessert fruit, and recommend the following preparation procedure:

Donald K. Tressler is a consultant and President of the Avi Publishing Co., Westport, Conn.

Table 23

The Desirability of 25 Frozen Fruit Products After One Year in Storage
at 0°F. ( − 18°C.)

| Fruit | Treatment | Form Packed[1] | Desirability |
|-------|-----------|----------------|--------------|
| Apple | cooked | butter, solid pack | excellent |
| Apple | cooked | sauce, solid pack | excellent |
| Apple | steamed | stew, semisolid pack | good |
| Apple | steamed | slices, loose pack | fair |
| Apple | boiling syrup | slices, solid pack | excellent |
| Apple | none | slices | poor, discolored |
| Apricot | steamed | halves, semisolid pack | good |
| Blackberry | steamed | whole, semisolid pack | good, color loss |
| Blackberry | boiling syrup | whole, solid pack | excellent |
| Blackberry | none | whole | fair, bitter |
| Blueberry | steamed | whole, semisolid pack | good |
| Blueberry | boiling syrup | whole, solid pack | excellent |
| Blueberry | none | whole, loose pack | poor, flavorless |
| Cherry | steamed | seeded, loose pack | fair, color loss |
| Cherry | boiling syrup | seeded, semisolid pack | excellent |
| Peach | | | |
|   Firm-flesh | steamed | slices, solid pack | good |
|   Firm-flesh | boiling syrup | slices, solid pack | very good |
|   Soft-flesh | steamed | slices, solid pack | poor, flavorless |
|   Soft-flesh | boiling syrup | slices, solid pack | fair, flavorless |
| Plum | steamed | seeded, semisolid pack | fair, flavorless |
| Plum | boiling syrup | seeded, semisolid pack | good |
| Plum | steamed | seeded, solid pack | excellent |
| Raspberry | steamed | whole, semisolid pack | fair, color loss |
| Raspberry | boiling syrup | whole, solid pack | excellent |
| Raspberry | none | whole, loose pack | fair, bitter |

Source: Woodroof and Atkinson (1945).
[1] The amount of sugar added to the various fruits varied, but all lots of the same fruit received the same amount.

"McIntosh apples were washed, peeled, and cored according to the method of Lee (1947), in which the blossom end is left on the apples. The apples were then cooked slowly in a 40 or 50% sugar syrup containing 0.1% calcium chloride until they were cooked through (approximately 5 to 8 min.). The apples were then cooled on a screen by a cold air blast. When cool, the apples were placed in paper cups such as are sometimes used for canned or frozen baked apples. The apples may be packaged and frozen immediately or the core cavities filled with an appropriate filling prior to freezing."

"After they are thawed out, the apples may be filled as desired by the consumer. In practice, we have found that whole cranberry sauce or fresh cranberry-orange relish makes a colorful filling and the flavor combination with the apple is quite acceptable."

## Baked Apples

Freezing preserves very well the flavor, color, and texture of baked apples, but as yet the product is not very popular.

Lee (1947) has studied the varietal suitability of some important New York State apples for use in the production of frozen baked apples. The varieties studied by Lee include Cortland, Rome Beauty, Rhode Island

Greening, Twenty Ounce, Red Twenty Ounce, McIntosh, Baldwin, and Northern Spy. In preparing the apples, Lee cored them in the usual fashion, cutting out the core from the stem end, but leaving the blossom end undisturbed, so as to prevent loss of syrup during the baking process. The skin was peeled off the top of the apple. The prepared apples were divided into four lots. To the core cavity of each apple in one lot was added approximately one-half ounce of a granulated sugar-ground cinnamon mixture (approximately 99% sugar and 1% cinnamon). A second lot of apples· received approximately ⅛ oz. lemon juice and a mixture of granulated sugar and nutmeg. A third lot was treated with brown sugar only. The fourth lot was sweetened by the addition of pure maple syrup to the core cavity. The prepared apples were baked at 400°F. (204°C.) until soft. After cooling, the apples were packed into quart-size Lily-Tulip cups, three to a cup, placing two pieces of moisture-proof Cellophane on top of each of the apples except the top one, which was covered with a single sheet of Cellophane before the insertion of the carton lid. The baked apples were stored for six months and then examined. The Cortland apples received the highest quality rating. The Rome Beauty, Baldwin, and Twenty Ounce were also rated high. In the case of the lots sweetened with either brown sugar or maple syrup, the Red Twenty Ounce and Northern Spy apples also received an excellent rating.

Rasmussen, Esselen, and Fellers (1948) compared the quality of frozen baked McIntosh, Baldwin, and Northern Spy apples. They concluded that Baldwin and Northern Spy apples retained their shape very well without added calcium but noted that frozen baked McIntosh apples were quite soft and mushy and did not retain their shape if prepared without added calcium chloride. However, satisfactory frozen baked apples of good texture can be prepared from the McIntosh variety if 0.05 to 0.10% of calcium chloride is used to maintain firmness.

## Scalloped Apples

One of the leading packers of high-quality precooked frozen foods has introduced frozen scalloped apples and found a market for the product. Scalloped apples are prepared by covering the greased bottom of an aluminum foil container with bread crumbs to which melted butter has been added. Then the container is half filled with sliced apples which are sprinkled with sugar, nutmeg, lemon juice, and grated lemon rind. After this, the container is filled with sliced apples which are again sprinkled with sugar, nutmeg, lemon juice, and grated lemon peel. The sliced apples are covered with buttered bread crumbs, and then baked for 40 min. in a moderate oven.

## AVOCADO PASTE OR GUACAMOLE

McColloch, Nielsen, and Beavens (1951) have worked out the following simple method of preparing and freezing a frozen avocado product called guacamole:

"Sound ripe fruit is thoroughly washed, preferably with a good detergent, and rinsed well with cold water so as to reduce microbial contamination to a minimum. The fruit is pared and all discolored spots, damaged portions, and the seed are removed. The fruit is then puréed by sieving or passing through a grinder. Sieving gives a product with a smoother texture, but many persons prefer the coarser texture produced from grinding. The avocado purée is then mixed with lemon or lime juice, salt, and onion powder in the following proportions (by weight):

|  | Parts |
|---|---|
| Avocado purée | 100 |
| Lemon or lime juice | 8–10[1] |
| Salt (sodium chloride) | 1–2[1] |
| Dehydrated onion powder | 0.3[2] |

The ingredients are blended and the finished product filled into a suitable container and frozen at 0° to −10°F. (−18° to −23°C.)."

When lime juice is employed instead of lemon juice, the amount added should be sufficient to bring the mixture to pH 4.5 for the preservation of green color.

Avocado paste finds its principal use as a spread to be used on canapés, potato chips, and crackers. See also Chapter 4, Volume 3.

## COCKTAILS AND SALADS

Heat-processed fruit cocktail and salad are very popular canned fruit items. Much frozen fruit is used by the homemaker, institutions, and restaurants as components in making so-called fresh fruit cocktails and salads. Often these cocktails and salads are mixtures of fresh and frozen fruits; sometimes canned fruits are also used as components.

Cruess, Afifi, and Glazewsky (1948) studied the freezing of a cocktail mix of the type commonly canned. The mix consisted of diced peaches and pears, pineapple pieces, sliced Maraschino cherries, and whole Thompson Seedless grapes. Half of each lot was packed in 40° Brix syrup without heating the fruit; half was heated in the syrup to boiling for about five minutes, cooled, and then packed. Some was canned, heat-processed, and

---

[1] These values represent the permissible range in the present formula for satisfactory retention of color for six months or more in the frozen state.

[2] Quantity may be varied according to taste, or the onion powder may be omitted if desired. Garlic powder may be used to vary the flavor of the product.

stored at 80°F. (26°C.). Cruess, Afifi, and Glazewsky report that, after one year's storage in cans at 0°F. (−18°C.) the raw cocktail had developed a noticeable hay-like flavor and odor, that which had been heated was unchanged from its original flavor and was much superior in flavor to that which had been preserved by sterilization by heat in cans.

Molded fruit salads can be prepared either from a mixture of frozen or fresh fruits. If frozen fruits are used, the fruits are thawed and drained. Gelatin, which has been dissolved in warm water and a little ascorbic acid, are added to the drained syrup. The drained fruits are mixed in the desired proportions. The fruit mixture is placed in cartons or other containers. The syrup containing the gelatin is allowed to cool until it forms a soft jelly, and is then poured over the fruit mixture in the cartons, which are then closed, overwrapped, and placed in a freezer.

The procedure is much the same if fresh fruit is used, except for the preliminary preparation of the fruit and the addition of corn or sugar syrup. Soft-ripe fruit is selected and washed. Pineapples are peeled, cored, sliced, and cut into pieces of the proper size. Peaches are peeled (see Chap. 3, Volume 3), pitted, and sliced. Sweet cherries are pitted. Seedless grapes are stemmed. Maraschino cherries are sliced. Pears are peeled, cored, and sliced. The fruits are mixed together. Gelatin and a small amount of ascorbic acid are dissolved in warm water. The solution of gelatin and ascorbic acid is mixed with corn or sugar syrup and the solution allowed to cool until it forms a soft jelly. The fruit mixture is placed in cartons or other containers, covered with the soft jelly. The containers are closed and placed in the freezer.

### FRUIT SALADS IN DEFROST POUCHES

A noteworthy new method of packaging, freezing, and defrosting fruit salad and prepared fruits has been introduced by three important packers of frozen fruits. This method involves the packing of the fruit salad to which has been added a little sugar and ascorbic acid, or a small amount of a sugar syrup containing a little ascorbic acid, in a heat-sealable polyethylene pouch, pulling a high vacuum, then sealing the pouch, after which it is packaged in a rectangular carton and quick frozen. When desired for use by the housewife, the pouch is immersed in a pan of running cold water, or lukewarm water, until the fruit is thawed but is still cold.

The packaging of the fruit under a vacuum maintains the color and flavor of the product almost perfectly. Rapid freezing and rapid thawing of the fruit aids materially in retaining both the color and flavor and also results in a product of better texture than that obtained if the fruit is thawed slowly while exposed to air.

## PIE FILLINGS

Heat-processed, canned pie fillings have long been an important article of commerce. On the other hand, fruits are commonly prepared for freezing either as whole, halved, or sliced fruit, or as fruit purée. The housewife or the baker uses these frozen fruits in making the pie fillings. If the frozen fruit packer would prepare and freeze the complete pie fillings, one step would be eliminated and pies of superior flavor should result. At present, some blueberry, elderberry, and pumpkin pie fillings are frozen, but as yet the business is relatively small.

Johnson (1950A) has studied the preparation of frozen fresh fruit pie mixes and published formulas and methods of preparation for the following mixes: apple, apricot, peach, red tart cherry, and blueberry. He recommends the use of either an Irish moss extractive or low methoxyl pectin. These thickening agents have a more definite gelling temperature and will not gel until the pie is cooled to this temperature. If low methoxyl pectin is used, approximately one-tenth as much monocalcium phosphate should be used. Johnson prefers fillings made with Irish moss extractives, since the latter make a very desirable clear soft gel. Johnson also recommends the use of ascorbic acid in the peach, apricot, apple, and cherry pie fillings. This antioxidant improves the flavor and prevents the discoloration of the fruit.

### Preparation of the Pie Mix

Johnson (1950A) indicates the following steps to be followed in preparing the dry mix:

"(1) A mixture containing the dry ingredients is first prepared. The sugar, thickening agent, antioxidant, and salt are thoroughly mixed. The composition of the dry mix may vary slightly with the particular fruit used but, in general, the composition will fall within the following limits: 2 to 3 lb. of Irish moss extractive (or 2.5 to 3.5 lb. of low methoxyl pectin containing 0.25 to 0.3 lb. of monocalcium phosphate), 0.2 lb. ascorbic acid, and 0.5 lb. of sugar. (2) The prepared fresh fruit is then mixed with the correct amount of the dry mixture. The mixture of the dry ingredients should be added in such a manner that uniform distribution is obtained for better protection of the fruit. This uniform distribution is more important for peaches than for some of the other fruits. . .

"When using cans, the dry mix can be added as the fruit is packed. Care should be taken to add the last part of the dry mix on top. (3) After the fruit and dry mix are packaged, it is frozen immediately and stored at 0°F. ($-18$°C.) or lower. The composition of the dry mix for various fruits is given in Table 24."

### Details of Preparation

**Apples.**—Apples are peeled and cored. Large apples should be sliced into 12 pieces and smaller ones into 8 pieces. The slices are dipped from 1

Table 24

Composition of Dry-Mix Given in Pounds

| Fruit | Wt. | Sugar | Irish Moss Extractive | Low Methoxyl Pectin | Monocalcium Phosphate (Anhydrous) | Ascorbic Acid | Salt |
|---|---|---|---|---|---|---|---|
| Apples | 100 lb. | 2.5 | — | — | 0.15 | 0.5 |  |
|  | " | — | 3.5 | 0.35 | " | " |  |
| Apricots | " | 2.25 | — | — | 0.2 | 0.5 |  |
|  | " | — | 3.5 | 0.35 | " | " |  |
| Cherries | " | 2.25 | — | — | 0.2 | 0.5 |  |
| (Red sour) | " | — | 3.5 | 0.35 | " | " |  |
| Peaches | " | 2.5 | — | — | 0.25 | 0.5 |  |
|  | " | — | 3.5 | 0.35 | " | " |  |
| Raspberries | " | 3.0 | — | — | — | 0.5 |  |
|  | " | — | 4.0 | 0.4 | — | " |  |
| Blueberries | " | 3.0 | — | — | — | 0.5 |  |
|  | " | — | 4.0 | 0.4 | — | " |  |

Source: Johnson (1950A).

to 2 min. in a bath containing 500 p.p.m. sulfur dioxide as sodium bisulfite and 0.25% citric acid. After draining, the slices are mixed with the dry mix in the proportion of 17 oz. of slices to 4.5 oz. of mix. This quantity is sufficient for a nine-inch pie.

**Apricots.**—Fully ripe apricots are washed, halved, pitted and then mixed with the dry mix in the proportion of 6 oz. of dry mix for each 20 oz. of halved apricots, which is a sufficient quantity for a 9-in. pie.

**Peaches.**—Soft ripe freestone peaches are peeled (see Chap. 3, Vol. 3) and cut into eight slices. Peach slices are mixed with the dry mix in the proportion of 1⅓ lb. of slices to 5 oz. of dry mix (enough for a 9-in. pie).

**Red Tart Cherries.**—Fully ripe cherries are chilled in ice water, washed, inspected, and pitted. The pitted cherries are mixed with the dry mix in the proportion of 1⅓ lb. of fruit to 6½ oz. of dry mix (enough for a 9-in. pie).

**Blueberries.**—After cleaning, washing, and inspecting the blueberries, they are mixed with the dry mix in the proportion of 18 oz. of berries to 4½ oz. dry mix (enough for a 9-in. pie).

## Baking of Pies from the Pie-Mix

If this pie-mix is packed in the right size cartons, each holding sufficient for a single pie, it is only necessary to thaw the fruit just enough so that the fruit pieces break apart readily. Then put the contents in a bowl and mix just enough to obtain a uniform mixture; place in an unbaked pie shell, put top crust in place, seal around edges and bake at 450°F. (232°C.) for 15 min. Reduce the temperature to 375°F. (190°C.) and continue baking for an additional 15 to 20 min.

## Pie Mix for Deep Dish Pies

## Cherry Pie Filling

Sayles and MacLennan (1965) give the following recipe and procedure for preparing and freezing filling for cherry pies.

### Ingredients per Deep Dish Pie

| | Oz. |
|---|---|
| Frozen cherries, thawed, well-drained | 8.00 |
| Cherry juice syrup | 2.75 |
| Vanilla extract | 0.10 |
| Orange "Tang" | 0.20 |
| Modified starch (e.g., "Purity 69") | 0.30 |

Procedure.—Slowly add the cherry juice syrup to the modified starch, add vanilla and "Tang." Heat to 180°F. (82°C.), stirring constantly. Combine cherries and syrup. Package in vacuum pouch, blast freeze.

## Apple Pie Filling

Sayles and MacLennan (1965) give the following recipe and procedure for preparation and freezing filling for deep dish apple pies.

### Ingredients per Deep Dish Apple Pie

| | Oz. |
|---|---|
| Apples, McIntosh, peeled, cored, and sliced | 6.0 |
| Lemon juice | 0.2 |
| Water | 3.5 |
| Sugar | 0.4 |
| Apple cider | 0.4 |
| Modified starch | 0.3 |
| Cinnamon | 0.05 |
| Orange "Tang" | 0.2 |
| Vanilla extract | 0.1 |

Procedure—Sprinkle lemon juice over apples. Cook slowly in covered saucepan 2-3 min. Combine water and sugar and cook 10–15 min. to reduce volume one-fourth. Slowly add cider to the modified starch and cinnamon. Stir until smooth. Add "Tang" and vanilla. Add to syrup. Heat to 180°F. (82°C.), stirring constantly. Combine apples and syrup. Package in vacuum pouch. Blast freeze.

## Blueberry Pie Filling

Sayles and MacLennan (1965) give the following recipe and procedure for preparing and freezing filling for blueberry pies.

**Ingredients per Deep Dish Pie**

|                                      | Oz. |
| ------------------------------------ | --- |
| Blueberries, fresh                   | 8.0 |
| Water                                | 3.5 |
| Sugar                                | 1.2 |
| Orange "Tang"                        | 0.2 |
| Vanilla extract                      | 0.1 |
| Modified starch (e.g., "Purity 69")  | 0.3 |

**Procedure.**—Combine half the water and sugar and cook 10–15 min. to reduce volume one-third. Slowly add remaining water to modified starch. Add to syrup. Heat to 180°F. (82°C.), stirring constantly. Combine blueberries and syrup. Package in vacuum pouch, blast freeze.

## Peach Pie Filling

**Ingredients per Deep Dish Peach Pie**

|                                      | Oz.  |
| ------------------------------------ | ---- |
| Peaches, canned, well-drained        | 8.75 |
| Water                                | 3.50 |
| Sugar                                | 1.20 |
| Orange "Tang"                        | 0.02 |
| Vanilla extract                      | 0.10 |
| Modified starch (e.g., "Purity 69")  | 0.30 |

**Procedure.**—Combine half of the water, and sugar and cook 10–15 min. to reduce volume one-third. Add "Tang" and vanilla. Slowly add remaining water to modified starch. Add to syrup. Heat to 180°F. (82°C.) stirring constantly. Combine peaches and syrup. Package in vacuum pouch. Blast freeze.

## PURÉES

### Frozen Purée Desserts

Many fruit purées, when diluted with sugar syrup and frozen rapidly, make delightful desserts of far better flavor and consistency than most sherbets and ices. Sorber (1942) recommends the following purée dilutions for use in the preparation of purées for dessert purposes:

| | |
|---|---|
| Cranberry, passion fruit | 1 vol. pulp—1 vol. 67% syrup |
| Montmorency cherry, Feijoa Loganberry, Santa Rosa and Claret plums, Boysenberry, strawberry, and Youngberry | 2 vols. pulp—1 vol. 67% syrup |

| | |
|---|---|
| Blackberry, Bing cherry, crabapple, Calimyrna fig, mango, New Boy nectarine, and Buerre Hardy pear | 3 vols. pulp—1 vol. 67% syrup |
| Hachiya persimmon | 4 vols. pulp—1 vol. 67% syrup |
| Apricot, Humbolt nectarine, and Ranaree raspberry | 1 vol. pulp—1 vol. 50% syrup |

In order to obtain a desirable dessert, it is essential to freeze the sweetened purée under conditions which will give a product of smooth texture. According to Sorber, the degree of smoothness depends upon: (1) the rate of heat exchange during freezing; (2) the percentage of water and soluble solids in the purée; (3) proportion, particle size, and distribution of insoluble solids (e.g., pulpy and colloidal material that make up the cellular structure of the fruit).

The nature of the protective colloids, e.g., pectin, and the amount of agitation employed during freezing are other important factors in controlling the smoothness of the frozen product.

When eaten at just the right temperature to have the proper degree of softness, these frozen sweetened fruit purées are delicious. If the products are too hard or are thawed, they are not pleasing. Since it is difficult to get the frozen purées at the right temperature, they may never be very popular.

**Velva Fruit.**—The Western Utilization Research Branch has suggested a different type of frozen dessert similar in composition to the pectinized purée, but containing gelatin instead of pectin as the stabilizer. The fruit purée-sugar-gelatin-solution mixture is frozen in an ice cream freezer to obtain a smooth texture and about 100% overrun.

The formulas recommended for fruits having a high acid and low pectin content are the following:

| A | Lb. | Oz. |
|---|---|---|
| Fruit purée | 640 | 0 |
| Sucrose | 265 | 0 |
| Gelatin (275 Bloom) | 5 | 13 |
| Water | 60 | 0 |

| B | Lb. | Oz. |
|---|---|---|
| Fruit purée | 610 | 0 |
| Sucrose | 170 | 0 |
| Enzyme-converted corn syrup (43°Bé.) | 125 | 0 |
| Gelatin (275 Bloom) | 5 | 13 |
| Water | 60 | 0 |

The soluble solids content, including the sugar of the fruit, should be about 37 to 38%.

The following formula is suggested for use with fruits of low acid and high pectin content:

C

|  | Lb. | Oz. |
|---|---|---|
| Purée | 680 | 0 |
| Sucrose | 225 | 0 |
| Gelatin (275 Bloom) | 5 | 13 |
| Water | 60 | 0 |
| Citric acid | 1 | 14 |

A soluble solids content of 34 to 35%, including the natural sugar of the fruit, is sufficient because of the lower acid content of these fruits. A 3 to 1 ratio of fruit to sugar is usually satisfactory, though even less sugar can sometimes be used.

In the preparation of a mix, the purée, sugar, and citric acid (if used) are mixed until the sugar and acid are completely dissolved. The gelatin is mixed with ten times its weight of water, and then heated to 180°F. (82°C.) to dissolve and sterilize it. The mix itself is not pasteurized. During the addition of the gelatin solution, the mix should be stirred in order to prevent the formation of a stringy mass.

The Velva Fruit purée mix is frozen in an ice cream freezer with sufficient agitation to produce about 100% overrun.

The Western Utilization Research and Development Division especially recommends raspberries, strawberries, Loganberries, Boysenberries, and Youngberries for making Velva Fruit. Apricots, Santa Rosa plums, and prune plums also give smooth-textured products of excellent flavor. Cantaloupe purée is said to produce a remarkably fine dessert. Peaches and nectarines are also suitable for making Velva Fruit. The Western Utilization Research and Development Division also recommends blends of berry with pear and apple purées.

MacArthur (1947) has described her experimental production of Velva Fruit from a number of purées. Of her products, the strawberry, black currant, and raspberry desserts were rated highest. She succeeded in making a satisfactory peach purée only when the peach halves were sprinkled with ascorbic acid and an ascorbic acid solution was allowed to drip into the purée container during the extraction of the purée with a tomato juicer. One-quarter of one per cent of ascorbic acid based on the weight of purée was required.

**Pectinized Purées for Ribbon Ice Cream.**—With the advent of fruit ribbon, ripple, or marble ice creams, there was a great demand for a new type of purée, one which could, without further treatment, be used directly in fruit ice creams. Such a product must have pronounced flavor and color, but it should not be too sweet; it should yield a frozen product of smooth texture, and must have a somewhat greater total solids content than the ice cream in which it is used, so that it will not be hard in the ice cream. Further, it should possess a heavy body so that it will not run out of the ice cream when it melts.

A total solids content ten per cent higher than the ice cream will give a purée which will be as soft or softer than the ice cream. If straight sucrose is used as the sweetening agent, the purée will not only be too sweet, but when frozen, it will be somewhat sandy because of the crystallization of the sugar. Replacement of half of the sucrose with a corn syrup of high sugar content, such as the enzyme-converted corn syrup, Sweetose, will take the edge off the sweetness, and also will cause the formation of very much smaller sugar crystals, because of the mixture of sugars present and the action of the protective colloid, dextrin, of the corn syrup.

The addition of pectin to the purée is advantageous both because of its action as a protective colloid (causing the formation of small crystals) and the increased body which it gives, thus causing purée to melt to a very soft jelly instead of to a liquid.

Most ice cream makers prefer a tart purée; this can be obtained by the addition of a little citric acid. Further, increasing the acidity increases the viscosity of the purée.

**Berry Purées.**—The preparation of raspberry, Boysenberry, Youngberry, blackberry, and blueberry pectinized purées is a relatively simple matter. A tested recipe is presented below (Tressler 1942):

|  | Lb. |
|---|---|
| Pulpy fruit juice or purée | 100 |
| Granulated sugar | 50 |
| Enzyme-converted corn syrup (43°Be.) | 60 |
| Pectin[3] (100 grade) | 2 |
| Citric acid | 1.5 |
| Water | 20 |

The pectin is stirred into 15 lb. of the enzyme-converted corn syrup, which has previously been warmed to about 160°F. (71°C.). This suspension of pectin in corn syrup is then slowly stirred into the water which has been brought just to the boiling point. The solution is agitated rapidly and kept hot for 5–10 min., or until the pectin forms a smooth syrupy solution. Heating is then discontinued, and, while the agitation is continued, the remainder of the enzyme-converted corn syrup is added. The fruit purée, to which has been previously added the granulated sugar and finely powdered citric acid, is then stirred with rapid agitation into the solution of the pectin in the corn syrup. Slow agitation is continued while the pectinized purée is being cooled. When its temperature has been reduced to 60°F. (15°C.) or

---

[3] Less pectin is required for black raspberry purée. One pound per 100 lb. of fruit will be sufficient.

lower, the product is run into 30- or 50-lb. enamel-lined slipcover cans and frozen at 0°F. (−18°C.) or lower. The total soluble solids content of the product will be approximately 50%.

The same formula and procedure can be used in making pectinized strawberry purée, except that berries which have been ground in a food chopper should be used instead of a seedless purée.

Another method of making pectinized fruit purées perfected by Johnson (1950B) is described on pp. 197–200, 203.

Guadagni (1954) studied the thawing of strawberry purée to which either ascorbic acid or sucrose had been added, but did not find that either retarded deteriorative changes.

**Peach, Nectarine, and Apricot Purées.**—The problem of making a pectinized purée from Elberta or a similar variety of peaches which browns easily is more difficult, since sufficient oxygen is introduced in the comminution process to cause rapid browning unless the oxidative enzymes are in some way inactivated. The following formula and procedure yield a very good product which does not discolor during long-continued cold storage.

|  | Lb. | Oz. |
|---|---|---|
| Ground peaches | 100 | 0 |
| Granulated sugar | 50 | 0 |
| Enzyme-converted corn syrup (43°Bé.) | 60 | 0 |
| Pectin | 2 | 8 |
| Citric acid | 1 | 4 |
| Water | 20 | 0 |

The solution of the pectin in the enzyme-converted corn syrup is obtained in exactly the same manner as described above under pectinized berry purée. In this case, the solution of the pectin in the enzyme-converted corn syrup is raised to and maintained at 175°F. (79°C.). The peaches are peeled either by scalding in boiling water for about 90 sec. or by immersion in hot lye solution (see also Volume 3). Peels are rubbed off, then the peaches are halved and the pits removed. The halved peaches are placed in the hopper of a food chopper, especially arranged to grind soft fruits, or in a similar grinding device, sprinkled with some of the sugar and some citric acid solution (prepared by dissolving the citric acid in a small amount of water). As fast as the peaches are ground, they are stirred directly into the pectin-corn syrup solution, which is maintained steadily at 175° F. (79°C.). When the proper weight of ground peaches has been added, any remaining sugar and citric acid is stirred into the batch. Then the pectinized purée is cooled by circulating cold water in the jacket of the kettle. When cooled to 60°F. (15°C.) or lower, the purée is run into enamel-lined cans and frozen.

Pectinized nectarine and apricot purée may be prepared according to the same procedure described for peaches. Mixtures of peach and nectarine purées and peach and apricot purées are even more inviting than the straight product. Straight peach purée does not have a particularly potent flavor and color. Addition of either nectarine or apricot purée strengthens flavor and color.

## CRANBERRY – ORANGE RELISH

Frozen cranberry-orange relish is now packed both in 11-oz. cans for sale at retail and in 40-oz. cans for the wholesale trade. It freezes well, retaining its color, flavor, and texture almost perfectly.

The process of manufacture is relatively simple. Fresh washed cranberries are ground in a food chopper. The oranges are quartered, the seeds removed, and then the orange quarters (without peeling) are put through a food chopper. Then ground cranberries, ground oranges, and sugar are mixed together in equal proportions by weight. The product is packaged in liquid-tight, moisture-vapor-proof cartons or fruit-enamel-lined cans, and frozen.

## SAUCES

### Cranberry Sauce

Boggs and Johnson (1947) studied the preparation of frozen jellied cranberry sauce and found that it was necessary to add high grade, rapid set citrus pectin to the cranberry purée in order to obtain a product the quality of which was not affected by syneresis. The first step in making the jellied cranberry sauce is to prepare a cranberry purée. This may be done either (1) by boiling cranberries with an equal weight of water in a steam-jacketed kettle for three minutes, then partially cooling and puréeing in a tomato juice extractor or similar device; or (2) the berries may be steamed on stainless steel trays for two minutes, cooled to 125°F. (51.5°C.), puréed (waste about 15% of the weight of the fruit), and diluted with water in the proportion of 118 lb. of water to 100 lb. of purée. The second step is the addition of pectin. For each 100 lb. of diluted purée, 0.42 to 0.58 lb. of rapid set, 150 grade citrus pectin is mixed with 13 lb. of the granulated sugar. Then this sugar-pectin mixture is stirred into the purée; stirring is continued for 15 min. in order to dissolve the pectin. Then 53.7 lb. of sugar are added to the purée-pectin mixture, which is stirred until all of the sugar dissolves. After the sugar has dissolved, the liquid mix is packaged in liquid-tight, moisture-proof cartons, or fruit-enamel-lined cans which are closed and allowed to stand at 70° to 80°F. (21° to 26.5°C.) for approximately 24 hr. During this time, the gel structure forms and strengthens.

The product is then frozen and stored at 0°F. ( − 18°C.) or lower.

According to Boggs and Johnson, the yield from 100 lb. of cranberries (85 lb. purée), 100 lb. water, 123.3 lb. sugar, and 0.8 lb. pectin is 309 lb. of frozen jellied cranberry sauce. Further, they report that the jellied sauce prepared from the Howes, Early Black, and McFarlin berries did not differ significantly in gel strength or syneresis.

### Apple Sauce

At one time, relatively large quantities of apple sauce were packed and frozen commercially, but the demand for the product has not held up. The frozen product is superior in flavor to most of the canned apple sauce on the market. If made from a given variety and maturity of apple, the canned sauce is somewhat lighter in color than the frozen product, owing to the bleaching of the sauce caused by the action of the malic acid of the apple on the tin of the can. This action also somewhat modifies the flavor of the canned product.

The process used by one important company in making and freezing apple sauce is summarized as follows (Anon. 1946):

The apples are first cored by a battery of seed-cellers. The cored apples are then elevated to a continuous steam peeler and then conveyed to a rotary spindle-type washer, where powerful jets of water knock off the loosened skins and force them through the bottom openings in the revolving cylinder to a waste conveyor below. The apples then pass over a long trimming and inspection table where adhering bits of skin, bruises, etc. are removed by women. The fruit is conveyed to a slicer, and then to a continuous cooker where the proper quantities of sugar and water are added. From the cooker the slices pass into a stainless steel pulper or puréer. The purée is pumped to a stainless steel tank, equipped with an agitator and heater. Then the purée is pumped through a Votator in which it is rapidly cooled. From the Votator the sauce passes to an automatic filler which fills measured amounts into cartons. The filled cartons are put in trays which, in turn, are placed on racks on pallets. The racks are moved into air-blast freezing tunnels. When frozen, the cartons are put into fiberboard shipping containers for storage or shipment.

### Spoonapple

A palatable frozen apple sauce, which needs no cooking, has been developed at Michigan State University by Robertson (Anon. 1963) and the late Dr. E. H. Lucas. Browning is prevented by inactivating enzymes by a patented process. After the apple has been peeled, cored, and pulped, the uncooked sauce is frozen. Robertson (1963) cites the following advantages for the frozen product:

"(1) improved storage of hard to store varieties, such as Chenango, Wealthy, and other early apples; (2) improved palatability; the product has been tested by packaging *Spoonapple* in a plastic container and selling it at cost to Michigan State students. The taste doesn't change with storage; characteristics of the apple variety from which it was made are retained."

## Pear, Peach, Apricot, and Fig Sauces

Cruess, Afifi, and Glazewsky (1948) prepared, froze, stored, and tested sauces made from pears, peaches, apricots, and figs and concluded that each of these fruits, when cooked and puréed, made a delicious sauce which retained its flavor very well during storage, whereas purées made from the raw fruits darkened and developed off-flavors and odors.

### FROZEN SPREADS AND JELLIES

Johnson and Boggs (1947) have developed two different types of fruit spreads which retain almost perfectly the natural full flavor, aroma, and color of the fresh fruit. These products are intended to be used as spreads, as are ordinary jellies and jams. A clear product, similar to jelly in appearance and texture, can be made with clear fruit juice. A jam-like product can be made with fruit purée. Since the products prepared according to the formulas and directions given by these workers not only contain less soluble solids than jams and jellies as defined by the Food and Drug Administration, but also differ from the standardized products in other respects, they should not be labeled as, or represented to be, jellies or jams.

Since heat is not applied to the fruit, fruit juices, or purées at any stage in the process of preparation, and since preservation is accomplished by storing at 0°F. ($-18$°C.) or lower, their volatile flavors and aromas are not lost, altered, or destroyed as in conventional methods of jelly and jam making which involve boiling.

These spreads require the addition of sugar, pectin, and, in some cases, a small amount of fruit acid, to the juice or purée. The cold process of gelation and the method of freezing preservation are identical for both the jam and jelly-like products. The procedures (Fig. 23) worked out by Johnson and Boggs (1947) are summarized as follows:

"The new products are made from freshly prepared fruit purées or juices, or those preserved by freezing without added sugar. Any fruit with a pH of approximately 3.0, or which can be adjusted to that pH by addition of fruit acid, can be used. The process involves the following steps: (1) Disperse and dissolve dry, rapid-set (high methoxyl) citrus pectin, mixed with sugar or glycerin, in fruit purée or juice. The soluble solids content should not be over 25% after the addition of the pectin. (2) Increase the soluble solids to 56.5% by the addition of sugar. (3) Package and allow the mixture to set to a gel before it is placed in freezing storage. As is usual, the products are defrosted prior to use.

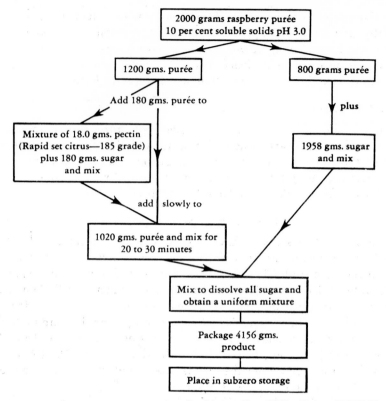

From Johnson and Boggs (1947) and Joslyn and Hohl (1948)

Fig. 23. Diagram illustrating preparation of raspberry Gelled Purée. Sugar is used for dispersing the pectin before it is mixed with the purée in the preparation of raspberry gelled fruit.

"The procedure of combining the ingredients as described below was adopted because it facilitates dispersion and dissolution of the pectin and because it involves a minimum introduction of air. Avoidance of aeration is particularly important when clarified fruit juices are used. Steps in the procedure are:

(1) The soluble solids content of the fruit purée or juice is measured with a refractometer, using the sucrose scale. pH is determined with a pH meter. If the pH of the fruit purée or juice is greater than 3.0, adjustment to pH 3.0 ± 0.05 is made by the addition of jelly maker's standard fruit acid.

(2) The purée or juice is divided into two portions in the ratio of 60 to 40.

(3) Rapid-set citrus pectin, approximately 0.45% of the weight of the final product (purée + sugar) for 185 to 200 grade, is dispersed and dissolved as follows: The pectin is mixed with 8 to 10 times its weight of sugar. An amount of purée or juice equal in weight to this sugar is taken from the 60% portion and added to the pectin-sugar mixture. The mixture is stirred until all of the sugar is dissolved. This step helps dispersion by allowing the particles to become wetted without much swelling. The concentrated pectin mixture is then added to the remainder of the

60% portion of purée or juice and mixed for 20–30 min. with a mechanical mixer of a type that does not beat air into the product. The soluble solids content at this stage should not exceed 25%. A higher sugar concentration will interfere with proper dissolving of the pectin. As an alternative and somewhat simpler procedure, the dry pectin can be mixed with approximately 2.5 times its weight of glycerin, and then added slowly to the 60% portion with constant stirring for 20 to 30 min. (Fig. 24). The small amount of glycerin needed to disperse the pectin makes it possible to dissolve pectin in purées already containing as high as 20 to 25% soluble solids. The addition of glycerin has other advantages which will be referred to below.

(4) The calculated amount of sugar required to increase the soluble solids of the final product to 56.5 to 57% is mixed into the 40% portion. The greater part of the sugar will dissolve. Amount of sugar required to increase soluble solids to 56.6% can be calculated from the following equation:

$$x = \{0.565y - [(s.s. / 100)(y)]\} / 0.435$$

where $x$ = weight of total amount of added sugar, $y$ = weight of fruit puree, and, $s.s$ = per cent soluble solids in fruit purée determined by Abbe refractometer, using the sucrose scale.

The amount of sugar to be added to the 40% portion then becomes $x$, less the amount of sugar or glycerin added to the pectin.

(5) This mixture is added to the 60% pectinized portion, and stirring is continued until all of the sugar is dissolved and a uniform mixture is obtained (approximately five minutes).

(6) The product is packaged in heavily waxed paper containers (six ounces or larger, if desired), and allowed to stand until properly gelled. This requires 20–24 hr.

(7) The gelled product is placed in freezer storage, 0°F. (−18°C.) or lower.

The composition of some of the purées and clarified juices and the spreads prepared from them by Johnson and Boggs is shown in Table 25.

Johnson and Boggs recommend storage at −10°F. (−23°C.) or lower if the flavor and texture are to be retained for seven months or longer. Samples held at +15°F. (−9.4°C.) retained texture well, but lost flavor in a few months. Those stored at +7°F. (−14°C.) became granulated and syneresis was apparent. At 0°F. (−18°C.) and below, the texture was maintained, but all samples stored at temperatures above −10°F. (−23°C.) showed some loss of flavor.

Later work by Brekke and Talburt (1950) has indicated sucrose hydrate crystals appear relatively rapidly when these spreads are stored at −10°F. (−23°C.). If these cold-processed spreads are to be stored for long periods, Brekke and Talburt suggest either that they be stored at a very low temperature, e.g., −30°F. (−34.4°C.), or that 30% of the sucrose requirements be replaced by invert sugar.

Johnson and Boggs report that some fruits require special preparation. Fruits having especially active oxidative enzymes, e.g., Santa Rosa plums, either must be subjected to a short heat treatment to inactivate the enzymes, or an antioxidant such as ascorbic acid must be added to the purée or juice. Concord grapes require a short heat treatment (e.g., a one-minute steam blanch) before juice extraction in order to extract the color and inactivate the enzymes. On the other hand, Boysenberries, blackberries, red and black currants, strawberries, and Youngberries require no special treatment before conversion into purées.

Although these cold-processed spreads will keep at ordinary room temperature

Table 25

Composition of Fruit Purées and Juices and Gels Prepared from Them

| Fruit | Fruit pH | Acid Added,[1] % | Gelled Fruit, pH | Soluble Solids of Fruit | Purée or Juice, Gm. | Sugar, Gm. | Soluble Solids in Gelled Fruit, % | Added Pectin,[2] Gm. | Added Pectin, % |
|---|---|---|---|---|---|---|---|---|---|
| Blackberry purée | 3.22 | 0.50 | 3.02 | 10.5 | 2000 | 2116 | 56.5 | 18.2 | 0.44 |
| Boysenberry purée[1] | 2.90 | 0.00 | 2.90 | 10.5 | 2000 | 2116 | 56.5 | 17.7 | 0.43 |
| Boysenberry purée[2] | 3.25 | 0.35 | 3.05 | 10.7 | 2000 | 2040 | 56.5 | 18.6[3] | 0.45 |
| Currant (red) juice | 2.85 | 0.00 | 2.85 | 9.5 | 2000 | 2110 (60 Gm. of glycerin) | 56.0 | 15.2 | 0.37 |
| Guava purée | 3.05 | 0.00 | 3.05 | 9.5 | 2000 | 2110 | 56.0 | 10.3 | 0.25 |
| Red raspberry purée | 3.15 | 0.25 | 3.00 | 10.0 | 2000 | 2145 | 56.5 | 18.2[3] | 0.44 |
| Red raspberry juice | 3.18 | 0.30 | 3.05 | 9.0 | 2000 | 2121 (60 Gm. of glycerin) | 56.5 | 18.8 | 0.45 |
| Strawberry purée | 3.22 | 0.30 | 3.05 | 8.0 | 2000 | 2224 | 56.5 | 19.0 | 0.45 |
| Strawberry juice | 3.40 | 0.70 | 3.02 | 9.0 | 2000 | 2100 | 56.5 | 19.6 | 0.48 |
| Santa Rosa plum purée | 3.00 | 0.00 | 3.00 | 11.0 | 2000 | 2090 | 56.5 | 18.4 | 0.45 |
| Youngberry | 3.15 | 0.30 | 3.02 | 10.7 | 2000 | 2100 | 56.5 | 18.2 | 0.45 |

Source: Johnson and Boggs (1947).
[1] On basis of purée or juice.
[2] Rapid-set citrus pectin grade 185.
[3] Grade 202.

for several days after thawing, their quality is retained better if held under refrigeration.

Kramer and Sunderlin (1953) have worked out a simple method of making uncooked jam in the home kitchen. Their method, which could be modified so as to be suitable for commercial use, follows:

### Red Raspberry Jam

| | |
|---|---|
| 12-oz. packages frozen red raspberries | 3 |
| Sugar (cups) | 5 |
| Powdered pectin (package) | 1 |
| Water (cup) | ¾ |

"After thawing, sieve or thoroughly mash the raspberries. Combine berries and sugar. Let stand about 20 min., stirring occasionally. Stir the pectin into the water, bring to boiling and boil rapidly one minute, stirring constantly. Remove from stove. Add the berries and stir about two minutes. Pour into jelly glasses. Cover and let stand at room temperature 24 hr., or until gelled. Seal with paraffin and store in a freezer. Or, the jam will keep several weeks at refrigerator temperatures. This makes about nine glasses.

Kramer and Sunderlin (1953) also studied making of frozen jam from purée made from frozen strawberries. In making jam from strawberry purée, more pectin was found to be necessary and a noticeable amount of syneresis occurred when the products were thawed.

Johnson (1950B) has suggested a novel process which consists of packing and freezing fruit (slices, or whole fruit in the case of berries) with 1.5 to 2 parts of sweetened pectinized purée containing 50% soluble solids. The sweetened pectinized purée can be made by the procedure described on p. 193, originally devised by Tressler (1942) or by that perfected by Johnson and Boggs (1947), summarized on p. 197–199, modified more recently by Johnson (1950B) and presented below:

Soft ripe berries (raspberries, blackberries, the Boysen, Logan, and Young varieties of dewberries, strawberries, and blueberries) are washed and sorted to eliminate defective berries and foreign matter. Two-thirds, or if a product containing more solid fruit is desired, four-sevenths of the fruit is converted into purée in a tapered screw expeller type of pulper with a 0.033 in. screen to remove seeds and coarse fibrous materials.

In preparing peaches, apricots, and nectarines, soft ripe fruit is washed, inspected, and then cut into halves or quarters, the pits removed, and the cut fruit immediately put through a pulper, fitted with a 0.062-in. sieve. Immediately after preparation, 200 mg. of ascorbic acid should be added to each pound of purée, in order to obtain a topping which will not discolor during thawing and use.

If the method proposed by Tressler is used in making the purée, it will not darken. However, the peach, apricot, or nectarine slices will slowly

darken if a small amount of ascorbic acid (e.g., 75 mg. per lb.) or other antioxidant is not incorporated in the topping.

The following are typical formulas for berry (raspberry, strawberry,
blackberry, etc.) and peach pectinized purées, and procedures for preparing and freezing the ice cream toppings (Johnson 1950B):

### Formulas and Methods of Preparation of Pectinized Purée

|  | Berry | Peach |
|---|---|---|
| Fruit (lb.) | 100 | 100 |
| Sugar (lb.) | 80 | 76 |
| Slow set citrus pectin | 17.3 | 17 |
| (oz.) 150 grade | | |
| Monocalcium phosphate (oz.) | 1.7 | 1.7 |
| Citric acid (oz.) | 0 | 4 |

"The amount of sugar used is such that the final soluble solids content is about
50%.

(1) The purée is divided into two portions in the ratio of 60 to 40.

(2) Slow-set citrus pectin, approximately 0.6% of the weight of final product
(purée plus sugar) for 150 grade, is dispersed and dissolved as follows:   The pectin
is mixed with about ten times its weight of sugar. An amount of purée equal in
weight to this sugar is taken from the 60% portion and added to the pectin-sugar
mixture. The mixture is stirred until all of the sugar is dissolved. This step helps
dispersion by allowing the particles to become wetted without much swelling. The
concentrated pectin mixture is then added to the remainder of the 60% portion of
purée to form mixture A, and is mixed for about 20 min. with a mechanical mixer
of a type that does not beat air into the product. The soluble solids content at this
stage should not exceed 25%. A higher sugar concentration will interfere with
proper dissolving of the pectin. As an alternative and somewhat simpler procedure,
the dry pectin can be mixed with approximately 2.5 times its weight of glycerin or
ten times its weight of invert sugar, and then added slowly to the 60% portion with
constant stirring for about 20 min.

(3) The calculated amount of sugar, required to increase the soluble solids of the
purée to 50% is mixed into the 40% portion. This will be referred to as mixture B.
The greater part of the sugar will dissolve. Amount of sugar required to increase
soluble solids to 50% can be calculated from the following equation:

$$x = \{ 0.50y - [(s.s / 100)(y)] \} / 0.50$$

where $x$ = weight of total amount of added sugar, $y$ = weight of fruit purée, and
$s.s$ = per cent soluble solids determined by refractometer using the sucrose scale.

The amount of sugar to be added to the 40% portion then becomes $x$, less the
amount of sugar, glycerin, or invert sugar added to the pectin.

(4) The mixture B is added to the 60% pectinized portions, (mixture A) and stirring is continued until all of the sugar is dissolved and a uniform mixture is obtained (approximately five minutes).

(5) Monocalcium phosphate is made into a slurry by the addition of small
amount of water. This slurry is then mixed into pectinized purée. When desired,
citric acid (50% solution) is also added at this stage.

(6) Two parts of the pectinized purée are then packed with 1 to 1.5 parts of

sliced fruit (peaches or strawberries) or whole berries (raspberries and other similar berries).

(7) After packaging, the product is placed into freezing storage. The mixing procedure for the preparation of the pectinized purée is graphically illustrated in Fig. 24.

The product has excellent fresh fruit flavor and good consistency for toppings for ice cream, cake, and shortcake. The soda fountain is a potential outlet for this product.

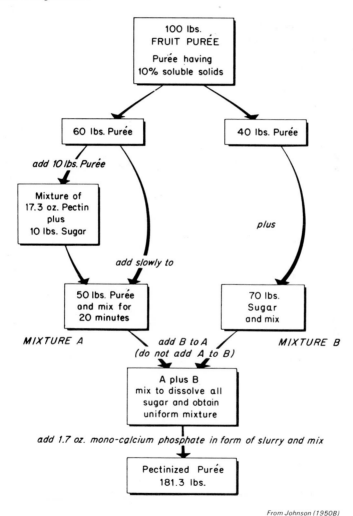

From Johnson (1950B)

Fig. 24.   Procedure for preparing pectinized purée.

## FROZEN PUNCH BLENDS

Although the freezing of fruit juices and fruit juice concentrates is covered in Chap. 4 of Volume 3, since punches are usually considered prepared fruit products, mention of the preparation and freezing of punch blends and bases is included in this chapter. Seale and Sherman (1960) developed a "Polynesian punch" with an enticing flavor; their formula follows:

|                                      | Parts |
|--------------------------------------|-------|
| Passion fruit juice                  | 18    |
| Pineapple concentrate                | 5     |
| Acerola purée                        | 4     |
| Pineapple juice                      | 3     |
| Orange concentrate                   | 4     |
| Lemon juice                          | 2     |
| Water                                | 8     |
| Sugar                                | 56    |
| Citric acid, enough to give an acidity of | 1.7 |

The ingredients are mixed in a blending tank; then citric acid is added to bring the acidity to 1.7 calculated as citric acid. The product is then filled into enamel-lined cans and frozen. When used, each can of blend is diluted with 4½ cans of water.

Another punch blend containing more acerola purée was also prepared by Seale and Sherman (1960). This formula follows:

|                      | Parts |
|----------------------|-------|
| Passion fruit juice  | 24    |
| Acerola purée        | 12    |
| Pineapple juice      | 10    |
| Orange concentrate   | 4     |
| Sugar                | 50    |

Enough citric acid was added to bring the acidity to 1.4–1.5% acidity calculated as citric acid.

In preparing a punch this base is diluted with four parts of water.

### BIBLIOGRAPHY

Anon. 1946. Velva Fruit—A new frozen fruit dessert. U.S. Dept. Agr. AIC 40, Rev. No. 1.

Anon. 1948. Frozen gel is packed by Washington rancher. Western Canner and Packer 40, No. 12, 59.

Anon. 1954. Apple dumpling plant opening. Quick Frozen Foods 17, No. 5, 70.

Anon. 1955A. New frozen coconut dessert developed. Western Canner and Packer 47, No. 10, 45.

Anon. 1955B. Magic Maid marketing frozen baked apples. Canner 120, No. 20, 26.

Anon. 1955C. Ocean Spray introduces frozen relish. Frosted Food Field *20*, No. 3, 26.

Anon. 1963. Spoonapple—palatable apple sauce needs no cooking. Canner/ Packer *132*, No. 9, 20.

Anon. 1967. Will defrost pouch fruit parallel growth of boilable bag vegetables in sauce. Quick Frozen Foods *29*, No. 89–90, 93–94, 96.

Baker, G. L., and Woodmansee, C. W. 1951. Frozen gelled fruits for the baker. Quick Frozen Foods *13*, No. 12, 60–61.

Boggs, M. M., and Johnson, G. 1947. How jellied cranberry sauce is preserved by freezing. Food Inds. *19*, 1067–1069, 1174–1176.

Brekke, J. E., and Talburt, W. F. 1950. Prevention of sucrose hydrate formation in cold-processed frozen fruit spreads. Food Technol. *4*, 383–386.

Cruess, W. V. 1955. New frozen fruit products coming out of the laboratory that may be tomorrow's best sellers. Frosted Food Field *20*, No. 3, 106.

Cruess, W. V., Afifi, A., and Glazewsky, I. G. A. 1948. Experiments on frozen fruits. Frozen Food Industry and Locker Plant Manual *4*, No. 1, 6–11.

Esselen, W. B., Jr., Fellers, C. R., and McConnell, J. E. W. 1949. Frozen apples and apple products. Food Technol. *3*, 121–126.

Fellers, C. R., and Esselen, W. B. 1955. Cranberries and cranberry products. Univ. Mass. Agr. Expt. Sta. Bull. *481*.

Guadagni, D. G. 1954. Effect of sucrose and ascorbic acid on quality retention in fresh and frozen strawberry purée. Food Research *19*, 396–401.

Johnson, G. 1950A. New frozen fresh fruit pie mixes. Quick Frozen Foods *13*, No. 1, 50–51, 100.

Johnson, G. 1950B. Frozen fresh fruit sundae-toppings. Colo. Agr. Expt. Sta. Mimeo. Circ. *471*, Misc. Series.

Johnson, G. 1951. New frozen apple product. Colo. Farm and Home Research *2*, No. 2.

Johnson, G., and Boggs, M. M. 1947. New fresh fruit spreads preserved by freezing. Food Inds. *9*, 1491–1494, 1612–1613.

Johnson, G., and Boggs, M. M. 1949. Cold processed fruit spread. U.S. Pat. 2,459,431. Jan. 18.

Johnson, G., and Johnson, D. K. 1952. Natural flavor retained in new frozen uncooked apple pulp. Food Technol. *6*, 242–245.

Joslyn, M. A., and Hohl, L. A. 1948. Commercial freezing of fruit products. Calif. Agr. Expt. Bull. *703*.

Kench, D. M. 1959. A continuous process centrifuge. A.S.A.E. Trans. 2, No. 1, 52–54, 57.

Kench, D. M., and Shaw, T. N. 1954. The development of a machine to extract juice from passion fruit. Univ. Hawaii Agr. Expt. Sta. Station Progress Notes *104*.

Kramer, M. A., and Sunderlin, G. 1953. The gelatin development of pectin in uncooked jam from frozen red raspberries and strawberries. J. Home Econ. *45*, 243–247. Jams with fresh fruit flavor. Ibid. *45*, 247.

Lee, F. A. 1947. The preservation of baked apples by freezing. Fruit Products J. 26, 366–367.

Loeffler, H. J. 1944. Velva Fruit—A new frozen fruit dessert. Ice and Refrig. *106*, No. 5, 263–266.

Loeffler, H. J. 1946. Rentention of ascorbic acid in strawberries during processing, frozen storage, and manufacture of Velva Fruit. Food Research *11*, 69–83.

MacArthur, M.  1947.  Frozen fruit desserts. Canadian Food Inds. *18*, No. 10, 37–39.

McColloch, R. J., Nielsen, B. W., and Beavens, E. A.  1951. A new frozen avocado product. U.S. Dept. Agr. AIC *305*.

Morris, E.  1952. A frozen apple creme. Quick Frozen Foods *14*, No. 9, 83.

Rasmussen, C. L., Esselen, W. B., Jr., and Fellers, C. R.  1948. Canned and frozen baked McIntosh apples. Fruit Products J. *27*, 228–229, 265.

Sayles, C. L., and MacLennan, H. A.  1965. Ready foods. Cornell University School of Hotel Administration Research Rept. *10*, Ithaca, N. Y.

Scott, F. J. Jr.  1955. Frozen passion fruit juice. Univ. Hawaii Agr. Expt. Sta. Agr. Econ. Rept. *25*.

Scott, F. S. Jr.  1956. Consumer preferences for frozen passion fruit juice. Univ. Hawaii Agr. Expt. Sta. Agr. Economics Rept. *29*.

Scott, F. S. Jr.  1957. Consumer uses of passion fruit juice. Univ. Hawaii Agr. Expt. Sta. Agr. Economics Rept. *31*.

Scott, F. S. Jr.  1958A. An analysis of marked development for frozen passion fruit juice. Univ. Hawaii Agr. Expt. Sta. Agr. Economics Bull. *11*.

Scott, F. S. Jr.  1958B. Commercial uses and consumer preferences for Hawaiian guava products. Univ. Hawaii Agr. Expt. Sta. Agr. Economics Bull. *13*.

Scott, F. S. Jr.  1958C. An economic analysis of the market for frozen guava nectar base. Univ. Hawaii Agr. Expt. Sta. Agr. Economics Bull. *14*.

Seale, P. E., and Sherman, J. D.  1960. Commercial passion fruit processing in Hawaii. Univ. Hawaii Agr. Expt. Sta. Circ. *58*.

Sorber, D. G.  1942. Frozen sliced, crushed and puréed fruits. Canner *94*, No. 7, 16–17, 36; No. 8, 18, 20, 22, 32.

Strachan, C. C., Atkinson, F. E., Moyls, A. W., Kitson, J. A., and Britton, D.  1954. Preparation of canned fruit pie fillings. Canadian Food Inds. *25*, No. 11, 16–23.

Tressler, D. K.  1942. Using fruit purées to get new flavors in ribbon ice cream. Food Inds. *14*, 49–51, 99.

Tressler, D. K.  1946. Frozen fruit purées in ice cream. Ice Cream Field *47*, No. 1, 32, 60–61.

Wolford, E. R., and Prescott, R. T.  1963. Frozen jelled fruits. U.S. Dept. Agr., Agr. Research Service ARS-74-27.

Woodroof, J. G., and Atkinson, I. S.  1945. Freezing cooked foods. Food Inds. *17*, 1041–1042, 1136–1138, 1179–1180, 1264–1265.

## CHAPTER 9

Donald K. Tressler | **Precooked Potatoes**

## INTRODUCTION

In 1945, French-fried potatoes were first frozen on a large scale by the Snow Flake Canning Co., a subsidiary of H. C. Baxter and Bros., Brunswick, Maine (Talburt and Smith 1967). Since then, the commercial production of this and other frozen potato products has had a phenomenal growth. In fact, more potatoes are now frozen than any other vegetable, constituting over 40% of the total frozen vegetable pack. See also Chapter 5, Volume 3.

The U.S. Department of Agriculture has estimated that 34,029,000 cwt. of potatoes from the 1966 crop were used to produce frozen French fries and an additional 5,602,000 cwt. for other frozen products, the total being approximately 14% of the potatoes used for food.

A large proportion of the total pack of frozen potato products goes to the hotels, restaurants, diners, and institutional users. The J. R. Simplot Co. of Caldwell, Idaho, developed an oil-blanched or partially fried product, called "parfried," for the institutional market. The popularity of this product stems largely from the fact that it requires only a very short reheating in a fry bath to prepare it for the table, and, since it is only partially fried, this reheating cooks it to the desired golden color.

Many restaurants, hotels, diners, and institutions have found that the use of these parfried potatoes is very desirable. It eliminates the laborious, time-consuming operations of washing, peeling, and cutting up potatoes. Further, since frying is accomplished in less time, there is less steam and oil vapor in the kitchen. The latter is especially desirable in a diner or small restaurant where the cooking is done right behind the counter or in a very small kitchen. In larger hotel kitchens where the potatoes are fried in two stages (two frybaths), the use of parfried potatoes eliminates the need for one bath. Further, the quality of the fried product is much more uniform when parfried frozen potatoes are used than when the restaurateur purchases his potatoes from day to day. Even when a hotel or restaurant buys in quantity and carries the potatoes in storage, the frying quality is likely to change from week to week, since few hotels or institutions have a storage maintained uniformly at the most desirable temperature to hold potatoes (50°F.; 10°C.).

Donald K. Tressler is a consultant and President of the Avi Publishing Company, Westport, Conn.

Table 26

Utilization of the 1964, 1965, and 1966 Crops of Potatoes

| Utilization Items | Crop, 1,000 Cwt. | | |
|---|---|---|---|
| | 1964[1] | 1965[1] | 1966 |
| (A) Sales | | | |
| (1) Table stock | 129,513 | 139,542 | 133,880 |
| (2) For processing | | | |
| (a) Chips and shoestrings | 28,783 | 31,292 | 32,729 |
| (b) Dehydration | 10,801 | 20,166 | 19,811 |
| (c) Frozen French fries | 20,494 | 32,263 | 34,029 |
| (d) Other frozen products | 3,160 | 5,039 | 5,602 |
| (e) Canned potatoes | 1,727 | 1,728 | 1,961 |
| (f) Other canned products (Hash, stews, soups) | 1,474 | 1,620 | 1,425 |
| (g) Starch and flour | 2,990 | 8,081 | 11,001 |
| Total | 69,429 | 100,189 | 106,558 |
| (3) Other sales | | | |
| (a) Livestock feed | 5,587 | 5,797 | 8,440 |
| (b) Seed | 14,203 | 16,922 | 16,144 |
| Total | 19,790 | 22,719 | 24,584 |
| Total sales | 218,732 | 262,450 | 265,022 |
| (B) Nonsales | | | |
| (1) Seed used on farms where grown | 7,363 | 6,510 | 8,118 |
| (2) Household use | 2,776 | 2,597 | 2,378 |
| (3) Feed | 1,871 | 2,179 | 2,930 |
| (4) Shrinkage and loss | 10,334 | 17,433 | 28,454 |
| Total nonsales | 22,344 | 28,719 | 41,880 |
| Total Production | 241,076 | 291,169 | 306,902 |

Source: U.S. Dept. Agr. Statistical Reporting Service, *Pot 1-3-(9-67)*.
[1] Revised.

Table 27

Pack of Frozen Potato Products

| Region | Pack of Recent Years by Region (In Thousands of Pounds) | | | |
|---|---|---|---|---|
| | 1962 | 1963 | 1964 | 1965 |
| East and South | 194,189 | 254,136 | 360,400 | 357,709 |
| West [1] | 567,420 | 607,401 | 757,482 | 860,820 |
| U.S. Total | 761,609 | 861,537 | 1,117,882 | 1,218,529 |

| Pack of Frozen Potato Products (By Container Size and Style of Pack) | | | |
|---|---|---|---|
| | 1963 | 1964 | 1965 |
| French-fried potatoes | | | |
| Retail sizes | | | |
| 9 oz. | | | 101,282,964 |
| 1 lb. | | | 73,490,075 |
| 2 and 2 1/2 lb. | n.a. | n.a. | 148,907,093 |
| 5 lb. | | | 32,163,148 |
| Special size: 12 to 24 oz. | | | 23,323,074 |
| Total French-fried for retail | | | 379,166,354 |
| Institutional sizes | | | |
| 4 and 4 1/2 lb. | | | 26,493,860 |
| 5 lb. | | | 518,266,266 |
| Special size: 7 1/2 to 15 lb. | n.a. | n.a. | 85,241,923 |
| 30 to 55 lb. | | | 45,328,179 |
| Total institutional distribution | | | 675,330,228 |
| Bulk for repack | | | 15,628,681 |
| Total all French-fries | 742,784,019 | 991,968,847 | 1,070,125,263 |
| Whipped and diced potatoes | 5,408,710 | 4,814,485 | 1,019,644 |
| Water blanched potatoes (any style, peeled, whole or cut) | 12,261,164 | 12,794,973 | 17,796,273 |
| Other potato products (hash browns, puffs, rissole, patties, shredded, stuffed, baked) | 104,083,287 | 108,304,641 | 129,587,672 |
| U.S. Total (all potato products) | 861,537,180 | 1,117,882,946 | 1,218,528,852 |

Source: National Association of Frozen Food Packers, Washington, D. C.
[1] Includes Midwest.
n.a.—Detail by container not available.

With the exception of Canada, the pack of frozen potatoes in other countries is not large; however Canadian production is becoming of considerable importance.

In cutting slices for French frying, a considerable quantity of "slivers" and short pieces are obtained. These are utilized in making patties, puffs, hash-brown, mashed potatoes, and other products which are frozen; they not only provide diversity but also contribute to the popularity of frozen potato products. The large variety of frozen potato products is indicated in Table 28.

Table 28

List of Frozen Potato Products Packed Individually and/or as Ingredients of Precooked Frozen Dinners

| | |
|---|---|
| French-fried | Potato rounds (shredded and extruded) |
|   Regular cuts | Baked stuffed |
|   Crinkle cuts | Puffs |
|   Par-fries (institutional) | Au gratin |
| Patties | Boiled |
|   Regular | Rissole |
|   Onion-flavored | Creamed |
| Mashed | Scalloped |
|   Riced | Delmonico |
|   Whipped | Cottage fried |
|   Cuts for mashing | Roasted |
|   Shredded for mashing | Dumplings or pirogen |
|   Dehydrofrozen | Knishes |
| Diced | Blintzes |
|   Regular | Pancakes |
|   Onion-flavored | Hashed in cream |
|   Dehydrofrozen | Cream of potato soup |
| Hash brown | Potatoes and peas in cream sauce |
|   Southern style—loose frozen | Stew mix |
|   Prescored—portion control | |

Source: Feustel and Kueneman (1966).

The Frozen Potato Products Institute was organized in 1959 for the purpose of expanding the sales and consumption of frozen potato products. This Institute conducts promotional and educational activities and also keeps pack and pack movement statistics.

### FROZEN FRENCH–FRIED POTATOES

**Convenience to User**

The use of frozen French-fried potatoes not only means great convenience and uniformity of quality to the restaurant and institution, but has equal or greater advantages to the housewife. She needs only to remove the product from package and put the frozen or thawed product in the oven for reheating. And if the frozen product has been packed in an aluminum foil package, the potatoes can be reheated right in the package. Relatively few homes do much deep-fat frying because it is difficult to keep a quantity of fat or oil for very long and if the oil of the frybath is discarded after each use, it makes the cost of frying potatoes prohibitive.

Some housewives complain that if frozen French-fried potatoes are reheated in an oven and not in a frybath, the product is likely to be inferior in color (too dark), texture, and flavor, compared to that made from fresh potatoes in a frybath. However, a product having superior palatability can be made by reheating frozen French-fried potatoes in a frying pan with a small quantity of cooking oil or shortening (Anon. 1964A).

On the whole, the quality of reheated frozen French-fried potatoes is good, being more uniform than that which the average housewife can produce when she buys fresh potatoes from the market. The reason is simply that the variety and maturity of the potatoes vary from season to season and seldom are just right for frying. Further, the fresh potatoes may be too high in soluble solids and therefore give a dark product; or conversely may be too low in sugars and not brown right and produce the right texture.

### INFLUENCE OF QUALITY OF RAW TUBERS ON QUALITY OF FRENCH–FRIED POTATOES

There are no standards of suitability of potatoes for processing which will assure the highest quality of frozen French fries. Most packers consider variety to be the most important single factor influencing processing quality and those varieties that are consistently high in solids content have generally proved best for processing. Unfortunately the composition of a given variety will often vary from one producing area to another and even from field to field. Further, growing conditions vary from year to year and these influence the composition and quality of the potato. However, the specific gravity (solids content) and the reducing sugar content are the most reliable guides in the selection of raw material for processing.

The reducing sugar content of the potatoes has a marked effect on the ease with which the strips brown during frying. If the sugar content is high, it is difficult to fry the potato strips without too much browning. When the potatoes are stored at a low temperature, e.g., 40°F. (4.5°C.) and less, sprouting is not a serious problem unless potatoes are stored into the springtime, but the sugar content builds up (Table 29). At a storage temperature of 55°F. (12.8°C.) there is relatively little change in the sugar content of the potatoes, but sprouting causes serious losses if storage is prolonged. At higher temperatures, respiration occurs at a faster rate and the sugar content decreases. If potatoes have been stored at low temperatures and consequently have a high sugar content, this accumulation of sugar may be reduced by holding the vegetable at a higher temperature (55° to 70°F.; (12.8°C. to 21°C.) for 5 to 20 days (Pentzer 1949; Gould 1954). The processor must know and control these conditions carefully.

### Varietal Suitability

Smith (1957) has indicated that Irish Cobbler, Russet Burbank, Russet Rural, Sebago, Kennebec, and Katahdin are among the best for French frying. Under some conditions, other varieties such as the Green Mountain accumulate so much reducing sugar that they yield dark and unattractive French fries and cannot be readily conditioned to satisfactory sugar levels.

Table 29

Total Sugar Content (in Per Cent) of Six Varieties of Potatoes from Several Locations
Stored at 40°F. or 55°F. (4.5° or 12.8°C.) in 1948 and 1949 [1]

| Variety and Location | 1948 | | | | 1949 | | | |
|---|---|---|---|---|---|---|---|---|
| | No Storage | 3 Mos. at 55°F. | 3 Mos. at 40°F. | 6 Mos. at 40°F. | No Storage | 3 Mos. at 55°F. | 3 Mos. at 40°F. | 6 Mos. at 40°F. |
| Chippewa | | | | | | | | |
| Indiana | 0.40 | 0.08 | 1.79 | 1.68 | 0.29 | 0.36 | 0.82 | 0.59 |
| Maine | 0.40 | 0.03 | 0.85 | 0.80 | 0.29 | 0.22 | 1.17 | 1.07 |
| Michigan | 0.63 | 0.38 | 1.14 | 1.34 | 0.44 | 0.31 | 1.23 | 1.32 |
| Green Mountain | | | | | | | | |
| Maine, I | 1.14 | 0.59 | 1.79 | 1.78 | 0.62 | 0.42 | 1.03 | 1.12 |
| Maine, II | 0.55 | 0.63 | 1.63 | 1.69 | 0.56 | 0.42 | 1.01 | 1.27 |
| New York | 0.58 | 0.60 | 1.69 | 1.92 | 1.00 | 1.10 | 2.15 | 2.01 |
| Irish Cobbler | | | | | | | | |
| Maine | 0.30 | 0.21 | 0.73 | 1.08 | 0.40 | 0.26 | 0.77 | 0.92 |
| North Dakota | 0.53 | 0.32 | 1.45 | 1.77 | 0.50 | 0.31 | 0.98 | 1.22 |
| Wisconsin | 0.31 | 0.21 | 1.02 | 1.37 | 0.41 | 0.28 | 1.05 | 1.34 |
| Katahdin | | | | | | | | |
| Colorado | 0.46 | 0.41 | 1.13 | 1.29 | 0.75 | 0.28 | 0.83 | 1.02 |
| Maine | 0.38 | 0.36 | 1.25 | 1.54 | 0.42 | 0.30 | 1.36 | 1.45 |
| Pennsylvania | 0.41 | 0.32 | 1.45 | 1.59 | 0.24 | 0.22 | 0.87 | 1.12 |
| Russet Burbank | | | | | | | | |
| Idaho, Aberdeen | 0.20 | 0.38 | 1.27 | 1.23 | 0.36 | 0.28 | 0.91 | 0.91 |
| Idaho, Ashton | 0.52 | 0.37 | 1.11 | 1.16 | 1.02 | 0.55 | 1.09 | 1.19 |
| Washington | 0.28 | 0.37 | 1.20 | 1.46 | 0.42 | 0.25 | 0.81 | 0.87 |
| Triumph | | | | | | | | |
| NorthDakota,Grand Forks | 0.67 | 0.74 | 2.10 | 2.64 | 1.00 | 0.56 | 1.54 | 1.75 |
| North Dakota, Walhalla | 0.70 | 0.64 | 1.80 | 2.17 | 0.81 | 0.64 | 1.70 | 1.95 |

Source: Heinze, Kirkpatrick, and Dochterman (1955).
[1] Each figure represents the mean of three analyses, all expressed on fresh-weight basis.

According to Gould (1954), in order to be satisfactory for processing, a potato variety must be fairly uniform in size, have shallow eyes, smooth shoulders or free from contours, free from defects, have a high specific gravity, and the ability to recondition (bring to a desirable soluble solids content) after any given storage period. The higher the specific gravity, the higher the starch and solids content, and, under most conditions, the better the quality. A high specific gravity is desirable in the raw potato from at least two standpoints: (1) greater yield of finished product from the same quantity of raw stock; and (2) less fat absorption per pound of potatoes.

## Specific Gravity and Quality

Kirkpatrick et al. (1956) of the U.S. Department of Agriculture carried out a comprehensive study of the effect of increasing specific gravity of the raw tubers on the mealiness, crispness, lack of oiliness, flavor, and tenderness of French-fried potatoes. Their data are summarized in Fig. 25 and Table 30.

They concluded that, with the exception of tenderness and oiliness, all of the characteristics listed above increased with increase in specific gravity. Oiliness decreased with increase of specific gravity (this is desirable), and crispness was optimum at about 1.085 sp. gr. (Fig. 25).

Within each variety lot, the percentage of dry matter in the raw samples increased with increasing specific gravity (Table 30). Kirkpatrick *et al.* also concluded that dry matter and yield of French fries tended to increase with higher specific gravity, although cooking time was also a factor.

## How Storage Temperature Affects Quality

Kirkpatrick *et al.* (1956) also studied the effect of length of storage and storage temperatures on the quality of the French fries made therefrom. They conclude: "Storage of potato tubers for 3 or 5 months at 40°F. (4°C.) caused accumulation of sugar in the raw tubers and excessively brown color and a burned flavor in the French-fried potatoes. In contrast, storage of tu-

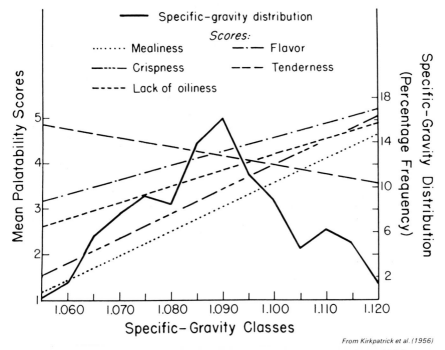

From Kirkpatrick et al. (1956)

Fig. 25. Specific gravity distribution of potatoes from six variety-locations, 1952 crop. Regression lines show mean scores for various characteristics on specific gravity (5 represents the optimum score and 1 the poorest for each quality attribute).

Table 30

Influence of Specific Gravity of Raw Tubers on Dry Matter, Cooking Time, Oil Content, Shear Force, and Yield of French-fried Potatoes, 1952 Crop

| Variety and Location | Raw Potatoes | | Cooking Time | | French-fried Potatoes | | | |
|---|---|---|---|---|---|---|---|---|
| | Specific Gravity | Dry Matter % | First-stage Fry Minutes | Second-stage Fry Minutes | Dry Matter % | Oil Content % | Shear Force Pounds | Yield[1] % |
| Chippewa: Maine | 1.060 | 16.1 | 4½ | 1½ | 46.3 | 13.6 | 2.2 | 46.8 |
| | 1.070 | 17.8 | 4½ | 1½ | 50.6 | 13.9 | 2.1 | 47.9 |
| | 1.075 | 18.5 | 4½ | 1½ | 49.8 | 13.3 | 2.0 | 50.8 |
| Irish Cobbler: Maine | 1.085 | 22.1 | 4 | 1½ | 54.4 | 12.6 | 3.7 | 50.6 |
| | 1.090 | 22.7 | 4 | 1½ | 56.3 | 12.1 | 3.4 | 50.3 |
| | 1.095 | 24.8 | 3½ | 1½ | 56.2 | 11.9 | 3.5 | 52.2 |
| Irish Cobbler: North Dakota | 1.090 | 22.3 | 4 | 1½ | 55.1 | 12.7 | 3.8 | 50.9 |
| | 1.095 | 24.1 | 3½ | 1½ | 54.5 | 12.1 | 4.3 | 52.3 |
| | 1.100 | 23.9 | 3½ | 1½ | 55.7 | 11.8 | 4.1 | 52.4 |
| | 1.110 | 27.0 | 2 | 1½ | 56.8 | 11.4 | 3.4 | 55.7 |
| Katahdin: Colorado | 1.085 | 22.4 | 4 | 1½ | 54.2 | 12.4 | 3.5 | 51.0 |
| | 1.090 | 21.5 | 4 | 1½ | 52.3 | 11.8 | 3.0 | 52.2 |
| | 1.095 | 24.4 | 3½ | 1½ | 54.4 | 11.6 | 3.2 | 54.2 |
| | 1.100 | 24.7 | 3½ | 1½ | 54.2 | 11.8 | 3.3 | 53.1 |
| Katahdin: Maine | 1.070 | 20.2 | 4½ | 1½ | 52.6 | 13.8 | 2.7 | 49.1 |
| | 1.075 | 20.8 | 4½ | 1½ | 54.0 | 13.6 | 3.4 | 48.4 |
| | 1.085 | 22.1 | 4 | 1½ | 54.1 | 12.6 | 2.6 | 50.5 |
| Russet Burbank: Washington | 1.100 | 26.2 | 3½ | 1½ | 56.6 | 12.1 | 4.4 | 55.7 |
| | 1.110 | 27.2 | 3 | 1½ | 57.4 | 11.2 | 5.1 | 56.2 |
| | 1.115 | 28.6 | 3 | 1½ | 58.1 | 10.6 | 4.8 | 56.9 |

Source: Kirkpatrick *et al.* (1956).
[1] Based on raw cut weight of selected strips.

bers for two months at 55°F. (13°C.) retarded sugar accumulation and gave French fries with much better color and flavor. Extensive investigations with the 1951 crop showed that color scores for French fries made from potatoes stored at 55° or 60°F. (13° or 15.5°C.), and flavor scores for French fries made from potatoes stored at 50°, 55°, or 60°F. (10°, 13°, or 15.5°C.) were significantly higher than from potatoes stored at lower temperatures."

Nevertheless, potatoes are stored at 40°F. (5°C.) or lower in many commercial storage cellars to minimize sprouting, withering, and spoilage (Feustel and Kueneman 1966). Under these conditions sugars accumulate and French-fried potatoes made therefrom will be too dark in color. When this occurs, the potatoes must be "conditioned" before processing, that is held at 70°F. (21°C.), or higher for 1 to 3 weeks prior to frying. This treatment lowers the reducing sugar content, but at the cost of actual weight losses (Feustel and Kueneman 1966). There are also trimming losses because the existing blemishes enlarge at the higher temperature.

### Inhibition of Sprouting

As indicated above, potatoes usually retain their initially good processing qualities when stored at 50°F. (10°C.) or higher. However, at these relatively high temperatures the potatoes will sprout during a long storage period if the tubers are not treated with a sprout-inhibiting chemical or irradiated. To prevent sprouting, potatoes may be treated with 3-chloro-isopropyl- N-carbamate (CIPC), maleic hydrazide (MH-40), with the methyl ester of alpha-naphthalene acetic acid (MENA), or with ionizing radiations.

Maleic hydrazide, when applied as a pre-harvest foliage spray has been shown to be effective in preventing sprouting of potatoes. The effectiveness of this chemical depends upon (1) the time and rate of application, (2) climatic and growing conditions, (3) treatment after harvest, (4) varieties, and other factors. Further information on these factors needs to be obtained before use of this chemical may be adopted generally.

Isopropyl-phenyl-carbamate (IPC) is being used in Great Britain in a limited way as a potato sprout inhibitor. The chlorinated derivative (CIPC) appears to be more effective.

Radiation with a dosage of 15,000 to 25,000 Rep has been shown to prevent sprouting of potatoes, even if they are stored at 70°F. (21°C.) (Desrosier and Rosenstock 1960). The U.S. Food and Drug Administration has recently approved the use of irradiation to prevent the sprouting of potatoes.

Sparks (1963, 1965) has found that forced circulation of highly humid air at the rate of 10 c.f.m. per ton of potatoes favors a low sugar content and markedly cuts shrinkage losses.

## Preparation for French Frying

Ziemba (1950), Tobin (1951), Jones (1953), Anon. (1955A), and Talburt and Smith (1967) have described in considerable detail the commercial preparation, frying, and freezing of French-fried potato strips. The various procedures may be summarized as follows: In the East, the potatoes are received in bags, each holding 100 lb. In Idaho, potatoes are sometimes handled in tote boxes but more commonly in sacks and bulk storage. The potatoes are emptied into a large metal-lined hopper set below the floor of the receiving room. From the hopper, the potatoes are moved by means of a drag conveyor or are flumed to the processing room where they enter a de-stoner, which removes pebbles and gives the tubers a preliminary washing as they are flumed through it in about three inches of water. Next, the potatoes drop into a flood-type washer and are pushed through a tank of rapidly circulating water by means of a chain conveyor. Here they get a 1½ min. washing, after which they are elevated by means of a flight conveyor to a belt conveyor which carries them to a scale hopper from which they are dumped into a high-pressure, steam-jacketed rotary pressure cooker in which the potatoes are subjected to steam pressure long enough to loosen the skins. In some plants, the peels are loosened by treatment in very hot (190° to 220°F.; 87.5° to 104.5°C.) caustic soda (lye) solution of about 9 to 22% concentration for 2 to 3 min. More severe peeling conditions are used on late storage potatoes.

From the cooker, the potatoes fall into a metal hopper where they are cooled with sprays of cold water. Then they are conveyed by means of a flight conveyor into a continuous peeler where rotating rubber rollers, four inches in diameter, spaced two inches apart, and a series of cold water sprays, remove most of the skins. tumbling drum washers fitted with high-pressure cold water sprays are used in some plants to remove the skins.

The peeled potatoes now pass on rubber belts along a trimming table where women trim off the sunburned, windburned, and cut parts, and remove eyes and defects (Fig. 26). For retail-size pack, potatoes over 4½

*Courtesy of J. R. Simplot Co*

Fig. 26.   Inspection of peeled potatoes in preparation for cutting into French fries.

in. thick are cut in half, discarding those with hollow centers. The trimmed potatoes are dropped on a moving center belt. Any that pass the operators move on to a return belt and again pass in front of the trimmers on an outside belt. The trimmed and peeled potatoes on the center belt are conveyed to a sizer where potatoes of less than 1¼ in. in diameter are eliminated for other uses. The main lot of larger potatoes move on a conveyor belt which empties them into a large stainless steel hopper filled with cold water. The potatoes then pass to the cutting and slitting machines which cut them into the strips for French frying. One type of machine used for this purpose is the Urschel strip cutter.

From the slitting machines, the strips pass to rotary-rod separators, or shaker type graders similar to those used for grading fruit, where they are tumbled under sprays of cold water.

Converted bean graders are also used to eliminate slivers. Nubbins may be separated by a vibrating screen after the slivers are removed. Some processors use a walking-beam grader (Fig. 27) for separating the under-

*Courtesy of J. R. Simplot Co. and Magnuson Engineers, Inc.*

Fig. 27.   Removing slivers and nubbins from French-fry cuts by means of a walking-beam grader.

sizes from those of suitable dimensions (Feustel and Kueneman 1966). This equipment consists of a series of cam-operated steps which align the strips across the length of each step. The slivers are first removed by adjusting the clearance between the steps and the nubbins are then eliminated by a series of adjustable slots built into each step. Separating the slivers from the nubbins is effected in this single unit.

The pieces that pass through rods set $\frac{3}{4}$ in. apart are separated and flumed to a whipped potato, mashed potato, hash brown potato, or potato puff line.

The main lot of strips falls on to a wire-mesh conveyor, where the strips are given a pre-blanch inspection. Any remaining small pieces and discolored pieces are picked out and discarded.

Next the strips are conveyed into a continuous circular drum blancher where the strips are blanched in water, just under the boiling point. Advantages of blanching include (a) more uniform color of fried products, (b) reduction in fat absorption, (c) reduced frying time, since the potato is partially cooked by blanching, and (d) improved texture of final product

(Feustel and Kueneman 1966). Although blanching leaches out some of the sugars on or near the surface of the slice, it does not eliminate the need for conditioning the potatoes to lower the overall reducing sugar content when this is too high for French fries of satisfactory color. However, adjustments can be made in time and temperature of blanching to minimize differences in sugar levels in different lots of potatoes since considerable variation in the raw material is encountered from time to time.

In some plants, two blanchers are used in series (Fig. 28). If the potatoes are very low in sugar, the second may contain a dilute sugar solution in order to adjust the surface sugar concentration to a level which gives the best color on frying.

Courtesy of Idaho Frozen Foods, Inc., and Christian Manufacturing Engineers, Inc.

Fig. 28.   Water blanchers in series used for French-fry cuts.

If the raw material has the optimum sugar content, hot water is used in both blanchers. The use of two blanchers instead of one increases the capacity of the plant.

The blanched strips fall onto a wire-mesh conveyor on which they are usually subjected to a hot-air blast in order to eliminate as much water as possible from the surface of the strips. Jones (1953) has described a specially designed unit for drying which may follow the dewatering screen. This consists of three horizontal belts placed one above the other. The potato strips fall from the first to the second belt while high-velocity air is blown past them as they fall.

## Frying

The next operation is frying (Fig. 29). Most packers use a two-stage fry bath—a preliminary and a final fry—in order to obtain the most uniform frying possible. As the strips are chuted to the preliminary fryer, they pass over a vibrator so that they can be evenly fed into shallow stainless steel, perforated frying baskets. The baskets filled with potato strips are attached

From Feustel, Juilly, and Harrington (1963)
Fig. 29. French fries emerging from a fryer.

to an endless chain which travels through a layer of hot fat. As a rule, just enough fat is used to keep the strips completely submerged. The frying time is varied from one lot of potatoes to another so as to obtain a uniformly colored product. As the partially fried potato stocks leave the preliminary fryer, a stainless steel wire-mesh conveyor with slats elevates the French fries and feeds them to the final fryer, which ordinarily is identical to the preliminary fryer. On the transfer from the first to the second fryer, the strips are turned over which insures even color development and avoids light areas caused by two or more pieces sticking together during the frying process.

Some plants use single stage fryers and achieve uniformity of color by turning or agitating the strips as they are conveyed through the fryer.

**Quality of Fat Used in Frying.**—Since the frozen French-fried potatoes may be stored for several months or even longer, it is important that the fat used in the frybath be of a high quality which will not deteriorate rapidly during use, nor will it develop rancidity during the storage of the product. Hydrogenated cottonseed oil and soybean oil are generally used for frying either alone or in combination (Feustel and Kueneman 1966). These hydrogenated oils have a relatively high smoke point and are resistant to foaming and gum formation. In a continuous frying operation, fresh oil is constantly added to the frybath. The number of hours required for the volume of fresh oil to equal the total content of the fryer is known as the "turn-over period." If this is relatively short, it is possible to operate the fry bath continuously without discarding any oil. A turn-over period of 10 to 16 hr. is considered satisfactory.

Particles of potatoes left behind in the fryer must be removed periodically or else they become charred and affect the quality of the oil adversely. These particles are removed either periodically or continuously by means of centrifugals or filters.

At high temperatures fatty oils may break down or deteriorate because of hydrolysis, oxidation, or polymerization. As previously pointed out, the potato slices should be free from surface moisture so as to keep hydrolysis low and prevent the build-up of free fatty acids in the frying oil.

If the oil of the frybath becomes oxidized, it will darken, may foam, and may develop off-odors and off-flavors. Further, potatoes fried in oxidized oil will have a relatively short storage life. Therefore, it is important to prevent aeration of the oil during centrifuging or filtration and to prevent contact with copper or other oxidation catalysts.

Deterioration by polymerization may cause formation of gum and gummy residues. Soybean oil is believed to be more subject to polymerization than is cottonseed oil.

### Oil Elimination and Cooling

As the strips leave the final fryer, they drop onto a wire-mesh conveyor. A vibrator drains off excess oil (Fig. 30), and distributes the French fries evenly on another mesh belt that carries them through a long cooling tunnel. Fans are used to pull cold air from outside the plant through filters and into the cooling tunnel. Some plants use refrigerated air to precool the strips. The cooled strips are usually passed over an inspection belt.

Potatoes for retail packages are fried to a golden brown so that only oven-warming is necesary for serving. Potato strips for sale to institutional outlets, hotels, and restaurants are fried to a stage where one minute additional frying in deep fat will prepare them for serving. These are called parfried potatoes.

From Feustel, Juilly, and Harrington (1963)

Fig. 30.   Defatting screen (right center) discharging on an inclined
cooling belt (center).

## Freezing

Some packers pack the precooled strips into consumer cartons which, after overwrapping and heat-sealing, are then frozen in plate freezers, e.g., Birdseye or Amerio multiplate freezers. Others freeze the strips before packaging by conveying them on wire-mesh conveyors through an air-blast freezing tunnel maintained at $-30°F.$ ($-34.5°C.$). Very rapid freezing is attained when the air blast is blown up through the perforated belt, thus attaining "fluidizing." Fluidized bed freezers are described in Chapter 5 of Volume 1.

## Packaging

The consumer pack of frozen strips is automatically filled into 9-oz. or 1-lb. cartons for the retail trade. They are also packed into poly bags, some of which hold as much as two pounds of the French-fried potatoes. The 9-oz. cartons are commonly packed 24 to the case and the larger sizes 12 per case.

Frozen parfried potatoes for the institutional trade may be packed six poly bags per 30-lb. case, or into 5-lb. cartons precision filled and automatically checkweighed (Fig. 31).

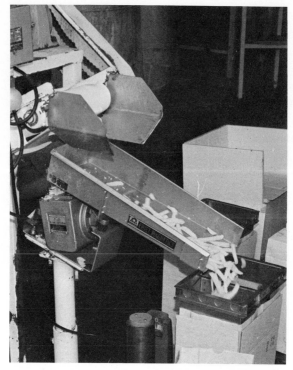

Fig. 31. Automatic filler for frozen French-fried potatoes. Potatoes are packed 10-lb. per kraft paper bag, 2 bags to the carton.

## Storage of Frozen French-Fried Potatoes

Workers at the Western Regional Research Laboratory, U.S. Dept. Agr., have found that frozen French fries are relatively more stable than most other frozen vegetables (Feustel and Kueneman 1966). They concluded that losses in quality from French-fried potatoes stored at 0°F. (−18°C.) for one year or more are insignificant. However, "oil-blanched" frozen French-fries held at ordinary refrigerator temperatures (55°F., 13°C.) for three days, then finish fried in deep fat, were significantly lower in flavor, texture, and color than those which had been held at 0°F. (−18°C.) (Boyle *et al.* 1965; Mitchener *et al.* 1965).

### OTHER POTATO PRODUCTS

As a rule, the other frozen potato products are prepared as by-products from the manufacture of frozen French fries (Fig. 32). Most of these products are listed in Table 28, p. 210.

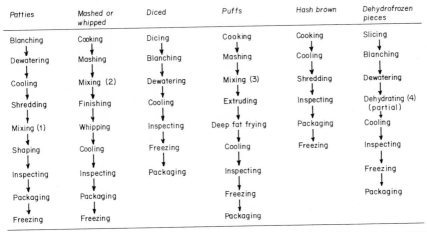

| Patties | Mashed or whipped | Diced | Puffs | Hash brown | Dehydrofrozen pieces |
|---------|-------------------|-------|-------|------------|---------------------|
| Blanching | Cooking | Dicing | Cooking | Cooking | Slicing |
| ↓ | ↓ | ↓ | ↓ | ↓ | ↓ |
| Dewatering | Mashing | Blanching | Mashing | Cooling | Blanching |
| ↓ | ↓ | ↓ | ↓ | ↓ | ↓ |
| Cooling | Mixing (2) | Dewatering | Mixing (3) | Shredding | Dewatering |
| ↓ | ↓ | ↓ | ↓ | ↓ | ↓ |
| Shredding | Finishing | Cooling | Extruding | Inspecting | Dehydrating (4) (partial) |
| ↓ | ↓ | ↓ | ↓ | ↓ | ↓ |
| Mixing (1) | Whipping | Inspecting | Deep fat frying | Packaging | Cooling |
| ↓ | ↓ | ↓ | ↓ | ↓ | ↓ |
| Shaping | Cooling | Freezing | Cooling | Freezing | Inspecting |
| ↓ | ↓ | ↓ | ↓ | | ↓ |
| Inspecting | Inspecting | Packaging | Inspecting | | Freezing |
| ↓ | ↓ | | ↓ | | ↓ |
| Packaging | Packaging | | Freezing | | Packaging |
| ↓ | ↓ | | ↓ | | |
| Freezing | Freezing | | Packaging | | |

From Feustel, Juilly, and Harrington (1963)

Fig. 32.    Partial flow sheets for processing frozen potato co-products. (1) Mixed with flour and seasoning; (2) Mixed with milk solids and salt; (3) Mixed with flour, egg solids, shortening, and seasoning; and (4) Dehydrated to 50% or more weight reduction.

## Potato Patties

Potato patties may be made from slivers and short pieces or nubbins separated from the French-fry line or from potatoes too small to be cut into French-fry strips economically. These small whole potatoes or pieces are cooked in a steam or hot water blancher, then shredded. The shredded or chopped material is mixed with potato or rice flour and salt, MSG, or other seasoning, such as onion powder. This mixture is fed to a patty forming machine which forms round or rectangular patties weighing three ounces each, and these are frozen either before or after packaging. The product can be fried in deep fat or oil, skillet-fried, boiled for mashing, baked, broiled, or prepared au gratin.

## Diced Potatoes

This product is usually prepared as hash-brown potatoes, but may be used for potato salad and in other ways.

As is the case with raw material for potato patties, small potatoes, slivers, and nubbins may be used (Fig. 33). They are run through a dicer to produce "dice" $\frac{3}{8} \times \frac{3}{8} \times \frac{3}{16}$ in. The diced product is dropped onto a blanching belt on which it is blanched in steam for three minutes. After "dewatering," the product is inspected, then mixed with seasoning, e.g., onion and salt. The product may be loose frozen on a belt or packaged and then frozen.

## Hash Brown Potatoes

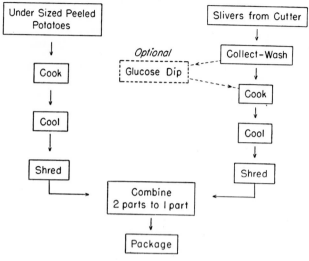

From Harrington et al. (1956)

Fig. 33.   Suggested flow sheet for production of hash-brown
potatoes.

### Whipped Potatoes

In many plants, whipped potatoes are a by-product of the production of French-fried potatoes described previously. The thin, broken, and small pieces of potatoes that are flumed from the rotary rod separators and pre-blanch inspection belt, are transferred to a wire-mesh conveyor and passed through a continuous steam blancher. Emerging from the blancher, the po-tato pieces pass to an inspection belt, where defective pieces are picked out and discarded. The potatoes are then conveyed to a pulper, where they are riced. The riced potatoes then fall into a portable bowl, which is rolled under beaters, which whip the product to the proper consistency. Finally, the whipped potatoes are hand-filled into cartons, check-weighed, closed, over-wrapped by machine with heat-sealable waxed paper, and frozen.

### Mashed Potatoes

In other plants, frozen mashed potatoes are made from the small potatoes and the thin, broken, and small strips separated from the main lot used for French frying. The small potatoes are flumed to a Model B Urschel or simi-lar cutter (Fig. 55, p. 333) then combined with the pieces and pumped to a blancher where, after dewatering, they are cooked. The cooked potatoes are conveyed to large stainless steel rolls which mash and drop the potatoes into a large mixing tank. Skim milk and salt are continuously added (amount regulated by a flowmeter) as the cooked potatoes enter the tank. The mixing is usually a continuous process. The mash is passed through a finisher to remove lumps and obtain a little aeration. The product is then filled into cartons which are placed on trays. The filled trays are put on portable racks, which, when filled, are moved into an air-blast tunnel for freezing.

In some plants, the finished mash is put through a ricer. The product is frozen on trays in an air-blast. The frozen shreds are passed through fingered breakers, filled into cartons, and cased for storage or shipment.

## Potato Puffs

Frozen potato puffs freeze well and are produced both for use as a component of frozen precooked meals and for freezing in consumer-size cartons. *Food Engineering* has suggested a formula and procedure for preparing potato puffs for freezing (Anon. 1955B), as follows:

|                          | %     |
|--------------------------|-------|
| Cooked, peeled potatoes  | 79.5  |
| Butter or margarine      | 4.5   |
| Cream (light)            | 9.0   |
| Egg yolk                 | 3.5   |
| Egg white                | 3.5   |
|                          | 100.0 |

"Whip peeled, boiled potatoes until free of lumps in beater-type mixer. Beat in butter and cream until batch is fluffy. Add well beaten egg yolks, and then fold in stiffly beaten egg whites. Form into 1½ to 2 in. diameter balls, place on greased bake sheets, brush with melted butter, and bake 15 to 20 min. in 375°F. (190.6°C.) oven. Pack cooked, cooled potato balls into consumer-size cartons, and finally freeze."

## Au Gratin Potatoes

According to Feustel and Kueneman (1966), a sauce consisting of milk, cheddar cheese, salt, MSG, and pepper is combined with cooked diced potatoes in the approximate ratio of ⅔ potato to ⅓ sauce. Rice flour, shortening, and sugar may also be added. A topping consisting of cheddar cheese, toasted bread crumbs, and margarine is sprinkled on the product preparatory to freezing.

## Potato Rounds

In order to make use of the slivers and short pieces obtained in the prep-

*Courtesy of J. R. Simplot Co.*

Fig. 34. Frozen potato rounds, a
shredded and extruded product.

aration of French-fried and par-fried potatoes, many packers are making a fried potato product known as potato rounds (Fig. 34).

Slivers, and short pieces are blanched, shredded, and mixed with potato flour, salt, and spices. The mixture is extruded, fried in deep fat, then frozen and packaged. The extruded pieces are usually ¾ in. in diameter and vary in length from ¾ to 1¼ in., depending upon the packer.

Rounds may be prepared for eating either by frying in deep fat or by heating in an oven. It is a popular hors d'oeuvre, but it is often served as the main potato dish of a meal.

**Potato Cakes**

Potato cakes are prepared by incorporating beaten eggs, chopped parsley, chopped celery or celery seed, grated onion, and salt with cold mashed potatoes or grated raw potatoes. The small and irregular blanched strips of potatoes rejected from the French-fry line may be used after they have been cooked further on a wire-mesh conveyor in a continuous steam blancher inspected and riced in a pulper. If grated raw potatoes are used, more eggs will be required to hold the cakes together than if either cold mashed potatoes or the steam-blanched, irregular strips from the French-fry line are used. After thoroughly mixing the ingredients, the potato mix is formed into cakes which are dipped either in fine bread or cracker crumbs, or flour, and then fried by the shallow fry method. Midway through the frying the cakes are flipped over and browned on the other side. After cooling, the potato cakes are packaged either in consumer-size cartons which are closed and overwrapped before freezing, or are placed on a tray as a component of a frozen precooked dinner.

## Dehydrofrozen Potato Products

Dehydrofreezing, a relatively new method of food preservation, was developed at the Western Regional Research Laboratory about a decade ago (Talburt and Ramage 1957; Van Arsdel and Copley 1964). Until recently, it was employed principally for the preservation of sliced apples, peas, and some other vegetables. This preservation method involves the dehydration of a fruit or vegetable until about one-half of the moisture content has been removed, after which it is packaged and frozen. Since dehydration is not carried to the point where the product quality is damaged; after refreshing, the fruit or vegetable still has high quality when the water is replaced. The reduction in weight and / or volume, which occurs during dehydration, makes possible substantial savings in container shipping, storage, and handling costs (refer to Chapter 12, Vol. 3, "Dehydrofreezing of fruits and vegetables" for more complete treatment).

Dehydrofreezing is also applied to the preservation of potato products, particularly mashed potatoes. This product is prepared by boiling potatoes cutting into half-inch slabs, then completing the cooking (Feustel and Kueneman 1966). The product is mashed and mixed with nonfat milk solids, after which it is extruded in a thin layer on a continuous belt drier, and dehydrated to approximately 15% moisture content. The dried product is milled slightly, inspected, packed in two-pound containers, and then frozen.

This frozen "concentrated" mashed potato is prepared for serving by adding boiling water, pressing the product into the water, adding additional milk and butter, if desired, and whipping.

## "Baked" Potatoes and Other Potato Products

Whipped potatoes are sometimes put in an aluminum foil container made in the shape of a half potato, which is then browned slightly in an oven, then packaged and frozen.

Potatoes are cooked in many other ways for use as a component of precooked frozen meals (see Chapter 24), such as oven browned, creamed, and scalloped potatoes, and boiled new potatoes.

### BIBLIOGRAPHY

Anon. 1955A. Potato "payoff" at Simplot. Western Canner and Packer 47, No. 11, 56–57, 60–61.
Anon. 1955B. Potato puff formula. Food Eng. 27, No. 10, 194.
Anon. 1957. The Ore-Ida potato pattie story. Western Canner and Packer 49, No. 5, 24–25.
Anon. 1958A. Ore-Ida potato products, a heat-and-eat item makes debut. Frosted Food Field 25, No. 3, 35.

Anon. 1958B. Potato freezing factory will establish mechanized production line. Frozen Foods *11*, No. 6, 60–62.

Anon. 1962. Fluidizing freezer offers unique flexibility. Food Eng. No. 11, 60–62.

Anon. 1963. Vegetable freezing modernization with a "fluidized" installation. Quick Frozen Foods *26*, No. 1, 46–47.

Anon. 1964A. Odd-size pieces in frozen French fried potatoes result in consumer complaints. Quick Frozen Foods *26*, No. 7, 127–131.

Anon. 1964B. How to buy frozen French fried potatoes. Canner / Packer *133*, No. 10, 4, 18.

Anon. 1964C. French fries hold on as best seller though competition narrows profits. Quick Frozen Foods *27*, No. 2, 101–104; *27*, No. 3, 249–250, 252, 254.

Anon. 1965A. Ore-Ida's Michigan plant packing million pounds of potatoes daily. Canner / Packer *134*, No. 13, 29–30.

Anon. 1965B. Perforated belt conveyors permit fast freezing of French fries. Quick Frozen Foods *27*, No. 12, 110.

Anon. 1965C. Modern potato products improved by sodium pyrophosphate. A Circular published by Victor Chemical Works Div., Stauffer Chem. Co., Chicago, Ill.

Anon. 1966A. Institutional growth frozen potatoes, based on specific cost control. Quick Frozen Foods *28*, No. 8, 105–107.

Anon. 1966B. Significant savings on frozen French fries over preparation from fresh potatoes. Quick Frozen Foods *29*, No. 2, 79–80.

Anon. 1967. Irish potatoes: utilization of the 1966 crop with comparisons. U.S. Dept. Agr., Statistical Reporting Service *Pot 1–3 (9–67)*.

Barackman, R. A., and Klis, J. B. 1962. Eliminates blackening of cooked potato products. Food Processing *23*, No. 7, 76–77.

Baxter, J. L. 1950. Prefrying treatment of potatoes. U.S. Pat. 2,498,024.

Baxter, J. L. 1957. Control over production capacity key to future French fry sales. Quick Frozen Foods *20*, No. 5, 123–125, 152.

Benes, C., Carlin, G. T., and Logan, P. 1941. Preparation of French fried potatoes in the restaurant kitchen. National Restaurant Assoc. Research Dept. Tech. Bull. *100*.

Boyle, F. P., Notter, G. F., Michener, H. D., and Guadagni, D. G. 1965. Stability of frozen French fries at refrigerator temperatures. 14th Natl. Potato Utilization Conference Rept. U.S. Dept. Agr. ARS *74–30*.

Chase, H. M. 1952. Frozen mashed potatoes. U.S. Pat. 2,597,067.

Chase, H M., and Chase, A. M. 1952. Process for preparing and preserving frozen potatoes. U.S. Pat. 2,597,066.

Davis, C. O., and Smith, O. 1964. Quality factors in the production of frozen French fries. Quick Frozen Foods *27*, No. 4, 76–79.

Desrosier, N. W., and Rosenstock, H. M. 1960. Radiation Technology in Food, Agriculture and Biology. Avi Publishing Co., Westport, Conn.

Feustel, I. C., and Kueneman, R. W. 1966. *In* Potato Processing. W. F. Talburt and O. Smith (Editors). Avi Publishing Co., Westport, Conn.

Gould, W. A. 1954. Watch color, flavor and texture when freezing French fried potatoes. Food Packer *25*, No. 2, 52–54.

Hatfield, F. H. 1964. Potato utilization in Canada. 41th Natl. Potato Conference Rept. U.S. Dept. Agr. ARS *74–30*.

Hayes, R. D. 1952. Effect of specific gravity, storage, preconditioning periods and processing methods on yield and quality of frozen French fried potatoes. M. S.

Thesis, Ohio S. Univ., Columbus, O.

Heinze, P. H., Kirkpatrick, M. E., and Dochterman, E. F. 1955. Cooking quality and compositional factors of potatoes of different varieties from several commercial locations. U.S. Dept. Agr. Tech. Bull. *1106*.

Hilliker, F. N. 1965. Ore-Ida's Michigan plant packing million pounds of potatoes daily. Canner / Packer *134*, No. 13, 29–30.

Jones, L. C. 1953. Simplot potato research leads to new quick frozen products. Western Canner and Packer *45*, No. 7, 13–15.

Kirkpatrick, M. E., Heinze, P. H., Croft, C. C., Mountjoy, B. M., and Falatko, C. E. 1956. French frying quality of potatoes as influenced by cooking methods, storage conditions and specific gravity of tubers. U.S. Dept. Agr. Tech. Bull. *1142*.

Lance, P. 1963. Seabrook Farms process improves frozen potato color. Canner / Packer *132*, No. 12, 28–29.

Lindstrom, H. R. 1961. Frozen French fried potatoes. Effect of size of pieces on consumer preferences. U.S. Dept. Agr. Marketing Research Rept. *514*.

Livingston, L. J. 1962. Lamb-Weston packs dehydrofrozen mashed and long cut French-fried potatoes by new methods. Canner / Packer *131*, No. 6, 28–29.

Livingston, L. J. 1966. French fry packer using electrical resistance of cooking oil to control heat. Canner / Packer *135*, No. 4, 37–38.

Longree, K. 1950. Quality problems in cooked frozen potatoes. Food Technol. *4*, 98–104.

Mitchener, H. D., Boyle, F. P., Notter, G. F., and Guadagni, D. G. 1965. Microbial growth on blanched French-cut potatoes. Bacteriological Proceedings, Abstracts of the 65th Ann. Meeting, Am. Soc. Microbiology.

National Association of Frozen Food Packers. 1960. Laboratory aids of research and development program. Packing and grading frozen French fried potatoes. Tech. Service Bull. *18*.

Pentzer, W. T. 1949. VIII. Storage and transportation of potatoes. U.S. Dept. Agr., Bur. Agr. and Ind. Chem. Publ., Proc., 2nd Ann. Conf. on Potatoes, *19–20*.

Porter, W. L., and Heinze, P. H. 1965. Changes in composition of potatoes in storage. Potato Handbook Potato Assoc. of America. New Brunswick, N.J.

Potter, A. L., and Belote, M. L. 1963. New potato snack item. Bakers Weekly *197*, No. 8, 42–43.

Rasmussen, C. L., Venstrom, D. W., Newman, H. J., Olson, R. L., Rockwell, W. C., and Strong, K. 1957. Latest dehydrofrozens cut costs. Food Eng. *29*, No. 12, 117–118.

Ross, L. R., and Treadway, R. H. 1962. A rapid method for determining fat in frozen French fried potatoes. Quick Frozen Foods 25, No. 1, 48, 107–108.

Schaal, B. 1955. Simplot a leader in frozen French fried potatoes. Food Packer 35, No. 2, 34–39.

Scheffel, K. G., and Klis, J. B. 1965. Use of Methocel produces uniformly golden brown—less greasy fried foods. Food Processing / Marketing 26, No. 10, 104–106, 110, 112.

Schwimmer, S., Hendel, C. E., Harrington, W. O., and Olson, R. L. 1957. Interrelation among measurements of browning of processed potatoes and sugar components. Am. Potato J. *34*, No. 5, 119–132.

Simmons, W. M. 1962. An economic study of the U.S. potato industry. U.S. Dept. Agr., Economic Research Service Agricultural Economic Rept. *6*.

Smith, O. 1951. Potato quality. Am. Potato J. *28*, No. 10, 732–737.

Smith, O.   1957.  High quality French-fries from the home kitchen.  Farm Research *23*, No. 3, 11.

Sparks. W. C.   1963.  Idaho potato storages—construction and management.  Univ. Idaho Bull. *410*.

Sparks, W. C.   1965.  Effect of storage temperatures on storage losses of Russet Burbank potatoes.  Am. Potato J. *42*, 241–246.

Talburt, W. F., and Ramage, W. D.   1957.  Dehydrofreezing of fruits and vegetables. *In* The Freezing Preservation of Foods, 3rd Edition. Vol. 1, by D. K. Tressler and C. F. Evers, Avi Publishing Co., Westport, Conn.

Talburt, W. F., and Smith, O.   1967.  Potato Processing. 2nd Edition. Avi Publishing Co., Westport, Conn.

Terman, G. L., Goven, M., and Cunningham, C. E.   1950.  Effect of storage temperature and size of French fry quality, shrinkage and specific gravity of Maine potatoes. Am. Potato J. *27*, 417–424.

Tobin, R. B.   1951.  How a Maine packer freezes French fries for 14 brands. Quick Frozen Foods *13*, No. 8, 104–105.

Treadway, R. H.   1956.  Recent developments in processed potato products. Am. Potato J. *33*, 300–312.

Tremain, H. E.   1962.  Packing quality frozen potatoes in Maine. Canner / Packer *131*, No. 8, 27–28.

U.S. Department of Agriculture.   1967.  United States Standards for grades of frozen French fried potatoes. Agr. Marketing Service, U.S. Dept. Agr.

Van Arsdel, W. B., and Copley, M. J.   1964.  Food Dehydration—Vol. 2, Products and Technology. Avi Publishing Co., Westport, Conn.

Ziemba, J. V.   1950.  Making French fries on continuous line. Food Indus. *22*, No. 5, 113–115.

## CHAPTER 10

Donald K. Tressler | Other Precooked Vegetables

## INTRODUCTION

Some vegetables, commonly sold merely as frozen vegetables, are in reality cooked products. Winter squash, pumpkin, and corn on the cob all have been steamed sufficiently long in preparation for freezing to cook them. These frozen products have been on the market since 1931 or 1932. The methods employed in preparing and freezing them have been considered in Chapter 5 of Volume 3; further details are presented in this chapter (p. 242).

Frozen "boil-in-the-bag" vegetables with either a cream sauce or a butter sauce have become very popular during the past five years. These products may be considered either as fresh or precooked. As a rule the sauce has already been cooked, but in most instances the vegetables require further cooking which is accomplished when the bags are boiled, for this reason "boil-in-the-bag" vegetables are considered in Volume 3, Chapter 5.

## ACCEPTABILITY

Although a large number of precooked vegetables are frozen commercially, either as a component of a frozen meal or of a prepared dish, such as chop suey, chicken pies, and the like, the quantities precooked and frozen are small with the exception of potatoes and onions. The list includes: Artichokes, asparagus, baked beans, green or snap beans, kidney beans, lima beans, pinto beans, soy beans, soy bean sprouts, cabbage, carrots, celery, water chestnuts, sweet corn, egg plant, okra, onions, blackeyed peas, field peas, green peas, green peppers, potatoes, pumpkin, rhubarb, rice, brown rice, wild rice, spinach, squash, sweet potatoes, tomatoes, turnips, yams, and zucchini.

Considering the large number of precooked vegetables frozen, the very considerable number of different ways of cooking each, and the great variety of combinations of vegetables which may be frozen, it is evident that detailed methods of preparation and cooking of each product cannot be given. With the exception of the methods of preparing and cooking potatoes, this chapter will be a consideration only of factors which affect the quality of the frozen product.

Woodroof and Atkinson (1945) compared the relative acceptability of

Donald K. Tressler is a consultant and President of the Avi Publishing Co., Westport, Conn.

Table 31

The Desirability of Nine Frozen Vegetables, Cooked and Uncooked, After
One Year in Storage at 0°F. ( − 18°C.)

| Vegetable | Treatment Before Freezing | Form Packed | Before Freezing | Desirability When Prepared for Serving after Freezing Storage |
|---|---|---|---|---|
| Beans, lima | steam blanched 3 min. | loose pack | — | very good |
| Beans, lima | cooked in steam 15 min. | loose pack | very good | fair |
| Beans, lima | water blanched 3 min. | loose pack | — | excellent |
| Beans, lima | cooked in water 15 min. | loose pack | excellent | poor |
| Beans, lima | cooked in water 15 min. | solid pack | excellent | very good |
| Beans, snap | steam blanched 2½ min. | loose pack | — | excellent |
| Beans, snap | cooked in steam 12 min. | loose pack | very good | fair |
| Beans, snap | cooked in water 12 min. | solid pack | excellent | very good |
| Beans, soya | steam blanched 4 min. | loose pack | — | excellent |
| Beans, soya | cooked in steam 20 min. | loose pack | very good | fair |
| Beans, soya | water blanched 4 min. | loose pack | — | excellent |
| Beans, soya | cooked in water 20 min. | loose pack | excellent | good |
| Beans, soya | cooked in water 20 min. | solid pack | excellent | very good |
| Corn | steam blanched 3½ min. | on cob, loose pack | — | poor |
| Corn | semi-cooked in steam 5 min. | on cob, loose pack | — | fair |
| Corn | cooked in steam 10 min. | on cob, loose pack | excellent | excellent |
| Corn | cooked in steam 10 min. | on cob, loose pack | very good | very good |
| Corn | steam blanched on cob 3½ min. | cut corn, cream style | — | excellent |
| Corn | semi-cooked on cob 5 min. | cut corn, cream style | — | fair |
| Corn | cooked in steam on cob 10 min. | cut corn, cream style | excellent | poor |
| Okra | steam blanched 3 min. | whole pod, loose pack | — | excellent |
| Okra | cooked in steam 12 min. | whole pod, loose pack | very good | fair |
| Okra | cooked in water 12 min. | whole pod, solid pack | excellent | very good |
| Peas, field | blanched in steam 1 min. | loose pack | — | excellent |
| Peas, field | cooked in steam 15 min. | loose pack | excellent | good |
| Peas, field | blanched in water 1 min. | loose pack | excellent | excellent |
| Peas, field | cooked in water 15 min. | loose pack | excellent | good |
| Peas, field | cooked in water 15 min. | solid pack | excellent | very good |
| Pumpkin | cooked in steam pressure 10 lb. 10 min. | purée | excellent | excellent |
| Rhubarb | none | sugar added 4:1, solid pack | — | excellent |
| Rhubarb | none | sliced, loose pack | — | very good |
| Rhubarb | steam-blanched 3 min. | sugar added 4:1, solid pack | — | good |
| Rhubarb | steam-blanched 3 min. | sliced, loose pack | — | fair |
| Rhubarb | cooked in steam | solid pack | excellent | excellent |
| Sweet potato | cooked in steam pressure 10 lb. 10 min. | purée, solid pack | excellent | excellent |

Source: Woodroof and Atkinson (1945).

several vegetables (a) when blanched and frozen and (b) when precooked
and frozen. In most instances, the blanched product was definitely superior
to that which had been precooked (Table 31). However, the corn on the
cob which had been cooked by steaming for ten minutes was much superi-
or to that which had been steam-blanched for only 3½ minutes. This indicates clearly the need for a long blanch, substantially cooking the product, in order to inactivate the enzymes of corn on the cob, if a stable product is to be obtained.

In discussing the results of the work summarized in Table 31, Woodroof and Atkinson state:

"Information in Table 31, shows that lima beans, snap beans, soy beans, okra, and cream-style corn kept in excellent condition when properly blanched and stored as a loose pack for one year at 0°F. ( −18°C.). However, when identical lots of these products were precooked (either with steam or by boiling), packaged the same way, and stored for one year, they were fair to poor in quality. None of these lots was covered with a solution or other medium while in storage, which possibly accounts for much of the loss of aroma and flavor. Numerous other tests were run which showed that as the amount of heating prior to freezing increased beyond that required to heat the pieces throughout, there was a gradual loss of fresh green color and a progressive loss of aroma and flavor developed in all lots which had been heated more than seven minutes and packed loosely. The texture also was poor.

"On the other hand, purée of pumpkins, sweet potatoes, and a few other vegetables that were cooked and solid-packed kept in excellent condition. Rhubarb kept in better condition when unblanched, and corn on the cob kept best when not only the corn was cooked but the cob as well."

### STORAGE LIFE

Hanson *et al.* (1950) carried out a detailed study of the relative storage qualities of blanched and precooked frozen peas, sweet corn, Kentucky Wonder beans, celery, carrots, lima beans, peppers, and Chinese water chestnuts. Table 32 is a summary of results of these tests. These results indicate that cooked peas develop an off-flavor in storage at a faster rate than do blanched peas. Since there was no difference in degree of off-flavor at the original evaluation, the difference in flavor is not caused by over-cooking of the peas before processing or during reheating. These data indicate the value of packing peas in a cream sauce or some other liquid in order to shut out the air from intimate contact with the cooked peas and thus prevent development of off-flavor during storage.

Hanson *et al.* also conclude that with careful control of processing conditions it is possible to produce precooked frozen vegetables of any desired degree of crispness. This can be accomplished by varying the cooking time before freezing and by rigid control of the reheating process.

Hanson *et al.* also studied the influence of the length of the reheating period on the color and texture of frozen precooked peas, sweet corn, snap beans, celery, carrots, lima beans, and peppers, varying the time in a steam bath from 25 to 40 min. Golden Cross Bantam sweet corn and Kentucky Wonder snap beans were the only ones not affected by increasing the re-

Table 32

Panel Mean Off-Flavor Scores[1] Showing Off-Flavor Development in
Frozen Peas[2]

| | | | Pre-Freezing Treatment | | |
|---|---|---|---|---|---|
| Variety | Size | Storage Time at 0°F. (—18°C.) (Months) | 65–73-Second Blanch at 212°F. (100°C.) | 5-Minute Cook at 212°F. (100°C.) | 5-Minute Cook, Solid Pack[3] |
| Wyola | 2 to 5 | 0 | 1.0 | 0.9 | 0.9 |
| | | 2 | 1.2 | 1.8 | 0.9 |
| | | 4 | 1.6 | 2.3 | 1.8 |
| | | 8 | 2.2 | 5.1 | 3.2 |
| | | 12 | 2.5 | 5.6 | 2.5 |
| McFee No. 9 | 3 to 6 | 0 | 0.2 | 0.3 | 0.2 |
| | | 2 | 1.1 | 1.5 | 0.9 |
| | | 4 | 1.4 | 3.0 | 1.4 |
| | | 8 | 1.9 | 4.8 | 1.5 |
| | | 12 | 2.8 | 5.3 | 2.2 |
| McFee No. 9 | 7 to 8 | 0 | 1.6 | 1.8 | 1.8 |
| | | 2 | 1.3 | 1.6 | 1.6 |
| | | 4 | 1.7 | 2.4 | 1.8 |
| | | 12 | 2.5 | 5.5 | 2.6 |

Source: Hanson, Winegarden, Horton, and Lineweaver (1950).
[1] 0 = no off-flavor; 3 = slight off-flavor; 7 = decided off-flavor; 10 = extreme off-flavor.
[2] White sauce added to cooked peas before freezing in No. 1 short unlacquered tin cans.
[3] In white sauce.

heating period beyond the recommended 25 min. The crisp texture of
Wyola peas (sizes 2 to 5), and of the McFee No. 9 peas (sizes 7 to 8) was
retained better than that of the McFee No. 9 peas (sizes 3 to 6). All of the
peas, however, deteriorated in color after an increase of five minutes
beyond the 25-min. period. All of the other vegetables studied showed a
significant deterioration in either color or texture or both after reheating for
5 to 10 min. beyond the 25-min. period.

These authors compared the deterioration of one lot of precooked and
blanched frozen peas during holding on a steam table and found that both
deteriorated in color and texture at the same rate.

Paul et al. (1952) studied the freezing of boiled asparagus, green beans,
carrots, broccoli, and cauliflower. They concluded that fully cooked vegetables after freezing, storage, and reheating were limp, watery, and mushy
and also usually had a stale, "warmed over" flavor. The off-flavor in reheated frozen cooked carrots was not so pronounced as in the case of the
other four vegetables studied.

### PRECOOKING AND FREEZING GREEN VEGETABLES

From Woodroof and Atkinson's (1945), Hanson et al. (1950) and Paul *et al.* (1952) studies of the preparation, precooking, freezing, and use of various green vegetables, certain conclusions may be reached:

(1) Certain cooked vegetables are difficult to freeze and reheat in the form of the whole vegetable or in large pieces without obtaining a product with a warmed-over appearance, color, flavor, and texture, e.g., asparagus, beet greens, and broccoli.

(2) Nearly all vegetables, when puréed, chopped, or otherwise comminuted, can be cooked, frozen, and then successfully reheated without marked loss of color or change in flavor. Thus, frozen precooked asparagus purée, chopped broccoli, chopped beet greens, and tomato purée are excellent products.

(3) Similarly, the addition of a white, cream, or other fluid or semifluid sauce, or combining vegetables, so as to get a semifluid or solid pack (e.g., combining other vegetables with tomatoes, as in preparing a scalloped vegetable, combining celery, mushrooms, onions, and bean sprouts, with chopped meat in the making of chop suey), usually results in a vegetable dish which freezes well and can be reheated without marked change in character, color, or flavor.

(4) The addition of monosodium glutamate to the sauce or combination of vegetables aids in retaining the flavor and preventing the development of "warmed-over" characteristics.

(5) Only vegetables at optimum maturity should be cooked for freezing. If the vegetable is immature, the product after reheating is likely to be of very soft texture and may be shriveled, e.g., immature peas. On the other hand, tough or stringy vegetables must not be selected for precooking, for it will be difficult to produce a tender product of good color and flavor therefrom. This is particularly important in the case of asparagus, snap beans, broccoli, kohlrabi, peas, rutabagas, turnips, and turnip greens. Of course, it is of greatest importance to use vegetables of uniform maturity. Quality graders (see Chapter 5 of Volume 3) may be used to eliminate overmature peas and lima beans by flotation in brine.

(6) The selection of a variety of any particular vegetable which cooks uniformly and freezes well is of considerable importance, e.g., Blue Lake and Kentucky Wonder snap beans have a pronounced bean flavor, deep color, and a desirable texture. For additional information concerning varietal suitability of vegetables commonly frozen, see Chapter 5 of Volume 2.

(7) The vegetables should be prepared for cooking by the same general procedures described in Chapter 5 of Volume 3, for the preparation of vegetables for blanching and subsequent freezing.

(8) As a rule, the vegetables should be slightly undercooked so that during cooling, freezing, and reheating it will not either become mushy or lose color and flavor and take on the characteristics of a warmed over product.

This is particularly important in the case of tender or immature vegetables.

(9) It follows logically that, immediately after precooking, the product should be rapidly cooled with a minimum of agitation; otherwise the hot product will continue to cook, with resultant loss of fresh flavor, color, and texture. Rapid cooling under sanitary conditions is also necessary to prevent multiplication of microorganisms.

(10) The product should be packaged in air-tight, moisture-vapor-proof, hermetically-sealed cartons or other containers, which preferably should be impermeable to oxygen. If small metal packages are used, hot filling, followed by immediate rapid cooling, is desirable. For further information concerning the packaging of precooked foods, see Chapter 4 of this volume.

(11) The packaged product should be rapidly frozen. Either an airblast freezer or a plate or some other type of quick freezer may be employed (see Chapters 5 and 6 of Volume 1).

(12) The product should be stored at a low temperature, 0°F. ($-18$°C.), or lower. A low storage temperature is absolutely essential in the case of loose-frozen products or those which are not protected with a cream sauce or gravy and not "solid" packed. Additional information concerning storage of precooked products are presented in Chapter 24 of this volume.

(13) When prepared for use, they should be quickly reheated to a temperature of 180° to 185°F. (82° to 85°C.). Most products do not need to be thawed before they are placed in a double boiler or other container for reheating. However, more uniform reheating will be effected if the containers of precooked foods are allowed to stand on a kitchen counter or table for an hour, or, if the products are packed in tin cans, the cans are floated in cold water for 30 to 45 min. prior to removal from the container. In any case the product will be best if served as soon as the precooked vegetable has reached serving temperature.

### Freezing Cabbage

Sather (1967) studied the freezing of the following cabbage dishes: (1) cabbage wedges with corned beef slices; (2) cabbage wedges with corned beef slices in horseradish flavored butter sauce; (3) cabbage chunks in butter sauce; (4) cabbage chunks in cheese sauce; (5) shredded cabbage in sweet and sour sauce; (6) shredded cabbage Hawaiian style with pineapple; (7) cabbage leaf rolls stuffed with hamburger with tomato sauce; (8) Chinese shredded cabbage (with soya sauce and sugar); and (9) chunk cabbage and meat balls in tomato sauce. She concluded that the cabbage was best if given a very short cook in steam or boiling water (2 or 3 min). She recommends reheating at 450°F. (232°C.) for 20 to 25 min. The cabbage chunks in cheese sauce and the cabbage wedges with corned beef in horseradish-flavored butter sauce were considered to be the most acceptable of all the cabbage products frozen.

### PREPARATION OF OTHER PRECOOKED VEGETABLES

#### Beans

**Dried Beans — Pork and Tomato Sauce Type**—Frozen precooked "Navy" or "pea" beans were suggested as a precooked frozen food item by the Western Regional Research Laboratory of the U.S. Department of Agriculture in 1943 (Anon. 1943A and B). The formula and procedure recommended for preparing, cooking, packaging, and freezing pork and beans of the tomato sauce type follows:

#### Yield

About 1775 one-pound packages.

#### Equipment

Steam or water blancher, vats for soaking the beans, retort, open or jacketed kettle, and packaging equipment.

#### Ingredients

Beans:　415 lb.
Pork:　56 lb. of trimmed meat.
Sauce:

| | |
|---|---|
| Tomato purée (1.035 sp. gr. basis) | 270 lb. |
| | (31 gal.) |
| Sugar | 47 lb. |
| Salt | 17 ¼ lb. |
| Onion, fresh (ground) | 6 lb. |
| Allspice, whole | 6 oz. |
| Cinnamon, whole | 7 oz. |
| Clove, whole | 6 oz. |
| Mace, whole | 4 oz. |
| Fat from the cooked pork | Amount available |
| Cornstarch | 13 ½ lb. |
| Pectin, citrus, slow-set (100 grade basis) | 5 ¼ lb. |
| Water to make 100 gal. of mixture weighing about 900 lb. Add 48 gal. (400 lb.) before cooking; then make up to volume after cooking. | |

#### Procedure

Beans:　Blanch small white beans for four minutes at 170°F. (76.5°C.). Then soak in soft, cold water about 16 hr., changing the water three times during the soaking period. Drain and cook in wire baskets 50 min. at 15-lb. steam pressure. Longer cooking yields a darker-brown bean but reduces the thiamine (vitamin $B_1$) content.

Pork: Cut the pork into ½-oz. pieces and cook in a covered pan in a retort for 30 min. at 15 lb. steam pressure.

Sauce: Tie the broken-up spices and ground onion in a cloth bag and cook them in the 48 gal. of water for about an hour in order to extract the flavor. Then remove the bag of spices and add 32 lb. of sugar, the salt, and the tomato purée. Mix together the pectin, cornstarch, and the remaining 15 lb. of sugar, and into this mixture stir the melted fat from the cooked pork and enough cold water to make a thin paste. Add this paste to the hot tomato-water-spice mixture and cook until the sauce loses its opaqueness and becomes clear (about five min.). Makes up to 100 gal.

### Packaging

Fill the packages with 48% cooked beans and 52% sauce by weight; make allowance for, and include in each one-pound package, a piece of cooked pork which weighed one-half ounce before cooking. The finished pork and beans with these proportions contains 69% moisture, which is within the 70% legal limit for canned pork and beans.

### Freezing and Storage

Freeze and store at 0°F. ( −18°C.) or lower temperature.

### Preparation for Serving

Partially thaw the pork and beans in the package in order to prevent overcooking and mashing of the outside layer before the center portion is thawed during cooking. Heat to serving temperature in a casserole in the oven or in a double boiler on top of the stove.

**Baked Beans.**—During World War II, canned baked beans were one of the many products curtailed in production by the restrictions on the use of tin cans. Because of this, many processors packed frozen baked beans (Hutchings and Evers 1947).

When the packers tried freezing oven baked beans, a mushy-textured product was obtained, if the beans received the same processing treatment as those packed in cans. When the baking time was reduced, a better-textured product was obtained but one which had poorer flavor and lacked the typical rich brown color of oven baked beans. Hutchings and Evers (1947) found that, if the ratio of water to syrup was lowered, the baked beans retained the desired texture and color and the flavor was characteristic of oven baked beans. A description of the procedure used follows:

"California small white beans, packed in 100-lb. bags, were emptied into a hopper which fed into a shaker-type screen cleaner. This removed some of the lighter foreign material. As the beans fell off the screen, they were subjected to a blower fan which further cleaned them. The raw product was then flumed into a riffle where heavier foreign matter, such as stones or sticks, were separated from the beans. A conveyor belt raised the beans and dropped them on a wide rubber sorting belt where defective beans were removed. This belt emptied the beans into large wooden tubs. Some moisture adhered to the beans from the cleaning process, so they were allowed to stand and drain completely. The beans were never soaked.

"A given quality of syrup was combined with several hundred pounds of cleaned beans in an iron pot. The beans were baked for approximately three hours in a gas-fired brick oven, then the fire was reduced and the dampers closed to develop the color. After five hours from the start of the bake, the beans were stirred, water added to the surface of the beans, and the salt pork placed over the beans on perforated trays. The beans were agitated only 2 or 3 times during the entire baking process. Usually, water was added only once during the bake. As the beans came from the oven, they were conveyed down a cooling chute where the syrup was diluted. Iron pots of the same type were used to collect the beans and carry them to the packing line. The amount of water added here was in direct proportion to the amount of evaporation during the baking."

Hutchings and Evers reported that after several weeks frozen storage, the product prepared as described above had a good color and texture, but had a rancid fatty flavor. However, they found that, when the pork was coarsely ground and mixed with the beans before baking, it did not become rancid during baking and / or subsequent freezing and storage. The commercial processing procedure was therefore changed accordingly.

A tested formula and procedure recommended for producing a frozen product resembling home-made baked beans follows:

**Ingredients**

| | |
|---|---|
| 10 lb. "pea" beans | 2.0 lb. dark molasses |
| 4 lb. fat salt pork | 6 oz. catsup |
| 2 oz. salt | 1 oz. dry ground mustard |
| 0.5 lb. sugar | |

The beans are sorted to eliminate dark beans and foreign matter, then washed. The washed beans are covered with cold water and soaked overnight. After draining, they are placed in a steam kettle covered with fresh water and heated slowly, keeping the water below the boiling point. The beans are cooked until the skins will burst when they are rapidly cooled. This is determined by withdrawing a few beans in a spoon and blowing on them. When sufficiently cooked, the cooking water is drained. The pork should be scalded, scraped, and then cut in ½-in. dice and mixed with the beans. The sugar, salt, molasses, catsup, and mustard are mixed and then stirred into a quart of boiling water. The pork and beans should be placed in a baking dish, preferably in a covered earthenware pot or crock. The mixture of sugar, salt, molasses, catsup, and mustard is added, then enough more boiling water to cover the beans, which should be baked in a slow oven (250°F., 121°C.) for about eight hours. The cover should be kept on the pot for the first seven hours, then removed for the last hour. Boiling water may be added if the beans appear dry at the end of the seven hours of baking.

Dried *kidney beans* may be substituted for the Navy or pea beans in the above baked bean recipe.

Dried *lima beans* also may be substituted for the Navy or pea beans. When lima beans are used, only about two hours baking is required. Soup stock is sometimes used to cover the beans, instead of boiling water.

## EGG PLANT

Egg plant is a vegetable which freezes very well in many forms. It may be sliced, dipped in batter, and fried in a shallow fryer. Or it may be cut into strips and fried in deep fat. It may be baked, broiled, boiled, scalloped, sautéed, creamed, prepared as egg plant creole, or cooked in many other ways. Further, the frozen product has no competition with the canned vegetable. Since fresh eggplant is available for only a relatively short season, the production and sale of the frozen vegetable should continue to increase.

French-Fried.—Egg plant, fried in deep fat, is an excellent dish, having commercial possibilities. In preparing this product the "eggs" are washed, peeled, cut into slices and then into strips, just as potatoes are prepared for French-frying (p. 215). The strips are blanched for four minutes. After draining, the strips are fried in a continuous deep fat fryer according to the procedure used in cooking French-fried potatoes (see p. 219). The fried product is drained of fat, cooled by fans, then either packaged in rectangular cartons, which are overwrapped, and quick frozen in a plate freezer, or frozen on a belt or on trays in an air blast, then packaged in cartons which are overwrapped.

## ONIONS

### French-fried

French-fried onion rings are becoming more and more popular, and consequently more packers are preparing and freezing them. Both the frozen breaded raw product, prepared for institutional use, and frozen French-fried onion rings ready for reheating by the housewife or the chef are marketed. The total production in 1965 was approximately 16,000,000 lb.

The procedure of preparing and frying onion rings may be summarized as follows: The butt ends of large Spanish or Bermuda onions 3 to 4 in. in diameter are cut off. Compressed air is then employed to blow off the peeling. Then they are thoroughly washed in cold water. The washed onions are mechanically cut into slices three-eights in. in thickness.

The slices are dropped into a tank of water in which they begin to separate into rings. They pass on to a vibrator separator where the separation into rings is completed. The rings are then dipped in batter. A dry batter mix which gives a satisfactory product has the following percentage composition: Dry nonfat milk 50; dry whole egg 8; wheat flour 26; and wheat gluten 16. The batter is prepared by stirring this mix into $\frac{2}{3}$ its weight of water.

After coating the rings with batter, they are immediately (within four seconds) dusted with breading mix. A breading which gives satisfactory results has the following composition:

|  | % |
|---|---|
| Corn flour | 48.3 |
| Wheat (bread) flour | 38.2 |
| Salt | 6.0 |
| Nonfat dry milk | 3.0 |
| Paprika | 1.6 |
| Whole egg powder | 1.0 |
| Monosodium glutamate | .6 |
| Onion powder | .3 |
| Soda | .2 |
| Sodium aluminum sulfate | .2 |
| White pepper | .2 |
| Celery salt | .2 |
| Red pepper | .1 |
| Rosemary, freshly ground | .1 |
|  | 100.0 |

The onions should be fried in deep fat at 350° to 385°F. (177° to 196°C.) until they become golden. After frying two minutes on one side, they should be flipped over, so as to fry both sides uniformly.

Some packers freeze the rings before packaging, then pack them in small bags; other packers pack the fried onion rings in layers in cartons and then quick freeze them.

**Storage Life of Frozen Onion Rings.**—According to Anon. (1965), if the onions have been fried in fresh oil, onion rings will retain their quality for one year at 0°F. (−18°C.). If, however, the oil has been used in the frybath for some time, the rings may turn rancid if held longer than six months at 0°F. (−18°C.).

### Freezing Prepared Uncooked Onions

Relatively small quantities of uncooked onions are frozen in Colorado. In this plant (Livingston 1963), the onions are flame-peeled, then washed with powerful sprays of water, after which they are trimmed. The trimmed product is rapidly frozen (IQF) in an air-blast tunnel, then either stored in bulk or packed into 50-lb. multi-wall bags.

#### STUFFED SWEET PEPPERS

Stuffed peppers can be frozen without great change and are a delicious luncheon dish. Their preparation is relatively simple; it may be described as follows:

Large green peppers are washed. One side is cut away and the seeds scraped out. The prepared peppers and pieces that have been cut away are steam blanched for five minutes, then cooled and filled with a "stuffing." This is made by grinding cooked ham, cooked corn beef, or raw beef, then mixing with an equal quantity of cold cooked rice. The blanched pieces cut from the green peppers are chopped and mixed with the stuffing. Four or six of the stuffed peppers are placed in a shallow aluminum foil pan, a tomato sauce is added; then the lid of the container is put in place and the product frozen in an air blast.

### WINTER SQUASH[1] AND PUMPKIN

Fully mature, hard shelled squash are washed, then cut up; the seeds and stringy material removed. The cut squash is cooked by steaming until it is soft; this requires 30 to 45 min. (Anon. 1953B). A continuous steamer may be used for the purpose. The steamed squash is conveyed to a finisher or pulper which separates most of the rind from the pulp. Use of a screen with about 0.04-in. openings is recommended. The squash is then rapidly cooled to prevent discoloration. This may be done in a shallow metal vat or trough which is partially immersed in running cold water. A screw conveyor may be used to move the squash through the cooling trough. The cool squash is filled into moisture-vapor-proof cartons and preferably quick frozen.

The Agricultural Marketing Service of the U.S. Department of Agriculture first published *United States Standards of Frozen Cooked Squash* effective October 5, 1953 (Anon. 1953B).

Pumpkin may be prepared according to the process described for squash. Blends of pumpkin and winter squash are also frozen commercially.

### SWEET POTATOES

**Varietal Suitability**

The types of sweet potatoes grown for food may be divided into two groups: (1) the so-called "dry-fleshed," more properly called firm, and (2) the so-called "moist-fleshed" or soft-varieties, popularly but erroneously called "yams." It is not the higher moisture content that makes a soft variety softer, after cooking, than a firm variety, but the character of the solids that it contains. Soft and firm describe the cooked flesh. When raw, the flesh on all varieties is hard.

Requirements of a variety for baking are that they be well flavored, easily cooked to the soft stage, and have a high moisture and sugar content.

Woodroof (1946) has indicated that the Porto Rico, Earlyport, and other moist- or soft-type varieties are preferable for purée and baked sweet potatoes for freezing. The Goldrush, Jersey Orange, Maryland Gold, and other dry- or firm-type are recommended by Woodroof and Shelor (1956) for candying.

Hoover and Pope (1959) have carried out a comprehensive study of the varietal suitability of 11 varieties of sweet potatoes cured for 7 days at 85°F. (29.5°C.), then stored at 55°F. (13°C.) until processed. The sweet potatoes were prepared for freezing by (1) peeling in 10% lye for 7 min., (2) rinsing, (3) trimming, (4) slicing into one-half inch thick slices, then (5) cooking in

---

[1] See also Chapter 4, Vol. 3.

Table 33

Palatability of Frozen Glazed Sweet Potatoes in Four Types of Glaze
Freshly Prepared and After Frozen Storage at 0°F. ( − 18°C.) for 0, 4, 8, and 12
Months [1]

| Glaze No. | Ingredients in Glazes | Storage Time, Months | Palatability Scores | | | |
|---|---|---|---|---|---|---|
| | | | Color | Flavor | Texture | Consistency of Glaze |
| 1 | Sugar 3 parts; brown sugar 3 parts; water 2 parts | fresh cooked | 4.4 | 4.6 | 4.7 | 4.6 |
| | | frozen, 0 | 4.0 | 4.0 | 4.3 | 4.6 |
| | | 4 | 4.0 | 3.7 | 3.6 | 4.0 |
| | | 8 | 3.8 | 3.5 | 3.6 | 3.5 |
| | | 12 | 3.9 | 3.5 | 2.9 | 3.0 |
| 2 | Sugar, brown sugar, water, orange juice; 64 parts glaze; No. 1 plus 9 parts orange juice | fresh cooked | 4.4 | 4.6 | 4.3 | 4.6 |
| | | frozen, 0 | 4.7 | 4.0 | 4.2 | 4.4 |
| | | 4 | 4.2 | 3.7 | 3.5 | 4.1 |
| | | 8 | 4.2 | 3.4 | 3.6 | 3.4 |
| | | 12 | 4.5 | 3.2 | 3.0 | 3.1 |
| 3 | Sugar 3 parts; corn syrup 3 parts; water 2 parts | fresh cooked | 4.7 | 4.6 | 4.4 | 4.5 |
| | | frozen, 0 | 4.7 | 4.1 | 4.3 | 4.3 |
| | | 4 | 3.7 | 3.5 | 3.3 | 4.2 |
| | | 8 | 4.0 | 2.9 | 3.1 | 3.2 |
| | | 12 | 3.5 | 2.9 | 2.7 | 2.6 |
| 4 | Sugar, corn syrup, water, orange juice; 64 parts No. 1 plus 9 parts orange juice | fresh cooked | 4.8 | 4.6 | 4.5 | 4.7 |
| | | frozen, 0 | 4.7 | 4.0 | 3.7 | 4.2 |
| | | 4 | 3.5 | 3.1 | 3.1 | 4.1 |
| | | 8 | 3.3 | 2.4 | 3.2 | 2.9 |
| | | 12 | 3.1 | 2.5 | 2.9 | 2.9 |

Source: Mountjoy and Kirkpatrick (1951).
[1] Mean scores of three judges from three replications; a score of 5 represents the highest score, 1 the lowest.

boiling 50% sugar syrup for 10 min. The cooked slices were packed into aluminum trays and frozen in an air blast at 0°F. ( − 18°C.).

Hoover and Pope's summary of the results is shown in Table 33. Color intensity was highest in frozen sweet potatoes of the Copper Skin Goldrush, Allgold, and Nugget varieties. The color of Kandee, Arcadian, Georgia Red, Nemagold, and Carogold varieties was quite acceptable for freezing but not entirely satisfactory in Porto Rico, Earlyport, and Redgold. They found that uniformity of color varied widely. Arcadian and Nemagold varieties were rated fairly high in color intensity, but were somewhat variegated. The color of frozen Goldrush, Allgold, Nugget, Georgia Red, and Kandee varieties was very uniform.

Hoover and Pope found that although discoloration was very pronounced in the frozen Nemagold and Redgold varieties, little or no discoloration was noted in the Kandee, Georgia Red, Goldrush, Allgold, and Nugget varieties.

The frozen Porto Rico, Georgia Red, and Allgold received the highest texture ratings. The flavor of the Porto Rico variety was preferred. However, all of the other varieties had a satisfactory flavor except the Goldrush, which seemed to have a slight off-flavor.

For a detailed consideration of sweet potato varieties, the reader is referred to the Department of Agriculture Farmers' Bulletin by Boswell (1950).

## Curing

If sweet potatoes are not properly cured at a high humidity, excessive loss by decay occurs during storage. Further, the quality of the cooked product may be inferior. Curing is best carried out by holding at 85°F. (29.5°C.) and a relative humidity of 85% for a period of ten days. Curing too long results in excessive sprouting and in a greater loss in weight than necessary. However, if curing is effected at a lower temperature, a longer period should be used. Thus, at 80°F. (27.7°C.) 12 to 16 days, at 75°F. (24°C.) 20 to 28 days, and at 70°F. (21°C.), 28 to 42 days are required (Lutz and Simons 1948). During curing, sweet potatoes lose water rather rapidly at first, but the rate becomes relatively slow after ten days. The following comments of Lutz and Simons concerning the changes in sweet potatoes during curing are noteworthy:

"Since most of the loss in weight is due to loss of water, one might suppose that the curing process causes the root to become more or less dried out. Many persons speak of well-cured sweet potatoes as being dried out; as a matter of fact although the roots have lost 5 to 10% in weight, there is almost the same proportion of water and dry matter in them as before curing. Thus the flesh of properly cured sweet potatoes, when baked or otherwise cooked, is apparently no less moist than the uncured ones. In fact, the flesh of baked cured sweet potatoes is apparently much more moist and juicy than that of similarly prepared uncured ones. Curing results in a decided improvement in the sweetness of the sweet potato because of a rapid change in much of the starch to dextrin and sugars."

Hoover and Pope (1959) also compared the effect of the various curing treatments on various quality factors. Surprisingly, there was little variability in the quality of the frozen product that could be attributed to curing. When the sweet potatoes were cooked in 30 to 45% syrup, the uncured samples had flavor superior to the cured samples. In general, the flavor of the cured samples improved as concentration of the syrup in which they were cooked increased. It also improved in the case of the uncured samples but reached a peak at 45% concentration, after which it tended to decline.

In general, longitudinally sliced frozen potatoes cooked in 45 to 60% sucrose were the best.

## Problems Encountered in Freezing

Fresh sweet potatoes do not store well and consequently are very scarce at certain seasons of the year. Raw sweet potatoes darken during freezing and subsequent storage. However, the cooked product freezes very well indeed; consequently one might expect that considerable quantities of cooked sweet potatoes would be frozen, but nevertheless it is not an important frozen food item. Some sweet potatoes are frozen in New Jersey, Pennsylvania, and Maryland. In addition some cooked sweet potatoes are used as a component of frozen precooked meals (Anon. 1955).

**Prevention of Discoloration.**—Woodroof and Atkinson (1944 A and B) indicated that puréed cooked sweet potatoes were satisfactorily preserved by freezing, and noted that the addition of 0.2% citric acid to the purée was effective in retaining the color during the storage of the frozen product. Dipping of slices of cooked sweet potatoes in a citric acid solution or in lemon juice before packaging for freezing has also been found to be similarly effective. Fenton and Darfler (1946) and Fenton (1951) recommended combining one part of orange juice with each four parts of mashed sweet potato prior to packaging for home freezing. For commercial use, the addition of citric acid, as recommended by Woodroof, would appear to be more practical.

More recently, Hoover (1964) has studied the use of phosphates (sodium acid pyrophosphate, tetrasodium pyrophosphate, and a 3:1 mixture of sodium acid pyrophosphate and tetrasodium pyrophosphate) as color preservatives for precooked, frozen sweet potatoes. In Hoover's experiments, small whole and sliced sweet potatoes were cooked in a 25% sucrose solution containing 0.0 to 1.0% of one of the phosphates listed above.

They concluded that sodium acid pyrophosphate was very effective in preventing discoloration of frozen sweet potatoes. However, in cut pieces it imparted a slightly acid flavor to the product when used alone in concentrations above 0.5% in the sucrose syrup. Tetrasodium pyrophosphate was effective in preventing discoloration; however in addition to off-flavor, a serious problem of sloughing of the outer tissue occurred when it was used alone at levels above 0.2%. A 3:1 mixture of sodium acid pyrophosphate and tetrasodium pyrophosphate was almost as effective as the acid form alone, and no off-flavor was noted when the mixture was used at higher concentrations; it did, however, cause some sloughing of the tissue when used at concentrations above 0.6%. Hoover concluded that the treated sweet potatoes should have a pH between 5.75 and 6.18 if they were to be free from off-flavors and sour flavors.

Mountjoy and Kirkpatrick (1951) have studied the freezing of glazed sweet potatoes in an effort to determine the type of glaze best suited for use in preparation of the frozen product which is to be cold stored for several months. A summary of their results is shown in Table 33. Mountjoy and Kirkpatrick conclude that of the four glazes tried on frozen precooked sweet potatoes, the brown sugar glaze with orange juice (No. 2) maintained the best color, and was one of the two glazes highest in flavor.

Based on the studies reported above, the following procedures are recommended for the preparation, cooking, and freezing of sweet potatoes:

## Mashed or Puréed Sweet Potatoes

Fully cured sweet potatoes should be washed. If the operations are conducted on a large scale, the washed sweet potatoes should be graded according to size, then immersed in a boiling lye solution containing 7 to 10% of caustic soda for 5 or 6 min. The treated potatoes should be washed in a squirrel-cage washer equipped with powerful sprays of water to wash off the peels and cool them. The peeled potatoes should be trimmed to eliminate pieces of peel and dark spots and then cooked in a retort under ten pounds steam pressure long enough to bring the temperature in the center of the potatoes to 190°F. (88°C.). The time required for steaming under ten pounds pressure varies depending on the size of the potatoes, as follows:

| Diameter of Potato in In. | Time in Min. |
|---|---|
| 4.5 | 30 |
| 4.0 | 25 |
| 3.5 | 23 |
| 3.0 | 20 |
| 2.5 | 15 |
| 2.0 | 7 |

Steam pressure higher than ten pounds is undesirable because the exterior of the potato will become too soft before the interior reaches 190°F. (88°C.).

The cooked, peeled sweet potatoes may be pulped in a ricer or in a rotary pulper. The riced or puréed potatoes are placed in the portable bowl of a large mixer. For each 100 lb. of the riced or puréed sweet potatoes, 4 to 6 oz. of citric acid, 1 lb. of salt, and some sugar (if desired) are added and the mixer operated until a uniform mix has been obtained. Then the product is packaged and frozen.

If the operations are conducted on a relatively small scale, the washed sweet potatoes may be cooked and the skins loosened in the same operation by steaming under ten pounds pressure. After the potatoes have cooled, the skins are removed with a knife. After trimming the potatoes are puréed, and mixed with citric acid etc. as directed above.

## Glazed Sweet Potatoes

The sweet potatoes are washed, inspected, and then cooked until tender either by boiling or steaming. The cooked potatoes are allowed to cool, then the peels are removed with a knife and the peeled potatoes trimmed to remove dark spots. A syrup is prepared by dissolving 32 parts of granulated sugar and 32 parts of brown sugar in 24 parts of water, heating the resultant syrup almost to the boiling point to obtain complete solution of the sugar. Then nine parts of orange juice and one-half part of butter are added and the whole mixed thoroughly. The peeled sweet potatoes are sliced into half-inch slices which are then dipped into the hot syrup and packed in liquid tight, moisture-vapor-proof cartons leaving only one-half inch headspace. Then sufficient syrup is poured over the slices to cover them. Approximately 3 oz. of syrup will be used on each 12 oz. of sweet potatoes.

If the glazed sweet potatoes are produced on a large scale, the washed potatoes may be lye peeled and cooked as directed under *Mashed or Puréed Sweet Potatoes* (p. 241).

## Baked Sweet Potatoes

According to Woodroof and Shelor (1956):

"Tests have shown that baking in-the-peel is the best method of cooking sweet potatoes to develop maximum natural sweetness and flavor. Those peeled before baking lacked the attractive appearance, sheen, and pronounced aroma and flavor of the ones baked unpeeled. Peeled potatoes baked in aluminum foil or in partially covered pans were superior to similar potatoes baked on a wire rack or baking sheets; but not as good as unpeeled potatoes baked on sheets. It was found desirable to grease the surface of unpeeled potatoes with butter or margarine before baking; and after baking they may be peeled and wrapped individually in aluminum foil or other moisture-proof sheets, or they may be packaged in the peel....

"Preference was shown, by a taste panel, for sweet potatoes that were baked for about ten minutes at 240°F. (115.5°C.) before freezing, and the baking process completed after the potatoes were thawed. The first heating inactivated enzymes and prevented darkening, while the second heating developed a fresh-from-the-oven flavor."

### ASPARAGUS

Some asparagus is cooked before being frozen. In fact, if only the tips are frozen, the steam blanch required to inactivate the enzymes, together with the reheating required to prepare it for the table is sufficient heating to cook it thoroughly.

One of the best asparagus dishes frozen is asparagus tips with Hollandaise sauce. In preparing the sauce, the suggestions of Mottern in Chapter 5 should be followed.

Another delicious dish that freezes well (provided the cream sauce formula includes waxy maize starch) is chopped asparagus in cream sauce. The asparagus used need not be just the tender tips; less tender parts of the stalk may be used provided they are not woody. This product may be frozen in evacuated "poly" bags (boil-in-the-bag).

### MUSHROOMS

## Sauté Mushrooms

Cooked mushrooms retain their flavor well during freezing and subsequent storage. The main difficulties are: (1) if they are not treated with sulfur dioxide or ascorbic acid before cooking, the mushrooms darken undesirably and may turn black. Blanching with steam or boiling water helps to prevent darkening, but this causes the mushrooms to shrink. Shrinking toughens the mushrooms.

Mushrooms sautéed in butter or margarine are delicious, and if they are sliced thinly before sautéeing, they freeze satisfactorily although the product may be undesirably dark. Unfortunately during cooking the mushrooms shrink; the sautéed product has only approximately half the original weight.

Mushrooms are important ingredients of many delicious frozen precooked dishes: e.g., beef stew, chicken stew, creamed chicken, creamed tuna, creamed chipped beef, creamed bacon, chicken livers, beef gravy with mushrooms, and many others. These dishes should be placed in "poly" bags (boil-in-the-bag) evacuated and quick frozen.

### BIBLIOGRAPHY

Anon. 1943A. Formula for quick frozen cooked pork and beans developed by W.R.R.L. staff. Western Canner and Packer 35, No. 12, 60–61.
Anon. 1943B. Information sheet on frozen pork and beans of the tomato sauce type. U.S. Dept. Agr. AIC-10.
Anon. 1943C. Freezing preservation of pumpkin pie stock. U.S. Dept. Agr. AIC-36.
Anon. 1953A. Birds Eye tests precooked egg plant. Quick Frozen Foods 15, No. 7, 77.
Anon. 1953B. United States standards for grades of frozen cooked squash. U.S. Dept. Agr. Production and Marketing Admin. 7CFR.
Anon. 1955. Military specification-meal, precooked, frozen, MIL-M-13966 OMC. Effective Feb. 14.
Anon. 1956. French-fried onions. Food Eng. 28, No. 4, 185.
Anon. 1963. Seafood packers invade onion ring field contributing to mounting popularity. Quick Frozen Foods 25, No. 10, 79–82.
Anon. 1965. Queries. The Refrigeration Research Foundation. No. 65–9. Washington, D.C.
Anon. 1967. Irish potatoes: utilization of the 1966 crop with comparisons. U.S. Dept. Agr., Statistical Reporting Service Pot 1–3 (9–67).
Arthur, J. C., Jr., and McLemore, T. A. 1956. Sweet potato dehydration: properties of polyphenolase causing discoloration of sweet potatoes during processing. J. Agr. Food Chem. 4, 553–555.
Boggs, M. M., Sinnott, C. E., Vasak, O. K., and Kester, E. B. 1951. Frozen cooked rice. Food Technol. 5, 230–232.
Boggs, M. M., Ward, A. C., Sinnott, C. N., and Kester, E. B. 1952. Frozen cooked rice. II. Brown rice. Food Technol 6, 53–54.
Boswell, V. R. 1950. Commercial growing and harvesting of sweet potatoes. U.S. Dept. Agr., Farmers' Bull. 2020.
Causey, K., and Fenton, F. 1951. Effect of reheating on palatability, nutritive value, and bacterial count of frozen cooked foods. I. Vegetables. J. Am. Dietetic Assoc. 27, 390–395.
Dawson, E. H., Gilpin, G. L., and Reynolds, H. 1950. Procedures for home freezing of vegetables, fruits, and prepared foods. U.S. Dept. Agr., Agr. Handbook 2.

Fenton, F. 1951. Foods from the freezer: precooked and prepared. Cornell Extens. Bull. 692 Rev.

Fenton, F., and Darfler, J. 1946. Foods from the freezer: precooked or prepared. Cornell Extens. Bull. 692.

Hanson, H. L., Winegarden, H. M., Horton, M. B., and Lineweaver, H. 1950. Preparation and storage of frozen cooked poultry and vegetables. Food Technol. 4, 430–434.

Hoover, M. W. 1963. Preservation of the natural color in processed sweet potato products. I. Flakes. Food Technol. 17, 636–638.

Hoover, M. W. 1964. Preservation of the natural color in processed sweet potato products. II. Precooked frozen. Food Technol. 18, No. 11, 135–138.

Hoover, M. W., and Pope, D. T. 1959. Factors influencing the quality of sliced precooked frozen sweet potatoes. Food Technol. 13, 448.

Hoover, M. W., and Stout, G. J. 1956. Studies relating to the freezing of sweet potatoes. Food Technol. 10, 250–253.

Hutchings, B. L., and Evers, C. F. 1947. Problems in the production of precooked frozen foods. Food Technol. 1, 421–426.

Kester, E. B., and Boggs, M. M. 1955. Frozen precooked rice in precooked frozen foods—A Symposium—Surveys of Progress on Military Subsistence Problems Series 1, No. 7, 22–26, Quartermaster Food and Container Institute, Chicago, Ill.

Kramer, A. 1965. Queries Refrig. Research Foundation No. 65-9. Oct. 20.

Livingston, L. 1963. Growers open first onion freezing plant. Canner / Packer 132, No. 9, 17–18.

Lutz, J. M., and Simons, J. W. 1948. Storage of sweet potatoes. U.S. Dept. Agr., Farmers' Bull. 1442 Rev.

Mountjoy, B. M., and Kirkpatrick, M. E. 1951. Freezing sweet potatoes—A progress report of research. Food Packer 32, No. 11, 23, 30.

Owen, R. F., Chase, J. T., and Van Duyne, F. O. 1951. Freezing cooked and prepared foods. Ill. Coll. Agr. Extens. Service Circ. 618.

Paul, P. C., Cole, B. I., and Friend, J. C. 1952. Precooked frozen vegetables. J. Home Econ. 44, 199–200.

Sather, L. A. 1967. Freezing cabbage-based foods: Products and procedures. Quick Frozen Foods 29, No. 8, 52.

Sistrunk, W. A. 1957. Problems involved in the prepeeling and packaging of sweet potatoes. Food Technol. 11, 336–339.

Sorber, D. G. 1943. Freezing baked beans and other prepared foods. Quick Frozen Foods 5, No. 8, 18–19, 24.

Stone, L. 1963. The breading of French fried onion rings. Quick Frozen Foods 25, No. 10, 77–78.

U.S. Department of Agriculture. 1953. United States Standards for grades of frozen cooked squash. Agr. Marketing Service. U.S. Dept. Agr.

U.S. Department of Agriculture. 1959. United States Standards for grades of frozen breaded onion rings. Agr. Marketing Service, U.S. Dept. Agr.

U.S. Department of Agriculture. 1962. United States Standards for grades of frozen sweet potatoes. Agr. Marketing Service, U.S. Dept. Agr.

Woodroof, J. G. 1946. Problems in freezing cooked foods. Quick Frozen Foods 8, No. 9, 90–91.

Woodroof, J. G., and Atkinson, I. S. 1944A. Preserving sweet potatoes by freezing. Georgia Expt. Sta. Bull. 232.

Woodroof, J. G., and Atkinson, I. S.  1944B.  Freezing provides an answer to sweet potato problem. Part II. Food Inds. *16*, 629–631.

Woodroof, J. G., and Atkinson, I. S.  1945. Freezing cooked foods. Food Inds. *17*, 1041–1042, 1136–1138, 1179–1180, 1264, 1266.

Woodroof, J. G., and Shelor, E.  1956.  Freezing sweet potatoes in the home. Ga. Expt. Sta. Leaflet *10*.

## CHAPTER 11

Donald K. Tressler

# Precooked Meat Dishes and Pot Pies

## STATUS OF THE INDUSTRY

The freezing preservation of packaged meats played an important part in the beginning of quick freezing in 1930, but these items went off the market for economic reasons. In the forties and early fifties, frozen precooked meat items began to appear on the market and had gained tremendous headway before packaged precut meats reappeared in retail frozen food cabinets.

Today, an amazing variety of frozen precooked meat items (entrées) help to fill the frozen food cabinets of the supermarkets and independent groceries.

Moreover, many airlines and some of the hotel chains serve frozen entrées (after reheating, of course). Some hospitals (see Chapter 15), especially those operating as a chain, also serve precooked frozen meats. The use of frozen entrées has many advantages for a chain of hotels or restaurants. It enables them to offer a great variety of entrées on the menu without loss because of leftovers, to serve entrées of uniformly high quality in all restaurants, and makes unnecessary the employment of a high-priced chef in each restaurant kitchen.

The number of frozen precooked meat entrées is very great. Some of the more popular are the following: beef: beef-barbecue, beef burgundy, beef stew, beef and vegetables with gravy, beef patty with gravy, beef goulash with noodles, beef in red wine sauce, Swiss steak, Yankee pot roast, beef with sour cream sauce, meat loaf with tomato sauce, Salisbury steak, beef slices with gravy, beef pot pie, beef pot pie filling, beef with green peppers and mushroom sauce, roast beef hash, braised beef with gravy, chopped beef with sauce, beef Stroganoff, Swedish meat balls, filet mignon; ham: ham with raisin sauce; ham slices with pineapple sauce, macaroni and cheese with ham; lamb: roast leg of lamb with gravy, lamb stew, lamb shanks; pork: loin of pork in barbecue sauce, roast pork with gravy; veal: veal scallopine, veal and Cornish Pojarsky, veal Pojarsky, veal Cordon Bleu, Ballotine of veal, veal goulash, veal Parmesan, veal Marsala, and veal Florentine.

Professor Christian of the Cornell School Administration organized a taste panel to determine the quality of these and many other entrées

Donald K. Tressler is a consultant and President of the Avi Publishing Co., Westport, Conn.

packed by nine different frozen food packers and he rated only one frozen meat product high enough in quality to be served in a "high check dining room"; curiously, that was *roast beef hash*, commonly considered a second-rate dish. However, many of the commercially frozen meat entrées were rated by Christian good enough to be served in a "medium check" dining room. These, which Christian (1965) and his panel rated in this category, were the following: beef stew; beef with sour cream sauce, meat loaf with tomato sauce, roast beef with brown gravy; macaroni and cheese with ham; veal Cordon Bleu; veal Florentine, beef in red wine sauce, sliced beef with gravy, ham and raisin sauce, pot roast of beef au jus, macaroni and beef, chopped beef with sauce, and barbecued beef slices.

PROBLEMS

Vail (1955) has given an excellent but condensed summary of the various studies that were made on precooked frozen meats over the past several years. Many of these papers are discussed in more detail in this chapter. Vail (1955) summarizes her report as follows:

"In conclusion it seems that the possibilities in the production of frozen cooked meats and meat dishes are great. Among the problems that remain to be solved might be mentioned the possible need for more efficient packaging of roasted and broiled meats to be frozen without a sauce or gravy; and perhaps another way of saying the same thing, the need for more work to determine how the 'warmed over' flavor can be avoided, especially in roasted meats and poultry; the need for additional study to determine whether or not meats cooked to a rare-done stage can be satisfactorily frozen and reheated; more effective methods for reheating the frozen product; and finally, perhaps the development of methods of preparing the lower grade meats to give a highly acceptable product in order that the demand for and acceptability of the less popular meats may be increased."

### Control of Rancidity during Storage

Harrison *et al.* (1953) studied the effects of storage temperature, length of storage, and the addition of certain antioxidants on precooked beef stew and pork stew. The antioxidants studied were NDGA (nordihydroguaiaretic acid), G-4 (propyl gallate, lecithin, and corn oil) and Tenox BHA (2-tertiary butyl-4-hydroxyanisole and 3-tertiary butyl-4-hydroxyanisole). They concluded that the use of these antioxidants contributed no beneficial effect to the keeping quality of the stews. They also reported that the stews decreased in desirability during the nine months' storage at 0°F. ($-18$°C.). Hence storage time and temperature were the most important factors in the retention of quality in these stews. For a review of similar work on Swiss steaks, see pp. 260–261.

## Control of Bacterial Growth

The effect of cooking on the bacteriologic flora of frozen beef stew and other precooked frozen foods was studied by Hussemann (1951). She purchased packages in the retail market for this test and reported that very low bacteria counts were noted in the beef stew samples. Organisms of possible intestinal origin were not found in any of the beef stew samples. Hussemann concluded that cooking reduced the numbers of all species of microorganisms, but did not completely destroy any type, if the type was originally present in the sample.

Proctor and Phillips (1947) concluded their microbiological study with the thought that meat stews (and other precooked frozen foods), if allowed to thaw and stand any length of time without refrigeration could serve as excellent substrates for the growth of microorganisms. They further concluded that extreme care should be used in all of the manufacturing operations, and recommended immediate freezing and continued storage at 0°F. (−18°C.) or below (see also Chapter 2).

### MEAT POT PIES

In view of the phenomenal success in the merchandising of frozen chicken pot pies (the first pot pies to be produced; see Chapter 7), it is not at all surprising that meat pies were soon offered. Today, there are a number of different kinds of meat pies available in the retail frozen food cabinet. At least one large meat packer is presently marketing frozen beef, pork, veal, and lamb pies. While beef pie is the one packed by the greatest number of packers and is also the biggest seller, there are many specialty meat pies on the market.

In making beef pies, many packers realize that quality is most important in a precooked frozen food and therefore use only top rounds and top sirloin in making this product. All fat and gristle are removed and the lean beef is diced into cubes. Among the best beef pies are those packed for the U.S. Air Force, prepared according to the following specification worked out by the Quartermaster Food and Container Institute (Anon. 1956A):

"3.2.34 *Beef for pot roasting or beef pot pie.*—Beef for pot roasting or for beef pot pie shall be fresh chilled (unfrozen) rounds, full-cut (rump and shank on), round (rump and shank off), or square-cuts chucks of grade C or better of Specification PP-B-221 and shall be from steers or heifers. The shank meat of the round shall not be used. The boneless major cuts (inside, outside, knuckle, and eye) of the round, singly or in combination, may be used in lieu of the bone in rounds provided all other requirements are complied with. In lieu of, or in addition to, the rounds or chucks of grade C, the regular roll or cube roll (eye of rib only—all fat cover excluded) of grade D or better of Specification PP-B-221 may be used.

"3.4.8 *Menu No. 8, beef pot pie (casserole)*.—Each casserole shall consist of:

| | Oz. |
|---|---|
| Beef | 2¾ |
| Gravy | 4¼ |
| Potato | 1 |
| Peas | 1 |
| Filling total | 9 |
| Crust | 2 (± ⅓) |
| Net total | 11 |

"3.4.8.1 *Beef*.—Beef shall be cut into ½- to ¾-inch pieces. Smaller pieces may be used not to exceed ten per cent by weight of the meat component. The beef shall then be rolled in flour, seasoned with salt, pepper, and monosodium glutamate and cooked in fat until brown. Water shall then be added, and the beef shall be cooked until tender.

"3.4.8.2 *Sauce and vegetables*.—The sauce shall be made of the following ingredients: beef stock, beef fat (rendered), flour, rice flour, salt, monosodium glutamate, pepper, onions, and water. Beef extract may be used. The onions shall be finely chopped and may be browned with the beef. The quality of onions used shall be such that the finished product shall not have a prominent onion flavor. The potatoes shall be diced as specified in 3.2.4 for diced carrots. The peas and potatoes shall be prepared as outlined in 3.3.1. The sauce must maintain a thin to light medium consistency after the product has been frozen, thawed, and reheated.

"3.4.8.3 *Crust*.—The crust shall be prepared as specified in 3.4.7.3."

Although the Military Specification calls for a prebaked crust, most frozen meat pies on the market have unbaked crusts when purchased.

Farkas (1956) recommends the following as an excellent formula and procedure for the preparation of a beef pot pie.

The contents of each beef pie is as follows:

| | Oz. |
|---|---|
| Diced cooked beef | 1½ |
| Crust | 2½ |
| Peas and carrots | 1 |
| Gravy | 3¼ |
| Total | 8¼ |

The recommended gravy formula in per cent by weight is as follows:

| | % |
|---|---|
| Broth (from cooking beef) | 62.00 |
| Water | 23.00 |
| Vegetable shortening | 6.00 |
| Flour | 5.83 |
| Commercial seasonings | 2.00 |
| Salt | 0.40 |
| Paprika | .25 |
| Dehydrated onion chips | .25 |
| Worcestershire sauce | .25 |
| Caramel (brown shade) | .01 |
| Burnt sugar shade | .01 |
| Total | 100.00 |

## Method of Making Gravy for Frozen Beef Pies

Melt shortening in kettle, slowly add weighed dry ingredients which have been mixed together stirring constantly and cook two minutes. Add remaining ingredients which have been combined, stirring constantly for 3 min. Dissolve weighed coloring in some of the weighed water. Blanch commercially frozen peas and carrots in a small amount of boiling water for 1½ min. This blanching water can be used as part of the water in making the gravy. Cool gravy to 40°F. (4.5°C.) or below before using.

## Cooking the Beef

Beef used in the making of frozen beef pies should be of a good commercial chuck or better, lean, and easily diced. The beef should be cooked slowly. Fast cooking has a tendency to toughen the beef fibers. Always skim fat from broth before using. Strain through a fine screen or muslin.

A shrinkage of from 25 to 40% will result in the cooking of the beef depending on the quality of beef and method of cooking. Too fat beef will produce a greasy gravy and waste meat as all fat will have to be discarded in the dicing of the cooked beef.

## Commercial Procedure

Most frozen meat pies are made on a pie machine. The empty rigid aluminum foil pie plates are stacked at the left end of this long narrow machine and the first operation is to place one plate in each of the four pockets that form a single cluster. Next, the dough for the bottom crust is rolled and placed over the four plates. A docker then forms the dough to the pie plates. The pies then go under a gravy filler and on past a section where weighed portions of beef or other products may be added and then to a section where a sheet of dough is rolled and placed by hand over the four pie plates to form the top crust. The top crust is then crimped in place and the trimmings cut away.

Then the completed pie usually passes to an automatic cartoning line where the pie is placed in a package and overwrapped; it is then ready for the freezer.

## Advantages of Cooking Meat Under Pressure

Contrary to the suggestions of Farkas, Foreman (1954) recommends cooking beef for use in meat pies at ten pounds pressure for approximately 30 min. which results in a uniform yield and controlled quality. He also recommends "small batch" cooking as giving a better product although admittedly it increases handling costs.

## Other Meat Pot Pies

As previously mentioned, in addition to beef pies, lamb, veal, ham, and pork pot pies are also being packed. In each of these pies there are variations in ingredients for reasons of color contrast, compatibility, or common custom. Even within pies made from the same type of meat there is likely to be some variation. For example, there is a considerable difference in the two beef pie ingredient formulas given in this chapter. Each packer has his own ideas on what the trade wants and that generally determines the choice of ingredients. The location of particular trade also plays a part in establishing the formula. For instance, it is generally recognized that the sale of lamb is confined to definite areas of the country. The particular preference for a specific type of fresh meat also would influence the sales of a precooked frozen product made from that meat. A similar situation exists on the inclusion of certain vegetables and also seasonings. In the South, especially in the Southwest, the preference is for more highly seasoned foods.

### MEAT STEWS

Not very many years ago stew was considered by many to be a poor man's dish. Today, that is hardly the situation in view of the present market costs of the various ingredients and the fact that meat stews are prepared and sold as a precooked frozen food. This does not imply that frozen foods are luxury items, but, obviously, there are costs in preparation, packing, freezing, storage, and distribution that the general public is willing to pay.

### Beef Stew

*Food Engineering* (Anon. 1956B) suggests the following formula and procedure for frozen beef stew:

|  | % |
|---|---|
| Beef (1 to 1½ in. cubes) | 30.50 |
| Diced potatoes | 25.00 |
| Diced carrots | 5.44 |
| Flour | 1.88 |
| Shortening | 1.88 |
| Diced onions | 0.88 |
| Salt | 0.52 |
| Pepper | 0.08 |
| Worcestershire sauce | 0.12 |
| Water | 33.70 |
|  | 100.00 |

As an alternate, one-fourth of the diced potatoes may be replaced with cooked peas (6.25% peas and 18.75% potatoes).

To prepare the beef stew, the beef is browned in a kettle with the shortening. Then approximately one-half of the water is heated and added to the browned meat which is then simmered until it is tender. The potatoes, carrots, and onions are cooked in another kettle in the remainder of the water until they become tender. Then the vegetables are added to the cooked meat.

The flour is made into a paste with cold water and added to the stew which is then heated with agitation until it becomes thick. It is seasoned with salt and pepper and simmered for about one-half hour; then cooled to 120° to 130°F. (49° to 54.5°C.) the Worcestershire sauce and cooked peas are added after which the stew is filled into suitable containers and frozen rapidly.

## Lamb Stew

Formula and procedure for lamb stew follows (Anon. 1956B):

|  | % |
|---|---|
| Lamb (1-in. cubes) | 31.87 |
| Diced potatoes | 29.75 |
| Hot water | 17.00 |
| Diced turnips | 8.50 |
| Peas (cooked) | 4.25 |
| Sliced onions | 4.25 |
| Tomato purée | 1.70 |
| Shortening | 1.25 |
| Flour | 0.85 |
| Salt | 0.50 |
| Ground pepper | 0.08 |
|  | 100.00 |

Lamb stew is prepared by lightly browning the lamb in shortening in a kettle and then adding sliced onions and salt. The pepper and flour are added and browned slightly. After the addition of the hot water and the tomato purée, the lamb is simmered until tender; this requires a little over an hour.

The potatoes, carrots, and turnips are cooked in a separate kettle until tender and then added to the stew, then cooled. After the excess fat has been skimmed off, the stew is filled into containers and frozen rapidly.

## Kidney Stew

|  | % |
|---|---|
| Beef kidneys (1-in. pieces) | 27.50 |
| Water | 27.50 |
| Diced potatoes | 13.70 |
| Canned tomatoes (drained) | 13.70 |
| Diced onion | 5.43 |
| Sliced carrots | 3.40 |
| Butter or margarine | 3.40 |
| Chopped celery tops | 3.30 |
| Barley (medium) | 1.65 |
| Salt | 0.28 |
| Ground pepper | 0.14 |
|  | 100.00 |

Also add crumpled bay leaves, to taste

The first step in preparing kidney stew is to soak washed barley in water for about two hours. Next the kidneys are "skinned" and trimmed free from fat and tough membranes after which they are cut into dice. The diced kidneys are browned in butter or màrgarine, then onions are added and the cooking is continued for about five minutes. The water, soaked barley, salt, tomatoes, pepper, and bay leaves are added. The kettle is covered and the stew simmered until both the barley and the kidneys are tender. This requires about an hour. Then the potatoes, carrots, and celery tops are added and the stew allowed to simmer for a half hour longer, or until the vegetables are tender. More water is added if necessary. The batch is cooled, filled into containers and rapidly frozen.

**Use of Glutamate in Stews.**—Kearns *et al.* (1955), studied the advantages of adding monosodium glutamate to frozen beef stews. They worked with levels of 0.125, 0.20, and 0.25% by weight of added monosodium glutamate and found that the 0.25% level resulted in the highest preference of the taste panel in four different examinations made over a period of a year. They drew the following conclusions from their results:

"The results of this study indicate that by adding the proper amount of monosodium glutamate the flavor of the products tested can be improved and that the improvement is still apparent after a year of storage.

"These results also imply that the frozen food packer can be assured that this product will reach the table of his consumer—several months after it is packed—with a better flavor because of the added monosodium glutamate."

**BEEF STROGANOFF[1]**

Yield: 10
Portion: 6½ oz. meat, 1 oz. mushrooms, and 7 oz. sauce

**Ingredients**

|  | Quantity |
|---|---|
| Beef, top round, strips | 6 lb. |
| 1¼ in. long and ½ in. thick | 7 oz. |
| Peanut oil | 7 oz. |
| Onions, chopped fine | 2 lb. |
| Butter | 3½ oz. |
| Hungarian paprika | ⅐ oz. |
| Water | 32 oz. |
| Dry red wine | 3½ oz. |
| Salt | 1 oz. |
| Pepper | 1/12 oz. |
| Dry sherry | 5 oz. |
| Modified starch | 3½ oz. |
| Modified cream | 5 oz. |
| Evaporated milk | 15 oz. |
| Instant onion | ½ oz. |
| Instant garlic | ¼ oz. |
| Mushrooms, sliced lengthwise and sautéed | 1½ lb. |

[1] Source:  Sayles and MacLennan (1965).

**Method**

Sauté meat in hot oil. Place in stew pan. Sauté onions in butter until transparent and add to meat. Add paprika, water, and wine. Cover and simmer for 1¼ hr. or until tender. Add salt and pepper.

Remove meat from sauce; should be two quarts plus 1 cup sauce. Bring to a boil. Slowly add the sherry to the modified starch and stir until smooth. Add modified cream and add to sauce. Heat to 180°F. (82°C.), stirring constantly.

Add evaporated milk, instant onion, and garlic. Blend well.

Package 6½ oz. meat in vacuum pouch (12 in. × 8 in.), and 1 oz. of mushrooms. Add 7 oz. sauce, evenly distributed. Yield 10 pouches. Blast freeze 30 min.

To Serve.—Heat pouch in boiling water to cover 6 min. May be served with 5 oz. cooked noodles. Noodles are cooked, packaged (8 in. × 6½ in.), and frozen separately.

## HUNGARIAN BEEF GULYAS[2]

Yield: 10
Portion: 10 oz. meat and 7 oz. sauce

| Ingredients | Quantity |
|---|---|
| Shank meat, trimmed, 1¼ in. cubes | 10 lb. |
| Oil | 7 oz. |
| Butter | ½ lb. |
| Onions, chopped | 2 lb. |
| Hungarian paprika | ⅓ oz. |
| Salt | 1 oz. |
| *Sachet bag* | |
| 3 cloves | |
| 1 bay leaf | |
| ⅒ oz. rosemary | |
| ⅒ oz. thyme | |
| Tomato sauce | 10½ oz. |
| Water | 2 qt. |
| Red wine | 8 oz. |
| Modified starch | 1 oz. |
| Instant onion | ½ oz. |
| Instant garlic | ¼ oz. |

**Method**

Heat oil and butter in deep pan. Add onions and sauté until transparent.

Add meat, paprika, salt, sachet bag, and blend well. Cover and *simmer* ½ hr., occasionally stirring from the bottom.

Add tomato sauce and water; cover and simmer 1½ hr. or until tender. Remove meat from sauce. Bring sauce to a boil. Remove sachet bag.

Slowly add wine to modified starch. Stir until smooth. Add to sauce and heat to 180°F. (82°C.), stirring constantly. Add instant onion and instant garlic. Blend well.

Package 10 oz. of meat in vacuum pouch (12 in. × 8 in.). Add 7 oz. of sauce, evenly distributed. Blast freeze for 30 min.

Spaetzli are cooked, packaged (8 in. × 6½ in.), and frozen separately.

[2] Source: Sayles and MacLennan (1965).

Fig. 35.    Preparing beef Stroganoff for serving.
When a customer orders beef Stroganoff, the
chef takes a pouch out of the freezer and puts it
in a boiling water bath. The dish is ready to
serve in minutes (with no leftovers).

To Serve.—Heat pouch in boiling water to cover 6 min. May be served with 5 oz. of cooked Spaetzli, Tarhonya, or rice.

## SWISS STEAKS

Both research workers and those in the industry have long recognized the fact that precooked frozen meats retain their best quality during storage when covered with a sauce or gravy (Hutchings and Evers 1946; Fenton and Darfler 1946; and Fitzgerald 1947). Since Swiss steaks are in this category, it is not surprising that several research workers chose this product for their studies and also that Swiss steaks were one of the earliest precooked frozen meat items to appear on the market.

Tinklin et al. (1950) made a study of frozen Swiss steaks including packaging, storage temperatures, and methods of reheating. While they found little difference in the packaging materials that they used, present day packaging materials might have given them better results. They stored Swiss steaks at +10°, 0°, and −10°F. (−12°, −18°, and −23°C.) for a period up to 29 weeks. Palatability scores at any one test were not entirely consistent with the generally expected result that the lower the storage temperature, the better the keeping quality. Perhaps if the storage test had been extended, greater difference would have been apparent. However, within the 29 weeks storage period, the lean of the steaks always received a higher desirability score than the fat of the steaks at any one storage temperature. Of the various reheating methods studied, reheating in a double boiler gave the best results with palatability scores that were comparable to those of freshly cooked meat. Here again. if these investigators had modern precooked food packaging materials, their results might have been different.

In a later study, Harrison *et al.* (1953) investigated the effects of storage temperature, length of storage, and the addition of certain antioxidants to Swiss steaks. Samples of the product were tested before freezing and at 0, 3, 6, and 9 months storage at 0°, $-10°$, and $-20°$F. ($-18°$, $-23°$, and $-29°$C.). They found little beneficial effect in keeping quality from the addition of the several antioxidants studied. However, they did conclude that storage time and temperature were deciding factors in the retention of quality of Swiss steaks. Over the nine months storage, there was a gradual decrease in the desirability of the product although the lower storage temperature ($-20°$F.; $-29°$C.) always gave a higher score than the higher temperatures, $-10°$F. ($-23°$C.) and 0°F. ($-18°$C.). In this same study, these investigators concluded, based on their palatability tests, of Swiss steaks before and immediately after freezing, that the precooked frozen product had slightly less overall acceptability than freshly prepared Swiss steaks.

Swiss steaks are included as a part of a frozen precooked meal covered in the Military Specification (Anon. 1956A) for that group of items. The requirements and methods of preparation are as follows:

"3.2.3.5 *Beef for Swiss steaks.*—Beef for Swiss steaks shall be fresh chilled (unfrozen) rounds, full-cut (rump and shank on), or round (rump and shank off) of grade D or better of Specification PP-B-221 and shall be from steers or heifers. The shank meat of the round shall not be used. The boneless major cuts (inside, outside, knuckle, and eye) of the round, singly or in combination, may be used in lieu of the bone-in rounds provided all other requirements are complied with.

"3.4.2.1 *Swiss steak and mushroom gravy.*—Swiss steak and mushroom gravy shall be prepared by searing mechanically tenderized meat which has been cut into slices ½ to ¾ in. in thickness. The meat shall be seasoned with salt, monosodium glutamate, and pepper, and cooked, using moist heat method, to a tender state. The gravy shall consist of beef stock, toasted flour or caramel coloring (or both combined), rice flour, tomatoes or tomato paste, salt, monosodium glutamate, pepper and mushrooms; Worcestershire sauce, onions, and beef extract may be added. The mushrooms shall be added to the gravy in such amount as to result in an average portion of not less than ¼ oz. per serving of steak. The gravy shall be thoroughly mixed before addition to steak to insure reasonably uniform distribution of mushroom pieces.'

Sayles and MacLennan (1965) studied the preparation of Swiss steak for freezing in a pouch (boil-in-bag) for later use by a hotel or restaurant. Their recipe for ten portions each in a bag follows:

| Ingredients | Quantity |
|---|---|
| Beef, bottom round, trimmed | 8 lb. |
| Salt | 1 oz. |
| White pepper | $\frac{1}{7}$ oz. |
| Peanut oil | 7 oz. |
| *Mirepoix* | |
| carrots, diced | 7 oz. |
| onions, diced | 7 oz. |
| celery, outside stalks | 7 oz. |
| Water | 80 oz. |
| *Sachet bag* | |
| 3 cloves | |
| 1 bay leaf | |
| $\frac{1}{10}$ oz. rosemary | |
| $\frac{1}{10}$ oz. thyme | |
| Red wine, domestic | 12 oz. |
| Modified starch | 3 oz. |
| Instant onion | $\frac{1}{2}$ oz. |
| Instant garlic | $\frac{1}{2}$ oz. |

**Method**

Cut meat into $9\frac{1}{2}$ oz. steaks and sprinkle with salt and pepper. Pound steaks on both sides to tenderize. Brown in hot oil. Add mirepoix and brown also.

Add water and sachet bag; cover and bring to a boil. Reduce heat and simmer 2 hr. or until tender.

Remove steaks and strain gravy. Slowly add wine to starch and stir until smooth. Add to gravy and heat to 180°F. (82°C.) stirring constantly.

Add instant onion and garlic.

Package $9\frac{1}{2}$ oz. steak in vacuum pouch (12 in. × 8 in.), evenly distributed. Add 7 oz. gravy. Blast freeze for 30 min.

**To Serve.**—Heat pouch in boiling water to cover 6 min.

### SALISBURY STEAKS

Hamburger was one of the first "prepared" meat items to be frozen in 1930 and it was believed that to have a completely satisfactory product, the meat should be chopped and not ground. It is possible that is the origin of the term "chopped steak," as all ground beef sold frozen in retail packages at that time carried that name. Today there seems to be no objection to the actual grinding of the meat although possibly it is not ground as fine as in those early lots prepared thirty-five years ago.

Some years later, after the protective value of added gravy was fully appreciated, precooked Salisbury steaks appeared on the market.

The Military Specification (Anon. 1956A) previously mentioned gives the following requirement for ground beef and preparation for precooked Salisbury steak:

"3.2.33 *Beef, ground.*—Ground beef shall be made by boning and grinding fresh chilled (unfrozen) rounds with or without rump, or square-cut chucks with or without clods, of grade D or better steers, heifers, or cows of Specification PP-B-221, and shall contain not more than 25% fat by analysis. Bull meat is not acceptable. All bone, cartilages, ligaments, bloody neck meat, periosteum, and thick tendons shall be removed and excluded. The beef shall be ground twice, first through a plate having holes 1 to 1½ in. in diameter, and then through a plate having holes ⅛ in. in diameter. Upon completion of the second grind, the temperature of the ground beef shall not exceed 50°F. (10°C.).

"3.4.3.1 *Beef patty (Salisbury steak).*—The ground beef shall be prepared with bread, beef stock, salt, monosodium glutamate, and pepper. Garlic, celery salt, Worcestershire sauce, beef extract, and milk may be added. The product, before being cooked, shall consist of a minimum of 80% by weight of beef. The meat shall be formed into a patty a minimum of ½-inch thick and large enough to yield four ounces after cooking and freezing. The patties shall be browned and cooked to a "medium" state of doneness (160° to 170°F.; 71° to 76.5°C. internal temperature).

"3.4.3.2 *Gravy.*—Gravy shall conform to the requirements for beef gravy as specified in 3.3.5.1. Additional ingredients shall consist of toasted flour or flour and caramel coloring (or both combined), rice flour, salt, monosodium glutamate, black pepper, onions, and water. Beef extract may be used as one of the ingredients. The onions shall be finely chopped, and the quantity used shall be such that the finished product shall not have a prominent onion flavor.

"3.3.5.1 *Fat, broth, and stock components for gravies.*—Fat, broth, and stock components for gravies to be used on beef products shall consist of shortening, beef fat (rendered), beef stock, or of beef extract (or a combination of any of these) in addition to other ingredients specified in 3.4. . . . Beef stock, . . . or beef fat derived during the cooking procedures shall be held not longer than 24 hr. at a temperature not exceeding 45°F. (7°C.)' "

## HAM AND BEEF STICKS

Following the phenomenal growth of fish sticks, frozen poultry sticks appeared on the market about 1953 and rapidly became a widely accepted product. Meat sticks became available about a year later and the ham stick was the first of the meat sticks.

The ham stick as produced by one large meat packer is made of cured ham which is chopped into uniform chunks and precooked. It is understood that coarse chopping gives the finished product the biting consistency of a center ham slice. These chunks which form the stick are coated with an egg batter and toasted bread crumbs and then packaged and frozen. The product needs no additional cooking for serving—only about a ten-minute heating in an oven.

The breading of fresh frozen meats preceded the development of sticks, and as is typical of any product that finds a readily acceptable market, some less scrupulous packers began to produce the product and reduced the quality from that which had built the market. As a result of this situation, the Meat Inspection Branch of the U.S. Department of Agriculture issued Memorandum No. 236 (Miller 1956) quoted below:

## "Preparation and Labeling of Breaded Meat and Meat Products

The use of a batter and breading coating on such articles as 'Breaded Ham Sticks,' 'Breaded Beef Sticks,' 'Breaded Beef Steaks,' 'Breaded Chopped Beef Steaks,' 'Breaded Pork Chops,' 'Breaded Chopped Pork Steaks,' 'Breaded Veal Cutlets,' 'Breaded Chopped Veal Steaks,' and the like shall not result in an increase of weight of more than 30% over that of the prebattered and breaded article.

When used, the ingredients of the batter and breading shall be shown in the order used in an ingredients statement.

This memorandum shall become effective December 1, 1956."

An earlier regulation (Anon. 1955) directed that pork muscle tissue used in frozen breaded products must be heated to a temperature not lower than 137°F. (58.3°C.) or held at a temperature of 5° to −20°F. (−15° to −29°C.) for a period of time depending on the temperature used and the thickness of the meat or inside dimensions of the container.

Beef sticks have been packed for institutional markets. Those packed to date have been made of seasoned beef, coated with a breading and then partially precooked. In that respect, they are similar to a type of precooked potatoes. The restaurant or other institutional user cooks the beef sticks, without thawing, by deep fat frying for approximately four minutes or by baking for 10 to 12 minutes.

### PORK SAUSAGE AND VEAL PATTIES

Watts and Peng (1947) compared the quality of pork sausage frozen before and after cooking. They reported that the precooked sausage kept better than the raw.

Apparently, the Quartermaster Food and Container Institute was unable to substantiate those findings or else they required a breakfast meat with a longer storage life as they specify a veal patty for that purpose. Their specifications (Anon. 1956A) state the following for the preparation of frozen precooked veal patties:

"3.2.40 *Veal for breakfast patty.*—Veal for breakfast patty shall be made by boning and trimming fresh-chilled (unfrozen) carcasses of veal without kidney knob, foreshank, and hindshank (140-lb. maximum weight); or hindquarters without kidney knob and shank (35-lb. maximum weight); or forequarters without shank (35-lb. maximum weight); or legs without shank (25-lb. maximum weight); or veal chucks without shanks (25-lb. maximum weight); or veal breasts (8-lb. maximum weight) or grade D or better of Specification PP-V-191, followed by mixing with fresh-chilled (unfrozen) beef codfat, white to slight yellow tint in color, and grinding. All bones, cartilages, ligaments, bloody neck meat, periosteum, and thick tendons shall be removed and excluded. Seventy-five per cent veal (by weight) and 25% beef codfat (by weight) which has been cut into pieces or strips shall be ground first through a plate having holes 1 to 1½ in. in diameter, thoroughly mixed with the prescribed seasoning ingredients, and then ground through a plate having holes 3/16 in. in diameter. Upon completion of the second grind, the temperature of the ground product shall not exceed 50°F. (10°C.). The product shall be held under proper refrigeration without the tissues containing ice crystals and shall show every evidence of freshness and quality up to the time of cooking.

"3.4.9.2 *Veal sausage patty.*—Breakfast sausage patty shall consist of 75% *lean veal and 25%* codfat, as specified in 3.2.40. To each 100 lb. of meat mixture, the following shall be added and mixed before the final grinding:

| | |
|---|---|
| Salt | 1¾ lb. |
| Sugar | 4 oz. |
| Pepper | 3 oz. |
| Sage | 2 oz. |
| Monosodium glutamate | 4 oz. |
| Rice (fully cooked weight) | 3 lb. |
| Water, cold | 3 lb. |

Sufficient quantity of meat shall be used so that, after cooking and freezing one patty shall weigh three ounces. Patties shall be browned and cooked to a medium state of doneness (160°F. to 170°F.; 71° to 76.5°C. internal temperature)."

## OTHER PRECOOKED MEATS

The demands of the airlines (also the Air Force) for inflight feeding has done much to foster the need for frozen precooked meats beyond what the industry might have produced for normal, everyday retail sale.

The advent of TV dinners has also led to the freezing of many types of precooked meats that otherwise would probably still be in the presently very small list of food items yet to be frozen. Numerous packers are of the opinion that some homemakers prefer to make up their own combination of dishes for a meal and, therefore, these packers are now merchandising as a separate item, the meat or meat and gravy that perhaps formerly was found only on a TV dinner. Hence, we find on the market such items as cooked, sliced corned beef, sliced roast beef in gravy, and beef pot roast and gravy.

The Military Specification (Anon. 1956A) gives the following procedure:

"3.4.5.1 *Beef pot roast and gravy.*—The meat shall be seasoned with salt, monosodium glutamate, and pepper, and shall be browned and cooked by a moist heat method. The gravy shall consist of tomato paste or tomatoes, salt, monosodium glutamate, pepper, onions, toasted flour or caramel coloring (or both combined), and rice flour. Celery salt may be added. The cooked meat shall be cut into slices ⅛ to 3/16 inch thick."

Frozen corned beef hash was one of the first prepared meat items to appear on the market in the late thirties and while it is still available, it is not the top seller that it once was, now that so many precooked meat items are to be found in the retail frozen food cabinet.

## BIBLIOGRAPHY

Anon.   1955. U.S. Dept. Agr. issues inspection rule on frozen, breaded pork. Quick Frozen Foods *18*, No. 2, 114.

Anon. 1956A. Meal, precooked, frozen. (Proposed revision ) Military Specification *MIL-M-13966A*, May 7.

Anon. 1956B. Frozen stews. Food Eng. *28*, No. 10, 170, 172.

Anon. 1963. Is breading part of frozen veal cutlet? Quick Frozen Foods *25*, No. 12, 151–153.

Anon. 1964. Wide market awaits lamb as precooked product. Enterprising packers wanted. Quick Frozen Foods *26*, No. 9, 149–151.

Anon. 1965A. A frozen boilable pouch entrée processing line. Quick Frozen Foods *27*, No. 8, 54, 75–76.

Anon. 1965B. What does the consumer think of frozen meat pies? Quick Frozen Foods *28*, No. 3, 166–170.

Atkinson, I. S., Cecil, S. R., Woodroof, J. G., and Shelor, E. 1947. Controlling rancidity in frozen sausage meat. Food Inds. *19*, No. 10, 102.

Butler, O. D., Jr. 1950. The effect of salt, pepper and sage on the stability of ground pork stored at zero degree Fahrenheit. J. Animal Sci. *9*, 30–36.

Causey, K., and Fenton, F. 1951. Effect of reheating on palatability, nutritive value and bacterial count of frozen cooked foods. II. Meat dishes. J. Am. Dietetic Assoc. *27*, 491–495.

Christian, V. A. 1965. Commercially pre-prepared frozen entrées. Cornell Hotel and Restaurant Admin. Quart. *6*, No. 3, 89–99.

Dahlinger, E. L., and Lewis, M. N. 1954. Precooked and fresh frozen beef roasts —total weight loss, drip loss and tenderness. J. Am. Dietet. Assoc. *30*, 362, 364.

Evers, C. F. 1955. Use of quality control programs. In Precooked Frozen Foods Surveys of Progress on Military Subsistence Problems, Series *1*, 39– on Military master Food and Container Institute, Chicago, Ill.

Farkas, L. D. 1956. Formula for frozen meat pie. Private communication. Donald K. Tressler and Assoc., Westport, Conn.

Fenton, F. 1951. Foods from the freezer. Precooked or prepared. Cornell Extens. Bull. *692* Rev.

Fenton, F., and Darfler, J. 1946. Foods from the freezer. Precooked or prepared. Cornell Extens. Bull. *692*.

Fitzgerald, G. A. 1947. How to control the quality of frozen cooked foods. Food Inds. *19*, No. 5, 623–625, 730, 732, 734.

Foreman, R. T. 1954. Converts locker plant to frozen-dinner processing. Food Eng. *26*, No. 9, 62–63, 205.

Harrison, D. L., Vail, G. E., and Kalen, J. 1953. Precooked frozen stews and Swiss steak. Food Technol. *7*, 139–142.

Hussemann, D. L. 1951. Effect of cooking on the bacteriologic flora of selected frozen precooked foods. J. Am. Dietetic Assoc. *27*, 855–858.

Hutchings, B. L., and Evers, C. F. 1945. Precooked frozen foods. Frozen Food Industry *1*, No. 2, 10–11, 40–43.

Hutchings, B. L., and Evers, C. F. 1946. Research and quality control of precooked frozen foods. Refrig. Eng. *51*, 26–29, 61, 78, 82. Food Inds. *18*, No. 2, 93–97. Fruit Products J. *25*, No. 6, 171–174, 189.

Hutchings, B. L., and Evers, C. F. 1947. Problems in the production of precooked frozen foods. Food Technol. *1*, 421–426.

Ice, R. M., Longree, K., Fenton, F., and Harris, K. W. 1952. Effect of holding on bacterial count and palatability of meat loaves. J. Am. Dietetic Assoc. *28*, 325–330.

Imhof, A. H. 1947. Precooked meat dishes *en casserole*. Frozen Food Industry *3*, No. 2, 21, 44–45.

Kearns, M. P., Fagerson, I. S., and Fellers, C. R. 1955. Tests prove improved frozen food flavor achieved with MSG lasts for a year. Quick Frozen Foods *17*, No. 11, 62–63, 248.

Knelman, F. H. 1956. MSG—A unique flavor enhancer. Food in Canada *16*, No. 10, 37–38.

Kraybill, H. R. 1955. Use of antioxidants in precooked frozen foods. In Precooked Frozen Foods—A Symposium. Surveys of Progress on Military Subsistence Problems, Series *1*, No. 7, 36–39, Quartermaster Food and Container Institute, Chicago, Ill.

Mathias, W. H. 1966. Packs 135 items in boil-in-bag. Food Processing and Marketing *27*, No. 9, 52–53.

Miller, A. R. 1956. Preparation and labeling of breaded meat and meat food products. U.S. Dept. Agr., Agr. Research Service, Meat Inspection Branch, Memorandum *236*.

Morse, R. E. 1955. How phosphates can benefit meats. Food Eng. *27*, No. 10, 84–86.

Owen, R. F., Chase, J. T., and Van Duyne, F. O. 1951. Freezing cooked and prepared foods. Ill. Coll. Agr. Extens. Service Circ. *618*.

Page, R. M. 1956. Growth of prepared frozen foods, meats behind distributors' 1956 profits. Frosted Food Field *23*, No. 3, 13, 29.

Proctor, B. E., and Phillips, A. W., Jr. 1947. Microbiological aspects of frozen precooked foods. Refrig. Eng. *53*, 30–33, 68.

Proctor, B. E., and Phillips, A. W., Jr. 1948. Frozen precooked foods, Am. J. Public Health *38*, 44–49.

Sandor, I. 1945. Freezing beef stew through quality control. Quick Frozen Foods *8*, No. 2, 56.

Sayles, G. I., and MacLennan, H. A. 1965. Ready foods. Cornell Hotel and Restaurant Adm. Quarterly *6*, No. 2, 21–43.

Shelor, E., and Woodroof, J. G. 1946. A promising precooked frozen food (Brunswick stew). Quick Frozen Foods *9*, No. 1, 136–137.

Straka, R. P., and Stokes, J. L. 1956. Microbiological hazards of precooked frozen foods. Quick Frozen Foods *18*, No. 7, 182–186.

Tinklin, G. L., Deck, C. Kalen, J., and Vail, G. E. 1950. Swiss steaks into the freezer and out. J. Am. Dietetic Assoc. *26*, 30–33.

Thorne, R. B. 1955. Some tips on pre-breading frozen meats. National Provisioner *133*, No. 2, 24.

Tressler, D. K. 1947. Fast cooling of cooked foods necessary before freezing. Frosted Food Field *4*, No. 3, 30–31.

Tressler, D. K. 1953. What's new in frozen foods? J. Am. Dietetic Assoc. *29*, 230–233.

Vail, G. E. 1955. Precooked frozen meat products. In Precooked Frozen Foods—A Symposium, Surveys of Progress on Military Subsistence Problems, Series *1*, No. 7, 11–18, Quartermaster Food and Container Institute, Chicago, Ill.

Watts, B. M., and Peng, D. H. 1947. Rancidity development in raw vs. precooked frozen pork sausage. J. Home Econ. *39*, No. 2, 88–92.

Ziemba, J. V. 1948. Frozen dinners. Food Inds. *20*, No. 10, 84–87.

## CHAPTER 12

Donald K. Tressler

# Prepared and Precooked Fish and Fishery Products

## INTRODUCTION

Until Rudy Wagner invented fish sticks in 1949, only small amounts of frozen precooked fish and fishery products were produced (see pp. 14–15, Chapter 1). Wagner's fish sticks were sawed from blocks of frozen fish, but were not cooked, as most of them now are. The fish stick idea caught on much more quickly than do most novel ideas. Various packers tried other shapes and sizes of "sticks" which also were cut from blocks of frozen fish. Now, precooked and / or breaded "portions" of uniform size and dimensions are produced in much greater quantity than the long narrow sticks (Table 1, p. 2). In fact, the demand for portions and sticks is so great that more than 200 million pounds of frozen fish blocks were imported in 1965 (see Fig. 36, Table 34 p. 270), and again in 1966, and about 6 million pounds of fish blocks were frozen in the United States in 1966.

Although far greater quantities of prepared and / or cooked fish sticks and portions are frozen than any other prepared or precooked product, still a great variety of fish "dishes" or entrées are frozen commercially (Anon. 1966A). The general items include fish puddings, fish flakes, fish cakes, fish chowder, rolls, turnovers, and fish and chips, and complete fish and assorted seafood meals.

Specialty fish items that are frozen in certain sections of the country include the following: codfish cakes; codfish portions, both plain and breaded; complete meals with codfish; haddock "dishes"; haddock "meals"; breaded halibut (see Fig. 37); halibut "meals"; breaded and / or precooked perch; breaded pike; breaded and / or precooked pollock; breaded salmon; sole "meals"; sole "dishes" with sauce; swordfish "meals"; breaded and boned trout; and tuna, cakes, "dishes", pies, sticks, and turnovers.

## BREADED FILLETS AND PIECES

Battered and breaded frozen fillets, and "bite-size" pieces of fish, and fish, ready for frying, are packed by a few fish freezers. In some smaller plants, the operations are carried out by hand. In many larger plants, the operations are largely mechanical. The procedure used in cutting the "bite-sized" pieces has been described by Holston (1956), as follows:

"Haddock, cod, flounder, or ocean perch fillets are carefully examined and freed of bones. The skins are removed, except in the case of ocean perch fillets. For

---

Donald K. Tressler is a consultant and President of the Avi Publishing Co., Westport, Conn.

bite-size portions, the fillets are then placed on a conveyor belt and run through a series of rotary knives. The knives cut the fillets into uniform pieces whose dimensions approximate 1 by 1 by ½ in. and whose weight is about 1 oz. each.[1] If breaded fillets are desired, the rotary knives are bypassed. The small portions of fish are collected in 25-lb.-capacity stainless steel containers and refrigerated (32° to 38°F.; 0° to 3°C.) until required for the breading operation."

The fillets or pieces of fillets are put into a wire-mesh basket and hand-dipped into batter (see p. 280) held in a large stainless steel rectangular dipping pan located at the beginning of the breading line. After dipping, the fillets or pieces are allowed to drain a moment and then are placed in a two-inch deep layer of bread crumbs on a plastic conveyor belt 2 ft. wide by 3 ft. long. As the fillets move along the belt, they are sprinkled with crumbs by an aluminum square-toothed roller. The breaded fillets and / or pieces of fillets then pass under a square-faced roller that uniformly presses the crumbs into them. The conveyor discharges the breaded fillets and pieces onto a slide grid. The crumbs remaining on the belt are chuted to a floor-level hopper of the breading machine, and then automatically conveyed to the sifter and reused. The breaded fillets or pieces are placed on metal trays which are roller conveyed to the packing station where girls pack them into 12-oz. cartons. The cartons are machine wrapped with a lithographed heat-sealable wrapper. The sealed cartons are loaded onto metal trays, 8 cartons to a tray and 12 trays to a rack. The racks are rolled into an air-blast freezer. Freezing requires about four hours (Anon. 1951).

### FRIED FILLETS AND PIECES

Fillets, pieces of fish, bite-size or larger, may be hand-dipped in batter, drained on a screen, then hand-breaded in bread crumbs, or a mixture of bread or cracker crumbs and wheat or corn flour, salt, monosodium glutamate, etc. (see pp. 276–282) and fried at about 375°F. (190°C.) in "batch" deep-fat fryers. Frying requires 1 to 2½ min. depending on the thickness, weight, and temperature of the pieces or fillets being fried. After removal from the frybath, the fillets or pieces are drained to eliminate excess oil. The drained fish are then cooled. This can be done on shallow trays in a refrigerated cabinet or on a conveyor belt. The cool fish are then packed into 10 or 12 oz. greaseproof packages, checkweighed, overwrapped, and loaded into a freezer.

In other plants, the breading operation is semi-automatic (as described under *Breaded Fillets and Pieces*) and the breaded fillets either fried in batches or automatically conveyed through a thermostatically controlled frybath as are fish sticks (p. 283). After draining, they are packed into cartons, which are overwrapped and frozen.

[1] In some plants, the pieces of fillets may be much larger, e.g., four inches in length (Anon. 1951).

Table 34

Sources and Disposition (in Thousand Pounds) of Fish Sticks and Fish Portions

| Year | Sources | | | | | | Disposition | | |
|---|---|---|---|---|---|---|---|---|---|
| | Fish Sticks | Fish Portions | Total | Imports | Beginning Stocks | Total | Ending Stocks | Apparent Consumption Total | Apparent Consumption per Capita Lb. |
| 1958 | 61,011 | 21,790 | 82,801 | 56 | 5,211 | 88,068 | 6,211 | 81,857 | 0.470 |
| 1959 | 60,378 | 37,147 | 97,525 | 41 | 6,211 | 103,777 | 6,875 | 96,902 | 0.547 |
| 1960 | 65,142 | 49,381 | 114,523 | 211 | 6,875 | 121,609 | 9,090 | 112,519 | 0.625 |
| 1961 | 69,824 | 59,847 | 129,671 | 493 | 9,090 | 139,164 | 10,511 | 128,653 | 0.703 |
| 1962 | 72,217 | 78,678 | 150,895 | 325 | 10,511 | 161,731 | 11,558 | 150,173 | 0.807 |
| 1963 | 79,302 | 94,644 | 173,946 | 377 | 11,558 | 185,881 | 13,614 | 172,267 | 0.912 |
| 1964 | 73,574 | 106,313 | 179,887 | 210 | 13,614 | 193,711 | 8,094 | 185,617 | 0.969 |
| 1965 | | | | | | | | | |
| 1st quarter | 21,391 | 30,788 | 52,179 | 94 | 8,094 | 60,367 | 6,359 | 54,008 | 0.280 |
| 2nd quarter | 18,696 | 32,590 | 51,286 | 75 | 6,359 | 57,720 | 9,258 | 48,462 | 0.250 |
| 3rd quarter | 19,384 | 38,941 | 58,325 | 48 | 9,258 | 67,631 | 8,958 | 58,673 | 0.302 |
| 4th quarter | 22,012 | 38,145 | 61,157 | 60 | 8,958 | 70,175 | 14,213 | 55,692 | 0.288 |
| Year | 82,483 | 140,464 | 222,947 | 277 | 8,094 | 231,318 | 14,213 | 217,105 | 1.120 |
| 1966 | | | | | | | | | |
| 1st quarter | 24,181 | 37,325 | 61,506 | 99 | 14,213 | 75,818 | 10,293 | 65,525 | 0.336 |
| 2nd quarter | 17,389 | 35,388 | 52,777 | 102 | 10,293 | 63,172 | 12,138 | 51,034 | 0.261 |
| 3rd quarter | 18,344 | 33,851 | 52,195 | 78 | 12,138 | 64,411 | 14,110 | 50,301 | 0.257 |
| 4th quarter | 21,381 | 40,073 | 61,454 | 105 | 14,110 | 75,669 | 19,460 | 56,209 | 0.286 |
| Year | 81,295 | 146,637 | 227,932 | 384 | 14,213 | 242,529 | 19,460 | 223,069 | 1.140 |

Source: Bureau of Commercial Fisheries, Fish and Wildlife Service.

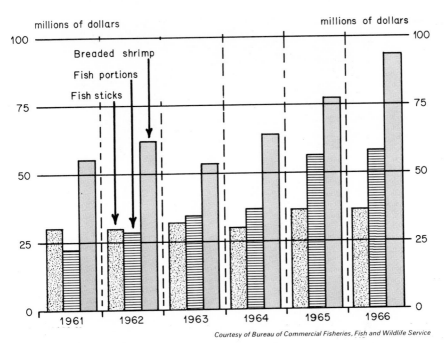

Fig. 36. Value of fish sticks, portions, and breaded shrimp, 1961–1966.

Almost any species of edible fish can be filleted and used in the preparation of frozen fried fillets and bite-size pieces. Commercially, however, small fillets, such as ocean perch, and fillets that are accidentally broken in handling, are generally used.

### COOKED FRESH-WATER FILLETS

Considerable quantities of cooked breaded fillets of fresh-water fish are also packed. One packer in Wheatley, Ontario, Canada cooks and freezes fillets of blue pike, yellow pike, whitefish, perch, and white bass. The procedure (Anon. 1955G) may be briefly described as follows: The fish are first filleted and sorted. Then the fillets are breaded by machine; after which the breaded fish are cooked in hot oil, cooled, and packaged. The packaged products are frozen in plate freezers at −20° to −30°F. (−29° to −34°C.).

### FISH STICKS

Fish sticks are uniformly shaped pieces of fish, usually 3¾ in. long, ⅞ in. wide, and ½ in. thick, dipped in batter, breaded, usually fried, and then frozen in consumer-sized packages. They are packed both in precooked and uncooked form. The precooked sticks, which have been deep-

Fig. 37.   Breaded Alaskan halibut is packed four servings to the
aluminum foil package.

fat fried before freezing, are easily heated in the oven at home for serving. The uncooked sticks are designed for those homemakers who prefer to do the frying themselves. Consumer acceptance of fish sticks has been so widespread that their production and that of portions (a similar product, see p. 2) has done for the fishing industry what orange concentrate had done for the citrus fruit trade. Production statistics are given in Figs. 1 and 2, (pp. 2–3) and Tables 34, 35, and 36.

Fish sticks are commonly marketed in 8-, 10-, 16-, and 20-oz. packages. Kahn and Stolting (1955, 1956) who carried out a national and regional survey of consumer preferences for breaded fish sticks found that in all areas housewives favored 8 sticks to the 10-oz. package with 10 sticks to the 10-oz. package a close second. Homemakers indicated some demand for a 12-oz. package. Consumers prefer chiefly medium breading and moderate seasoning. About 12% of those answering questionnaires preferred no seasoning.

*Courtesy of Bumble Bee Seafoods, Inc.*

Fig. 38.   Sawing fish sticks in Columbia River packers' plant.
Note that they are cut from bars, not blocks.

Both imported and domestic fish are used in fish stick manufacture. The sticks produced in 1953 were composed chiefly of cod and other groundfish. More recently, the great bulk of the fish used in making fish sticks is imported as fish blocks; nearly all of this is prepared from cod fillets. On the other hand, many different species of fish are now used in the United States for making fish blocks for fish sticks and portions.

More fish stick plants are located in Massachusetts and California than in other sections of the country. However, fish sticks are also packed in Florida, Georgia, Maine, Maryland, Michigan, Minnesota, New Jersey, New York, Ohio, Pennsylvania, Rhode Island, Virginia, Washington, and Wisconsin.

### Fish Fillet Blocks

Both fish sticks and portions are sawed or cut from frozen blocks of fish fillets. A fish fillet block is a uniform compact and cohering mass of skinless fillets frozen together under pressure.

There are many shapes and sizes of blocks. The shape and size of block is determined principally by (1) the manufacturer's methods of cutting fish sticks or portions, and (2) the size and weight of the fish sticks or portions to be produced.

**Forming Fillet Blocks.**—The method of forming a block has been described by Holston (1956) as follows:

"The carefully prepared boneless and skinless fillets are laid in a waxed kraft fiberboard container (some pans are used), either parallel or perpendicular to the long axis of the container. The latter procedure is claimed by its advocates to minimize breakage of the sticks during processing. In either case, the thick portion of the fillet is placed adjacent to the edge of the container, and the thin portion in the center. The depression so formed is built up with fillets until the desired weight is obtained. Most processors add an extra one-fourth pound of fillets over and above the indicated net weight to insure against 'void' formation during freezing."

**Freezing Fish Fillet Blocks.**—The containers of fillets are then placed in a multiplate freezer with spacers $\frac{3}{32}$ in. less in depth than the cartons of fillets. This results in a single compression of the cartons of fillets when the freezer plates are closed. The compression smooths the surfaces of the containers of fillets. Further, when the fillets freeze into a block, they expand about seven per cent, thus forcing the expanding fish fillets to fill each carton completely and also to fuse together to form a single block.

**Sawing or Cutting Fillet Blocks Into Sticks.**—Many types of machines have been used for cutting fish blocks into sticks or portions. These include scoring machines, heated cutting wires, bandsaws, gangsaws, and guillotine-type cutting machines (Figs. 38 and 39). The latter three are most commonly used; the use of each has both advantages and disadvantages.

According to Holston (1956), these are as follows:

**Cutting with a Bandsaw.**—Advantages:—(1) the sticks produced are very uniform in shape and size; sawdust losses are relatively low when a blade of satisfactory characteristics is used; positioning of the blade is easily checked or adjusted. The disadvantages are that (1) the costs are higher, owing to slow repetitive operations; (2) more labor is required, than with other types of cutting machinery; and (3) because of the exposed blades, the element of danger to the operator is always present.

**Gangsaw Cutting.**—"Gangsaw equipment is usually designed by the manufacturer to fit a specific operator's cutting operation. The assembly ordinarily consists of a series of circular saw blades, set at precise distances apart, on a single axis and is usually enclosed to allow room only for the entry of the block. The block is forced through the gangsaw blades as a result of pressure exerted by the operator on a block immediately behind it. The advantages of such a machine are: (1) it makes many cuts at one operation, reducing time and labor requirements; (2) it is

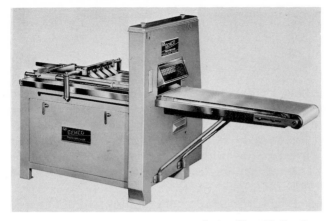

*Courtesy of General Machinery Corp.*

Fig. 39.   The Gemco automatic frozen food slicer. The Gemco food slicer shears with an action somewhat similar to a paper cutter. This action is both down and across the product thus minimizing breakage and distortion. The Gemco slicer's automatic feed mechanism can be adjusted for any size of stick. It will cut 800 fish sticks per minute.

*Courtesy of Bureau of Commercial Fisheries, U.S. Fish and Wildlife Service*

Fig. 40.   Fish sticks coming out of batter.

safer to operate than a bandsaw, since the gangsaw blades are totally enclosed." (Holston 1956).

"Two of the disadvantages of such machines are: (1) the difficulty of replacing the blade, and adjusting it, or in checking its position; (2) the relatively large saw-dust loss." (Holston 1956).

**Guillotine-type Cutting Operation.**—The guillotine-type cutting machine consists of a very heavy beveled chrome-steel, horizontal or vertical reciprocating blade hydraulically driven at about 50 strokes per minute. The slabs of fish are fed past the knife either by gravity or by means of a belt. The knife is propelled with sufficient force to shear off successive portions of the slabs as they are fed into the machine. There is no sawdust. However, incorrect design or improper use leads to other types of losses; e.g., splitting of the blocks, shaving of the sticks, and distorted sticks lacking the required dimensions.

As a rule, three separate cutting operations must be made in order to make fish sticks from most shapes of fish blocks. Only two cutting operations are necessary if the blocks are only $\frac{1}{2}$ or $\frac{7}{8}$ in. thick. However, if thin blocks are prepared there is much greater danger of breakage. For this reason the blocks are commonly prepared in thicknesses of two or three multiples of $\frac{7}{8}$ in.

Generally, in the first cutting operation, the $1\frac{1}{2}$ in. thick block is divided by means of a bandsaw into three portions parallel to the long axis of the block. The second cutting operation splits the three portions into six slabs, each being one-half as thick as the original portion. This operation may be carried out either by bandsaws or gangsaws. The third cutting operation usually carried out by a guillotine-type cutter divides each of the six slabs into individual sticks.

### Coating the Raw Fish Sticks

Most of the batter mixes and breading materials are commercial products made in plants specializing in the manufacture of these materials which are not only used for breading fish sticks but, also, for shrimp and many other foods which are fried in deep fat. In 1954, in which year only 50 million pounds of fish sticks and portions were packed, these packers brought 12,500,000 lb. of breading and batter mixes and mix ingredients.

**Types of Coating Materials.**—According to Holston (1956), most commercial batter mixes are prepared from ground corn flour and corn meal and contain spices and nonfat dry milk solids. Breading materials are based on the use of (1) ground, soft winter wheat cereals, (2) dried bread crumbs, or (3) mixtures of these products. Some breadings contain small quantities of cracker meal, soy, and potato flour. The choice of a particular type or blend of ingredients is usually determined by the processor in conferences of his sales and production staffs with technical representatives of the suppliers of the breadings.

**Batter Mix.**—The following formula is recommended for use in making a batter mix suitable for use on fish sticks and other seafood:

| Ingredients | % |
|---|---|
| All purpose wheat flour or | |
| a mixture of wheat and corn flours | 72.30 |
| Salt | 1.00 |
| Baking powder | 1.70 |
| Dehydrated whole eggs | 8.15 |
| Nonfat milk powder | 6.00 |
| Melted hydrogenated | |
| vegetable shortening | 9.00 |
| Monosodium glutamate | 1.85 |
| | 100.00 |

Mix all dry ingredients together. Add melted shortening. Mix thoroughly. Chill, preferably in freezer. Put through a hammermill. Mix again. Prepare batter by stirring the batter mix into $1\frac{1}{2}$ times its weight of water.

**Properties of Batter Materials.**—Holston (1956) has given a good summary of the properties of batters and batter materials and factors controlling them, as follows:

"Viscosity, the degree of resistance to flow, can be related to batter-solids content and to weight pickup by the fish sticks during the coating process. (Fig. 40). A sufficiently accurate measurement can be made by noting the time required for a certain quantity of batter at a given temperature to flow through a small orifice in a container. Such figures are comparative only and should be related to time-measurements of a standard batter found to be satisfactory by the quality-control group. Other more elaborate apparatus may be used that measures viscosity directly.

"The adhesion of batter to the frozen surface seems to be enhanced by predusting the sticks with dry batter mix prior to the application of the batter. The dry-mix-solids provide a rough surface on which the batter adheres.

"The amount of breading material pickup is determined by the viscosity (or rather, solids content) of the batter. Lirot (1955) found the relationship to be semi-logarithmic. To a certain degree, the more viscous (or more concentrated) the batter, the greater the pickup of breading material.

" A higher solids content also appears to reduce weight losses during the subsequent cooking operation (Lirot 1955). Portions of the prepared mixes break down during heating to form glutens, which appear to seal off the surface of the flesh, minimizing moisture losses. Too high a solids content, however, prevents thorough cooking of the batter and results in a mushy, pasty coating on the finished sticks even after they are reheated in the home. Usually, from 3 to 4 gal. of batter are prepared at a time, as needed, throughout the day. This procedure prevents (1) too long a period of use of one batch during which the balance of the batter may become bacterially contaminated or (2) loss by requiring the discarding of batches of batter during the several daily cleanings of the batter equipment."

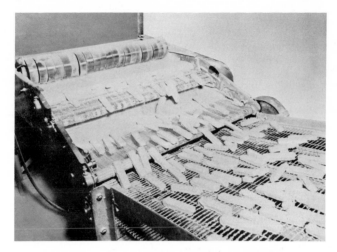

*Courtesy of J. W. Greer Div. Joy Mfg. Co.*

Fig. 41.   Close-up view of delivery end of breader.

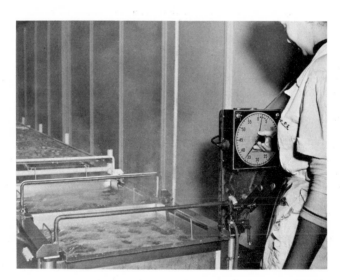

*Courtesy of Columbia River Packers Assoc.*

Fig. 42.   Frying fish sticks. Time and temperature are precisely controlled. Oil is constantly filtered and tested.

**Breading Mix.**—The following formula is suitable for use in breading fish sticks and other seafood:

| Ingredients | % |
|---|---|
| All purpose wheat flour or a mixture of wheat and corn flours | 40.00 |
| Dehydrated whole eggs | 10.00 |
| Nonfat milk powder | 2.50 |
| Salt | 1.00 |
| Fine cracker crumbs (meal) | 45.85 |
| Monosodium glutamate | 0.65 |
| | 100.00 |

Mix and sift all ingredients together.

**All—Purpose Mixes.**

Some commercial mixes may be used dry for breading, and, with the addition of the proper amount of water, produce a satisfactory batter.

### IMPORTANCE OF USING MONOSODIUM GLUTAMATE IN FISH STICKS

The U.S. Testing Company carried out a test of the effectiveness of monosodium glutamate as a flavor-enhancing ingredient in breaded fish products (Foster 1954). Fish sticks were carefully prepared to assure uniformity in the finished product. The only difference among the batches of coded fish sticks was in their glutamate content. The first test compared the flavor acceptance of samples treated with glutamate at an 0.18% concentration by weight of fish with samples containing no glutamate. In this case, the glutamate had been added to the dry batter mix. The results of this comparison are shown in Fig. 43. It was found that 64% of the consumers preferred the fish sticks with the glutamate, while only 36% preferred those without glutamate. The second test compared fish sticks with and without glutamate at the 0.18% level, but this time the glutamate had been added to the breading instead of the batter. In this case 67% of the consumers preferred the fish sticks with glutamate. The final test compared fish sticks with glutamate at an 0.18% level, with those containing 0.05% glutamate. Again 67% of the consumers preferred the fish sticks treated at the 0.18% level.

Kearns, Fagerson, and Fellers (1955) report that the improved flavor obtained by the addition of monosodium glutamate to cooked frozen seafoods is retained during storage.

**Factors Controlling Quality of Breading.**—According to Holston (1955A), the hue of the finished sticks is primarily determined by the type of breading material. Breading mixes based on cracker meal result in a golden-yellow hue; those based on wheat a golden-brown hue; and those

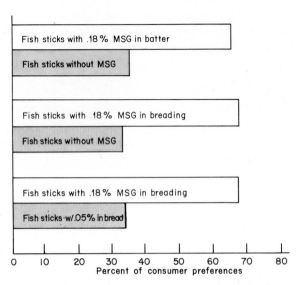

From Foster (1954)

Fig. 43.   Consumer preferences for fish sticks prepared with and without monosodium glutamate. This chart indicates that two-thirds of the panel preferred the fish sticks treated at the 0.18% level.

based on bread crumbs, a reddish-brown hue. As the ratio of bread crumbs to wheat cereal base mix is increased, the shade of color obtained at a given temperature and cooking time is deepened. Fish sticks prepared from cracker meal do not deepen in shade noticeably, even during extended storage.

### Methods of Applying Batter to Fish Sticks

**Semiautomatic Processes.**—In many of the smaller plants (Holston

Table 35
Production (in Million Pounds) of Fish Portions by Product Forms

| Year | Breaded Portions | | Unbreaded Portions Raw | Total Portions |
|------|--------|-----|--------|--------|
|      | Cooked | Raw |        |        |
| 1960 | 8.5  | 38.8  | 2.1 | 49.4  |
| 1961 | 11.0 | 46.8  | 2.0 | 59.8  |
| 1962 | 14.0 | 62.3  | 2.4 | 78.7  |
| 1963 | 16.6 | 75.0  | 3.0 | 94.6  |
| 1964 | 21.0 | 82.8  | 2.5 | 106.3 |
| 1965 | 30.5 | 107.4 | 2.6 | 140.5 |
| 1966 | 33.3 | 109.2 | 4.1 | 146.6 |

Source: Bureau of Commercial Fisheries, Fish and Wildlife Service.

1956), the solidly-frozen raw sticks are conveyed to a wedge-shaped batter tank. This tank, is usually mounted on a stand about 4 ft. high, is commonly about 4 ft. wide. It is very shallow at the feeding end and about 18 in. deep at the lower or product end. Batter is pumped from the reservoir at the deep end through a perforated manifold along the top of the tank. The batter under pressure flows in a smooth stream from the shallow feeding end of the tank to the deep product end, where the pumping operation is repeated. An expanded metallic mesh conveyor belt extends over the deep portion of the tank through which the batter flows.

The fish sticks are dropped by attendants into the flume; the flow of the batter carries the sticks to the end of the tank, where they are caught on the conveyor belt and transferred to the breader.

According to Holston 1956, this type of operation has several disadvantages:

(1) The free-flowing sticks freeze together when they touch, necessitating separation by attendants and return to the batter tank in order that they can be recoated with batter.

(2) Several attendants are necessary to make sure that each stick receives an adequate coating of batter.

(3) Carryover of excess batter on sticks and conveyor belt, unless removed, causes lump formation in the loose breader materials at the next step in the operation.

**Automatic Processes of Applying Batter and Breading.**—The frozen sticks are fed onto a set of parallel bars spaced about the same distance above a flat conveyor belt. The bars are vibrated while the endless belt moves toward the batter tank. The vibration of this unscrambler separates the sticks and feeds them in equidistant rows onto the metallic mesh belt of the batter machine.

The batter in the machine is usually refrigerated to below 50°F. (10°C.), so as to minimize bacterial growth. Batter is pumped from the bottom of the tank into a manifold extending over and about three inches above the conveyor belt. A steady curtain of batter falls from the manifold onto the sticks; the excess forms a small puddle around the belt and drains back into the tank. Thus, all sides of the sticks are coated. The coated sticks next pass under a blower which removes the excess batter from both sticks and belt. The coated sticks are then moved on a conveyor to the breader.

The spaced, aligned, batter-coated sticks on the conveyor pass beneath a curtain of falling breading (Fig. 41) which covers the sticks to a depth of about 2½ in. This procedure makes certain that all sides of the sticks receive an adequate coating. The coating is then pressed into the batter. This is done either by a roller or by a series of ascending and descending flexi-

Table 36
Production (in Million Pounds) of Fish Sticks, by Product Forms

| Year | Breaded Cooked | Breaded Raw | Total |
|------|------|------|------|
| 1960 | 60.4 | 4.7 | 65.1 |
| 1961 | 65.0 | 4.8 | 69.8 |
| 1962 | 66.8 | 5.4 | 72.2 |
| 1963 | 74.1 | 5.2 | 79.3 |
| 1964 | 67.8 | 5.8 | 73.6 |
| 1965 | 77.3 | 5.1 | 82.5 |
| 1966 | 77.0 | 4.3 | 81.3 |

Source: Bureau of Commercial Fisheries, Fish and Wildlife Service.

ble rings actuated by a rod connected to an eccentric gear. The conveyor then passes through a vibration zone which frees the sticks of most of the excess breading. The sticks are then turned over in a fall to a lower belt which dislodges all remaining loose breading. This is important in order to prevent loose breading from getting into the oil in the cooker into which the sticks are conveyed.

Another automatic breader is a rotary machine resembling a concrete mixer open at each end. In this machine raw batter-covered sticks are dropped onto a layer of loose breading. The sticks and loose breading are carried toward the other end by rotation of the "mixer" which has spiral baffles. The sticks and surplus breading drop out onto a second conveyor made of wire screening. The excess breading falls through the screening before the sticks reach the frybath (cooker).

### Precooking the Coated Fish Sticks

**Methods of Frying Fish Sticks.**—Two different methods of frying breaded fish sticks are in common use: the batch process, and the continuous process. In the batch process, loaded trays of fish sticks are immersed in hot oil; whereas in the continuous process, an endless belt conveys the sticks through the hot oil.

A typical batch fryer is initially charged with about 275 lb. of oil or shortening and produces from 175 to 200 lb. of fish sticks per hour. A typical continuous cooker may be designed to cook as much as 2,000 lb. of fish sticks per hour in either hydrogenated or untreated vegetable oil. An initial charge of oil may be as much as 200 gal.

**Selection of Equipment.**—In selecting batch frying equipment for frying sticks, it is important to choose a bath which will hold the proper amount of fat required to do the frying job. Since copper catalyzes the development of rancidity, copper and copper-containing metals should be avoided. The design should be such that hot spots and local overheating will be avoided.

**Selection of Batter and Breading Mix.**—Select the batter and breading that will give the desired color and flavor. Care should be taken to remove as many loose crumbs as possible before placing the sticks in the frybath.

**Selection of Shortening.**—Hoyer (1952) has indicated that a good shortening should have the following characteristics: (1) its melting point should be near body temperature to insure the best eating quality; (2) select hydrogenation to assure stability and long kettle life; and (3) a high smoke point, e.g., 450°F. (232°C.).

Table 37

Effect of Cooking Time and Oil Temperature on the Shade
(Brilliance of Color) of Fish Sticks

| Cooking Time, Sec. | Shade[1] (Brilliance of Color) Cooking Temperature | | | |
|---|---|---|---|---|
| | 360°F. (182°C.) | 375°F. (190°C.) | 390°F. (199°C.) | 405°F. (207°C.) |
| | Shade No. | | | |
| 45 | 2 | 3 | 3 | 5 |
| 60 | 3 | 4 | 5 | 6 |
| 75 | 4 | 4 | 6 | 7 |
| 90 | 4 | 6 | 8 | 8 |
| 120 | 5 | 7 | 8 | — |
| 150 | 7 | — | — | — |
| 180 | 8 | — | — | — |

Source: Holston (1955A).
[1] The color shade designations (1 to 10) were arbitrarily developed for this experiment. A very pale product differing little from an uncooked item, merited designation "1." A moderately dark product was given a "7," while a moderately-colored product was rate a "4." Lithographed pictures of fish sticks were used as guides for the range "4" to "7." The shades of color rated as acceptable to one or more members of the laboratory staff ranged from about "3" to "8." The shade preferred by the average panel member was about "6."

Hoyer also indicates the importance of melting solid fats before addition to the frybath. The preheated shortening should be run into the frying kettle at a definite rate to replace shortening absorbed by the food being fried. Discarding of the used fat when the equipment is being cleaned is also recommended.

**Frybath Practices.**—Temperatures recommended for the frybath (Fig. 42) vary from 350° to 390°F. (177° to 199°C.). A frybath temperature of 375°F. (190°C.) is common. Holston (1955A) determined the effect of cooking time and oil temperature upon the shade of color; his results are shown in Table 37. These data show the importance of close control of cooking times and oil temperature in the production of a uniform shade of fish stick color.

The finished fish stick will, as a rule, contain approximately ten per cent of absorbed fat (see Table 38). It is of course necessary to add some fresh

Table 38

Determination of Gain and Loss of Weight of Fifty Fish Sticks
During Battering, Breading, Frying, and Cooling

|  | Test A | Test B |
|---|---|---|
| Wt.[1] raw sticks | 1002 | 1010 |
| Wt. breaded sticks | 1348 | 1401 |
| % gain | 34.5 | 38.7 |
| Wt. fried | 1339 | 1405 |
| % gain | 33.6 | 39.1 |
| Wt. fat absorbed | 81.5 | 85.0 |
| % fat absorbed | 8.1 | 8.4 |
| Wt. water lost | 90.5 | 84.5 |
| % water lost | 9.0 | 8.3 |
| Wt. after cooling | 1292.0 | 1365.0 |
| Fat drainage | 21.0 | 21.0 |
| Wt. water lost | 26.0 | 19.0 |
| % water lost | 2.0 | 1.3 |
| Overall increase in weight (%) | 29.0 | 35.0 |

Source: Umpleby, Pincus, and Block (1955).
[1] All weights in grams.

fat to the frybath from time to time, and little of the fat remains in the hot frybath for a long time. In larger installations, continuous filters are sometimes used to remove crumbs and bits of fish and batter which fall from the sticks as they are being fried. It is important to filter the frybath oil or fat at the end of each day's run.

Grimm (1955) recommends filtering the frybath oil twice daily, once during the noon hour and again at the end of the working day, or continuously if much finely divided material gets into the bath during the cooking operation.

Robertson (1953) indicates that good frying practices, reduced to simplest terms, consist of (1) choosing the highest quality of raw ingredients; (2) keeping to a minimum the changes which normally occur in fats under frying conditions; and (3) compensating as much as possible for the changes that do occur. He suggests the following check-list of do's and don'ts of good frying practice:

(1) Use the correct frying fat.

(2) Use the proper frying equipment—equipment designed to insure a proper frying life.

(3) Keep equipment functioning properly by frequent check-up.

(a) Correct any development of hot spots.

(b) Keep thermostats accurate.

(c) Replace worn coils, heating elements, etc.

(d) Repair worn spots or holes in kettles where heat is applied.

(4) Clean frying kettle and equipment as needed to remove gum accumulation and dirt.

(5) Clean hood over frying equipment and avoid return to the kettle of drippings which accumulate and condense on the hood.

(6) Rinse all equipment thoroughly after cleaning to remove traces of materials used for cleaning.

(7) Prepare foods properly.

    (a) Check to avoid excessive moisture.

    (b) Check to avoid loose crumbs.

(8) Fry properly.

    (a) Avoid scorching and burning of fresh fat when adding it to an empty kettle. Use "low" heat for melting.

    (b) Regulate the heating of the frying fat by adjusting heating elements and burners properly to avoid local overheating.

    (c) Avoid holding fat at idling temperatures, or worse yet at high temperatures, unnecessarily.

    (d) Avoid frying temperature above 400°F. (204°C.).

    (e) Check idling temperatures and keep them as low as possible.

    (f) Maintain a rapid or high "fat turnover."

        (1) Avoid too much fat in the kettle for the amount of food being fried.

        (2) Avoid using too big a kettle for the amount of food being fried.

    (g) Clarify the fat frequently to avoid accumulation of burned particles.

(9) Avoid contamination with metals which hasten breakdown, not only in the kettle but in all auxiliary equipment with which the fat comes in contact."

Quammen (1955) list the six common "trouble factors" encountered in frying foods as follows: (1) excessive heat; (2) metallic contamination; (3) soap and caustic residues left after cleaning equipment; (4) burnt food particles; (5) inadequate filtering; and (6) insufficient turnover of frying fat. Quammen has presented data (Table 39) which show that higher temper-

Table 39

Effect of Frybath Temperature on Color and Free-Fatty Acid
Content of Fat

| Temperature | Lovibond Red Color | | Free Fatty Acid | |
|---|---|---|---|---|
| | Control (No Frying) | After 5 Days' Frying | Control (No Frying) | After 5 Days' Frying |
| 350°F. (177°C.) | 4.1 | 37.2 | 0.05 | 0.23 |
| 385°F. (197°C.) | 4.1 | 123.0 | 0.05 | 0.36 |

Source: Quammen (1955).

atures speed up color and free fatty acid development. Prevention of development of free fatty acid formation is important, if a long storage life of the fried product is required.

### Cooling, Packaging, and Freezing Fish Sticks

**The Cooling of Fish Sticks.**—After frying, the fish sticks must be cooled to approximately 90°F. (32°C.) before packaging, Otherwise, if the fish sticks are packaged while they are still warm, moisture vapor will condense as frost within the package during freezing. The cooling equipment may be a very simple plywood box equipped with a fan to blow air on the racks of trays of fish sticks, or it may be a tunnel, equipped with fans and an air filter, through which the fish sticks are slowly conveyed on a belt.

**Packaging.**—The cool fish sticks are conveyed to a packaging line, which usually consists of a long table with three endless plastic or rubber belts running down the center. The lowest belt is flush with the table top, the middle belt is about 12 in. above the table, and the highest belt about 21 in. above the table top. The lowest belt carries the cool fish sticks, and the top belt the empty containers. The middle belt conveys the filled containers to the wrapping machines. Any sticks rejected (those that are poorly breaded, broken sticks, etc.) are allowed to proceed to the end of the line where they are packed in large containers for institutional use.

**Freezing.**—Several types of freezing systems are in use for the freezing of fish sticks. These include multiplate freezers, simple sharp freezers, and various types of air-blast freezers.

### Uncooked Breaded Fish Sticks

Considerable quantities of uncooked breaded fish sticks are also packed. In general, the methods of preparation are the same as those described for the frozen precooked product, except the breaded sticks are frozen without frying in deep fat.

Packers of the uncooked product claim superiority over the precooked product (Anon. 1954D), since it has "the same fresh flavor of fresh fish cooked to order—so superior to warmed over fish" and "permits a wide range of cooking preparation—broil, bake, saute, pan fry, or deep-fat fry."

### FISH PORTIONS OR SQUARES

As indicated previously, fish sticks are long and narrow, usually 3¾ in. long, ⅞ in., wide, and ½ in. thick. As a rule, they are breaded and fried in deep fat. Fish sticks became very popular, but before long it became evident that there was a need for larger rectangular or square pieces of uniform size sawed or cut from frozen blocks of fillets in the same way that sticks are made. These larger pieces of uniform size came to be known as portions or squares (see Chapter 1).

## Cutting Portions

Many sizes and shapes of fish portions are packed. All are cut or sawed from fish blocks. The latter are made exactly as they are for fish sticks except the size and dimensions of the blocks usually are different. The dimensions of the block are those which permit it to be cut into the desired size and shape of portions required. Since the making of frozen blocks from fish fillets has been described on p. 274, it will not be repeated here.

A popular size of portions is 4 by 3 by $15/32$ in. The raw-fish weight is generally adjusted so that the breaded portion weighs approximately four ounces and is the right size for the entrée of a fish "dinner." Portions of this size may be sawed from a block $12\frac{1}{8}$ by $9\frac{1}{8}$ by 1 in. The whole block is run through a guide and into a gangsaw. This cuts the block into three pieces, each 4 by 9 by 1 in. Each of these is sawed in two; thus obtaining 6 slabs each measuring 4 by 9 by $15/32$ in. The final cut produces 18 portions each 4 by 3 by $15/32$ in.

## Battering

The portions or "squares" are coated with batter and then breaded, usually in an automatic machine, exactly as fish sticks are battered and breaded. Although nearly all of the fish sticks produced are fried in deep fat, in 1966 approximately three-fourths of the fish portions produced are merely battered and breaded and put into cold storage without cooking.

## Frying

The breaded fish portions which are to be cooked are fried in deep fat in the same way as fish sticks are fried (p. 282). Since the fried portions are much heavier than fish sticks, it takes longer to cool them.

### FISH CAKES

Cooked fish cakes freeze without marked change, and, after reheating, taste like the freshly cooked product. They may be prepared from salted or either fresh or frozen fish. Fourteen food freezers packed frozen fish cakes or patties in 1966.

## Preparation

The method recommended by *Food Engineering* (Anon. 1955H) for preparing fish cakes from salt cod follows:

"Soak 12½ lb. of shredded salt cod for three hours in cold water. Then shred and introduce fish into steam-jacketed kettle and add water. Heat to boiling and drain off water.

"Now boil the fish with fresh water, plus 22½ lb. of potatoes, until well done. Drain water and grind fish and potato mix through a ¼-in. plate.

"Blend thoroughly groundfish and potatoes in vertical-type bowl mixer along with 2 lb. of beaten eggs, 1½ lb. of butter or margarine, 2½ lb. of diced onions, and ¾ oz. of pepper.

"Form mixture into cakes, dip into beaten eggs, roll in bread crumbs, and fry until light brown."

If fresh or frozen fish are used, the same general formula and procedure can be used; however, certain modifications are necessary. It will, of course, be unnecessary to soak the fish. Almost any species of fish can be used; however, marine groundfish, such as cod, haddock, cusk, and pollock give a superior product. When salmon is used, delicious fish cakes are obtained. One Chicago packer uses salmon to make "salmon patties" and a Philadelphia company is freezing salmon croquettes. When fresh fish are used, it is probably better to boil the boned fish or fillets and potatoes separately. When the fish and boiled potatoes are blended in a mixer, beaten eggs, margarine or butter, and diced onions are added in the proportion of 4 oz. eggs, ½ oz. butter or margarine, and ¾ oz. onions for each pound of fish-potato mixture. The mixture should be seasoned with pepper and monosodium glutamate.

After forming the mixture into patties, they should be dipped in beaten eggs or batter mix (see p. 277), then breaded with breading mix (see p. 279); midway through the fryer, the cakes should be flipped over and fried on the other side. The fish cakes are cooled on trays, then packaged in cold-waxed cartons using waxed paper separators. The cartons are closed, then overwrapped with a lithographed wrapper, and frozen either in a plate or air-blast freezer. After freezing, the cartons are packed in fiberboard containers for storage or shipping.

### FISH BURGERS

Recently, a novel product called a "fillet fish burger," similar to fish cakes except they are steamed and not fried, has been introduced on the Pacific Coast (Anon. 1954B). This product is prepared from cod fillets frozen in five- and ten-pound blocks. The method used has been described as follows:

"After slicing, the frozen fish is ground and the ground material is added to the batter mix and blended with eggs, potatoes, seasoning, onion powder, and cracker meal. The patties are formed in a press, which permits precision molding of the patty, equipped with an automatic paper feed that provides waxed paper separation for each patty.

"The burgers are partially cooked by a steam process. After machine forming, the patties are stacked six deep, and are wrapped in vaporproof wraps, double-weight waxed paper, four to a group. They are then packed 24 to a carton and sharp frozen. Each burger is 3¼ in. in diameter, ½ in. thick, and 2 oz. in weight."

## TUNA AND OTHER FISH PIES

In 1966, there were seven packers freezing fish pies in as many different states. Five of these were packing tuna pies, the other packers, simply "fish pies." Although this product has not attained the popularity of chicken pie, its production is increasing and it may some day be very popular.

### Formula and Procedure

The following formula makes a highly acceptable "gravy" for tuna pies:

| Ingredients | % |
|---|---|
| Frozen peas, or peas and carrots | 7.50 |
| Hydrogenated vegetable shortening | 6.00 |
| Dry nonfat milk | 6.00 |
| Flour, all-purpose wheat | 5.50 |
| Tomato purée | 1.00 |
| Salt | 0.70 |
| Canned green Bell peppers | 0.25 |
| Canned red Bell peppers | 0.25 |
| Monosodium glutamate | 0.20 |
| Dehydrated onion | 0.04 |
| Black pepper | 0.01 |
| Water | 72.55 |
| | 100.00 |

The shortening is melted in a steam-jacketed kettle, the flour is stirred in, then the tomato purée and one-half the water are added. The dry nonfat milk is then stirred in; stirring is continued until all lumps are eliminated. The remainder of the water and the vegetables and other ingredients are added. Heating and stirring are continued until the temperature reaches 190°F. (88°C.). The mixture is then cooled to about 100°F. (38°C.). A thin-rolled sheet of pie crust, slightly larger than the pan, is placed on the bottom of a small, shallow, heavy weight, aluminum foil pie pan. The usual size of pan is 5 in. in diameter at the top and 3 in. at the bottom. Five ounces of "gravy" (see formula given above) are added, then 1½ oz. of pieces of canned tuna are placed on top and lightly pressed into the "gravy." A thin-rolled sheet of pie crust slightly larger than the pan is placed on top; then the pies pass through a machine which cuts off surplus crust and crimps the edge. Usually 2 oz. crust, 4½ oz. gravy, and 1½ oz. of tuna are used in each individual pie.

The little pies are packaged in heavily parafinned cartons which are mechanically overwrapped and heat-sealed with a lithographed wrapper.

## TU-NOODLE

This product was not on the market in 1966 but appears to have possibilities, and so the method of preparation is described here. White sauce, canned tuna, and sharp cheddar cheese are required. The white sauce is prepared as follows:

| Ingredients | % |
|---|---|
| Margarine | 11.2 |
| Flour | 3.7 |
| Nonfat dry milk | 84.5 |
| Salt | 0.4 |
| Monosodium glutamate | 0.2 |
| | 100.0 |

The margarine is melted in a steam kettle (or in a double boiler, if a small lot is being prepared). The flour is slowly stirred in. Stirring and heating is continued until a temperature of about 190°F. (88°C.) is reached, then the milk, salt, and monosodium glutamate are stirred in; cooking is continued until the sauce is thick.

If the product is packed in 14-oz. aluminum containers, two ounces of cooked drained egg noodles are placed on the bottom of the container, 1½ oz. of pieces of canned tuna are spread over the noodles and then one ounce of the grated sharp cheddar cheese. A layer of two ounces of cooked drained noodles is added, then 7½ oz. of white sauce is spread on top. The top is then sprinkled with rolled cracker crumbs which have been mixed with paprika.

## FISH STEW

See p. 157.

## BIBLIOGRAPHY

Anon. 1951. Fillet breading now mechanized. Food Eng. 23, No. 10, 145, 169.
Anon. 1953A. To prepare fried fish. Food Eng. 25, No. 3, 182, 184.
Anon. 1953B. Frozen fish in new form and tailored sizes. Food Eng. 25, No. 4, 192.
Anon. 1954A. Fish stix biz a-buzz. Pacific Fisherman 52, No. 10, 21–23.
Anon. 1954B. Frozen "fillet burger" packed by Berkoff. Pacific Fisherman 52, No. 10, 64.
Anon. 1954C. Eardley fisheries feature distinctive fish sticks. Pacific Fisherman 52, No. 8, 53.
Anon. 1954D. Cutting of fish sticks important operation. Fishing Gaz. 71, No. 6, 45, 104.
Anon. 1954E. Michigan fish stick producer. Fishing Gaz. 71, No. 9, 42, 44–45.

Anon.   1955A. Fish sticks at the plant of Gorton-Pew Fisheries Ltd. of Gloucester, Mass. Fishing Gaz. 72, No. 1, 49, 117.
Anon.   1955B. The Blue Water story. Quick Frozen Foods 17, No. 6, 75, 77, 79, 81, 83–87.
Anon.   1955C. Frozen seafood growth spurs new advances in automation. Quick Frozen Foods 17, No. 9, 105–107, 125–126.
Anon.   1955D. Canadian fish stick operations at plant at Lunenburg Sea Products, Ltd. Fishing Gaz. 72, No. 6, 41, 98.
Anon.   1955E. Streamlined fish stick production. Fishing Gaz. 72, No. 2, 50–51.
Anon.   1955F. Booth sets up new plant for frozen fish sticks. Food Packer 36, No. 1, 34.
Anon.   1955G. Olmstead boosts freshwater fillet pack to million pounds annually. Quick Frozen Foods 17, No. 12, 80–82.
Anon.   1955H. Preparing fish cakes. Food Eng. 27, No. 3, 187.
Anon.   1955I. Automatic breading, frying. Food Processing 16, No. 1, 60–62.
Anon.   1956. Well-designed production line spreads output, cuts labor. Quick Frozen Foods 18, No. 10, 53, 184.
Anon.   1966A. Quick Frozen Foods 1965–1966 Directory of Frozen Food Processors. E. W. Williams Publications, New York.
Anon.   1966B. Fish sticks, fish portions, and breaded shrimp. U.S. Dept. Interior, Fish and Wildlife Service, Bureau Commercial Fisheries. C.F.S. 4122.
Anon.   1967. Food fish—Situation and outlook. U.S. Dept. Interior, Fish and Wildlife Service, Bureau of Commercial Fisheries. Annual Review Issue 1966. CEA-F2.
Barkalow, F.   1954. Breaded, cooked fish era spurs mechanization of process line. Quick Frozen Foods 17, No. 3, 104, 106.
Block, Z.   1964. Frying. Chapter 50 in Volume 3, Food Processing Operations. M. A. Joslyn, and J. L. Heid, Editors. Avi Publishing Co., Westport, Conn.
Cocca, F. J.   1957. Some factors affecting "sawdust" losses during the cutting of fish sticks. Commercial Fisheries Rev. 19, No. 1, 41.
Crowther, H. E., and Hopkinson, L. T.   1953. Method of preparing fish fillet block. U.S. Pat. 2,643,952.
FE Staff.   1954. Fish sticks—Their acceptance mounts; processing detailed. Food Eng. 26, No. 1, 44, 202–203.
Foster, D.   1954. Use of MSG at proper level doubles product's consumer acceptance. Quick Frozen Foods 17, No. 3, 51–52.
Greer, Co., J. W.   1956. Continuous frying oil filters cut costs, boosts QC. Food Eng. 28, No. 2, 123.
Grimm, R. T.   1955. This filtering of frying oil assures better looking, tasting, lasting products. Food Eng. 27, No. 6, 113.
Holston, J. A.   1955A. Some factors affecting the color of fish sticks. U.S. Fish and Wildlife Service, Commercial Fisheries Rev. 17, No. 11, 15.
Holston, J. A.   1955B. Weight changes during the cooking of fish sticks. Commercial Fisheries Rev. 17, No. 4, 30–33.
Holston, J. A.   1955C. Effect of cooking oil, quality, and storage conditions on the keeping quality of frozen fried fish sticks. U.S. Fish and Wildlife Service, Commercial Fisheries Rev. 17, No. 11, 15.
Holston, J. A.   1956. Raw breaded or precooked seafoods. Section 3, Part 4, of Refrigeration of Fish. Fish and Wildlife Service Fishery Leaflet 430.

Hope, G. W., and Chipman, E. W. 1957. Comparison of sauces made from fresh and frozen rhubarb. Canadian Food Inds. *28*, No. 12, 11.

Hoyer, H. G. 1952. Deep fat frying of breaded fish and shellfish. Fishing Gaz. *69*, No. 13 (Annual Rev. No.) 166, 263–264.

Kahn, R. A., and Stolting, W. H. 1955. Household consumer preferences for breaded shrimp and breaded fish sticks. Part I—National and regional summary. U.S. Fish and Wildlife Service, Fishery Leaflet 424. Part II—Summary by farm and nonfarm rural city size groups. *Ibid.* Fishery Leaflet *425.*

Kahn, R. A., and Stolting, W. H. 1956. Household consumer preferences for breaded shrimp and breaded fish sticks. Part III—Summary by income groups, household size, homemaker age groups, and occupation. U.S. Fish and Wildlife Service, Fishery Leaflet *426.*

Kearns, M. P., Fagerson, I. S., and Fellers, C. R. 1955. Tests prove improved frozen food flavor achieved with MSG lasts for a year. Quick Frozen Foods *17*, No. 11, 62–63, 248.

Lawler, F. K. 1955. With idea for premium quality at premium price, Sea Pak achieves quick success through new know-how. Food Eng. *27*, No. 2, 72–76, 118–121.

Lee, C. F. 1954. Composition of cooked fish dishes. U.S. Fish and Wildlife Service, Circ. *29.*

Lirot, S. J. 1955. A study of some factors affecting the quality of frozen fish sticks. M.S. Thesis. Massachusetts Institute of Technology.

Lirot, S. J., and Nickerson, J. T. R. 1956. Quality variables pinpointed for fish-stick makers. Food Eng. *28*, No. 6, 88–90, 189.

Martin, S. 1967. The rise of prepared and precooked frozen foods. Unnumbered pamphlet. Nat'l Prepared Frozen Food Processors Assoc., Hicksville, New York. *See also* Chapter 1, of this book.

Osterhaug, K. L., and Bucher, D. L. 1945. Precooked frozen fish preparations. U.S. Fish and Wildlife Service, Fishery Leaflet *144.*

Patashnik, M., and Dassow, J. A. 1956. Storage tests on frozen fried fish sticks prepared from Pacific cod. Commercial Fisheries Rev. *18*, 15–18.

Peters, J. A. 1964. Time-temperature tolerance of frozen seafood. ASHRAE J. *6*, No. 8, 72–75, 91.

Peters, J. A., and Slavin, J. W. 1962. Time-temperature tolerance of frozen seafood: Influence of storage time, packaging, and humidity on the keeping quality of fish blocks and sticks. Annexe 1962-1, Suppl. Bull. Instit. Intern. Froid. 533–542.

Quammen, W. A. 1955. For top-quality fried foods curb these six trouble factors. Food Eng. *27*, No. 8, 76–77.

Robertson, C. J. 1953. Good frying practices. A talk made before the New England Fish Technologists Soc. in Boston, Oct. 13, 1953.

Ryan, J. J., and Evers, B. 1964. Precooked and prepared foods. In ASHRAE Guide and Data Book Applications Volume, Chap. 48, 585–588. Am. Soc. Heating Refrigerating and Air-Conditioning Engineers, Inc. New York.

Stansby, M. E. 1963. Processing of seafoods. In Food Processing Operations, M. A. Joslyn, and J. L. Heid, Editors. Avi Publishing Co., Westport, Conn.

Stix, R. L. 1965. American market for fishery products going through complete revolution. Quick Frozen Foods *28*, No. 4, 96.

Tenney, R. D., and Ryan, J. J. 1963. Inspectors' instructions for grading frozen fried fish sticks. Second issue. Bureau of Commercial Fisheries, Fish and Wildlife Service.

Tenney, R. D., and Ryan, J. J.   1964. Inspectors' instructions for grading frozen raw, breaded fish sticks. First issue. Bureau of Commercial Fisheries, Fish and Wildlife Service.

Tenney, R. D., and Ryan, J. J.   1964. Inspectors' instructions for grading frozen fried fish portions. First issue Bureau of Commercial Fisheries, Fish and Wildlife Service.

Tenney, R. D., and Ryan, J. J.   1964. Inspectors' instructions for grading frozen raw, breaded fish portions. Second issue. Bureau of Commerical Fisheries, Fish and Wildlife Service.

Trauberman, L.   1956. Controlled cooling key to quality fish sticks. Food Eng. 28, No. 5, 61, 189.

Umpleby, J., Pincus, B., and Block, Z.   1955. Tests determine range of breader pickup. Quick Frozen Foods 17, No. 6, 63, 68–69.

Wolfe, L. P.   1955A. Breaded, fried, and frozen seafoods. Fishing Gaz. 72, No. 2, 55–56; No. 3, 42, 67.

Wolfe, L. P.   1955B. Pointers on breading and frying sticks. Quick Frozen Foods 17, No. 6, 63.

Woods, L. C.   1955. Frying oils and fats. Fishing Gaz. 71, No. 13, (Annual Rev. No.) 174, 184.

Ziemba, J. V.   1953. Frying breaded fish non-stop. Food Eng. 25, No. 12, 84–85, 138, 140.

## CHAPTER 13

Donald K. Tressler | **Prepared and Precooked Shellfish**

## INTRODUCTION

A great variety of seafoods other than fish are frozen either in a prepared or precooked form. At present, breaded shrimp is the leading frozen prepared shellfish product, but there are many other precooked products of considerable importance. The list includes broiled and French-fried shrimp, shrimp croquettes, cutlets, paste, cakes, sticks, cocktail, patties, and pies; abalone patties, sticks, and breaded steaks; clam chowder (see p. 154), patties, deviled clams, fried clams, minced clams, and stuffed clams; conch; many inviting crab products; lobster cakes, cocktails, cutlets, pies, and tails; oyster cakes, pies, stews (see p. 153), and breaded oysters; breaded scallops and cooked scallops; king crab meat; and seafood dinners (see p. 516).

Although the list is long, it is continually growing longer, for new products are frequently coming on the market. Since the homemaker does not like the odor of cooking shellfish and does not like to prepare them for cooking, she buys frozen cooked shellfish if the products have the quality she demands. There is also an important market for cooked breaded shrimp. Taken as a whole, 104,040,000 lb., valued at $93,607,000, of breaded shrimp were frozen in the United States in 1966. Considerable quantities of other shrimp specialties were also frozen, the most important being stuffed shrimp, and shrimp dinners, in 1965 the values of which were $1,237,566 and $817,600 respectively. See also Volume 3, Chapter 9, Part 2.

The U.S. Armed Forces have used frozen uncooked lightly breaded shrimp since 1952 (Tressler and Evers 1957), Military specification MIL-S-4326A, published on Dec. 3, 1965, presents detailed specifications which must be met by frozen raw, lightly breaded shrimp purchased by the U.S. Military procurement agencies.

This Federal Specification indicates that the shrimp shall be clean and sound; shall be free of unsound shrimp such as those that are discolored, mashed, mutilated, or decomposed; shall be free from rancidity, from bacterial spoilage odors, and from off-odors of any kind, except that they shall be practically free from an iodoform odor. The breaded shrimp shall be free of black spots. The frozen shrimp shall have been in storage not longer than 90 days and the storage temperature shall have been not higher than 0°F. ($-18$°C.). The frozen shrimp, in addition, shall show no evidence of freezer burn, desiccation, discoloration, or other deterioration.

Donald K. Tressler is a consultant and President of the Avi Publishing Co., Westport, Conn.

The breading must not constitute more than 35% of the weight of the product. The maximum permissible standard plate count is 500,000 per gram.

## COMMERCIAL PROCEDURES FOR BREADING
### AND FREEZING SHRIMP

The process used in the SeaPak Corporation's plant on St. Simons Island, Ga., has been described by Lawler (1955) as follows:

"Iced fresh shrimp are washed, inspected, and mechanically graded into four sizes. Then they go to automatic peeling and deveining machines, and a water flume carries the peeled shrimp to a series of three spray-wash belts, the last discharging onto inspection belts.

"Pans of shrimp now go to pinning line, specially built by SeaPak. Here girls slip the tail of each shrimp over a pin on a metal bar to permit individual quality breading and freezing. Conveyors move pans of shrimp to the workers, and racks of pinned shrimp to the next operation. Tail-suspended shrimp, 325 to a rack, are dunked in batter, then transferred to a box and covered with a breading mix. Next they go into a −60°F. (−51°C.) air-blast freezing tunnel.

"After freezing, the shrimp are knocked off their pins by bumping a rack against a conveyor belt. This belt carries them to girls who do the cartoning and weighing. Retail-size cartons are then machine-wrapped, placed into shipping cases, and trucked to sub-zero storage."

Certain points concerning the procedure and equipment used at SeaPak are worthy of special note. The water used in washing the fresh shrimp is iced and chlorinated to 10 p.p.m. Another is the battery of 12 machines which peel the shrimp and take out the vein at a rate of 125 lb. per minute per machine for medium to large shrimp. Each of these peeler-deveiners is fed manually, one shrimp at a time, through an oval opening. Two small belts running face to face catch the shrimp and move it against the knives and a water jet. The knives take the peel off and the vein out, but leave the tails on for the fantail style. The jet washes waste to a flume. The peeled shrimp discharge into another flume that takes them to a series of spray-wash conveyors and inspection belts. These machines save a lot of man hours. Using eight of them on a shift with a total of 36 workers—machine feeders, inspectors, supervisors—SeaPak peels as many shrimp as 90 to 100 workers formerly turned out by hand operation.

The battering and breading operations are also ingenious. The batter is contained in a waist-high pan with a horizontal center section and upward sloping wings on either side. A rack of tail suspended shrimp is placed on supports over the center section, immersing the shrimp, but not the rack, in batter. Then the rack is slid onto one of the inclined wings to drain. This treatment is repeated in order to obtain a uniform coating of batter. To apply the breading mix, the rack is transferred to a box where it rests on supports to permit the shrimp to hang downward. Breading is scooped over the entire rack and a coating adheres to the batter on the shrimp (Fig. 44).

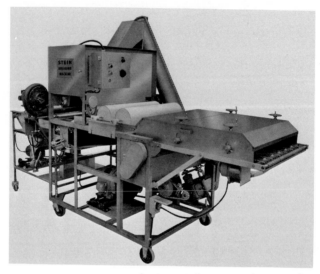

Fig. 44.   Stein batter and breading machine. Designed for continuous breading of shrimp and other seafoods.

## Boiled Shrimp

Frozen shrimp, precooked by boiling or steaming, are popular. If properly prepared from fresh or frozen shrimp of high quality and marketed without a long storage period, it is a delicious product. The amount of salt used in the cooking water should be small (Lewis 1947; Fieger 1954); further, it should be low in calcium, or the cooked shrimp will become rancid and tough during cold storage. Moreover, the package should not permit desiccation, since the desiccated product is likely to be tough (Lewis 1947).

The process used by Envoldsen Shrimp, Inc. in producing precooked frozen shrimp of high quality, has been described as follows (Anon. 1953B):

"The frozen shrimp reach the Envoldsen plant usually in five-pound institutional boxes, packed in master cartons. These are held in freezer storage until they are needed in the plant. They are thawed only as needed, the thawing time being rigidly controlled so that the shrimp are ready for the girls to peel without excess waiting time. As the girls peel the shrimp they are placed in a flume where the water carries them to an Envoldsen grader which separates them into four accurate grades. As these peeled shrimp are weighed out, the container for each 15-lb. lot is tagged with the size designation, which follows them through the deveining and cooking process and into the cooler so that they may be packed according to size without further grading.

"The shrimp are carried from the grading operation to the deveining tables where they are placed, five at a time, in a holder to facilitate the deveining operation. One girl slits the back of each shrimp in a lightning-like movement and the holders full of shrimp are then passed on to the operator on the rotary brush which whisks the vein out. The shrimp are then removed from the holder and sent to the beginning of the cooking line. Here 20 lb. of peeled and deveined shrimp are placed in a Monel cooking basket in a tank of brine solution. These baskets are picked up on a chain conveyor, which pushes them through the brine and into the hot, salty, spiced solution where the shrimp are cooked as the conveyor carries them through. Brine and spices are added after each basket leaves the solution, to keep the level of the salt and spice constant in the solution. The cooking time is rigidly controlled with adjustments made for each size of shrimp cooked.

"As the conveyor pulls the shrimp out of the hot cooking vat, the basket is immediately dipped into a container of chilled water to lower the temperature quickly. The shrimp are immediately removed from the basket and washed and inspected under a shower of ice water to bring them to a 40°F. (4°C.) temperature four minutes after they leave the cooking solution. After this cooling and inspection, shrimp are immediately placed in the cooler where their temperature is reduced to 33° or 34°F. (0.5° to 1.0°C.) in a few hours.

"As a rule, shrimp remain in the cooler overnight and are packed the following day. Only one pan of shrimp is removed from the cooler at a time and placed on the inspection and packing table. Here a rigid final inspection is made of each shrimp as they are packed in hand overwrapped cartons . . .

"Immediately after packaging and overwrapping, the packaged shrimp are placed on pallet-type freezing trays and placed in the blast freezer. The construction of these aluminum trays is such that the air circulates freely between each layer of packages, assuring equal freezing throughout. Packages are removed from the freezer and packed in master cartons for shipment.

## Other Frozen Precooked Shrimp Products

**Shrimp Sticks.**—In 1955, shrimp sticks were introduced. Both eight- and ten-ounce packages containing ten breaded and cooked shrimp sticks have been offered (Anon. 1955). These are produced by a process somewhat similar to that employed in preparing fish sticks (see pp. 275–286).

**Curried Shrimp**[1]

| Ingredients | Quantity |
|---|---|
| Frozen shrimp, medium, peeled, deveined, butterfly or cut in half lengthwise | 2½ lb. |
| Butter | 3½ oz. |
| Curry powder | ⅔ oz. |
| Salt | ¼ oz. |
| Instant onion | ½ oz. |
| Celery, finely diced | 1½ oz. |
| Broth (made from raw shrimp shells and fish bones) | 2 lb. |
| Evaporated milk | 10½ oz. |
| Modified starch[2] | 2½ oz. |
| Apples, peeled and finely diced | 3½ oz. |
| Mango chutney | 1 oz. |
| Modified cream (Pream) | 1½ oz. |
| Cooked rice | 1 lb. 14 oz. |

**Method.**—Reserve broth from cooked shrimp for fish broth.

Sauté shrimp in butter 5 min., stirring often. Add curry powder, salt and celery, and instant onion. Simmer covered 5 min. Remove shrimp and add fish broth.

Slowly add evaporated milk to starch and stir until smooth. Add to broth. Heat to 180°F. (82°C.), stirring constantly.

Add apples and chutney and stir until well blended. Add modified cream and stir until dissolved.

Package 6 oz. shrimp in each vacuum pouch (12 in. × 8 in.), evenly distributed with 7 oz. sauce. Blast freeze for 30 min.

**To Serve.**—Heat pouch in boiling water to cover 6 min. Serve in a 1-in. deep heated dish. Serve with 3 oz. of rice.

Sayles and MacLennan (1965) have estimated the cost and quantities of foods required for curried shrimp prepared in a hotel kitchen following the above recipe to be that indicated in Table 40.

[1] Source: Sayles and MacLennan (1965).
[2] Purity 69 or equivalent.

**Shrimp Creole**[3]

| Ingredients | Quantity |
|---|---|
| Shrimp, medium size, cooked, shelled and deveined | 2½ lb. |
| Peanut oil | 3½ oz. |
| Salt | ⅐ oz. |
| Spanish paprika | ⅑ oz. |
| Onions, 1 in. squares | 7 oz. |
| Instant onions | ½ oz. |
| Instant garlic | ¼ oz. |
| Green pepper, ½ in. squares, precooked | ¼ lb. |
| Italian tomatoes (canned), peeled, chopped, and seeds removed | 1 lb. |
| Tomato sauce | 1 lb. 2 oz. |
| Pimiento, ¼ in. diced | 3 oz. |
| Chili peppers | ¼ oz. |
| Rice, cooked | 1 lb. 14 oz. |

**Method.**—Sauté shrimp in peanut oil over high heat for 2 to 3 min.

Add salt, paprika, onions, instant onions, garlic, and green pepper. Cover and simmer 5 min.

Remove shrimp, add tomatoes, tomato sauce, pimiento, and chili peppers. Blend well.

Package 6 oz. shrimp and 7 oz. creole sauce in each vacuum pouch, evenly distributed. Blast freeze 30 min. Yield 6 pouches.

**To Serve:** Heat pouch in boiling water to cover 6 min. Serve in a 1-in. deep dish. Serve with 5 oz. of rice.

Sayles and MacLennan (1965) have estimated the cost of 1,000 portions of shrimp creole (prepared following the recipe given above in a hotel kitchen) for freezing and later use in a hotel restaurant to be that indicated in Table 41. These costs do not include the cost of freezing and storage of the product.

**Shrimp Pilau**

| Ingredients | Small Recipe | Quantity |
|---|---|---|
| Rice | 1 cup | 20 qt. |
| Water | 2 cup | 10 gal. |
| Salt | ½ tsp. | 1½ qt. |
| Onion | 1 large | 4 qt. |
| Fat | 4 tbsp. | 6 lb. |
| Green pepper | 1 | 3 qt. |
| Tomatoes, No. 2 can | 1 | 80 lb. |
| Shrimp (cooked) | 1 lb. | 80 lb. |

---

[3] Source: Sayles and MacLennan (1965).

Table 40

Estimated Quantities and Costs for 1,000 Portions

| Ingredients | Quantity, Lb. | Unit Price | Amount |
|---|---|---|---|
| Shrimp | 415 | $1.30 | $539.50 |
| Celery | 15 | 0.10 | 1.50 |
| Apples | 75 | 4.00/box | 8.00 |
| Purity 69 starch | 18 | 0.25 | 4.50 |
| Evaporated milk | 110 | 0.15/14 oz. | 17.60 |
| Pream | 14.5 | 0.89/14 oz. | 14.50 |
| Instant onion | 7.3 | 1.85 | 13.57 |
| Mango chutney | 11 | 0.86/9 oz. | 17.20 |
| Curry powder | 7.3 | 0.70 | 5.13 |
| Butter | 25 | 0.64 | 16.00 |
| Seasoning | — | — | 2.00 |
| Shredded coconut | 10 | 0.40 | 4.00 |
| Rice | 120 | 0.18 | 71.60 |
| Total estimated ingredient cost | | | $715.10 |

| Preparation and Cooking | Time Hr. | Rate | Amount |
|---|---|---|---|
| 1 Fireman | 5 | $1.75 | $ 8.75 |
| 2 Firemen, 2 hr. each | 4 | 1.75 | 7.00 |
| 1 Sauce cook | 4 | 3.75 | 15.00 |
| 3 Kitchen helpers | 7 | 1.75 | 12.25 |
| Employee benefits (22%) | — | — | 9.46 |
| Total estimated wage cost | | | $ 53.46 |
| Cost of Pouches (1,050 at $36.48/M) | | | 38.30 |
| Total estimated cost of 1,000 portions | | | $806.86 |
| Estimated Cost Per Portion 80.6 cents | | | |

**Method.**—Cook rice in boiling water (salted) until tender. Drain. Brown onion and green pepper in hot fat. Add tomatoes. Bring to rolling boil. Add rice and shrimp. Simmer for 10 min. Package while hot. Freeze rapidly.

## Frozen Prepared and Precooked Crab Products—Blue Crabs

The popularity of frozen precooked crab products has increased markedly during the past few years. The list of products now offered is long, including the following: Crab meat (see Volume 3, Chap. 9), both blue and king, crabettes, deviled crab cakes, deviled crabs, crab cakes, cocktails, loaf, rolls, sticks, legs, stuffed crabs, crab imperial, and soft shell crabs.

Most of these crab products are prepared from the blue crab, *Callinectes sapidus*, but cooked crabs and cooked crab legs are prepared using the dungeness crab, *Cancer magister*, and the king crab, *Paralithodes camtschatica*. The latter two species are caught on the Pacific Coast and in Alaskan waters.

**Crab Meat.**—All frozen crabs, with the exception of some frozen soft crabs, are steamed, and in most cases the meat is picked out, prior to freez-

Table 41

Estimated Quantities and Cost of 1,000 Portions

| Ingredients | Quantity Lb. | Unit Price | Amount |
|---|---|---|---|
| Shrimp | 415 | $1.30 | $539.50 |
| Canned tomatoes | 150 | 0.95/6½ lb. | 21.85 |
| Onions | 75 | 0.10 | 7.50 |
| Green peppers, cooked | 35 | 0.28 | 9.80 |
| Pimientos | 30 | 0.28 | 8.40 |
| Dried peppers | 1¾ | 0.46/14 oz. | .92 |
| Instant garlic | 3¾ | 1.85 | 6.95 |
| Instant onion | 7⅓ | 1.85 | 13.57 |
| Peanut oil | 37 | 2.69/128 oz. | 12.37 |
| Tomato sauce | 185 | 0.11/6 oz. | 54.23 |
| Seasoning | — | — | 2.00 |
| Spanish paprika | 3¾ | 0.99 | 3.67 |
| Rice | 120 | 0.18 | 21.60 |
| Total estimated ingredient cost | | | $702.36 |

| Preparation and Cooking | Time Hr. | Rate | Amount |
|---|---|---|---|
| 1 Fireman | 7 | $1.75 | $ 12.25 |
| 1 Fireman | 2 | 1.75 | 3.50 |
| 1 Sauce cook | 4 | 3.75 | 15.00 |
| 3 Kitchen helpers | 7 | 1.75 | 12.25 |
| Employee benefits (22%) | | | 9.46 |
| Total estimated wage cost | | | $ 52.46 |
| Cost of Pouches (1,050 at $36.48 per M) | | | $ 38.30 |
| | | | $793.12 |

Estimated Cost per Portion 79.3 cents

ing. Consequently, the product is in reality cooked and without further cooking may be used directly in crab cocktail and salad. The methods of steaming crabs and picking out the meat have been described in Chapter 9 of Volume 3, and therefore the procedures will not be repeated here.

**Deviled Crabs.**—Deviled crabs have always been very popular in Maryland, Virginia, and many other states along the seacoast. The preparation of this product is time-consuming; consequently it is not surprising that the frozen product has found ready acceptance. One packer alone produces 25,000 or more daily. The procedure followed by the Eat-All Frozen Food Co., Philadelphia, Pa., has been described by the *Food Engineering* Staff (1954) as follows:

"(1) Cream sauce is prepared in stainless steel, steam-jacketed kettles, then blended with seasoning and other ingredients in a horizontal, batch-type mixer.

"(2) Deviled crab mix is then charged into the hopper of an automatic patty-forming machine. Here, a screw feeds mix to five cylinders bored into a revolving disk that serves as the forming unit and as a circular conveyor. Below each forming cylinder are a cam operated piston and piston rod. Deviled crab patty is shaped in the cylinder under pressure of the screw feed and just as the piston rod passes over the cam. Patty then is forced up to the top of the revolving disk. When piston is in discharge position, a circular knife, revolving in opposite direction, but parallel with the disk, removes the patty.

"(3) Crab-shaped patties then are placed on the edible pastry shells and loaded onto trays for transfer to the egg-batter station. Here, deviled crabs go into a small stainless steel vat holding several gallons of batter. From this small vat, a three-foot, pulley-driven, inclined, wire-mesh belt picks up the 'crabs,' draining excess batter from them as they are discharged into a wooden tray containing bread crumbs.

"(4) A trayload of breaded deviled crabs is then submerged for a few minutes in a batch-type, deep-fat fryer. Temperatures of the frying fat (hydrogenated vegetable oil) is 375°F. (190.5°C.). Next each tray is elevated out of the fryer to permit draining of excess cooking fat.

"(5) Trays are now loaded onto racks that are rolled into a blower-type pre-chill room at 25°F. ($-3.5$°C.). Product then is moved to a $-30$°F. ($-34.4$°C.) blast freezer, where it is flash-frozen in about 30 min.

"(6) Girls finally pack two three-ounce deviled crabs in a laminated carton. Product-packed cartons are then belt conveyed to a wrapping machine that applies a heat-sealable, waxed paper overwrap. Cartons subsequently are packed into shipping cases for freezer storing prior to shipment"

**Deviled Crab Formula.**—The formula below was developed by one of the authors and is *not* that used by the packer whose operations are described above.

| Ingredients | Quantity required for 100 3¼ oz. Crabs | |
|---|---|---|
| | Lb. | Oz. |
| Whole fluid milk | 6 | 13 |
| "Instant" milk powder | | 6 |
| Waxy maize starch | | 12.5 |
| Shortening (hydrogenated vegetable) | 2 | 4 |
| Dry mustard | | 1 |
| Worcestershire sauce | | 3 |
| Cayenne pepper | | ⅓₀ |
| Dehydrated parsley | | 1 |
| Salt | | 3 |
| Chopped green peppers | | 10 |
| Monosodium glutamate | | 1 |
| Dehydrated egg yolk | | 8 |
| Lemon juice | | 2 |
| Blue crab meat | 6 | 0 |

**Procedure.**—Six pounds of fluid milk are placed in a six-quart aluminum or stainless steel pan or bowl. The milk is agitated with a high-speed electric mixer, then slowly the "Instant" dry nonfat milk is added and agitation is continued until the nonfat milk is completely dissolved.

The hydrogenated vegetable shortening is melted in a steam-jacketed kettle equipped with a variable speed agitator. The waxy maize starch is stirred in and the mixture stirred until smooth, then the temperature is raised until it reaches 180°F. (82°C.). The milk is slowly stirred into the mixture; then the product is heated to 180°F. (82°C.).

The dehydrated egg yolk is placed in an eight-quart bowl of a Hobart mixer. After starting the mixer, the remaining milk (13 oz.) is slowly added; the mixture is stirred until smooth after each addition of milk. When all the milk has been added, a small portion of the hot milk-melted shortening-starch mixture is added. The slow stirring in the milk-melted shortening-starch mixture is continued until half of it has been added. Then this egg-milk-shortening-starch mixture is poured into the remaining half of the milk-shortening-starch mixture which has been kept at 180°F. (82°C.) in the steam-jacketed kettle. This entire mixture is slowly stirred until it is homogeneous, with simultaneously heating to bring the temperature back to 180°F. (82°C.).

The remaining ingredients, mustard, Cayenne pepper, dehydrated parsley, salt, monosodium glutamate, lemon juice, Worcestershire sauce, and finally the crab meat, are added. Mixing is continued slowly until the temperature has reached 160°F. (71°C.). It is then cooled, either by running cool water through the jacket, or by placing it in shallow two-quart aluminum pans and floating the pans first in cold water and then packing in crushed ice. If the preliminary cooling is carried out by running cold water through the jacket, the final cooling to 50°F. (10°C.) can be effected either by removing the deviled crab from the kettle and placing it in aluminum pans packed in crushed ice or placed in a large refrigerator.

The product is filled into pastry shells which have been fried in deep fat for ten seconds at 375°F. (190.5°C.) 3¼ oz. to the crab, and sprinkled with bread crumbs which have been mixed with hydrogenated vegetable shortening in the proportion of five ounces bread crumbs to one ounce shortening.

Each deviled crab is placed in a transparent moisture-proof envelope which preferably is then heat-sealed. The crabs are then packed in shallow cartons, one layer to a carton. After removal from the freezer the cartons are packed into fiberboard shipping containers for storage.

## Crab Imperial

Another cooked crab product, filled into imitation crab shells in the same way as deviled crab, is "crab imperial" which resembles the "deviled" product but is less highly seasoned. A tested formula and procedure for making this product follows:

| Ingredients | Quantity Required for 100 3¼-oz. Crabs Lb. | Oz. |
|---|---|---|
| Chopped green peppers (blanched) | | 14¼ |
| Onion powder | | ½ |
| Paprika | | ¼ |
| Salt | | 2 |
| Lemon juice | | 7 |
| Monosodium glutamate | | ¾ |
| Either white sauce or an emulsified salad dressing (such as "Miracle Whip") | 6 | 14 |
| Crab meat (lump) | 12 | 14 |

**Preparation of White Sauce**

| Ingredients | | |
|---|---|---|
| Dehydrated egg yolk | | 2 |
| Vegetable shortening | | 8½ |
| Flour, all purpose wheat | | 7½ |
| Salt | | ½ |
| Nonfat milk powder, instant | | 3½ |
| Water | 5 | 8 |
| Total | 6 | 14 |

The shortening is melted in a double boiler, or if a large batch is being prepared, in a steam kettle; the flour is added; stirring is continued until the mixture is smooth. Nonfat milk powder is dissolved in water, then slowly stirred into the fat-flour mixture. The mixture is cooked until thick and smooth, with slow stirring. The sauce is cooled to 140°F. (60°C.) then some of it is added to the egg yolk solids. Slow stirring is continued until the sauce is smooth. The egg yolk mix is then stirred into the main lot of cream sauce, with slow heating, and continued cooking and stirring until the sauce is smooth and near the boiling point. After addition of salt, the sauce is cooled.

**Preparation of Crab Imperial.**—Chopped peppers, onion powder, monosodium glutamate, salt, and paprika are mixed together. Cool white sauce or salad dressing is added; the mixture is stirred until uniformly mixed; then crab meat is carefully folded in with sufficient mixing to obtain a uniform product. It is filled into imitation or sterilized crab shells, sprinkled with brown cracker crumbs, prepared by combining one ounce melted shortening with five ounces brown cracker crumbs. The "crabs" are placed in transparent moisture-proof envelopes which are heat-sealed. The envelopes containing the "crabs" are packed in shallow cartons which are placed on metal trays for freezing on racks in an air-blast freezer at −10°F. (−23°C.), or below. After removal from the freezer, the cartons are packed into fiberboard shipping containers for storage or shipment.

## Crab Cakes

The product is somewhat similar in composition to that used in deviled crabs. However, it usually is less highly seasoned. The following formula will produce 100 two-ounce crab cakes:

| Ingredients | Lb. | Oz. |
|---|---|---|
| All purpose wheat flour | 1 | |
| Hydrogenated vegetable short-ening | 1 | 4 |
| Nonfat milk powder, instant | | 5 |
| Dry mustard | | ¾ |
| Whole egg or yolk solids | | 1¾ |
| Salt | | 2 |
| Dehydrated onion powder | | ¼ |
| Fresh lemon juice | | 1¾ |
| Cracker crumbs | | 10 |
| Dehydrated parsley | | ½ |
| Monosodium glutamate | | ¼ |
| Crab meat | 5 | |
| Water | 4 | |

**Preparation Procedure.**—The instant nonfat milk powder is stirred into the water in a stock pot. The hydrogenated vegetable shortening is melted in a steam-jacketed kettle, equipped with a variable speed stirrer, and the flour slowly blended in, with continuous agitation. Then a sauce is made by stirring in all but about a pint of the water. The remaining water is used to make a thin paste of the egg yolk. About a pint of the warm sauce mixture is stirred into the yolk solution and stirring is continued until the product is smooth, then it is added to the main lot of warm sauce, and heated to 180°F. (82°C.). The crab meat and remaining ingredients, except for the lemon juice, are stirred in with thorough mixing. The mixture is heated to 160°F. (71°C.) then the lemon juice is added. The product is cooled in

*Courtesy of John H. Dulany and Son, Inc.*

Fig. 45.   Crab cake forming machine. A carefully blended mixture of sauce and crab meat is put into the hopper of the machine which forms the cakes.

*Courtesy of John H. Dulany and Son, Inc.*

Fig. 46. Arranging crab cakes on trays for frying.

a refrigerator to 60°F. (15.5°C.) or lower. It is then formed into two-ounce cakes (Fig. 45 and 46), which are dipped first in batter, then in cracker crumbs or breading, and fried in deep fat at 365°F. (185°C.) until golden brown. The cakes are cooled, packaged, overwrapped, and frozen on trays placed on racks in an air-blast freezer at −10°F. (−23°C.).

## Crab "Cocktail Balls"

Another interesting crab product is cocktail balls which after reheating can be served on tooth picks as an hors d'ouevre, or with a cream sauce as the main dish of a meal. The formula and procedure for making this product follows:

| Ingredients | % |
|---|---|
| Crab meat, finely chopped | 52.60 |
| Cracker meal, rolled fine | 13.30 |
| Hydrogenated vegetable shortening | 10.00 |
| Blanched parsley, chopped fine | 4.30 |
| Whole egg solids | 1.60 |
| Salt | 1.00 |
| Monosodium glutamate | 0.20 |
| Dehydrated onion powder | 0.16 |
| Dehydrated garlic powder | 0.08 |
| Worcestershire sauce | 0.03 |
| Water | 16.73 |
| | 100.00 |

**Procedure.**—All dry ingredients are mixed together. The Worcestershire sauce and water are mixed separately and then stirred into dry mixture. When a homogeneous mixture has been obtained, the mixture is pressed into small balls each weighing about one-sixth ounce. The balls are dipped first into a batter mix (see p. 277), then in breading mix (see p. 279). The balls are fried in deep fat at 370° to 375°F. (188° to 190.5°C.) until golden brown, then drained, cooled, packaged, and frozen.

## KING CRAB

The freezing of Alaskan crab on an important scale was begun during the year 1952 in which 359,892 lb. was frozen. The pack of this delicious crustacean has steadily increased; in 1964, 7,924,888 lb. was packed.

All of the Alaskan crab meat marketed in the United States has been cooked, much of it on board large factory ships which operate off the coasts of Alaska and the Aleutians.

The procedure followed in preparing, cooking, packing, and freezing king crab meat may be described as follows (see also chapter 9, Volume 3): The king crabs (Fig. 47) are caught in huge "pots" or traps many of which are 8 ft. square and 36 in. deep. Usually the frames are made of steel rods with nylon mesh lashed to an inner frame, usually a wooden dowel which, in turn, is lashed to the pots. A 9½ in. knotted nylon mesh forms the sides, bottom and top of the pot, and 3½ in. knotted or knotless nylon is used in the tunnel (entrance to the trap) which is tipped upward toward the top of the pot.

Frozen herring or halibut heads are used as bait. The pots are hoisted to

*Courtesy of Wakefield Seafoods, Inc.*

Fig. 47. A ten-pound king crab. Several crab pots (traps) are in the background.

the deck of the fishing vessel every 2 or 3 days. On deck the crabs are removed and placed in a live tank.

After the fishing vessel has pulled all of the traps, the catch is brought directly to the processor, either a floating or a shorebased factory. The crabs are put in huge baskets in which they are weighed and then placed in the processors live tanks. All dead crabs are discarded.

The crab is butchered by grasping the legs and striking the bottom of the shell sharply against a dull bladed knife. This operation separates the carapace and viscera from the legs, claws, and shoulders (Fig. 48).

The legs, claws, and shoulder "section" of the crabs are immediately placed on a continuous conveyor on which they are conveyed through boiling water (some processors use fresh water, others sea water). The sections are held in the cooker long enough to cook them thoroughly. On the Wakefield factory ship Akutan the cooked sections are automatically ejected into a stainless steel tube 22 in. in diameter and 42 ft. long through which cold seawater is pumped continuously. The sea water cools the sections to approximately 45°F. (7.2°C.) and conveys them to the head of the processing line.

At this point, the legs are separated and graded into those from which the meat will be removed and the legs which will be packed as king crab legs in the shell. From this point on, two separate and distinct procedures are used in packaging and freezing.

When sections are to be packed in the shell, they are degilled, scrubbed, the barnacles are removed, and then the legs are packed in metal pans and placed in a blast freezer. From the blast freezer the sections are moved to a glazing station where the legs are dipped in cold fresh water to glaze them. They are then packed in corrugated fiberboard containers and placed in low-temperature storage awaiting shipment.

The legs from which the meat is to be extracted are cut into shorter pieces; these are put on a flat conveyor belt which carries them to meat extractors or wringers. These wringers are constructed much like a laundry wringer. They crush the shell and squeeze out the meat which drops on the feeding side of the wringer into a trough in which it is conveyed by water to a packing table. There it is packed into lined metal trays which hold 15 lb. of meat. The crab meat is frozen in 15 lb. blocks either in a plate freezer or in an air-blast freezer. The frozen meat is glazed and packed into cases for cold storage prior to shipment. The 15 lb. blocks are in two shapes; some are 11 by 15 by 3 in., others 5 by 3 by 33 in.

When prepared for retail sale, these blocks are cut with a saw and packaged in 6, 8, 12, and twin 8 oz. consumer packages and, in addition, some are cut into 1, 2½, and 5 lb. institutional packs. (Fig. 49).

The 11 by 15 by 3 in. blocks are first cut into three 11 by 5 by 3 in.

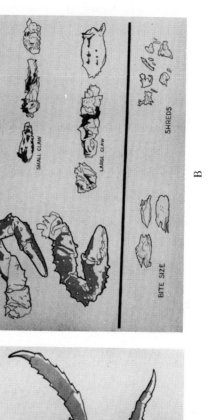

Fig. 48A and B. Edible portions of the king crab are shown in the two illustrations above. (A) Location of edible portions. (B) Shoulders, legs, and claws after separation. Note that only these parts are used for food. The merus is bright red. Because of its size and attractive color, it is often placed in the upper part of the package of crab meat.

*Courtesy of the National Fisherman*

Fig. 49. Cutting 15-lb. blocks of frozen king crab meat into 6-, 8-, and 12-oz. pieces which are packaged for the retail market. The work is done in refrigerated areas to prevent thawing of the crab meat.

blocks; then cut again to yield portions 3 by 5 in. by the thickness required to produce 6, 8, or 12 oz. portions (Fig. 49).

As a matter of fact, the "15 lb." blocks frozen in Alaska are about 15 lb. 10 oz. in weight. This 10 oz. of extra meat makes up for losses due to desiccation and the "sawdust" which is lost when the blocks are sawed into the size needed for retail cartons. For retail sale the portions are placed in cardboard cartons, which are each sealed in a waxed paper overwrap.

A special "fancy" or "fry leg" pack is also produced. This pack is made up of the meros piece only and is packed in 3½ lb. units by dividing the standard 15 lb. tray into four separate sections and lining each section with a waxed carton.

### LOBSTER

As in the case of crabs, practically all of the lobster frozen is first steamed for about 15 min. This steaming cooks it so that, without further preparation, the meat may be used in salads and cocktails. These statements also apply to spiny crawfish, marketed commercially under the name of lobster tails, South African lobster tails, and the like. Since the freezing of lobster meat has been presented in Chapter 9 of Volume 3, no further consideration will be given here. The discussion which follows will be devoted to prepared lobster dishes. The principal frozen lobster dishes offered commercially are lobster cakes and cutlets, pies, Newburg, "thermidor," and stuffed lobster.

**Lobster Newburg**

|  |  | Quantity |
| --- | --- | --- |
| Ingredients | Lb. | Oz. |
| Lobster meat | 15 | |
| Butter | 2 | 8 |
| Waxy maize or waxy rice starch | | 6 |
| Egg yolk solids | 1 | 2 |
| Instant nonfat milk powder | 2 | |
| Salt | | 3 |
| Monosodium glutamate | | 1.5 |
| Paprika | | 1.5 |
| Red pepper | | 1.5 |
| Ground nutmeg | | 1 |
| Water | 16 | |
| Sherry | 1 | 8 |

**Procedure.**—Diced boiled lobster meat is sautéed for 3 to 5 min. in the melted butter in a steam-jacketed kettle. A cream sauce, prepared using the water, starch, nonfat milk powder, and egg yolk solids, is added with slow stirring and heating. The mixture is slowly brought to the boiling point and simmered for three minutes. After the batch has been cooled to about 100°F. (38°C.), the sherry wine is added. Then the product is packaged and frozen.

## Lobster Thermidor

The first step in preparing lobster thermidor is to steam the lobsters under ten pounds pressure. After cooling, the lobster meat is removed both from the body and the claws. The shells are washed, dried, and chilled. The lobster meat is diced and sautéed in sherry wine. The meat is then placed in the cleaned shells (Anon. 1951B) and covered with a cream sauce filling. The filled lobsters are frozen on trays. When frozen, they are placed in cold-waxed cartons which are overwrapped.

### ABALONE

Abalone is frozen in California as breaded steaks and in the form of sticks and patties. The industry is located principally in Santa Barbara, Long Beach, and Morro Bay, Calif.

One processor (Anon. 1951A) is utilizing abalone trimmings, which were formerly of little value, in the preparation of breaded frozen fresh abalone patties. The product is being made from the too-thin steaks, edgings, and pieces broken from the steaks in pounding.

The pieces of abalone trimmings are first minced in a mechanical meat grinder and the ground meat then forced under pressure into a metal tube 24 in. long and 3 in. in diameter. The "cores" made in this manner are stacked in a freezer. After freezing, the meat is released in a solid frozen loaf by running water over the core. The loaf of abalone meat is sliced into pieces ¼-in. thick. These thin patties are dipped into batter and cracker crumbs. The patties are packed four to a Cellophane bag, are put into cartons; 12 or 24 cartons are packed in each shipping container for storage or shipment.

## BIBLIOGRAPHY

Anon.  1951A.  Abalone patties, breaded and frozen. Pacific Fisherman 49, No. 6, 51–52.

Anon.  1951B.  Two cooked lobster dishes. Quick Frozen Foods 14, No. 1, 57.

Anon.  1952.  Frozen cooked lobsters retain fresh qualities. Food Eng. 24, No. 2, 169–170.

Anon.  1953A.  Wants to make crab cakes. Food Eng. 25, No. 9, 210–211.

Anon.  1953B.  The Envoldsen story. Southern Fisherman Yearbook 13, 72–73, 77.

Anon.  1954.  Breading machine scores in plant tests. Quick Frozen Foods 16, No. 7, 214.

Anon.  1955.  Shrimp sticks seen winning favor. Quick Frozen Foods 17, No. 12, 80.

Anon.  1956A.  Making lobster Newburg. Food Eng. 28, No. 4, 177.

Anon.  1956B.  Tips on hand-breading of shrimp are listed for processors. Quick Frozen Foods 18, No. 7, 324, 326.

Anon.  1956C.  Present shrimp operations expensive. Frozen breaded shrimp plant engineering survey indicates need for plant reorganization. Fishing Gaz. 73, No. 6, 50–51, 84, 146.

Anon.  1956D.  Breaded shrimp plant engineering survey. U.S. Fish and Wildlife Service, Com. Fisheries Rev. 18, No. 6, 37–38.

Anon.  1965.  Military specification: Shrimp, frozen, raw, lightly breaded. MIL-S-43269A. 3 December.

Anon.  1967.  Shellfish situation and outlook. Fish and Wildlife Service, Bureau of Commercial Fisheries, Current Economic Analysis 56.

Dugan, J. R.  1954.  Handling shrimp in the breading plant. Southern Fisherman Yearbook 14, 62–64.

FE Staff.  1954.  Deviled crabs: 25,000 daily. Food Eng. 26, No. 11, 99, 176.

FE Staff.  1956.  Method maintains quality in crab cakes. Food Eng. 28, No. 2, 92–93.

Fieger, E. A.  1954.  How long cooking time, what brine strength? Study on losses resulting from cooling, peeling of shrimp. Canner 118, No. 14, 9–11.

Grimm, R. T.  1955.  This filtering of frying oil assures better looking, testing, lasting products. Food Eng. 27, 27, No. 6, 113.

Heerdt, M., and Dassow, J. A.  1952.  Freezing and cold storage of Pacific Northwest fish and shellfish. Part 2. King crab. U.S. Fish and Wildlife Service, Com. Fisheries Rev. 14, No. 12a, 29–35.

Kahn, R. A., and Stolting, W. H.  1955.  Household consumer preferences for breaded shrimp and breaded fish sticks. Part I—National and Regional Summary. U.S. Fish and Wildlife Service, Fishery Leaflet 424. Part II—Summary by farm and nonfarm rural and city size groups. Ibid. Fishery Leaflet 425

Kahn, R. A., and Stolting, W. H.  1956.  Household consumer preferences for breaded shrimp and breaded fish sticks. Part III—Summary by income groups, household size, homemaker age groups, and occupation. U.S. Fish and Wildlife Service, Fishery Leaflet 426.

Kerr, R.   1950. Fish cookery for one hundred. U.S. Fish and Wildlife Service, Text Kitchen Series 1.

Lawler, F. K.   1955. With idea for premium quality at premium price, SeaPak achieves quick success through new know-how. Food Eng. 27, No. 2, 72–76, 118–121.

Lewis, H.   1947. What effects do cooking time and packing have on frozen boiled shrimp? Food Freezing 1, No. 3, 48–49.

Lyles, C. H.   1967. Statistical data on U.S. process products. U.S. Fish and Wildlife Service, Bureau of Commercial Fisheries, Letter dated April 10.

Osterhaug, K. L., and Bucher, D. L.   1945. Precooked frozen fish preparations. U.S. Fish and Wildlife Service, Fishery Leaflet 144.

Quammen, W. A.   1955. For top-quality fried foods curb these six trouble factors. Food Eng. 27, No. 8, 76–77.

Sayles, C. I., and MacLennan, H. A.   1965. Ready foods. Cornell Hotel and Restaurant Administration Research Rept. 10.

Tressler, D. K., and Evers, C. F.   1957. The Freezing Preservation of Foods, 3rd Edition. Vol. 1 Fresh Foods. Vol. 2 Precooked and Prepared Foods. Avi Publishing Co., Westport, Conn.

Watts, B. M., Lewis, H., Gardner, E. A., and Wentworth, J.   1956. Progress in preservation studies on Southern oysters. Fishing Gaz. 73, No. 7, 42, 60–61.

## CHAPTER 14

Sauces and Gravies;

Thickened Desserts and Fillings;

Helen Hanson Palmer

Whipped Toppings;

Salad Dressings and Soufflés

## INTRODUCTION

Sauces, gravies, thickened desserts, salad dressings, soufflés, and whip toppings at first glance appear to have little in common. They are included in the same chapter because all have characteristic structures that may be damaged during freezing, storage, and thawing. Sauces and gravies have a characteristic smooth, viscous consistency. Salad dressings have a stiff, uniform consistency that is dependent on maintenance of their emulsion structure. Whip toppings, soft meringues, and soufflés have foam or sponge structures. Custards, puddings, and thickened fillings have gel structures. The maintenance of the characteristic structures in some of these products depends on selection or modification of key ingredients (the starch in the sauces and gravies, the oil and starch in salad dressings); in others storage temperature and processing methods are important.

### SAUCES AND GRAVIES

Sauces and gravies were originally frozen as an adjunct to meat or poultry in products such as chicken à la king, Swiss steak, stews, and pot pies. They are now used in increasing amounts in "boil-in-the-bag" vegetables and entrées. In addition to contributing their own distinctive flavors, sauces and gravies are important for their role in increasing the flavor stability of the meat or vegetables. They perform this function by eliminating air from the package and delaying development of rancidity and other off-flavors. Commercially prepared sauces and gravies are also frozen individually in wide variety for the restaurant and institutional market, ready for quick thawing and reheating in a steamer or in hot water. Thus they eliminate the need for a large inventory of ingredients and the daily need for the labor required in their preparation.

Commercially prepared frozen meat sauces include Hollandaise, Bearnaise, Bordelaise, Madère, Smitane, Suprême, Eugenie, Hongroise, Mornay, cheese and mushroom; dessert sauces include Jubilee and Suzette. These sauces contain a wide variety of basic and exotic ingredients: broth,

Helen Hanson Palmer is Head Product Stability Investigations, Poultry Laboratory, Western Utilization Research and Development Division, Agricultural Research Service, U.S. Dept. of Agr., Albany, Calif.

milk, sour cream, tomatoes, wine, fruit juices, brandy, liqueurs, cheese, mushrooms, cherries, spices, and herbs. Some are thickened with starch or flour and others are cooked to the desired paste consistency. Those containing starchy thickening agents present special problems in preserving their desirable consistency after freezing and thawing.

### Starch-thickened Sauces and Gravies

Sauces and gravies thickened with the common cereal flours and starches appear curdled after freezing and thawing. Liquid separates from those that are thawed after storage of a few weeks at 0°F. (−18°C.), and the amount of separation increases with increase in storage time or temperature. The change is most apparent in products that are thawed to refrigerator or room temperature (Fig. 50). Heating to serving temperature improves the appearance, and stirring is also beneficial; but heating and stirring do not entirely restore the smooth appearance of the unfrozen sauce. Since stirring may damage diced meats and tender vegetables in some products and since "boil-in-the-bag" products cannot be stirred during heating, studies were conducted over a number of years to develop sauces that remain smooth without stirring during thawing.

Early research on the stability problem showed that the starch fraction of the thickening agent is the constituent directly responsible for stability (Hanson *et al.* 1951). This study also showed that waxy cereal starches and flours produce more stable frozen sauces or gravies than do the common cereal products. Among the waxy cereals, waxy rice produces greatest stability. Sauces or gravies thickened with waxy rice flour may be stored for a

Fig. 50. White sauce thickened with waxy rice flour (left) and wheat flour (right), thawed at 77°F. (25°C.) after 5 months at 0°F. (−18°C.).

year at 0°F. ( −18°C.) with little or no change in appearance on thawing. Even if storage is prolonged or higher storage temperatures are used, so that curdling or liquid separation occur, the sauces become smooth without stirring when heated to serving temperature.

Waxy rice and other waxy cereals differ from common cereals primarily in the composition of the starch fraction (see also Chapter 2). Approximately 17 to 30% of the starch from common cereal flours consists of unbranched starch chains, and the remainder consists of branched starch chains. Waxy cereal flours contain only branched starch chains. The unbranched starch chains "retrograde" or associate, with elimination of water, more rapidly than do the branched chains during freezing and frozen storage. Branched starch molecules which undergo retrogradation are readily redispersed by heating to 122°F. (50°C.) (Schoch and French 1947). Retrogradation of the common cereal starches as the major factor affecting stability was confirmed by Osman and Cummisford (1959).

The explanation for the superior stability of waxy rice products is not known; it may be related to the small size of the rice starch granule or to some anomalous difference in its chemical structure (Schoch 1966). Waxy corn, sorghum, and rice differ from each other in size and extent of branching of their starch molecules. Although sauces thickened with waxy rice are stable for a year at 0°F. ( −18°C.) those thickened with waxy corn and sorghum are stable for about two months. Aqueous five per cent waxy rice starch pastes show no liquid separation after 20 freeze-thaw cycles (Schoch 1966). The method for measuring freeze-thaw stability is given on p. 52. Sauces containing mixtures of waxy rice and wheat flour show stability intermediate between that of rice and wheat alone; but if the waxy rice flour constitutes 40% of the mixture, liquid separation and the curdled appearance disappear when the sauce is heated for serving. The addition of stabilizers increases the time that the products containing waxy cereal thickeners can be held under adverse conditions without noticeable change (Hanson et al. 1957). Sauces thickened with waxy rice flour separate after about 1 to 2 months' storage at 10°F. ( −12°C.); addition of one per cent citrus pectin increases the stability to a year at this temperature. Other stabilizers tested, including gums, gelatin, and Irish moss, were less effective than citrus pectin. The additives are generally ineffective in markedly improving the stability of the usual wheat flour sauce held at 10°F. ( −12°C.). Other additives or higher concentrations of those tested might, of course, prove to be effective. Algin derivatives are used in chicken pie gravies and for frozen meat slices with gravies. Use of carrageenin has been reported to increase the cling of the sauce to frozen vegetables, to impart an attractive sheen to the vegetables and improve richness of the product.

Research on the chemical modification of waxy starches has produced a number of "freeze-resistant" starches for use in sauces and gravies that are to be frozen. Most of these are waxy corn or maize starches, chemically modified so that they will give cooked pastes of desirable consistency and stability. Through cross-bonding of the molecules and addition of ester groups, deficiencies of the untreated starches are reduced or eliminated. Such treatments reduce the stringy cohesive character of the cooked waxy starch paste, the tendency to break down under mechanical agitation, autoclaving, or acid conditions, and improve the freeze-thaw stability (Powell 1966; Schoch, pp. 53 of this volume). It is of interest that waxy rice flour, which is the commercially available product, produces the typical "short" texture of a wheat flour paste, while waxy rice starch produces the same stringy texture as other waxy starches.

Thickening agents are tested in each formula to make sure the resulting product has the desired consistency in combination with other ingredients and with the specific processing methods used, and that they have the required stability for commercial storage. In frozen meat pot pies some wheat flour is used to give the expected flavor, opacity, and texture. Freeze-thaw stability is attained by using waxy starch or flour with the wheat flour, normally at about a 50:50 ratio. Waxy corn starch is modified as described above to reduce its stringy, cohesive character, and to improve its stability. In some cases a three-way blend of wheat flour-modified waxy-unmodified waxy rice has more desirable characteristics than the 50-50 blend of wheat flour and waxy rice flour. In the frozen Chinese type foods the sauce must be clear and smooth with a viscous flow, but not too stringy. Here, single or dual modified waxy starches are used straight, without wheat flour or other cloudy thickeners (Powell 1966). Most of the major starch companies now prepare several formulated thickening agents designed specifically for use in a variety of precooked foods.

In preparation for cooking of sauces the dry ingredients may be slurried in the liquid at about 100°F. (38°C.) and the temperature raised to 190° –200°F. (88°–93°C.) as rapidly as possible. Or a separate slurry of the starch-flour mixture in about one-fourth of the liquid is stirred gradually into the hot solution of all other ingredients in the remainder of the liquid, the temperature being maintained above 180°F. (82°C.) during the addition. The temperature of the entire mass is then brought to 210°F. (99°C.), then cooled to 60°F. (15.5°C.) as rapidly as possible with constant and relatively vigorous agitation (Buchanan 1966).

Sauces may be cooked in open steam kettles with agitators that scrape the sides such as the Groen kettles. Or continuous flow, swept surface heat exchangers may be used for both cooking and cooling steps. Various direct steam injection "jets" are also used to get rapid, uniform continuous cooking. Flash evaporation has been used to cool the mix, although this is normally a batch operation (Powell 1966). Certain carrageenin products have been found effective in improving filling operations for gravies in frozen TV dinners. In these cases a thickener is needed that prevents splashing and "slopping over" of gravies as they are filled and travel down the production line. However, no additional viscosity is desired at the higher eating temperatures, and carrageenin provides these characteristics (Rapp 1967).

## Other Sauces

Some sauces can be prepared with a thick enough consistency that no starchy thickening agent is needed. They present no particular stability problem and include a variety of formulas and ingredients. Cocktail and creole sauces are examples of this group. A typical cocktail sauce for use on seafoods requires no preparation other than thorough mixing (Tressler and Evers 1957).

### Cocktail Sauce

| Ingredients | % |
|---|---|
| Catsup | 68.0 |
| Vinegar or lemon juice | 16.0 |
| Celery, finely chopped | 10.0 |
| Horseradish, grated | 4.5 |
| Tabasco sauce | 0.5 |
| Salt | 1.0 |
| | 100.0 |

Directions for preparing shrimp creole for freezing have been published by the Cornell University School of Hotel Administration (Sayles and Mac-Lennan 1965). The formula for the sauce contains no thickening agent and includes canned tomatoes, onions, green peppers, pimentos, dried peppers, instant garlic, instant onion, peanut oil, tomato sauce, seasoning, and Spanish paprika. The publication includes proportions and methods of preparation for 6 and 1,000 portions.

Use of carrageenin reportedly controls water damage from pizza sauce and provides a richer body to the sauce. Sheen is also improved and color is not impaired (Rapp 1967).

### THICKENED DESSERTS AND FILLINGS

Maintenance of the characteristic gel structure in custards, puddings, and fillings that depend on starch or egg for their structural characteristics was a problem of the prepared food industry for many years (Tressler and Evers 1957), and is still not completely solved. In products with a gel structure that contains a high concentration of cooked egg white, the gel structure contracts and liquid exudes after freezing and storage. Maintenance of the firm gel structure of a typical baked custard after freezing and storage has not been achieved. Similar problems occur during freezing of products such as cornstarch pudding that depend on a starch gel for their characteristic structure. However, substitution of more stable ingredients or alteration in the proportion of ingredients has made possible the successful freezing and limited storage of puddings, soft custard type desserts, and thickened fillings.

The stability of gelled products containing cooked eggs increases with an increase in the proportion of egg yolk to egg white. This is not surprising, since hard cooked egg yolks can be frozen and stored at 0°F. (−18°C.) for at least a year without significant texture change, but the white of hard cooked eggs becomes rubbery or granular and watery and separates into clumps or layers due to the mechanical effects of ice crystal formation (Davis et al. 1952). During freezing, migration of water from within the gel structure results in ice crystal growth followed by contraction of the gel structure. Soft custard type desserts of limited storage stability [2 to 4 months at 0°F. (−18°C.)] can be prepared by using egg yolk in place of whole egg and supplementing it with waxy rice flour (Hanson et al. 1953). Puddings without eggs, stable for 6 to 9 months at 0°F. (−18°C.) can be made by substituting waxy rice flour for cornstarch and adding gelatin to provide a soft gel structure. The latter are stable for over a year at −10°F. (−23°C.) but for less than a month at 10°F. (−12°C.). Temperatures fluctuating for even brief periods to 10°F. (−12°C.) damage the texture of these products. To improve the stability of the soft-custard type products containing egg yolk and waxy rice flour, various stabilizers (slow setting citrus pectin, gelatin, gum karaya, gum tragacanth, and Irish moss extractive) were added at 0.4 and 1.0% concentrations (Hanson et al. 1957). The lower concentration is ineffective; but a concentration of one per cent of citrus pectin or gum tragacanth reduces separation from custard puddings to less than three per cent liquid separation after storage of approximately a year at 10°F. (−12°C.). Slight decreases in the smooth appearance of the product occur after shorter storage times, but they are probably not sufficient to affect acceptability.

In cream pies that are to be frozen, some ordinary cornstarch may be blended with a modified waxy cornstarch or dry milk solids may be used since some cloudiness is desired. Or, a highly cross-bonded waxy starch is used straight to give a soft, buttery texture with some cloud (Powell 1966). Carrageenin can be used as a setting agent in frozen cream pies (Rapp 1967). A cold swelling type of carrageenin is used to increase viscosity of cream and custard pie fillings to prevent splattering and "slopping over" during filling and processing. Carrageenin aids in providing a "set" and in controlling syneresis in certain frozen cream pie fillings that are prepared as whipped emulsions. A carrageenin product with cold milk solubility properties is available for use in a whipped dessert that is frozen in the home freezer compartment before serving. Carrageenin helps control ice crystal size for a smoother product with even melt-down (Rapp 1967). Fruit juice concentrates have been heated to 145°F. (62.8°C.) with monoglycerides to produce a mix which may be frozen in a conventional ice cream freezer. The resulting products have from 100 to 200% overrun with good body and smooth consistency (Neu and Lee 1961). Microcrystalline cellulose prepared by acid treatment of alpha-cellulose under special processing conditions is used to reduce crystal formation and control overrun in frozen desserts (Glicksman 1963).

For fruit pies that are to be frozen and thawed, retention of clarity, gloss, and sheen are important. Modified waxy starches are used. The low pH and high mechanical shear in some processing machines has led to the adoption of those with an intermediate degree of cross-bonding. In some cases the modified waxy starch is pregelatinized to simplify processing and aid flavor retention in the raw-frozen type pies. Frozen fruit can be partially thawed, sweetened, and thickened without ever being cooked before the housewife bakes the frozen pie. With the pregelatinized thickeners, cost and the tendency to get lumps or "fish-eyes" are problems. Premixing the starch with dry sugar reduces lumping. Savings on labor, heating, and cooking costs tend to off-set the extra starch cost. More of the pregelatinized starch is needed compared to the corresponding raw parent waxy starch to arrive at the same viscosity (Powell 1966).

## WHIPPED TOPPINGS

### Armed Forces Topping

A specification for frozen dessert and bakery toppings for use by the Armed Forces was published by the Department of Defense (Anon. 1957). The product must be pasteurized and homogenized, and it must be frozen immediately after packaging. One type specifies inclusion of nonfat milk solids; the other specifies inclusion of edible protein. The required and optional ingredients are described in Table 42.

The performance requirements include a minimum overrun of 100% within 15 min. after the start of whipping. Whipping is conducted under standard conditions of mixer, mixer speed, quantity of mix, and product temperature. The whipped product must show no serum separation, weeping, rancidity, or change in color in 6 hr. at 70°F. (21°C.) when removed from the whipping bowl and heaped to a depth not less than 4 in. on a flat, nonabsorbent surface. The product must be stable enough to pass the

Table 42

Army Frozen Topping

| | % |
|---|---|
| Required | |
|    Vegetable fat | Not less than 20 |
|    Nonfat milk solids (Type I only) | Not less than 5 |
|    Edible protein (Type II only) | Not less than 1.25 |
|    Total added sugar | Not less than 15 |
|    Moisture | Not more than 50 |
| Optional | |
|    Emulsifiers and stabilizers | Not more than 3 |
|    Flavoring | — |
|    Coloring | — |

whipping test after four months' storage at 20°F. ($-6.6$°C.) and shall not develop oxidized or other undesirable off-flavors during this period.

## Durkees Whipped Toppings

Formulas for preparing whipped toppings that can be frozen were supplied by Durkee Famous Foods (Ryberg 1967). One formula is used for a product that is whipped before freezing; the other is whipped after defrosting. The manufacturing steps are described in Tables 43 and 44. The functions of the ingredients used and the effects of certain processing steps are described in the following paragraphs.

The sucrose provides the desired sweetness in the topping and also provides solids. The sodium caseinate helps to stabilize the emulsion. Soya proteins can also be used, but the finished product will not have as good a flavor. The stabilizer gums are used to prevent syneresis. The stabilizers also function to modify the crystal size of the water, restricting the growth

Table 43

Whipped Topping—Freeze-Thaw Stable After Whipping

(Durkee Formula LDS-269-W)

| Ingredient | % |
|---|---|
| Sucrose | 14.00 |
| Sodium caseinate | 2.00 |
| Carrageenan | 0.05 |
| Guar gum | 0.05 |
| Water | 59.05 |
| Durkee's Paramount C with lecithin | 16.00 |
| Durkee's Hydrol 92 | 8.00 |
| Durkee's SL 100 (glycerol lacto palmitate) | 0.50 |
| Polysorbate 60 | 0.20 |
| Sorbitan monostearate | 0.15 |
| Total | 100.00 |

Table 44

Frozen Whipped Topping

| Ingredients | % |
|---|---|
| Sugar | 10.00 |
| Sodium caseinate | 2.00 |
| Cellulose gum[1] | 0.65 |
| Water | 61.40 |
| Durkee's Paramount C | 20.00 |
| Durkee's Hydrol 92 | 5.00 |
| Durkee's SL-100 | 0.70 |
| Polysorbate 60 | 0.25 |
| Flavor and color | (optional) |
| Total | 100.00 |

[1] "Avicel-RC"—made by FMC Corp., American Viscose Division.

of water crystals and thus, further stabilizing the emulsion during freezing and thawing.

Durkee's Paramount C is a lauric hard butter. This type of fat is characterized by the high per cent of solid fat and a very sharp melting point close to body temperature. This type of high-solids fat will whip better over a wider range of temperatures and stands up better when whipped. The eating qualities are excellent. Hydrol 92 is a 92°F. (33°C.) melting coconut oil. Blending of fats yields lower viscosities in. the mix and yields better whipping performance.

The blend of emulsifiers acts synergistically to yield an overall effect. The glycerol lacto palmitate is used for its aeration properties. The polysorbate and sorbitan esters provide stability during freezing and thawing. The Polysorbate 60 also acts to lower the viscosity of the mix and promote aeration. The GLP also aids in keeping the viscosity of the mix low. In a product such as this, mono and diglycerides could contribute to a higher viscosity.

During homogenization, the second stage reduces clumping of the fat globules. The rapid cooling keeps the viscosity of the mix low and tends to prevent destabilization of the mix. Toppings are aged at least 12 hr. so that the fat crystal transformations are completed and the emulsion is well stabilized.

Procedure.—Dry mix sugar, sodium caseinate, and stabilizers. Add to water. Mix well to disperse solids. Heat mix to 110°F. (43°C.) and add remaining ingredients. Heat mix to 160°F. for 30 min. Homogenize mix at 1,500 and 500 p.s.i. through a two-stage homogenizer. Cool mix as rapidly as possible to 40°F. (4°C.). Age mix at 40°F. (4°C.) for at least 12 hr. Whip mix to desired gravity. Package whipped topping and freeze as rapidly as possible to 10° to 20°F. (−12° to −7°C.). Defrost topping at 40°F. (4°C.) before use.

Procedure.—Dry mix sugar, sodium caseinate, and cellulose. Add to water. Mix well to disperse solids. Add remainder of ingredients and pasteurize mix at 160°F.

(71°C.) for 30 min. Homogenize mix at 1000 and 500 p.s.i. through two-stage homogenizer. Cool mix to 40°F. (4°C.), package, and freeze mix as rapidly as possible to −10° to −20°F. (−23° to −29°C.). Defrost mix at 40°F. (4°C.) before whipping.

## Whipped Cream

Whipped cream, with and without added sugar, is stable during frozen storage. Glabau (1953A and 1953B) reported that there was no danger of destroying the overall properties of whipped cream subjected to freezing temperatures from −10° to −20°F. (−23° to −29°C.). He reported that an algin stabilizer reduced seepage of liquid. Unpublished results of tests conducted in the author's laboratory showed little or no drainage from samples thawed and held two hours at room temperature after a year's storage at 0° or −10°F. (−18° or −23°C.). Off-flavors which developed in samples after three months at 10° and 20°F. (−12° and −6°C.) preclude storage at those temperatures for extended periods. Cream frozen without whipping is damaged by freezing so that a satisfactory foam volume cannot be produced after thawing (Dahle and Josephson 1944). Carrageenin can be used to improve appearance, body, and texture of frozen whipped cream (Downs et al. 1960). A carrageenin product with cold milk solubility properties is available for use in a whipped cream dessert that is frozen in the home freezer compartment before serving. Carrageenin helps control ice crystal size for a smoother product with even melt-down (Rapp 1967).

### SALAD DRESSINGS

Salad dressings stable to freezing and frozen storage are used commercially in frozen sandwich fillings and salads for vending service, catering, transportation systems, and various other mass feeding establishments. Mayonnaise, however, cannot be successfully frozen; oil separates from it after it thaws. Although mayonnaise and salad dressings both contain concentrated emulsions of oil in an aqueous liquid, with egg yolk as the emulsifying agent, they differ in that salad dressings contain less oil and contain a starch paste as well as an emulsion.

Salad dressings now being frozen conform to the U. S. Food and Drug Administration definitions and standard of identity. Salad dressing is described as an emulsified semi-solid food prepared from edible vegetable oil, acidifying ingredients, egg-yolk-containing ingredients, a starchy paste, and optional seasoning or flavor ingredients. Water may be added in the preparation of the paste. Salad dressing contains not less than 30% by weight of vegetable oil and "not less egg-yolk-containing ingredient than is equivalent in egg-yolk solids content to 4% by weight of liquid egg yolks." It may contain in addition to egg yolk, specified optional emulsifying ingredients or mixtures of not more than 0.75% by weight of the finished salad dressing. It may also contain limited amounts of other specified ingredients.

Salad dressing emulsions consist of oil globules surrounded by the egg yolk emulsifying layer within a liquid phase which contains such acidifying ingredients as vinegar or lemon juice. Oil separation occurs when oil fractions crystallize at low temperatures, penetrate through the emulsifying film, and coalesce as the temperature rises. At refrigerator temperature, a fraction of most oils crystallizes. Lowering the temperature for frozen storage increases the fraction that crystallizes. Thus, the nature of the oil in salad dressings that are to be frozen is more critical than in refrigerated salad dressing. In the latter, oils are selected or modified to limit or reduce the fractions that solidify in crystalline form at the refrigerator temperature. Cottonseed oil is generally "winterized," a process that involves holding the oil at low temperature and removing fractions that crystallize at that temperature. Corn and soybean oils do not require winterization for storage at refrigerator temperature.

Two approaches have been used by research groups to prepare salad dressings stable to freezing. One approach is the use of crystallization-resistant oil and suitable concentrations and types of other ingredients (Hanson and Fletcher 1961, 1965). It is important that oil used does not solidify in crystalline form, crystallizes only to a limited extent, or crystallizes slowly. Corn, soybean, cottonseed, and olive oils crystallize to such an extent at usual frozen storage temperatures that large amounts of oil separate after thawing of salad dressings containing them; and winterization of the oils for such low temperatures removes such large amounts of crystalline material that it is not practical. Safflower and peanut oils are superior to other salad oils in their solidification characteristics. Safflower oil does not solidify at 20°F. (−7°C.), and the small fraction that crystallizes at 10°F. (−12°C.) can be removed by winterizing. At lower storage temperatures, however, winterization is not effective because too high a proportion of the oil crystallizes. Although peanut oil solidifies to a considerable extent in the temperature range of frozen storage, it can be used for frozen salad dressings, apparently because it solidifies in an amorphous rather than in a crystalline form, and in this form it does not break through the emulsifying layer and coalesce. Salad dressings prepared in the course of this research to illustrate the effect of type of oil on stability are shown in Fig. 51. Salad dressings prepared with other oils, e.g., cottonseed, can be stored indefinitely without oil separation on thawing if the temperature is low enough to cause rapid freezing. Although the oils solidify almost completely at −29° to −51°F. (−34° to −46°C.), they solidify in an amorphous rather than a crystalline form. The product temperature is apparently lowered through the critical crystallization range too fast for crystallization to take place.

Fig. 51.    Salad dressing containing peanut oil (left) and cottonseed oil (right),
thawed at 77°F. (25°C.) after 3 months at 0°F. (−18°C.).

Suitable selection of other ingredients minimizes oil separation from
these salad dressings. Although frozen salted yolks are generally used in
salad dressing manufacture, the use of freshly prepared yolks usually produces a more stable salad dressing (Hanson and Fletcher 1961). The lower
the temperature at which frozen salted yolks are held, the greater is the
damage to their emulsifying ability. Even holding the yolks at 35°F. (2°C.)
for 48 hr. has a slight damaging effect similar to that caused by freezing of
the salted yolks. Increasing the concentration of the yolk, whether fresh or
frozen, in the range of 4 to 8% improves the stability of the salad dressings
significantly.

The difference in the composition of salad dressing and mayonnaise and
the difference in their stability to freezing and frozen storage indicates that
the starch paste contributes to the stability of salad dressing. The selection
of a stable starchy thickening agent has value in salad dressings as it had in
sauces and gravies discussed earlier in this chapter. Under optimum conditions of oil and egg yolk selection, additional stability is achieved by selection of a suitable thickening agent. A freeze-resistant starch such as waxy
rice flour improves salad dressing stability under conditions in which only a
small proportion of the oil fraction coalesces (Hanson and Fletcher 1961).
The improvement due to the use of a freeze-resistant starch is not sufficient
to be effective in salad dressings containing oil which crystallizes to a large
extent during frozen storage. The higher the proportion of starch paste to
emulsion in a salad dressing, the greater is the stability of the product. Increasing the salt concentration in salad dressings over the range 0.5 to 1.7%
also decreases oil separation from frozen, thawed salad dressings. When
peanut oil is used and other conditions are optimum, oil separation can be

prevented for 3 months at 0°F. ( −18°C.) and for 6 months at all other temperatures from 20° to −30°F. ( −6° to −34°C.).

A different approach to frozen salad dressing stability is described in two patents assigned to the National Dairy Products Corp. (Partyka 1963; Krett and Gennuso 1963). Standard salad dressings containing 30% fat and diet dressings containing 5 to 35% fat are covered by patents. The standard salad dressing contains substantial amounts of hard fat components which were considered to be deleterious to the stability of emulsions. The use of hydrogenated fat or nonwinterized oil was based on the observation that butter and margarine, which contain hard fat and consist of water-in-oil emulsions, can be frozen without separation; whereas salad dressings, which consist of oil-in-water emulsions, separate after freezing (Mottern 1967; Partyka 1967). Any of the usual edible liquid oils is satisfactory in this type of salad dressing; winterizable components need not be removed. The oil should cloud in less than 5.5 hr. in ice water in accordance with the cold test of the American Oil Chemists' Society. Hard fat may be added to the liquid oil or the oil may be hydrogenated. The salad dressing may be prepared using only oil that is highly unsaturated, and then this dressing may be "cut" with melted hydrogenated oil (Example 1, Partyka 1963). The iodine value of the oil should be in excess of 75 and that of the product is usually between 90 and 115. The emulsifying agent is usually egg yolk, present in not less than eight per cent of the soft oil. In one example cited, soybean oil with an iodine value of 127, was used at a level of 3.7% of the salad dressing; the ratio of yolk to fat in the product was 0.123 but the ratio of yolk to soft oil was 0.246. Additional yolk facilitates formation of the emulsion but does not improve stability. The starch should be a freeze-resistant starch such as a chemically-modified waxy starch or a blend that provides a freezer-resistant gel. Preparation methods and equipment used do not differ from those normally used in salad dressing manufacture. Oil does not separate from products held a week at −10°F. ( −23.3°C.) before warming to room temperature.

The diet dressings are stable at −10° and −40°F. ( −23° and −40°C.) for a week or more (Krett and Gennuso 1963). They contain 5 to 35% edible salad oil. Winterized oil may be used, but winterizable components need not be removed. The ratio of yolk to oil is in excess of 0.12. The authors believe that important factors in stability include use of a type and amount of starch that prevents breakdown of the starch gel, a ratio of egg yolk to oil of at least 0.12, and a maximum oil content of 35%.

## SOUFFLÉS

Sweetened dessert soufflés, soft pie meringues, and unsweetened soufflés used as entrées have foam or sponge structures that may be damaged by freezing and frozen storage. The time and skill required in their preparation show there are advantages in having them available in frozen form. Recent tests have shown that with appropriate formulation and storage temperature, the characteristic texture of several of these sponge products can be retained during frozen storage and height loss can be limited (Cimino *et al.* 1967). These soufflés or meringues can be thawed as needed and reheated in an oven.

Sweetened whole egg dessert soufflés can be frozen and stored at 0° to −10°F. (−18° to −23°C.) for 6 months with less than 10% loss in height. To achieve this stability the flour concentration is increased from 4 to almost 8%; with higher flour concentrations it is difficult to combine the very thick white sauce with the egg white foam. Variation in yolk or salt concentration has little effect on stability of these soufflés. Off-flavors develop at storage temperatures above 0°F.; souffle height decreases more rapidly below −10°F. (−23°C.) than in the range of 0° to −10°F. (−18° to −23°C.).

Height loss is generally more of a problem in unsweetened whole egg soufflés than in sweetened soufflés, but an increase in flour concentration and the addition of cheese or methylcellulose improves their stability.

The stability of baked egg white dessert soufflés is directly related to sugar concentration. The most stable formula tested contained the highest sugar concentration, 46%, a composition similar to that of a soft pie meringue. Unlike the whole egg dessert soufflés, egg white soufflés are equally stable at temperatures ranging from 0°F. to −30°F. (−18° to −34°C.).

Because of the instability of soufflés frozen before baking, baking before freezing is recommended (Cimino *et al.* 1967). Unbaked sweetened whole egg soufflés lose their characteristic structure and develop a custard-like texture if exposed to a relatively high storage temperature, 20°F. (−6°C.), even for short periods. Unbaked plain whole egg soufflés frozen before baking are also less stable than if baked before freezing. Unbaked cheese soufflés frozen before baking develop off-flavors at usual commercial frozen storage temperatures.

Reference to a company or product name does not imply approval or recommendation of the product by the U.S. Dept. Agr. to the exclusion of others that may be suitable.

## BIBLIOGRAPHY

Anon.   1957. Topping, dessert and bakery products, frozen. Military Specification MIL-T-35024, June 11.
Buchanan, B. F.   1966. Private communication. Tarrytown, N. Y.
Cimino, S. L., Elliott, L. F., and Palmer, H. H.   1967. The stability of soufflés subjected to frozen storage. Food Technol. *21*, No. 8, 97–100.

Dahle, C. D., and Josephson, D. V. 1944. Properties of quick frozen cream. Ice Cream Field 44, No. 5, 36–37, 48.

Davis, J. G., Hanson, H. L., and Lineweaver, H. 1952. Characterization of the effect of freezing on cooked egg white. Food Res. 17, 393–401.

Downs, D., Wilkinson, B., and Hedrick, T. I. 1960. Developing and marketing dairy product foods. 1. Frozen whipped cream. Quarterly Bulletin, Michigan Agricultural Experiment Station 42, No. 4, 871–877.

Glabau, C. A. 1953A. How bakery products react to low temperature freezing. Part XII. Problems which arise in freezing products containing whipped cream. Bakers' Weekly 157, No. 3, 47, 48, 70.

Glabau, C. A. 1953B. How bakery products react to low temperature freezing. Part 20. Problems that arise in freezing products containing whipped cream. Bakers' Weekly 157, No. 4, 43–44.

Glicksman, M. 1963. Utilization of synthetic gums in the food industry. Advances in Food Res. 12, 283–366.

Hanson, H. L., Campbell, A., and Lineweaver, H. 1951. Preparation of stable frozen sauces and gravies. Food Technol. 5, 432–440.

Hanson, H. L., and Fletcher, L. R. 1961. Salad dressings stable to frozen storage. Food Technol. 15, 256–262.

Hanson, H. L., and Fletcher, L. R. 1965. Preparation of precooked frozen poultry products. U.S. Pat. 3,169,069, February 9.

Hanson, H. L., Fletcher, L. R., and Campbell, A. A. 1957. The time-temperature tolerance of frozen foods. V. Texture stability of thickened precooked frozen foods as influenced by composition and storage conditions. Food Technol. 11, 339–343.

Hanson, H. L., Nishita, K. D., and Lineweaver, H. 1953. Preparation of stable frozen puddings. Food Technol. 7, 462–465.

Krett, O. J., and Gennuso, S. L. 1963. Salad dressing. U.S. Pat. 3,093,486, June 11.

Mottern, H. H. 1967. Private communication. New Orleans, La.

Neu, G. D., and Lee, L. J. 1961. Whipped dessert toppings, whipped salad toppings, low calorie frozen desserts. Food Processing 22, No. 5, 58–61.

Osman, E. M., and Cummisford, P. D. 1959. Some factors affecting the stability of frozen white sauces. Food Research 24, 595–604.

Partyka, A. 1963. Salad dressing. U.S. Pat. 3,093,485, June 11.

Partyka, A. 1967. Private communication to H. H. Mottern. Chicago, Ill.

Powell, E. L. 1966. Private communication. Ruby, Ind.

Rapp, H. 1967. Private communication. Hinsdale, Ill.

Ryberg, J. R. 1967. Private communication. Santa Monica, Calif.

Sayles, C. I., and MacLennan, H. A. 1965. Ready foods. Cornell School of Hotel and Restaurant Admin. Quart. 6, No. 2, 21–43.

Schoch, T. J. 1966. Properties and uses of rice starch. In Starch: Chemistry and Technology, Vol. 2, R. L. Whistler and E. F. Paschall (Editors), Academic Press, New York.

Schoch, T. J., and French, D. 1947. Studies on bread staling. 1. The role of starch, Cereal Chem. 24, 231–249.

Tressler, D. K., and Evers, C. F. 1957. The Freezing Preservation of Foods, 3rd Edition, Vol. II. Avi Publishing Co., Westport, Connecticut.

## CHAPTER 15

Donald K. Tressler

# Infant Foods—Dietetic and Geriatric Foods

## INTRODUCTION—INFANT FOODS

From time to time, the possibilities of producing and marketing frozen strained and chopped vegetables, fruits, and meats for use as infant and junior foods, have been indicated. Hohl (1944) and Hohl and Smith (1944) showed that frozen strained vegetables and fruits have a high vitamin content and suggested that their use would have nutritional advantages over that of the canned products.

Although frozen chopped spinach and broccoli, and frozen apple sauce and other fruit purees, have often been used for the feeding of infants and young children, until 1956 no company packed a line of frozen strained or chopped vegetables prepared especially for infants and junior children. A line of strained vegetables, which includes strained carrots, green beans, peas, and spinach, is now available (Anon. 1956A). These products are prepared without salt or other seasoning and, consequently, are suitable for feeding persons suffering from peptic ulcers, diverticulosis, and colitis, as well as for people with high blood pressure and other individuals whose diet must be as nearly sodium free as possible.

## STRAINED VEGETABLES

The procedure suggested for the manufacture of strained baby foods from vegetables may be summarized as follows:

### From Frozen Vegetables

Frozen vegetables, packed for remanufacture, or institutional-size packs, are allowed to thaw partially by standing overnight in a cool room. Circulating air may be provided by fans to hasten thawing. The partially or completely thawed product is placed in a steam kettle, covered with water, and cooked until tender; the amount of water used and the length of time required for cooking will depend, of course, on the kind, maturity, and size of pieces of the vegetable used. If the product is to be salted, salt (0.25%) and monosodium glutamate (0.15%) are added, then the cooked vegetable is converted while still hot into a purée by putting it through a paddle-type finisher with a screen having 0.027-in. holes (Fig. 52). The purée is homogenized at 3,000 to 4,000 lb. per sq. in. pressure. It is then sterilized by

---

Donald K. Tressler is a consultant and President of the Avi Publishing Co., Westport, Conn.

329

*Courtesy of F. H. Langsenkamp Co.*

Fig. 52. A stainless steel Indiana model B "E-Z Adjust" pulper or finisher used for making strained infant foods. The front portion of the impeller is provided with sharp, jagged teeth that tear and shred the incoming material before forcing it through the crusher partition, which puts the raw stock in condition for the effective action of the paddles in the pulping chamber. The paddle assembly of this pulper consists of a unit of four paddles attached to front and rear paddle arms which can be adjusted for clearance quickly and easily. The trailing edges of the paddles are curved. This construction assists centrifugal force, which throws the product through the screen perforations. The tapered shape of the screen allows a horizontal reaction from the pressure of the paddles which spreads the incoming material over the entire screen surface.

pumping through a tubular heat exchanger of the small-tube, high-velocity type, in which it is heated to about 280°F. (137°C.) (Figs. 53, and 54). If tin cans are used as containers, the purée is filled, after cooling to 200° to 210°F. (93.5° to 99°C.) in a tubular heat exchanger. If it is packed into cartons, or composite cartons with metal ends, the purée should be continuously cooled without delay to 100°F. (38°C.) or lower before filling. This cooling is best effected in another tubular heat exchanger.

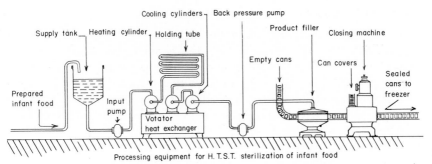

Processing equipment for H. T.S.T. sterilization of infant food

Fig. 53. Flow sheet of processing equipment for the high-temperature short-time sterilization of infant foods. In this schematic drawing a *Votator* heat exchanger replaces the homogenizer and tubular heat exchanger used for cooling the product from the sterilization temperature down to the proper filling temperature.

Fig. 54. Processing equipment for high-temperature, short-time sterilization. Much of the equipment indicated in Fig. 53 is shown in this picture. The supply tank is on the left. The *Votator* heat exchanger is in the center. Above it is the holding tube, where the product is held for a sufficient number of seconds to effect sterilization. The back-pressure pump draws the product from the cooling cylinder of the Votator and pumps it to the supply tank above the filler (not shown).

## From Fresh Vegetables

If fresh vegetables are used as the raw material, the procedure will be the same as that followed in making the product from frozen vegetables (described above), except that great care must be taken to free the vegetables from dirt, sand, weeds, thistles and thistle buds, decayed and discolored parts, and foreign matter, by shaking, soaking, washing, trimming, inspecting, etc., according to the conventional methods of preparing vegetables for freezing described briefly in Chapter 10 of this volume, and in far greater detail in Chapter 5 of Volume 3. It should be noted that fresh vegetables require longer time for cooking than do frozen ones.

Owing to the fact that fresh beets and carrots are generally available throughout much of the year, and further, since these fresh vegetables can be stored for several months, they are not commonly frozen for remanufacture, but the fresh vegetables are used for making infant foods. These vegetables are usually cleaned, trimmed, and thoroughly washed, first in a soaker, then in powerful sprays of water, inspected, after which they are peeled, usually by first subjecting the vegetable to high-pressure steam, and then to high-pressure water sprays. The peeled vegetables are passed over an inspection belt where vegetables with crowns not completely removed, or discolored and improperly peeled portions, etc., are hand trimmed. The vegetables are then chopped in a stainless steel chopper or otherwise comminuted into small pieces. The chopped vegetables are cooked until tender in a steam-jacketed kettle with about three times their weight of water; 0.15% of monosodium glutamate and 0.25% of salt are usually added. After cooking, the mixture (vegetables plus cooking water) is passed through a stainless steel paddle type finisher (Fig. 52 p. 330), equipped with a screen having 0.027-in. diameter perforations. This finisher should be equipped with steam inlets on either end so that there will be a steam atmosphere at all times during the straining operation. The chopped product is homogenized at 3,000 to 4,000 lb. per sq. in. pressure, after which it is sterilized at about 270°F. (132°C.) by pumping it through a tubular heat exchanger of the small-tube, high-velocity type. This will effect almost complete sterilization of the product. The purée is then passed through another heat exchanger in which it is cooled to the desired filling temperature. If packed in tin cans, they should be filled at 200° to 212°F. (93.5° to 100°C.), closed immediately, and promptly cooled by cold water sprays. If packed in composite or other moisture-vapor-proof cartons, the filling temperature should be 100°F. (38°C.) or lower.

### CHOPPED VEGETABLES

The methods recommended for the manufacture of frozen chopped infant foods from frozen vegetables are summarized as follows:

## Preparation from Frozen Vegetables

Frozen vegetables packed for remanufacture or in institutional size packages are allowed to thaw overnight in a cool room. The thawed, or nearly thawed, product is chopped in a vegetable chopper, usually adjusted so as to produce an average size of piece not greater than $\frac{1}{16}$ in. in diameter. Spinach and other greens, and broccoli, which are commonly frozen in chopped form, are often comminuted to a quarter-inch piece size, using an Urschel dicer (Fig. 55) or similar chopper. These frozen chopped vegetables are blanched but not ordinarily cooked by the frozen food packer.

*Courtesy of Urschel Laboratories, Inc.*

Fig. 55. The feed roll and strip cutting and dicing knives of the Model J Urschel dicer. This dicer will cut spinach and other greens, broccoli, etc., into standard square cuts of $\frac{1}{4}$, $\frac{3}{8}$, and $\frac{1}{2}$ in. The thickness of the square will be the thickness of the original product. The product to be cut is fed onto a high-speed conveyor belt which conveys the product to the cutting parts. A feed roll 6 in. in diameter is mounted directly over the end of the conveyor belt. This feed roll serves two purposes. It flattens the product before entering the knives and it forces the product into the knives. This feed roll meshes into the circular knives which causes a positive transfer of the product to the knives. The circular knives cut the product into strips. These knives do not run on the belt but run into grooves in a stationary feed plate. The strip cut product is removed from the circular knives by a shear plate which also acts as a cutting block for the cross-cut knives. As the strips of product are ejected from the circular knives, the strips are cut into squares by the cross-cut knives. The diced product is then thrown into the discharge spout.

They may be used as raw material for the preparation of both precooked chopped junior foods and precooked strained infant foods. The chopped vegetable is transferred to a steam-jacketed kettle; a small amount of water, 0.15% monosodium glutamate, and 0.25% of salt are added, and the vegetable cooked until tender. If the chopped vegetable is packed in tin cans, it is run into a steam-jacketed holding tank, equipped with an agitator, located above an automatic filler which fills the cans with the hot product. If composite or other cartons are used, it should be cooled before filling. If the quantity to be cooled is small, cooling can be done with sufficient rapidity merely by running cold water in the jacket of the kettle while the chopped product is being slowly agitated. If the scale of operations is large, a heat exchanger suitable for handling a semifluid product should be used. Chopped spinach and other relatively fluid products can be pumped through a tubular heat exchanger, provided the pump used will handle fluids containing small pieces of vegetables.

### Preparation from Fresh Vegetables

If fresh vegetables are used as the raw material for the making of frozen chopped baby foods, the procedures will be the same as those described above for making the product from frozen raw material, except that it will be necessary to prepare, clean, wash, sort, and do all of the other things required in the usual operations carried out in the preparation of vegetables for freezing.

As in the case of strained baby foods (see previous section), chopped carrots and beets are commonly prepared from the fresh vegetables. The methods followed in preparing frozen chopped carrots and frozen chopped beets will be the same as those outlined above for preparing strained carrots and strained beets up to the point where the chopped vegetables are obtained; then, instead of converting this product into a purée, homogenizing, and sterilizing it, it is only necessary to add the desired amount of salt (usually 0.25%) and monosodium glutamate (0.15%), fill hot, if cans are used, or cool and fill into cartons or composite cartons, then quick freeze.

In order to obtain a product from spinach and other greens, and broccoli, suited for feeding both juniors and old persons, it may be advantageous to comminute them to a piece size larger than $\frac{1}{16}$ in. in diameter (recommended for feeding very small children). This may be done by an Urschel dicer (Fig. 55), which chops these vegetables into quarter-inch "dice."

### QUALITY CONTROL

To obtain a commercially acceptable product, it is necessary to produce strained and chopped vegetables of low bacterial content, free from coliform organisms, having bright colors, and of uniformly high quality and uniform viscosity and / or total solids content. Sterilization of the strained vegetables in a tubular flash heater followed by rapid cooling in a heat exchanger will reduce the bacterial content to a very low level (substantially zero) and kill any coliforms which may be present. The thorough cooking of the chopped products similarly will kill all vegetative cells and nearly all spores.

In the case of strained spinach and other strained vegetables, either the total solids content or the viscosity of the products should be standardized. In most instances, it is impossible to standardize both, since the pectin and other colloids of the vegetables do not vary as do the total solids. As a rule, it is better to adopt a standard viscosity for strained baby foods; when this is done the homemaker will think that the product is of uniform composition even though the total solids content varies widely. Uniform viscosity of product may be maintained by determining the viscosity of the product after it passes through the homogenizer and adjusting it to a standard viscosity by adding either water or homogenized material from a thicker batch.

STRAINED FRUITS

Strained prunes, strained apples and apricots, and apple sauce are popular baby foods.

### Preparation of Strained Prunes

Dried prunes are washed, then soaked overnight in water, using about twice as much warm water by weight as prunes. The drained fruit is placed in a steam-jacketed kettle and covered with the soaking water, cooked for 10 to 15 min., then converted into a purée and pitted in a paddle-type finisher (Fig. 52, p. 330), fitted with a screen with 0.027-in. openings. The finisher should have steam inlets at both ends so that there will be a steam atmosphere at all times inside. The resulting purée is homogenized at about 2000 lb. p.s.i. pressure, pumped through a tubular sterilizer (of the small-tube, high-velocity type) in which the temperature is quickly raised to about 270°F. (132°C.) and then immediately cooled to the desired filling temperature in a tubular heat exchanger.

### Preparation of Strained Apple Sauce

The procedures used in preparing apple sauce for freezing have been described on p. 196. The same general methods are used in preparing strained apple sauce for infant food, except for three additional steps: (1) Sugar equivalent to ten per cent of the total weight of apples and water is usually added to the cooked mixture just before the cooking is finished. (2)

The sauce coming from the finisher (Fig. 52 p. 330), is put through an homogenizer, (3) after which it is pumped through a tubular sterilizer (small-tube, high-velocity type) in which its temperature is raised to about 200°F. (93.5°C.) and then through a tubular heat exchanger in which it is rapidly cooled to the filling temperature. If it is to be packed in tin cans, filling and closing temperatures preferably should be about 200°F. (93.5°C.) so that there will be a vacuum in the headspace when the sauce cools. If the product is put into cartons or composite cartons, the temperature should be much lower (e.g., 100°F. or 38°C.), the exact temperature will depend upon the type of carton used and the methods used in cooling and freezing the product.

### Strained Apples and Apricots

Dried apricots are washed, and then soaked overnight in about three times their weight of water. The next day the fruit is cooked in the soaking water for about 15 min. A quantity of apple sauce, either frozen or freshly prepared, twice the weight of the dried apricots used, is added to the cooked apricots, and mixed thoroughly. The mixture is then converted into a purée by running it through a rotary finisher fitted with a screen with 0.027-in. openings (Fig. 52, p. 330). The resulting purée is homogenized, pumped through a flash sterilizer (tubular heat exchanger), and then cooled to the proper filling temperature by passage through another heat exchanger.

CHOPPED FRUITS

### Prunes

Dried prunes are washed, then placed in twice their weight of warm water, and soaked overnight. The next day after they are pitted, the prunes are chopped in a chopper which will produce an average particle size of $\frac{1}{16}$ in. in diameter or less. The chopped prunes are cooked in the soaking water for about 25 min. Additional water is added, if necessary, to produce the desired consistency. If packed in cans, the chopped prunes can be filled without cooling. If the product is to be put into cartons or composite cartons with metal ends, it should be cooled. This may be done by pumping it through a heat exchanger, provided the pump used will handle a product containing the small pieces of prunes.

## STRAINED MEAT STEWS

**Strained Vegetables with Beef**

| Ingredients | Quantity Lb. | Oz. |
|---|---|---|
| Ground beef | 140 | — |
| Carrots | 106 | — |
| Potatoes | 110 | — |
| Tomato juice | 111 | — |
| Celery stalks | 35 | 10 |
| Waxy rice flour | 22 | — |
| Rice | 10 | — |
| Dehydrated onion powder | 1 | — |
| Salt | 3 | — |
| Monosodium glutamate | 1 | 6 |
| | 540 | — |

Yield—100 gal.

**Procedure.**—The ground beef is cooked in a steam-jacketed kettle in 35 gal. of water for 30 min. The partially cooked meat is then comminuted in a Fitzpatrick mill, or equivalent. The comminuted product is returned to the kettle. The rice and salt are added and cooking is continued for 15 more minutes. The potatoes are washed, then peeled in an abrasive peeler, or by some other method. The carrots are washed, trimmed, and peeled. The celery is washed and trimmed. After chopping, the potatoes, carrots, and celery are added to the stew and the cooking continued for about 25 min. The tomato juice, salt, monosodium glutamate, and an aqueous slurry of waxy rice flour and onion powder is stirred in. The batch is then made up to 100 gal. with additional water. The stew is then put through a rotary cylindrical finisher (Fig. 52, p. 330) fitted with a screen having 0.033-in. openings. The resultant purée is then pumped through a tubular flash-heater or sterilizer to raise the temperature to about 270°F. (132°C.). It is then immediately cooled to the filling temperature by passing it through a heat exchanger.

**Chopped Vegetables with Beef.**—The formula used for this product is exactly the same as that previously indicated for making *Strained Vegetables with Beef*, presented above.

**Procedure.**—Small pieces (e.g., one-inch cubes) are cooked in a steam-jacketed kettle in 35 gal. of water for 30 min. The partially cooked meat is chopped in a Buffalo cutter (Fig. 56). The remainder of the procedure is exactly that described for the *Procedure* of making *Strained Vegetables with Beef* (p. 329) up to the point where the finished stew is run through the finisher. Instead of putting the product through the finisher, it is either immediately filled into tin cans or cooled and packaged in cartons.

## Strained Vegetables with Beef Liver

| Ingredients | Quantity Lb. | Oz. |
|---|---|---|
| Beef liver | 128 | — |
| Tomato juice | 130 | — |
| Potatoes | 110 | — |
| Carrots | 106 | — |
| Celery stalks | 35 | 8 |
| Waxy rice flour | 24 | 8 |
| Beef fat (suet) | 5 | — |
| Rice | 5 | — |
| Salt | 3 | 8 |
| Monosodium glutamate | 1 | 8 |
| Dehydrated onion powder | 1 | — |
| | 550 | 0 |

Yield—100 gal.

**Procedure.**—The beef liver and suet are sliced into thin slices, then chopped into small pieces (about 1 in. by ½ in.) The chopped liver and suet are cooked in a steam-jacketed kettle in about 30 gal. of water for 15 min. The partially cooked liver is then comminuted in a Fitzpatrick mill, or equivalent. The comminuted cooked liver and cooking water are put through a rotary finisher, using a screen with 0.033-in. openings, to remove gristle-like particles. The strained liver is returned to the kettle; the rice, monosodium glutamate, and salt added, and the cooking continued for 15 min. The prepared chopped vegetables and dehydrated onion powder are added and cooked for 25 min. The tomato juice and slurry of waxy rice flour are then added. Sufficient water is added to bring the volume to 100 gal. and boiling continued for five minutes. Then the stew is converted to a purée by putting it through a rotary paddle-type finisher fitted with a sceen with 0.033-in. openings. The purée is sterilized at about 270°F. (132°C.) in a tubular flash heater, then immediately cooled to the desired temperature for filling by pumping it through a heat exchanger.

### Chopped Vegetables with Liver (Liver Stew)

The formula used for this product is exactly the same as that previously indicated for making *Strained Vegetables with Beef Liver.*

**Procedure.**—Small pieces (e.g., each about 1 by ½ in.) of liver and suet are cooked in a steam-jacketed kettle in about 30 gal. of water for 15 min. The partially cooked liver is then chopped in a Buffalo chopper (Fig. 56). The remainder of the procedure is exactly that described for the *Procedure* of making *Strained Vegetables with Beef Liver* up to the point where the finished stew is run through the rotary finisher. Instead of putting the product through the finisher, it is either filled into cans, or cooled to the desired temperature, and packed in cartons.

## FREEZING INFANT FOODS

The method of freezing and type of freezer employed in freezing infant foods will depend to a considerable extent upon the container in which the purées or chopped foods are packed. If tin containers are used, they may

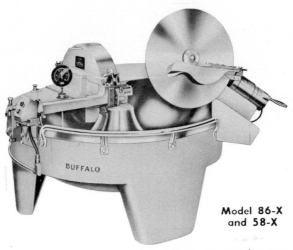

**Model 86-X
and 58-X**

*Courtesy of John E. Smith's Sons Co.*

Fig. 56.   The Buffalo direct-cutting converter or chopper designed for chopping meat. The cutting mechanism consists of a set of curved knives which revolve at a high rate of speed, passing within a fraction of an inch of the more slowly revolving bowl, then through the closely fitted slot of the comb. The meat is given a clean, sheer, draw cut without any mashing or beating. All lumps or cords are eliminated and the meat is thoroughly mixed.

be rapidly frozen in either low-temperature alcohol "brine," such as is used in the Food Machinery and Chemical Corp.'s Round Shell Freezer (see Fig. 16, p. 160), or in any type of air-blast freezer. If the infant foods are in rectangular cartons, they may be frozen in any of several types of plate freezers, or in an air-blast freezer.

Since the cans or cartons used are small, usually of the 3¼- or 6¾-oz. size, little difficulty is encountered in obtaining a rapid freeze.

### NUTRITIVE VALUE OF FROZEN INFANT FOODS

As indicated on p. 340, Hohl (1944), and Hohl and Smith (1944) have shown that fruit and vegetable purées retain their ascorbic acid, riboflavin, and thiamine content very well during manufacture and storage. Data indicating retention of these vitamins in vegetables are shown in Table 45. It should be noted that the vitamin changes recorded include all losses which occurred during processing and subsequent storage, as they were calculated on the basis of the original composition of the fresh vegetable.

These workers also report that "all of precooked frozen vegetable purées retained excellent color and flavor during storage periods of a year or more when held at 0°F. ( −18°C. )."

Table 45

Vitamin Retention of Frozen Vegetables Purées

| Kind of Purée | Period of Storage Months | Vitamin | % of Original Retained After Storage |
|---|---|---|---|
| Asparagus | 6 | C | 92 |
| Peas | 6½ | C | 76 |
| Spinach | 12 | C | 63 |
| Asparagus | 4 | B[1] | 93 |
| Asparagus | 13 | B[1] | 81 |
| Carrots | 12 | B[1] | 83 |
| Peas | 13 | B[1] | 77 |
| Spinach | 12 | B[1] | 53 |
| Asparagus | 13 | B[2] | 84 |
| Peas | 7 | B[2] | 95 |
| Spinach | 12 | B[2] | 81 |

Source: Hohl (1944).

Hohl also reported that purées made from a number of blanched fruits (apricots, peaches, and pears) retained excellent color and flavor during one year's storage at 0°F. ($-18$°C.). Hohl suggests that fruit combinations such as apricot and apple, apricot and nectarine, and apricot and peaches may have great possibilities as baby food because of their pleasing flavors.

### DIETETIC AND GERIATRIC FOODS

An important development in recent years has been the general use of frozen specially prepared precooked dietetic foods in a number of hospitals. Two factors which are hastening this are the great increase in the number of hospital patients, especially the elderly, and the great shortage and high cost of help in hospital kitchens.

A large proportion of the hospital patients require special diets. Many must have food low in sodium, others should have a diet low in calories, still others need foods low in saturated fats, etc. Because of the great variety of specially prepared foods needed, a great deal more labor is required for food preparation than is the case in other institutions.

The general use of specially prepared, precooked frozen foods packed in small packages has been found to reduce greatly the kitchen help needed, especially cooks and others trained in food preparation. An important factor in the introduction of precooked foods in certain hospitals has been the discovery that food in aluminum containers can be very quickly thawed and reheated in a microwave oven if the aluminum foil has been coated with plastic. The use of these plastic coated aluminum containers eliminates the troublesome arcing and burning of the food, and permits very rapid thawing and reheating without the great difficulties encountered previously with food packed in ordinary aluminum foil containers.

Some hospitals that serve frozen precooked dietetic foods reheated in microwave ovens have been able to dispense completely with kitchens for cooking food. About the only items that are not purchased frozen and reheated in microwave ovens are shell eggs (Anon. 1966D).

Some of the large processors of frozen foods are cooperating by freezing in small containers containing individual servings (usually three ounces) the great variety of dietetic foods required by the large hospitals.

### TESTS OF FROZEN MEALS PREPARED WITH POLYUNSATURATED FATS

A team of physicians from the Arteriosclerosis Research Center in Montclair, N.J., studied the benefits of a diet of frozen meals low in saturated fats involving 200 male test subjects (coronary patients) between the ages of 20 and 50. A preliminary report (Anon. 1966B) of the results of these studies indicated that the men on the special diet were much less subject to coronary attacks than the controls who did not eat the meals in which the saturated fats were largely replaced by polyunsaturated fats.

The foods provided on the special diet were flavorful, including such gourmet items as lobster Nairobi, chicken sauté marengo, and corn fiesta. Desserts included frozen pies topped with mellorine made with corn oil. This research is being continued in order to obtain more data on the value of polyunsaturated fats in the diet.

### FOOD AND DRUG ADMINISTRATION REGULATIONS FOR SPECIAL DIET FOODS

Recently, new standards affecting labeling or content or both of special diet foods have been announced by the Food and Drug Administration (Anon. 1966A).

Fortified foods cannot be sold if the labeling or advertising contains any statements or pictures implying any of the following: (1) that the food is adequate or effective for the treatment of any disease or condition; (2) that a diet of ordinary foods will not supply adequate amounts of vitamins and minerals; (3) that significant segments of the U.S. population are suffering, or are in danger of suffering, from a deficiency of vitamins or minerals.

Foods which are marketed for weight control must include on the label the statement "for calorie restricted diets." The label must also state the number of available calories in a specified serving and compare it with the number of calories in an equivalent serving of the ordinary food. A reduction of at least 50% must be obtained to support the claim for calorie restricted diets. The label shall also state the quantity in grams of protein, fat, and carbohydrate in a specified serving of the food.

A packer may claim on the label of a food for calories restricted diets that it is lower in calories or a similar phrase. However, the declaration "low calorie" may be made only if the food contains not more than 15 calories in a serving, and not more than 30 calories in the average total daily consumption of the food. The label of such a product must indicate that the food contains an artificial sweetener which is non-nutritive. The use of the artificial sweetener must reduce the caloric content by at least 50% if the food is offered for calorie restriction.

Manufacturers of foods for diabetics must also include on the label a prominent statement, immediately before or after the name of the food, reading "for the diets of diabetics." The label shall also state the quantity in grams of protein, fat, carbohydrate, and available calories in 100 gm. of the food. The label must also state whether an artificial sweetener has been added and that the sweetener is nonnutritive.

Labels of foods for persons on salt-restrictive diets must state the content of sodium in milligrams in 100 gm. of the food.

Fruit purées and other fruit products for infants may have a minimum of 30 mg. and not more than 60 mg. added ascorbic acid per 4 oz. of serving.

### BIBLIOGRAPHY *

Anon.    1954. Flavor in special-purpose foods now a factor. J. Agr. Food Chem. 2, 766.

Anon.    1956A. Frozen baby foods show advantages over jars; wide dietetic use anticipated. Quick Frozen Foods 18, No. 8, 139.

Anon.    1956B. Two frozen diet meals sold in single package. Food Field Reporter 24, No. 4, 1.

Anon.    1966A. Know these rules. Food Eng. 38, No. 8, 56–57.

Anon.    1966B. Frozen meals with polyunsaturated fats reduced deaths 250% in coronary test. Quick Frozen Foods 28, No. 10, 97, 99–102.

Anon.    1966C. Frozen prepared meals cut labor costs sharply in German hospitals. Quick Frozen Foods, Internat. Ed. 7, No. 4, 129–130.

Anon.    1966D. Hospital converts to frozen meals heated by mobile plug-in microwave ovens. Quick Frozen Foods 28, No. 10, 111–114.

Hohl, L. A.    1944. Experiments prove value of freezing baby foods. Quick Frozen Foods 6, No. 13, 30, 36.

Hohl, L. A., and Smith, M.    1944. Comparison of the vitamin content and palatability of frozen, canned, and dehydrated vegetable purées. Fruit Products J. 24, 54–56, 62.

Williams, E. W.    1956. Frozen foods forum—baby foods. Quick Frozen Foods 18, No. 9, 47.

<table>
<tr><td>Donald K. Tressler</td><td>Chinese, Kosher, Mexican, and<br>Other Nationality Foods</td></tr>
</table>

## IMPORTANCE OF FOREIGN FOODS

It is difficult to ascertain just when "nationality foods" came into being as frozen precooked foods. It is known that frozen chop suey was packed during World War II; however, to the Chinese, that product is an American dish and unknown in China or in an American-Chinese household (Kan 1956).

As various frozen precooked foods appeared on the market, at least some nationality foods came into being at about the same time or shortly thereafter. According to Martin (1966), the sales of "nationalities" are increasing steadily. In 1965, the dollar value of these foods ranked third in the list of prepared specialty foods, being surpassed only by platters (frozen meals on trays) and baked goods. Taking 1965 only into consideration, the value of nationality foods sold was $146 million, an increase over 1964 of 15% in the sale of these foods, most of which was due to the increasing popularity of Italian foods. Approximately one half of the value of the Italian foods, or $49 million, was pizza.

Among the more important of the nationality foods, are the following:

**Oriental.**—Chop sueys, chow meins, egg rolls, Chinese soups, egg foo young, and fried rice dishes.

**Jewish.**—Blintzes, knishes, kreplach, and a general line of kosher foods.

**Mexican.**—Tamales, enchiladas, tacos, and tortillas.

**Italian.**—Pizza, ravioli, lasagna, and spaghetti and meat balls.

**Other Nationalities.**—Hungarian and Swedish foods.

## CHINESE FOODS

A vegetable chop suey was packed during the war years of the forties by one of the large frozen food packers. Since meat rationing was in effect at that time, food processors could not obtain meat for their requirements beyond a percentage of what they had used in previous years. Since this was a new item, there was no previous use, hence, the product had to be produced as a meat-less item; namely, a vegetable chop suey. In going ahead with the production of this item, the packer reasoned that it might find a ready market as a meat extender, suggesting that the housewife add whatever meat was available to her.

---

Donald K. Tressler is a consultant and President of the Avi Publishing Co., Westport, Conn.

Just about ten years later, another packer entered the field with a variety of precooked frozen Chinese foods believing that the American public was ready for a type of meal that was different from the usual and / or average American diet and also that for those who relished Chinese foods, these items would save a trip to a Chinese restaurant or save detailed preparation in the home. Apparently that belief was correct, judging from present day sales of the various Chinese frozen precooked foods.

### Chop Suey and Chow Mein

Excluding any meat that may be packed with Chinese food, there appears to be no basic difference between chop suey and chow mein. It seems to be a matter of personal choice by the packer as to which name is used to designate this product. However, chow mein is commonly served over fried noodles. The basic ingredients in either chop suey or chow mein appear to be, celery, onions, bean sprouts, monosodium glutamate, sugar, salt, soy sauce, chicken broth or beef stock or bouillon, and spices. In a study of numerous ingredient labels the complete absence of water chestnuts was very noticeable. It is believed that all fine Chinese restaurants serving chop suey or chow mein include water chestnuts in the recipe. Could it be that water chestnuts are an expensive ingredient and for that reason are omitted from the frozen product in view of the competition that exists between different packers' brands? If water chestnuts were an item that did not freeze well, this might be some explanation, but Hanson (1954) reports that Chinese water chestnuts are one of the few vegetables that retains its texture during both cooking and freezing.

*Food Engineering* (Anon. 1956E) offers the following recipe for preparing chop suey:

"In a kettle, lightly brown 37½ lb. of sliced onions in 6 lb. of lard. Introduce 24 lb. of celery (¼ in. pieces) and 4½ gal. of water, and simmer ½ hr. Add 4½ lb. of meat concentrate (Armour's Vitalox or Wilson's B-V) dissolved in a little water.
"Now add 6 lb. of sliced mushrooms, 6 lb. of sliced green pepper, and 18 lb. of bean sprouts. Bring to boil, and thicken with paste consisting of 2 lb. of cornstarch and 1½ qt. of cold water. Fill into suitable containers, and freeze."

One of several types of meat, or shellfish or chicken may be added to a vegetable chop suey base thereby making it a meat chop suey with a more descriptive name. Examples are chicken chop suey, pork chop suey, beef chop suey, and shrimp chop suey. For some unknown reason when chicken meat is added, the resulting product is more frequently called chicken chow mein. The product name, mushroom chow mein is also more familiar. Almonds are often added to the different types of chop suey. At least one packer has a shrimp chow mein.

Typical for just about all precooked frozen foods, chop suey, after it is cooked, is rapidly cooled prior to filling and packing. The chop suey or some particular type of chop suey may be packaged as is and sold as that item. Packers of Chinese or Cantonese dinners may use the same product as the main ingredient on the dinner tray.

## Egg Rolls

Another item, packed and sold as is or added to the tray and sold as a Chinese dinner is egg roll. These are often made with the following ingredients, celery, shrimp, flour, pork, vegetable shortening, eggs, onions, water, scallions, salt, sugar, monosodium glutamate, and spices.

Ziemba (1954) describes the packing of egg rolls in one plant as follows:

"Shrimp, celery, pork, and onions are diced, then mixed along with spices in approximately 40-lb. batches. An Urschel slicer cuts celery into ⅛-in. dice. About two oz. of this mix is placed on a sheet of egg-noodle dough (purchased according to specifications from a local macaroni manufacturer), and then hand-formed into a roll (1¼ × 5 in.). An egg paste is used to seal the dough.

"Rolls are packed 72 to a wire-basket tray, and 20 trays are loaded onto a portable rack that's pushed to the kitchen. Here, a trayload of egg rolls is submerged 2½ min. in one of the three batch-type, deep-fat fryers. Temperature of the cooking fat is 350°F. (177°C.).

"The trayload of rolls is then removed from the fryer and placed on an inclined table attached to the fryer. Draining of excess fat takes about two minutes.

"Trays are then loaded onto racks for room-temperature cooling. Then the rolls are packed three to each carton. Cartons are Cellophane-wrapped by a Hayssen machine.

"Furthermore, the egg rolls are also packed two to a plastic bag as well as 25, 50, or 100 to a carton for institutions and restaurants."

## Egg Cantonese

The following recipe for egg Cantonese was furnished by the Poultry and Egg National Board (Anon. 1961C):

| Ingredients | Quantity Gm. |
|---|---|
| Eggs, 12 | |
| Crushed pineapple | 567 |
| Pineapple tidbits | 567 |
| Brown sugar | 250 |
| Cornstarch | 28 |
| Salt | 2 |
| Monosodium glutamate | 1.5 |
| Vinegar | 230 |
| Red pimientos (canned) | 90 |
| Green pepper | 40 |
| Hot (cooked) rice | 300 |
| Soy sauce | 12.5 |

**Manufacture.**—The pineapple, green pepper, and onion are ground together and drained. The resulting juice plus that previously drained from the pineapple is combined with brown sugar, cornstarch, salt, vinegar, and soy sauce, and cooked until slightly thickened.

The eggs are steamed until hard cooked, peeled, ground with the finest plate, and added to the other ground ingredients. This mixture is then blended with the thickened juice and the glutamate and pimiento added. The hot mixture is then filled into a pouch and sealed.

The rice is cooked, drained, and filled into a pouch and sealed.

**Package.**—A polyethylene boil-in-bag double-pouch package is suitable for this product. The sealed package with the rice in one pouch and the egg mixture in the other is inserted into a shell, overwrapped and frozen.

**Use.**—The double pouch is dropped into boiling water to thaw and heat for serving. The pouches are then opened and the egg mixture spooned over the rice.

FROZEN COOKED RICE

## Steamed Rice

**Using Polished Rice.**—Boggs *et al.* (1951) studied the preparation, freezing, and storage of rice cooked by slowly boiling it for ten minutes and then steaming it for an additional 25 min. They found that, after reheating, the product was fully equal to the freshly cooked product in every respect. Both polished Texas Patna (a long grain rice) and California Pearl (short grain) were studied and compared. The frozen cooked Pearl rice was stickier than the product prepared from the Texas Patna variety. For this reason, the latter variety probably is superior for freezing.

The commercial procedure recommended by these workers may be summarized as follows:

"The rice would be removed from storage by bucket conveyor and washed in a rod-reel washer. Next, it would be conveyed by belt to hoppers and measured into stainless-steel jacketed kettles equipped with removable wire-lined baskets. Water would be added in the proportion of 1.28 lb. per pound dry rice, and the mass boiled. Following complete absorption of water, the basket of partially cooked rice would be lifted out of the kettle by hoist and dumped into a hopper, which would feed the rice into a steamer for completion of cooking. The steamer would be one similar to a large blancher in general design, and equipped with stainless-steel mesh belts."

"Following cooking, the rice would be discharged onto a stainless-steel mesh belt (to allow draining) conveyed through an air-blast cooler and cooled to approximately room temperature, and then packaged in 12-oz. cardboard cartons. The latter would be transported to a refrigerated warehouse, where they would be frozen and held in storage until marketed."

"Facilities for one week's storage of dry rice are assumed to be adequate for the proposed operations. In the calculations, the bulk densities of raw and cooked rice are taken as 36 and 43 lb. per cu. ft., respectively. The cost of long-grain rice is assumed to be eleven cents per pound, that of packaging materials $12.00 per thousand cartons, and lithographed overwraps $4.50 per thousand."

Table 46

Estimated Cost (in Cents) of Manufacture for 12-Oz. Carton of
Frozen Cooked Rice

| | Product per Hr., Lb. | | |
|---|---|---|---|
| | 1,500 | 4,500 | 9,000 |
| Raw materials and packaging supplies | 5.1 | 5.1 | 5.1 |
| Processing and packaging cost | 1.1 | 0.6 | 0.5 |
| Transportation and casing | 1.0 | 0.9 | 0.9 |
| Freezing and storage | 1.2 | 1.2 | 1.2 |
| Indicated manufacturing cost | 8.4 | 7.8 | 7.7 |

Source: Boggs *et al.* (1951).

It is assumed that steam required for processing would be available from the parent plant at the rate of 75 cents per 1,000 lb. of steam. Estimated manufacturing costs for 12-oz. cartons of frozen cooked rice are shown in Table 46.

"If normal mark-ups for processor, broker, distributor, and retailer are added to the cost of manufacture, the indicated retail price of frozen cooked rice would be in the range of 13 to 15 cents per 12-oz. carton.

"It is recognized that the cooking of rice on a commercial scale would vary somewhat from the laboratory procedure. The cooking time for example, would need to be adjusted to allow for the longer period required to bring the raw rice to boiling temperature. The optimum rice loading on steaming belts has not been determined. The variations, however, should not result in any loss of quality of finished product."

Boggs *et al.* (1951) studied the storage of frozen steamed rice and reported that it retained its palatability for eight months at +10°F. (−12°C.)

**Improved Method of Cooking Rice for Freezing.**[1]—Use a premium, long grained variety such as Patna or Blue Bonnet. These are easily distinguished from the medium and short grained varieties which are more common from West Coast production.

(1) Place in an excess of water at 130° to 140°F. (50.5°–60°C.) which has received enough citric acid to give it a pH of 4–5.5. Enough water should be used to completely cover the rice after it has soaked for two hours.

(2) After two hours, drain off the soak water and rinse with more of the same pH adjusted water to remove fines.

(3) Drain thoroughly, tapping the screen to shake loose the adhering water, or by blowing the rice layer with air.

(4) Meanwhile, place a small volume of water in the bottom of a pressure cooker and heat to boiling with the cover on to heat up the apparatus. Place the soaked, drained rice in layers 2 in. deep or less over screens which are supported above the water in the vessel. Close the vessel and heat with the vent open until steam is emitted, then close off the vent and raise the pressure to 12–15 p.s.i. and hold for

---

[1]  Method suggested by Mr. George C. Briley.

12 to 15 min. Then blow off steam gradually enough to prevent violent boiling and flashing of the hot water.

(5) Remove the hot, steamed rice. It should have a rubbery texture. Place in an excess of hot water at 200° to 210°F. (93°–99°C.) and without stirring let it imbibe water until the grains are large, tender, and quite free. Stirring will cause it to become sticky. The rice should be held in a perforated vessel so that water may circulate freely through it. *Do not boil the rice*.

(6) Cooking should require only 10 to 15 min. following the step described in (4). Drain off the hot water, rinse twice with cool or cold water having the pH adjustment described in (1) above.

(7) Tap and shake to remove excess free water; or better still if you have the equipment suck off free water over a vacuum filter.

(8) The thoroughly cooked, tender, and free-flowing rice is now ready for freezing.

### Brown Rice

Boggs *et al.* (1952) have studied the preparation, cooking, and freezing of brown rice. They prepared both the long grain (brown Patna) and short grain (brown Pearl) rice by boiling for 15 min., then steaming for 50 min., air cooling, packaging, and freezing the packaged product at −10°F. (−23°C.). After storage for periods of 1 week, 2, 6, and 12 months, the reheated product was scarcely distinguishable from freshly cooked brown rice in every respect, even after one year of storage.

The methods recommended for preparation, cooking, packaging, and freezing on a commercial scale are the same as those suggested by Boggs *et al.* (1951) for polished rice (pp. 346 and 347), except longer periods of time are required both for the boiling and for the steaming operations.

### Fried Rice

Ziemba (1954) describes the preparation of fried rice in one plant as follows:

"Boiled rice is mixed and fried with fresh eggs, pork, soy sauce, onions, and selected spices. Batches (40 lb.) are then cooled and packaged in the same manner as chow mein."

### Soy Rice

Another rice dish popular both with the Chinese and the Polynesians is soy rice. This is prepared from freshly cooked, polished rice, seasoned with soy sauce, salt, monosodium glutamate, and mushroom powder with the addition of chopped green peppers and pimientos; a recipe follows:

| Ingredients | Quantity Gm. |
|---|---|
| Vegetable oil | 12 |
| Hot cooked rice | 450 |
| Soy sauce | 25 |
| Salt | 2 |
| Sugar | 2 |
| Monosodium glutamate | 1 |
| Mushroom powder | 0.3 |
| Chopped green pepper | 12 |
| Chopped pimiento | 12 |

**Method.**—Mix the oil with the rice. Add soy sauce, salt, sugar, and monosodium glutamate. Sprinkle in mushroom powder. Add pepper and pimiento.

## Chinese Soups

Today there are various kinds of Chinese soups available in the retail frozen food cabinet. These include, chicken noodle soup, egg drop soup, and Won Ton soup. Ziemba (1954) describes the making of the latter as follows:

"Making this specialty soup involves wrapping a small ball of precooked ground pork in a 2½ × 2½ in. sheet of dough to form kreplach. These are parboiled and packed nine to a paper cup along with chicken broth and chopped Chinese cabbage."

When these soups first appeared on the market they were packaged in paperboard tubs. Today most of them are packed in lithographed tin cans.

## Sweet and Sour Pork

Another very popular entrée of both the Chinese and Polynesians is sweet and sour pork. A recipe for this item follows:

Sweet and Sour Pork Recipe

| Ingredients | Quantity Gm. |
|---|---|
| Soy sauce | 100 |
| Fresh ginger root | 20 |
| Scallions, cut in 4 in. pieces | 20 |
| Cloves garlic, slightly crushed | 10 |
| Salt | 8 |
| Passion fruit nectar | 17 |
| Pork, cut in ¾ in. cubes | 450 |
| Water | 385 |
| Oil, vegetable | 28 |
| Cloves garlic, slightly crushed | 5 |
| Chili sauce | 40 |
| Sweet mixed pickle juice | 60 |
| Pineapple syrup (canned) | 380 |
| Pineapple tidbits | 190 |
| Water chestnuts (¼ in. slice), canned | 78 |
| Pickles, sweet, mixed (½ to 1 in. pieces) | 80 |
| Pimientos, coarsely diced (½ in. pieces) | 64 |
| Fresh green pepper, coarsely diced (½ to ¾ in.) | 57 |
| Cornstarch | 24 |
| Water | 35 |

Method.—Combine 75 gm. soy sauce, ginger root, scallions, 4 cloves garlic (10 gm.), salt, passion fruit nectar, and pork; mix well. Let stand for 2 hr. Add 350 gm. water and place in pressure cooker. Cook under 15 lb. pressure for 12 min. Cool immediately. Let meat cool in stock. Drain and pick out pieces of ginger, garlic, and scallion.

Heat oil and add 2 cloves garlic (10 gm.); let sizzle for 5 sec. Remove garlic and add remainder of soy sauce (25 gm.), chili sauce, pickle juice, and pineapple syrup. Heat to boiling point. Combine cornstarch, and 3 tbsp. water; mix until blended and add to hot liquid. Cook, stirring constantly, until mixture thickens. Add pork and remaining ingredients. Package and freeze.

## Sweet-Sour Spareribs

Sweet-sour spareribs is a delicious dish, very popular in China.

**Spareribs for "Sweet Sour Spareribs"**

| Ingredients | Quantity |
|---|---|
| Soy sauce | 65 gm. |
| Fresh ginger root, slices | 2 |
| Scallions, stalks in | |
| 4-in. lengths | 2 |
| Garlic cloves, slightly crushed | 4 |
| Salt | 8 gm. |
| Passion fruit nectar | 17 gm. |
| Spareribs cut in | |
| 1-in. lengths | 900 gm. |
| Water | 340 gm. |
| Sweet 'n Sour sauce, heated | 900 gm. |

Combine soy sauce, ginger, scallions, garlic, salt, and nectar. Add spareribs and marinate for two hours, turning over once at the end of one hour. Place spareribs, marinating sauce, and 340 gm. water in a pressure cooker. Cook under 15 lb. pressure for 15 min. Let ribs cool before removing from liquid.

Reheat cooked spareribs in pre-heated oven at 250°F. (121°C.) for 10 minutes. Add heated Sweet 'n Sour Sauce.

**Sweet 'n Sour Sauce**

| Ingredients | Quantity Gm. |
|---|---|
| Garlic, crushed | 5 |
| Vegetable oil | 24 |
| Soy sauce | 25 |
| Chili sauce | 22 |
| Sweet mixed pickle juice | 57 |
| Pineapple tidbits | 190 |
| Water chestnuts, sliced | 78 |
| Sweet pickles, sliced | 80 |
| Diced pimiento | 57 |
| Diced green pepper | 57 |
| Cornstarch | 16 |
| Water | 24 |
| Weight of product | 900 |

**Method.**—Let garlic sizzle in oil for a few seconds. Discard garlic cloves. Combine soy sauce, chili sauce, pickle juice, and pineapple juice and add to the hot oil and mix well. Add pineapple, chestnuts, pickles, pimiento, and green pepper. Bring to a boil. Blend cornstarch and water. Stir into sauce mixture. Cook, stirring constantly, until mixture comes to a boil.

POLYNESIAN FOODS

Chicken Curry (CHICKEN MAI-KAI)

| Ingredients | Quantity Gm. |
|---|---|
| Margarine | 43 |
| Chopped onion | 114 |
| Clove garlic, crushed | 1.5 |
| Uncooked ham, diced ($\frac{3}{8}$ in. square) | 88 |
| Chopped canned mushrooms | 56 |
| Curry powder | 5 |
| All-purpose flour | 18 |
| Chicken stock (unsalted) | 285 |
| Lemon juice | 14 |
| Heavy cream | 118 |
| Pineapple tidbits | 134 |
| Diced cooked chicken ($\frac{1}{2}$ in.) | 135 |
| Salt | 8 |

Method.—Melt margarine and add onion, garlic, ham, and mushrooms. Cook, stirring occasionally, until onion is tender. Stir in curry powder and flour. Continue cooking, stirring frequently, for two minutes. Add chicken stock and lemon juice and cook until mixture comes to a boil. Stir in remaining ingredients and heat to serving temperature.

Light or Confetti Rice

| Ingredients | Quantity Gm. |
|---|---|
| Egg | 72 |
| Salt | 1.5 |
| Vegetable | 42 |
| Cold, unsalted, cooked rice | 450 |
| Sugar, granulated | 2 |
| Monosodium glutamate | 1.3 |
| Finely chopped scallion ($\frac{1}{16}$-in.) | 26 |
| Medium diced pimiento ($\frac{1}{8} \times \frac{1}{8}$-in.) | 30 |

Method.—Combine egg and 1 gm. salt; beat until blended. Heat (4 gm.) oil in small skillet. Add egg and scramble until firm. Break into small pieces ($\frac{1}{4}$ in.).

Heat 28 gm. oil in large skillet. Add rice and stir until coated with oil. Add salt, sugar, and monosodium glutamate. Mix until well blended. Add scallion, pimiento, and scrambled egg. Stir until evenly mixed.

**Chicken Tahiti**

| Ingredients | Quantity Gm. |
|---|---|
| Butter or margarine | 200 |
| Flour | 90 |
| Chicken stock, heated | 910 |
| Cream heavy | 115 |
| Celery strips | 320 |
| Chinese cabbage stems, sliced | 320 |
| Chicken, cooked, diced | 675 |
| Bamboo shoots, canned, sliced | 40 |
| Water chestnuts, canned, sliced | 80 |
| Pimiento, canned diced | 40 |
| Almonds, slivered, toasted | 80 |
| Coconut, fresh, diced | 150 |

**Method.**—Melt butter; add flour and stir over low heat for 2 to 3 min. Add chicken stock and cook, stirring constantly, until mixture comes to a boil. Stir in cream, celery, and cabbage. Heat again to a boil. Stir in remaining ingredients and season with salt and pepper to taste. Heat to serving temperature. Serve over cooked rice.

### JEWISH (KOSHER) FOODS

Probably the most important, traditionally Jewish frozen food item is blintzes. Basically a blintz is a thin outer egg-leaf pancake folded over fillings of cheese, fruit, or potatoes. In France, a blintz has another name, (crêpes suzette) which term and the product is familiar to all epicureans. It is believed that the blintzes are not so thin a pancake as those used for the French crepes, but the amount of filling is usually more generous. The ingredient label usually reads, fresh eggs, flour, sugar, cornstarch, salt and pepper, plus whatever the filling might be, such as fresh cottage cheese, or frozen strawberries.

Blintzes filled with frozen fruits or fruit preserves are eaten anytime, but the blintzes filled with cheese are eaten especially during the Jewish holiday of Shavuos. Frozen blintzes are available in the market with a number of different fillings such as cheese, blueberries, potatoes, strawberries with cheese, and cherries.

These and all other products to be truly kosher must be certified by the adherence to kosher dietary laws is under the constant supervision of a product accepted by them carries the seal. All food preparation under strict adherence to kosher dietary laws is under the constant supervision of a rabbi during the entire working day.

Some of the kosher products that are available as frozen prepared or pre-cooked foods include roast chicken dinner, breast of beef dinner, chopped chicken livers, meat kreplach (which is, similar to ravioli), stuffed cabbage, baked corned beef hash and knishes. A knish is a nonsweet meat or vegetable filled baked pastry. Some knishes are filled with beef or liver (Anon. 1955B). While the sale of these frozen items is quite large in certain cities of the country, a new market is rapidly developing. Hospital dieticians are finding the frozen kosher foods solve the problem of feeding their orthodox Jewish patients.

## MEXICAN FOODS

The popularity of Mexican frozen foods is steadily increasing. It is reported (Anon. 1956C) that Mexican foods were listed among the five best-selling frozen food specialities by ten per cent of the brokers polled in a survey. As would be expected, these products have their greatest distribution in the southwestern part of this country although they are beginning to appear in other markets.

These products are presently available as single items packed in individual cartons and are also used as a part of combination Mexican dinners. Enchiladas and beef tacos are two of the leading Mexican foods. One packer (Anon. 1956C) describes some of his basic ingredients as follows:

"The Spanish rice used in the Mexican dinner is the Minute rice that housewives all over the country prefer; Orega chile, world-reknowned for its fine qualities is used exclusively; Quaker oats are incorporated into his corn tortillas; in addition, the sweet chili peppers . . . are grown in areas noted for fine chili peppers. All beef is U.S. inspected so that the product may be sold interstate, and well-aged natural cheddar cheese ... is used exclusively."

"The newest product . . . is 'Avoca'te,' a Mexican-American delicacy made with whipped avocado and a special blend of seasonings, adaptable for use in Vichysoisse-Mexicana, a cream soup served hot or cold; as a spread to be added to hamburgers; or as a gelatin salad mold to surround chicken or shrimp."

The above frozen avocado dip is made up of avocados, fruit juices, onions, peppers, and flavorings. As a paste, it is designed for hors d'oeuvres, sandwiches, and salads. See Chapter 5, Part 1.

One Mexican style dinner is composed of two tamales wrapped in corn husks, one enchilada covered with a sauce, and cheddar cheese, Spanish rice, chili, and Pinto beans. The ingredient label reads, water, beef, corn flour, beans, rice, cheese, spices, tomato puree, flavoring, pork, wheat flour, vegetable oil, beef fat, and monosodium glutamate.

The packer of the above dinner states (Floyd 1956) that he obtains the highest grade of peppers and spices, with appealing flavor and not too much fire; the highest quality of red meat free from tendons, gristle and sinew; selected recleaned frijoles; long grain converted rice; tortillas made from white corn flour; aged cheddar cheese; white Spanish onions to make enchiladas, with an enchilada sauce containing peppers and spices, onions and a tomato puree made from Italian vine-ripened tomatoes.

*Food Engineering* (Anon. 1956H) lists two interesting formulas and procedures for the manufacture of tamale pies. Since no mention is made as to whether the formulas given can be frozen, they are not being quoted. However, the details given in that article may be used as a guide in preparing tamale pies under test for freezing preservation.

Robe (1956) describes several pieces of equipment that were recently developed to serve the Mexican food producing industry.

One is a new continuous tamale making machine. This machine extrudes the filling and the ground corn covering in one operation, cuts the product to proper length, and delivers them to a continuous conveyor for packaging. The machine is a taco fryer which takes the flat, thin tortilla, folds it without breaking it, fries it in thermostatically controlled deep fat, and delivers a crisp and flaky shell to the operator for filling. Robe (1956) advises that filling the deep-fried shell with hamburger, lettuce, grated cheese, fresh onion, and chili sauce completes the taco (Mexico sandwich).

A description of enchiladas as given by Robe (1956) is as follows:

"Enchiladas, another highly popular Mexican dish, differs from tacos both in method of production and manner of eating. A filling of chopped onion and cheese is rolled in a tortilla like a jelly roll, then covered with a chili sauce. It is eaten with a fork, in contrast to the sandwich type of handling given the taco. Filling of both products is still largely a manual operation."

*Courtesy of Rosarita Products*

Fig. 57.   Making tortillas. This view shows the specially-made ovens used for the making of tortillas for a frozen enchilada dinner and for tacos. These ovens are completely automatic and operate at a capacity of 4,000 tortillas per hour.

The tortilla seems to be the base for most Mexican dishes. Hence, the above mentioned automatic corn tortilla oven appears to be a piece of equipment that will play a big part in the possible expansion of the production of frozen Mexican dishes (Fig. 57). Ovens similar to the above and wet corn grinders are two pieces of equipment that appear to be the basis for any Mexican food operation. The corn grinder is used for making the dough for tortillas and tamales. The grinder is also used for making a chili purée or sauce for Mexican foods.

## ITALIAN FOODS

Although pizza pies are the number one item in any consideration of frozen Italian foods, ravioli, lasagne, manicotti, spaghetti and meat balls, spaghetti with meat sauce, chicken cacciatore, turkey tetrazini, egg plant parmigiana, veal scallopini, veal parmigiana, and an old favorite, macaroni and cheese are all popular. Other specialty items include veal with mushrooms, beef and macaroni in tomato sauce, meat balls in sauce, and mussels in sauce. Italian dinners—including spaghetti dinners, ravioli dinners, and veal dinners are also available frozen. Many kinds of pasta are also obtainable frozen, including egg noodles, green noodles, rigitoni, carvatelli, and gnocchi.

### Pastas with Sauces

Various Italian sauces are frozen including meat sauce, meatless tomato sauce, and mushroom sauce.

### Frozen Pizza

Freezing is the only way to preserve and market pizza. Frozen pizza is amazingly popular. Teenage children are especially fond of it. There are many reasons for its popularity. One is that it is not only rather difficult and time-consuming for the housewife to prepare, but also it requires a special sauce and powdered cheese not commonly stocked in the home kitchen. Further, it has many uses: it can be eaten as a snack, an appetizer, or as a main course. Pizza is not only delicious, but is nutritious as well. In frozen form, it can be kept in the home freezer for an emergency which may arise when a meal is needed in a hurry, since it can be quickly and easily prepared, merely by reheating in a hot oven.

Commercially, the making and freezing of pizza can be a straight line procedure. The first operation is the preparation of the dough. A modified biscuit flour mix will give a tender crust, provided a minimum of mixing is used. The following is a suitable formula:

| Ingredients | % |
|---|---|
| All purpose flour | 80.04 |
| Shortening | 12.67 |
| Sugar | 1.81 |
| Salt | 1.81 |
| Anhydrous calcium phosphate | 1.60 |
| Soda | 1.27 |
| Nonfat milk solids | 0.80 |
| | 100.00 |

This "biscuit mix" can be prepared in advance and made into a dough in an Artofex mixer and kneader with the addition of one-half its weight of lukewarm water containing a suspension of five per cent of active dry yeast or its equivalent of compressed yeast. The dough is allowed to stand for 20 or 30 min.; then it is pressed into pie-shape crusts about ¼ in. thick with the edge turned up and the top pricked at about one-inch intervals so as to allow the escape of the steam and gas during baking. The two most common sizes produced commercially are (1) 5-in. (individual), and (2) 10-in. (family size). Five ounces of dough are required for the 5-in. size and 10 oz. for a 10-in. pizza. The pizza crusts are baked for approximately 3½ min. in a 500°F. (260°C.) oven. After the pizza crusts have cooled to 100°F. (38°C.) or lower, the upper side of the crust is brushed or sprayed with margarine. Then a pizza sauce is added. A basil-flavored tomato sauce is popular; however, each packer has his own specially flavored sauce. The following is a very good pizza sauce:

| Ingredients | % |
|---|---|
| Tomato paste | 81.00 |
| Chopped canned tomatoes (drained) | 17.80 |
| Salt | 1.04 |
| Basil, dried, ground | 0.16 |
| | 100.00 |

Five ounces of this sauce should be spread on each 10-in. pizza, and 2½ oz. on each 5-in. pie. Most pizzas are dusted with dehydrated cheese. The following is a good cheese blend:

| Ingredients | % |
|---|---|
| Parmesan (grated) | 24.9 |
| Romano (grated) | 24.9 |
| Mozzarella (chopped) | 49.9 |
| Oregano (dried, ground) | 0.3 |
| | 100.00 |

Some pizza bakers do not use a blend of cheese but use straight dried mozzarella cheese.

In some sections of the country pizzas topped with sliced Italian sausage instead of cheese are popular. Pepperoni is the kind of sausage commonly used, and some pizzas are topped with mushrooms.

A recent survey of the popularity of various brands of pizzas, by Quick Frozen Foods (Anon. 1964), indicated that the large round pizzas with a thin crust are most popular. Pizzas with a thick crust and the square and rectangular shapes are much less in demand. Cheese pizzas are most popular in all sections of the country. Nevertheless there is a considerable demand for sausage and pepperoni pizzas in the Midwest and far West. In the East and Midwest some mushroom pizzas are sold.

Some packers place the pizzas directly on trays on which they are frozen in an air-blast freezer then package them in cartons. Others put the baked pizzas in packages which are in turn placed in an air-blast freezer.

## Ravioli

Two other especially important frozen Italian foods are ravioli and lasagne. Raviolis are produced as several different types and a cheese ravioli normally contains durum flour, one or several types of cheese, water, eggs, parsley, salt, pepper, and spice. The raviolis and the sauce are packed in separate packages. The sauce formula of one packer is reported (Anon. 1951) to include tomato puree, onion, garlic, beef, carrots, celery, mushrooms, olive oil, salt, parsley, and spices.

## Lasagne

Lasagne is often made of beef and vegetable broth, tomatoes, one or several types of cheese (such as mozzarella, ricotta, and Parmesan cheese), beef, flour, water, durum flour, semolina, eggs, wheat germ, wheat gluten, butter, salt dehydrated onions, olive oil, wine, sugar, plant protein, monosodium glutamate, dehydrated carrots, and flavorings.

### THE FUTURE

In view of the rapid increase in the production of frozen nationality foods and the fact that more and more food items within any one nationality are gradually entering the frozen food market, it is expected that within the next few years many more items than those mentioned in this chapter will come into being. Also it is expected that there will be foods of additional countries produced by packers in this country.

### BIBLIOGRAPHY

Anon.   1951. Mushroom gravy is canned and frozen. Western Canner and Packer 43, No. 5, 29–30.
Anon.   1955A. Freezing opens markets for kosher specialties. Quick Frozen Foods 17, No. 7, 84.
Anon.   1955B. Frying noodles. Food Eng. 27, No. 7, 169.
Anon.   1956A. "Flight to the suburbs" inspired successful Chinese frozen food business. Quick Frozen Foods 19, No. 3, 130–132.

Anon. 1956B. Packers give pizza "new look" in effort to gain their share of vast market. Quick Frozen Foods 19, No. 1, 113–114, 116–118.

Anon. 1956C. Popularity of Mexican frozen food causes Moreno's to triple plant size; extend distribution. Quick Frozen Foods 19, No. 2, 90–91.

Anon. 1956D. Mah Chena proves truth of old Chinese adage—quality is the foundation of success. Meat 44, No. 5, 88, 90, 92.

Anon. 1956E. Preparing chop suey. Food Eng. 28, No. 5, 187.

Anon. 1956F. 1955 prepared foods pack placed at 534 million pounds by U.S. Dept. Agr. Quick Frozen Foods 18, No. 8, 107–109.

Anon. 1956G. Prepared foods prove boon to agriculture; now represent 35% of total frozen food sales. Quick Frozen Foods 18, No. 10, 61–63.

Anon. 1956H. Preparing tamale pies. Food Eng. 28, No. 11, 181.

Anon. 1961A. Italian foods—the favorite nationality dishes. Quick Frozen Foods 23, No. 9, 93–94.

Anon. 1961B. Frozen pizza sales top $200–250 million market. Quick Frozen Foods 23, No. 9, 99–100.

Anon. 1961C. Profit making opportunities in the 60's with eggs. Poultry and Egg Nat'l. Board. Special Bull.

Anon. 1963. Kosher frozen meals form basis of successful retail business. Quick Frozen Foods 26, No. 1, 93–94.

Anon. 1964. Pizza packers find tight freezer space will stretch for profitable large size. Quick Frozen Foods 26, No. 10, 75–79; No. 11, 117–121.

Anon. 1965. Placing prepared foods in proper perspective. Quick Frozen Foods 27, No. 6, 89–92.

Anon. 1966A. El Chico doubles Mexican style food output at 80,000 sq, ft. complex. Quick Frozen Foods 29, No. 3, 149–150.

Anon. 1966B. Military sales average 2500 weekly for Vorgos Pizza Crust Company. Quick Frozen Foods 29, No. 4, 96–97.

Boggs, M. M., Sinnott, C. N., Vasak, O. R., and Kester, E. B. 1951. Frozen cooked rice. Food Technol. 5, 230–232.

Boggs, M. M., Ward, A. C., Sinnott, C. N., and Kester, E. B. 1952. Frozen cooked rice. II. Brown rice. Food Technol. 6, 53–54.

Floyd, R. T. 1956. Private communication. Pan-Am Foods, Inc., Brownsville, Texas.

Hanson, H L. 1954. Recent developments in precooked frozen foods. J. Am. Dietet. Assoc. 30, 241–244.

Kan, J. J. 1956. Private communication, Kan's Restaurant, San Francisco, Calif.

Martin, S. 1966. The state of the industry. Quick Frozen Foods 29, No. 4, 35–41, 116.

Robe, K. 1956. Mexican foods popularity grows, new machines help supply demand. Food processing 4, No. 11, 19.

Tenor, J. 1967. Big money backs nationality foods as freezing makes them universal. Quick Frozen Foods 29, No. 6, 91–94.

Ziemba, J. V. 1954. Precooked frozen Chinese food. Food Eng. 26, No. 4, 92–93.

## CHAPTER 17

Marjorie Heid | Frozen Batters and Doughs

## INTRODUCTION

The perishability of bakery products is a problem not only on the shelf but at each step during production. Freezing at some stage of processing prolongs the duration of freshness. At room temperature cakes in general have a longer shelf-life than most baked products, but the staling rate of cakes during the first few hours after baking is faster. Cakes and quick breads freeze very successfully at the batter stage, as well as after baking if certain requirements are met.

### FROZEN BATTERS

Stockpiling batters in frozen form can make possible more efficient batch scheduling, with larger batch runs and tighter control over production labor and inventory. This, in turn, can assure tighter cost control and fewer stale losses. It may make possible a greater daily assortment of fresh merchandise and permit some diversion of labor to special orders and holiday attractions. Today's shopper expects variety in the daily fare as well as a stock of convenience products for busy days. Gourmet and holiday specials are always big sellers. With frozen batters in reserve, items which sell out early in the day can be replenished for the late shoppers who are often faced with empty shelves. The enticing aroma of this periodic point-of-sale baking stimulates impulse buying.

Research on frozen cake batters was initiated early in the 1940's by Home Economics staff members at several Universities and State Colleges. During the forties and early fifties, interest was directed toward applications for homemakers in home freezers. Results and conclusions were at times in variance. There was a sparsity of background information on certain types of key ingredients, namely baking powders and shortenings, and on freezing of bakery products, either baked or unbaked. Interest in commercial applications of freezing cake batters was reflected at an annual meeting of the American Society of Bakery Engineers (Anon. 1955). Some of the problems and possibilities of this new type of product were presented and discussed (Pickens 1955).

Pillsbury Co. (1966) reported that over half the retail bakers in this country now freeze some products at one or more stages of processing as a

Marjorie Heid is Research Food Technologist, Western Utilization Research and Development Division, Agricultural Research Service, U.S. Dept. Agr., Albany, Calif.

means of minimizing the extreme perishability and extending the shelf-life of bakery products.

## Importance of Baking Powder

Observations of progressive decrease in volume of cakes baked from frozen batters as storage periods increased led to several comparisons by early researchers of the performance of the available types of baking powders in cake batters which were to be held in frozen storage for later bake-off. Under comparable conditions of frozen storage similar cake formulations retained better volume with sulfate-phosphate baking powder than with tartrate (Zaehringer and Mayfield 1951; Mackey et al. 1952). During identical frozen storage situations, shortened cake batters containing phosphate baking powder were observed to release carbon dioxide at a slower rate than similar batters with either sulfate-phosphate or tartrate powders as measured by the AACC gasometric method with a Chittrick apparatus adapted to the determination of the $CO_2$ content of cake batters (Moore et al. 1954). A stabilized dicalcium phosphate baking powder was developed which remains alkaline in the batters until heat is applied during the baking process (Joslin and Ziemke 1955). Only then is carbon dioxide released from the soda fraction. It is geared to commercial bakery conditions and is especially tailored for use in frozen cake batters. Several modifications of this type of powder are now available to commercial bakers. Research conducted by Pickens (1955) and by the author in 1959 demonstrated the need to increase the baking powder level in commercial cake batters to be held in frozen storage by 0.2 to 0.25% above the level required in the same batters when baked immediately after mixing. This partially compensates for the loss of air from batters during frozen storage and baking (Pickens 1955; Pillsbury Co. 1966).

## Type of Shortening

Although butter was given higher ratings on texture and cell characteristics in some studies (Graul and Lowe 1947; Mackey et al. 1952) others reported better results with hydrogenated vegetable shortening (Zaehringer and Mayfield 1951) in batters stored at freezing temperatures for later bake-off. Butter and lard oxidized in frozen batters during storage for 6 months at $-30°F.$ ($-34°C.$), and developed rancid odors and flavors (Mackey et al. 1952). Hydrogenated vegetable shortening is the one strongly recommended for commercial production. In the author's laboratory, satisfactory results were achieved also with liquid shortening when it was used with an emulsifier (sorbitan monostearate with polyoxyethylene sorbitan monostearate) in yellow cake batters which were held in frozen storage at $-10°F.$ ($-23°C.$) over a 12-week period. Improved cell structure was reported in white and chocolate cakes baked from frozen batters made with either butter or hydrogenated vegetable oil when an emulsifier (glyceryl monostearate) was used at levels of 5 and 10% (Mackey *et al*. 1952). In the author's laboratory, greater air inclusion during mixing, more uniformity in cell structure and grain, and better volume were noted in yellow and chocolate cakes baked from frozen batters when an emulsifier (sorbitan monostearate with polyoxyethylene sorbitan monostearate or glyceryl monostearate) was used at levels up to four per cent. An explanation of why air is lost from cake batters during frozen storage was offered by Mackey (1955). In the freshly prepared batters microscopic examination depicted the fat dispersed in aerated particles as thin patches with filmy edges where it was in contact with the aqueous phase. Closely packed air bubbles clustered within the fat particle. Globules of fat appeared only occasionally. As frozen storage at 0°F. (−18°C.) progressed over a period of 12 weeks, the fat tended to pull away from the aqueous phase and form globules with distinct rather than filmy boundaries. The tiny air bubbles seemed to coalesce into larger bubbles. These escaped from the warm batter during the early stages of baking. This redistribution of air bubbles in the stored batters was reflected in increasingly coarse texture and steadily diminishing volume in the test cakes after baking as storage period progressed. These observations were supported during storage tests by the author and by statements by commercial bakers that "air is squeezed out of cake batter under adverse frozen storage conditions and changes the grain and volume of the cakes after baking" (Pickens 1955) and "air bubbles in the fat particles of cake batters tend to unite during storage at low temperatures" (Pillsbury Co. 1966).

### Importance of Temperature

The relationship of storage temperature to the rate of deterioration in quality factors of frozen batters was observed and recorded as early as 1947. Cakes baked from batters stored at −10°F. (−23°C.) up to four months showed no significant differences from freshly baked cakes, whereas similar batters stored at 0°F. (−18°C.) were inferior in aroma, flavor, color, and volume (Graul and Lowe 1947). Batters stored at −30°F. (−34.5°C.) retained good volume up to six months (Mackey *et al*. 1952). Pickens (1955) recorded a time-temperature curve to demonstrate graphically the stages through which cake batter passes at various temperatures enroute to 0°F. (−18°C.). At 20°F. (−7°C.) the batter is still pliable. It becomes firm somewhere between 10° (−12°C.) and 0°F. (−18°C.), but is actually only 65 to 70% frozen at this stage. It is not completely frozen until it reaches a temperature of about −20°F. (−29°C.). Pickens' cake batter curve was very similar to his curve depicting the gradual absorption of latent heat at falling temperatures in the freezing range, and the freezing point of a sugar solution having the same sugar-liquid ratio as he used in his cake batter. The high sugar content is responsible for the long heat of fusion period and the low freezing point of cake batters, as well as for rapid defrosting when batters are exposed to temperatures above their freezing point. Studies in the author's laboratory strongly support use of rapid freezing at a temperature well below the freezing point of the cake batter, with subsequent storage at $-10°F.$ ($-23°C.$), or below if batters are to be stored more than a few weeks. Unpublished time-temperature-tolerance investigations by the author in 1966 suggest safe storage periods at several temperature levels for four common commercial cake batters. Table 47 shows results of a four-month storage test. Cakes baked from the stored batters maintained quality factors comparable to those of freshly prepared batters during the period noted for each temperature.

Temperature stability is essential to quality maintenance in stored frozen batters. Volume, grain, and texture are damaged by fluctuations in storage temperatures, especially in angel, sponge, and chiffon batters. These quickly break down, air bubbles escape, and water separates from the batters. This settles to the bottom of the pans and results in an unbaked layer at the bottom of the baked cake. The texture of the baked cake is then unpalatably coarse. Although shortened batters show more tolerance than the sponge types to temperature fluctuations, their period of quality preservation is considerably abbreviated. Because of their high sugar content cake batters thaw rapidly when exposed, for even short periods, to temperatures above $0°F.$ ($-18°C.$). Air, which was incorporated during the mixing, is freed. Decreasing volume, coarsening of texture, and irregularity in cell structure will parallel the amount of air lost.

## Formulation and Mixing

Any well balanced cake formula can be frozen at the batter stage with but slight modifications in formulation and mixing. The choice of leav-

Table 47

Storage Tolerance of Frozen Batters

| Type of Cake | Storage Temperature and Time (Weeks) | | |
|---|---|---|---|
| | —30°F. (—34.5°C.) | —10°F. (—23°C.) | 0°F. (—18°C.) |
| Yellow | 18 | 14 | 14 |
| Chocolate | 18 | 14 | 14 |
| Angel (dried whites) | 10 | 10 | 8 |
| Angel (liquid whites) | 10 | 8 | 6 |
| Chiffon | 14 | 9 | 6 |

ening agent is all-important. The dicalcium phosphate and sodium acid pyrophosphate varieties have records of good performance, but the tartrate
powder loses leavening action during frozen storage. Hydrogenated vegetable oil is the recommended shortening. A high shortening level and high
sugar ratio give better results in cakes baked from frozen shortened batters
than do the leaner formulations. An emulsifier will increase the potential
air inclusion during mixing and thus improve volume, cell structure, and
symmetry in the baked cake. It helps stabilize the air distribution in the
frozen batter during storage. The optimum level of emulsifier will be dictated by the kind of emulsifier (there are several types available), the type
or brand of shortening, and the particular formulation. The commercial
manufacturer of the shortening or emulsifier is best qualified to make recommendations for his own product. In scanning a variety of available
emulsifiers, the author found that the optimum levels ranged from 4 to 10%.

Cake batters tend to lose some of their entrapped air during frozen storage (Fig. 58). This can be compensated for by whipping in more air during
mixing and by increasing the baking powder level by 0.2 to 0.25% of the
level required in similar batters intended for immediate bake-off.

Dried egg whites perform as well as liquid whites in frozen angel batters;
in fact, they may even show a slight edge over the liquid whites for frozen
storage tolerance and for volume. The cakes with the liquid whites, however, may be preferred for flavor and texture.

Chemically leavened novelty breads, such as banana bread, date-nut,
etc., which are made from muffin-type mixtures, may be frozen at the bat-

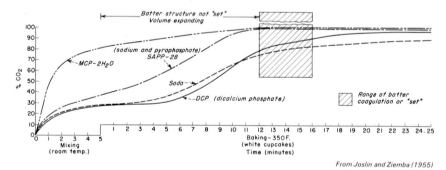

*From Joslin and Ziemba (1955)*

Fig. 58.    Rate of release of carbon dioxide during baking of cup cakes containing a
stabilized form of dicalcium phosphate. This new leavener is especially good for preparing batters to be frozen since the phosphate does not react with the soda until the batter is heated. Essential to baking of cup cakes with new leavener is the delay in coagulation until leavening gas is released. Cake batters have more sugar than biscuit batters
and coagulate at higher temperatures. Cakes must be baked in slow ovens to permit
more time for leavening action. SAPP-28 = sodium acid pyrophosphate; MCP-2$H_2O$
= monocalcium phosphate. DC$\overline{P}$ = the stabilized dicalcium phosphate.

ter stage providing: (1) they are reasonably high in sugar and shortening; (2) they are mixed by the emulsion or cake method, not by the standard muffin method; (3) no more than a 5 to 6-week storage period is planned. These batters, when prepared by the muffin method, have no tolerance for freezing. They break down during the freezing process and develop an extremely coarse texture and undesirably large and uneven cell structure. Because these mixtures are lower in shortening and sugar than the cake batters, they are not stable to prolonged storage periods.

## Packaging and Freezing

The container has several specific requirements: rigidity to shape the cake during baking, both low and high temperature tolerances, and prevention of moisture and volatile odor transfer to or from the batters. It must be capable of an airtight seal. Aluminum foil pans fulfill these requirements and are good heat conductors both in the freezer and in the oven. Needless to say, cake batters should be packaged immediately after mixing, and should be frozen without delay. Rapid freezing at a temperature below the freezing point of the cake batter is desirable if available facilities permit.

## Thawing and Baking

Angel, sponge, and chiffon batters bake quite successfully from the frozen state. Shortened batters, on the other hand, achieve better volume, cell structure, and symmetry if they are thawed at room temperature before baking. The high sugar content induces rapid thawing. Usually 20 to 30 min. is a sufficient time for batters up to 1 in. in depth. For both sponge and shortened batters the normal baking temperature should be reduced by 20° to 25°F. (11° to 14°C.), and the bake-off period increased, as needed, to complete the baking.

## Conclusions

Bakeries, in general, face their peak load at week's end. The volume of sales can be affected by weather conditions and holidays. A supply of batters in frozen storage will help to balance shortages and excesses. The small operator can reduce operation costs by increasing batch volume and reducing the number of batches run per day. This will also conserve time lost in change-over. Production time thus saved can be applied toward new product development, increased variety and special orders. For the large operator there may be untapped potentials for distribution of cakes in frozen batter form for bake-off as needed at point of sale in supermarkets, in restaurants, hotels, institutions, hospitals, and the like, whose variable needs are not easily accommodated by their own baking resources. In a survey of cur-

rent commercial practices in freezing bakery products, Rollag and Enochian (1964) point out the possible economies associated with large-scale
production of frozen unbaked products at a central plant, with the baking
shifted to the institutional operator or retail outlet, and also mention reports of higher sales resulting from the appealing aromas of sales-point baking. Of the 109 bakeries surveyed on this subject, the authors reported that,
at that time, only six per cent were freezing cakes at the batter stage, partly
because baked cakes freeze so well, and partly because frozen batters require a larger inventory of cake pans.

Distribution through retail outlets and supermarkets to consumers, for
bake-off in the home, would be a risky operation at best, because frozen
batters are so susceptible to damage from temperature fluctuations.

Experience with frozen batters at the Western Regional Research Laboratory suggests these guidelines:

(1) Use a well-balanced formula. (2) For shortened batters, use a high-
ratio sugar and shortening level. (3) Choose the proper leavening agent,
one designed specifically for use in frozen batters. Increase the normal
level of the baking powder by 0.2 to 0.25% above the level required for immediate bake-off. (4) Include an emulsifier. (5) Store batters in tightly covered containers of a material which prevents moisture and odor migration,
and has both low and high temperature tolerance. (6) Lose no time in
packaging and freezing batters. (7) Freeze batters as rapidly as possible to
−20°F. (−29°C.), or below. Store at temperatures below 0°F. (−18°C.).
Avoid temperature fluctuations. (8) Thaw shortened batters 20 to 30 min.
at room temperature before baking. Bake angel, sponge, and chiffon batters
directly from the frozen state. (9) Decrease normal baking temperature 20
to 25°F. (11° to 14°C.) and adjust the baking period as needed.

## Cake Formulas

The following commercial-type cake formulas were used for frozen batter
studies at the Western Laboratory. They are scaled to laboratory batch size
and may require some adjustment if scaled to production-batch size.

## Yellow Layer Cake

| Ingredients | Quantity Lb. | Oz. |
|---|---|---|
| Cake flour | 3 | 12 |
| Baker's sugar | 4 | 8 |
| Salt | | 2¼ |
| Baking powder | | 2¾ |
| (sodium-acid-pyrophosphate[1]) | | |

Sift together 3 times.

| | | |
|---|---|---|
| Shortening | 2 | 3½ |
| Emulsifier (sorbitan monostearate | | 1½ |
| with polyoxyethylene sorbitan | | |
| monostearate[1]) | | |

Combine with dry ingredients in mixer. Blend on low for 1 min. Add liquid milk.

| | | |
|---|---|---|
| Liquid milk | 2 | 3½ |

Blend on low for 5 min. Scrape.

| | | |
|---|---|---|
| Eggs | 2 | 3½ |
| Liquid milk | 2 | 1½ |
| Vanilla (combine with milk) | | 1½ |

Add eggs and liquid mixture alternately on low. Blend on low for 2 min. Scrape. Blend for 4 min. Scrape. Package; freeze; store.
Upon removal from freezer thaw at room temperature for 20 to 30 min. Bake at 345°F. (174°C.). Time required will depend on size of pan and depth of batter.

## Chocolate Cake

| Ingredients | Quantity Lb. | Oz. |
|---|---|---|
| Cake flour | 1 | 8 |
| Baker's sugar | 2 | 10 |
| Nonfat milk solids | | 6 |
| Cocoa | | 6 |
| Salt | | 1¼ |
| Baking powder | | 1½ |
| (sodium-acid-pyrophosphate) | | |

Sift together 3 times.

| | | |
|---|---|---|
| Shortening | 1 | 4 |
| Emulsifier (sorbitan monostearate | | ¾ |
| with polyoxyethylene sorbitan | | |
| monostearate) | | |

Combine with dry ingredients in mixer. Blend on low for 6 min. Scrape after 2 min. and at end.

| | | |
|---|---|---|
| Water | | 15 |

[1] A different type of baking powder or emulsifier may require adjustment in the level indicated here.

Add slowly on low; blend for 2 min.; scrape; blend for 2 min., scrape.

| | | |
|---|---|---|
| Water | 1 | |
| Eggs | 1 | 6½ |
| Vanilla | | ⅔ |

Combine and add one-half; blend on low for 2 min.; add second half and blend for 3 min. Scrape. Package; freeze; store. Upon removal from freezer thaw for 20 to 30 min. at room temperature. Bake at 340°F. (171°C.). Time required will depend on size of pan, depth of batter and temperature of batters.

### Chiffon Cake

| | Quantity | |
|---|---|---|
| **Ingredients** | **Lb.** | **Oz.** |
| Cake flour | 1 | 2 |
| Baking powder | | ¾ |
| Sugar | 1 | |
| Salt | | ½ |
| Sift together 3 times. | | |
| Egg whites[2] | 1 | 2¾ |
| Cream of tartar | | ⅛ |
| Sugar | | 8¾ |

Whip whites on medium speed to foamy stage. Add cream of tartar and whip to a soft peak. Gradually add sugar. Whip on high speed to stiff peak.

| | | |
|---|---|---|
| Oil[2] | | 9¼ |
| Egg yolks[2] | | 9¼ |
| Water[2] | | 14 |
| Vanilla | | ¼ |

Combine and add to flour mixture as soon as sugar is added to egg whites. Blend on low speed for 45 sec. Scrape. Blend on low for 30 sec. Add to beaten whites. Blend on low for 30 sec., then fold by hand until the two mixtures are blended. Package[3], and freeze immediately; store. Bake from frozen or partially thawed stage (no more than 10 to 15 min. at room temperature). Invert pans for cooling.

### Angel Cake

| | Quantity | |
|---|---|---|
| **Ingredients** | **Lb.** | **Oz.** |
| Cake flour | | 14¾ |
| Salt | | ½ |
| Powdered sugar | | 8½ |
| Baker's sugar | | 11¼ |
| Sift together 3 times. | | |
| Angel egg albumen | | 5¼ |
| Baker's sugar | 1 | 6 |
| Tart-o-cream | | ⅛ |

---

[2] Have eggs, oil, and water at room temperature, 68° to 70°F. (20° to 21°C.).

[3] This batter breaks down quickly after mixing. No time should lapse before packaging and freezing. As each pan is loaded tap on bench top 3 to 4 times to remove large bubbles.

Sift together. Add to water.

Water (50°F. or 10°C.)                                                                    1       9½

Whip on medium speed 1 min.; scrape; continue whipping 3 min., then increase to high speed and whip for ½ min.

Water (50°F. or 10°C.)                                                                            11

Gradually add to white mixture during ½ min. Reduce speed to medium and continue whipping for 2 min. Increase speed to high and continue whipping for 1 min. (variable) to soft peak stage. Sift in flour mixture in 3 parts. Whip on low speed for 10 sec. after each addition. Remove whip and fold by hand until blended. Package; tap each package on bench top several times to remove large air bubbles. Freeze at once; store. Bake from frozen state at 350°F. (177°C.). Baking time required will depend upon size of pan and depth of batter. Invert pans for cooling.

### FROZEN DOUGHS

The 3rd Edition of *The Freezing Preservation of Foods* (1957) states: "In 1955 two companies were marketing frozen roll dough, one in Illinois and the other in Massachusetts. It is likely that others would enter the business, were it not for the relatively short storage life of the product." A survey by Rollag and Enochian in 1964 boosts this figure to 29 companies marketing frozen dough for bread and roll bake-off either at the point-of-sale in supermarkets, retail bakeries, and various types of institutional food service establishments, or in the kitchens of consumers. The competition of frozen bread dough with prebaked frozen breads in retail cabinets seems to have started in Vancouver, British Columbia, Canada, in 1963 and spread southward to Los Angeles, Calif., gaining momentum along the way. The trend then spread eastward to Denver, Colorado (Anon. 1963A). This increase in on-premise baking in supermarkets has been due to a number of factors, including (1) consumer demand for one-stop shopping, (2) the effect of aroma and eye-appeal in increasing purchases of bakery items and increasing total store sales, (3) competition among supermarkets, (4) effectiveness of in-store baking in reducing distribution costs and problems, and (5) more purchases of bakery products because of growth in consumer incomes (Anon. 1967G). Several bakery trade journals in the early part of 1967 announced current new ventures by large chain supermarkets into hot on-premise frozen bake-off operations within their supermarkets in the Chicago and Minneapolis areas. Bread and all other dough items were to be frozen raw at their central processing plants, then trucked to the bake-offs in other locations. One of these organizations predicted that with an in-store bake-off, where baking is done as required by sales, throw away or loss could be held to an absolute minimum, possibly one per cent or less. This point-of-sale bake-off concept has received increasing consideration during the past decade because it offers the supermarket operator a higher operating profit than is possible with a complete process in-store bakery (Gelber 1966). Savings are possible largely because of (1) the economies in purchasing ingredients in large quantities, (2) lower labor costs in the modified bakery than in the complete on-premise bakery because of the employment of less skilled personnel, and (3) lower capital investment in each individual on-premise bakery (Anon. 1967G).

## The Problem[4]

The literature on frozen unbaked bread dough is neither comprehensive nor conclusive, but contains certain threads of consistency as follows:

(1) If prepared by the straight dough procedure, only very short fermentation periods are possible without encountering serious loss of yeast viability and gassing power during frozen storage (Anon. 1963C; Merritt 1960; Godkin and Cathcart 1949; McPherson and Lamb 1948; Meyer *et al.* 1956) and,

(2) Doughs made by the conventional sponge and dough process are particularly unstable in the frozen state (Anon. 1964; Lorenz 1965) and, accordingly, have not been used for this purpose.

A further problem encountered in studies at the Western Laboratory (Kline and Sugihara 1967) is that weak or slack dough and poor gas retention during proofing may also accompany the dying of yeast cells during frozen storage. This weakness-of-dough defect may be a consequence of the release of reducing substances from the dead yeast cells (Peppler 1960; Reed 1966) and, experimentally, may be counteracted by the addition of substantial levels of bromate or other oxidizing agents (Anon. 1965; Kline and Sugihara 1967). Addition of bromate, however, has no beneficial effect on yeast stability *per se* during frozen storage (Kline and Sugihara 1967).

It seems clear, both from the literature and results obtained to date at the Western Laboratory that the principal problem with frozen unbaked bread doughs is the retention of sufficient yeast viability and gassing power during frozen storage to avoid excessive or even impossible proofing times after thawing the frozen product. Minor variations in quality of the thawed product can be achieved by manipulation of sugar content, shortening, type of yeast, use of milk or milk solids, or oxidizing agents, and by re-working the dough after thawing; but these are of little consequence if the yeast activity is not maintained, and the thawed dough will not rise.

### Factors Affecting Stability of Yeast

Factors affecting the yeast stability in frozen unbaked bread doughs pre-

[4] Dr. Leo Kline, Western Utilization Research and Development Division, Agricultural Research Service, U.S. Dept. of Agr., Albany, Calif., has contributed this discussion of "The Problem," part of which is based on his own research, as yet unpublished.

Table 48

Instability of Frozen Bread Doughs Prepared by Conventional Procedures

| A. Straight Dough (3% Yeast) | | | | |
|---|---|---|---|---|
| Fermentation Time, Hr. | Yeast Count/Gm. Dough × 10⁶ | | Pan Proof Time Hr.:Min. | |
| | Fresh | 15 Wk. at 0°F. (—18°C.) | Fresh | 15 Wk. at 0°F. (—18°C.) |
| None | 250 | 192 | 1:27 | 2:10 |
| 1 | 250 | 45 | 0:52 | >5:00 |
| 2 | 220 | 10 | 0:44 | >5:00 |

| B. Sponge and Dough (2% Yeast) | | | | |
|---|---|---|---|---|
| Sponge Time Hr. | Yeast Count/Gm. Dough × 10⁶ | | Pan Proof Time Hr.:Min. | |
| | Fresh | 15 Wk. at 0°F. (—18°C.) | Fresh | 15 Wk. at 0°F. (—18°C.) |
| 4 | 180 | 3 | 0:55 | >5:00 |

pared both by the straight dough and the sponge and dough methods have been recently examined at the Western Laboratory (Kline and Sugihara 1967). Results shown in Table 48 verify those reports in the literature that yeast stability and proofing power in a frozen straight dough decrease sharply with substantial fermentation times prior to molding and freezing. Thus a fermentation time of one hour or longer may cause an 80 to 95% loss during extended storage in the number of viable yeast cells, and a proofing time on thawing in excess of five hours or, on occasion, an actual loss of ability to rise significantly. No indication of this loss of stability is, however, suggested by the yeast counts in the fresh dough, which remain virtually constant with increasing fermentation time. However, these counts were determined by the usual plate count procedure and, as pointed out by Thorn and Ross (1960), such counts do not reflect incipient growth or budding, in which state the yeast cells are unstable in frozen storage.

As also noted in Table 48, the yeast cells in a dough prepared by a conventional sponge and dough procedure with a 4-hr. sponge time are extremely unstable in frozen storage.

One method of achieving some stability of yeast in frozen bread dough is illustrated by the data in Table 49 for straight doughs, where the use of a higher yeast level, roughly double that conventionally used, is combined with a minimum possible fermentation time (Kline and Sugihara 1967). In this case a minimum time of about 15 min. at about 80° to 82°F. (27°–28°C.) was necessary to make the dough workable. Longer times at lower temperatures are also possible and, for practical purposes, have the advantage of introducing the dough into the freezing step at a lower temperature. As shown in Table 49, use of a six per cent yeast level and a 15-min. fermentation time resulted in a very substantial yeast count of $335 \times 10^6$ per gm.

Table 49

Effects of Increased Yeast Level (6%) and Shortened Fermentation Times on Stability
of Frozen Straight Dough

| Fermentation Time | Yeast Count/Gm. Dough × 10⁶ | | Pan Proof Time Hr.:Min. | |
|---|---|---|---|---|
| | Fresh | 15 Wk. at 0°F. (—18°C.) | Fresh | 15 Wk. at 0°F. (—18°C.) |
| None | 520 | 460 | 0:57 | 1:28 |
| 15 min. | 580 | 335 | 0:39 | 1:26 |
| 30 min. | 510 | 192 | 0:34 | 1:57 |
| 1 hr. | 510 | 60 | 0:30 | 3:08 |
| 2 hr. | 550 | 45 | 0:28 | >5:00 |

dough after 15 weeks of storage at 0°F. ( − 18°C.), and a respectable proof time of approximately 1½ hr. In the view of workers at the Western Laboratory (Kline and Sugihara 1967), the above stability appears to be achieved, however, at the expense of oven aroma and bread flavor and, to a certain extent, loaf volume.

Stability in the frozen state is not as readily achieved using the sponge and dough method. Nevertheless, possibilities were explored because it was felt that this method offered more probability for combining extensive sponge fermentation and, accordingly, flavor and aroma in the end product, with yeast stability. In the conventional sponge and dough all the yeast is, of course, added at the first mixing or sponge stage. Spiking with additional yeast at the second mixing or dough stage and shortening the dough handling period as much as possible (30 min. or less) was explored as a possibility of introducing "dormant" yeast cells and achieving stability. However, as shown in data from the Western Laboratory (Kline and Sugihara 1967) in Table 50 (second frozen sample) this device was no better than the standard procedure with yeast introduced only at the sponge stage (first frozen sample). It was subsequently found that several modifications of procedure could be introduced to achieve increasing stability of the yeast added at the second stage. These included (Table 50) shortening the sponge time, buffering the sponge with nonfat milk solids, chilling the sponge (and dough) at the second mixing stage, and further increasing the yeast level added at the dough stage. Under these conditions good retention of yeast count (266 × 10⁶ per gm. dough) and proof time (approximately 1 ½ hr.) were again obtained after 15 weeks at 0°F. ( − 18°C.).

At the present time it is probable that most frozen unbaked bread dough being offered commercially is being made by the first procedure demonstrated, i.e., straight dough with increased initial yeast level and a very short fermentation period. Such a procedure offers economies in procedure which are reflected in the low final price. Whether or not the modified sponge and dough procedure will become attractive commercially will, of course, hinge on the improvement in flavor and oven aroma it may offer.

Table 50

Sponge and Dough Effects of Various Factors on Frozen Storage Stability

| Yeast Level, % | | Sponge Time, Hr. | Dough Temp. | | Added NFMS[1] | Yeast Count per Gm. Dough × 10⁶ | Pan Proof Time Hr.:Min. |
| Sponge | Dough | | °F. | °C. | | | |
| --- | --- | --- | --- | --- | --- | --- | --- |
| A. Fresh |  |  |  |  |  |  |  |
| 2 | 0 | 4 | 84 | 29 | — | 180 | 0:57 |
| B. Frozen 15 wk. |  |  |  |  |  |  |  |
| 2 | 0 | 4 | 84 | 29 | — | 3 | >5:00 |
| at 0° F. (—18° C.) 2 | 2 | 4 | 84 | 29 | — | 2 | >5:00 |
| 2 | 2 | 1 | 84 | 29 | — | 71 | 4:30 |
| 2 | 2 | 1 | 64 | 18 | — | 128 | 2:47 |
| 2 | 3 | 1 | 64 | 18 | + | 266 | 1:27 |

[1] Nonfat milk solids.

This is currently (July 1967) being evaluated at the Western Laboratory (Western Utilization Research and Development Division).

It should be mentioned that the above limitations of frozen unbaked bread doughs are primarily applicable to the retail product subjected to a necessary shelf-life of over two months. Frozen products intended for institutional baking and which are going to be held in frozen storage for less than three weeks may be fermented for longer periods (up to an hour) prior to freezing.

## Ingredients

Yeast.—Merritt (1960) defines stability in a frozen dough as its ability to ferment, rise, and expand after thawing and baking. This ability is directly proportional to the viability of the yeast. Different brands of commercially prepared yeast as well as different lots of the same brand may vary in their ability to withstand sub-freezing storage. Also the rate at which yeast is frozen apparently affects its longevity (Godkin and Cathcart 1949). These workers demonstrated that yeast spores are considerably more cold-resistant than vegetative yeast cells—in other words, that the yeast cells in unfermented frozen doughs were more resistant to low-temperature storage than those in fermented frozen doughs; they observed that yeast cells died off at a faster rate in the fermented doughs during the test period than those in the unfermented doughs. These authors, however, concluded that although yeast cells appeared to lose their reproductive ability as low temperature storage progressed, some still retained fermentative activity, inasmuch as good bake tests resulted in some samples which showed poor yeast counts (Fig. 59).

Both compressed and dry yeasts are satisfactory for use in doughs to be frozen. The recommended range for compressed yeast is 6 to 10% of the flour weight, and for active dry yeast 3 to 5%. These ranges are higher than those used in doughs intended for immediate processing and bake-off. The

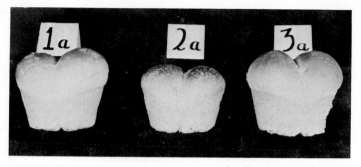

From Meyer, Buckley, and Moore (1952)

Fig. 59.  Yeast rolls after one month of freezer storage. (1a) Baked before freezing; (2a) Frozen in dough state, shaped before freezing; and (3a) Frozen in dough state, shaped after freezing.

quantity in each range depends on the speed of proofing desired. Since active dry yeast requires a slightly longer induction period than compressed yeast, Merritt (1960) suggests that it may offer some advantage and that this short period of inactivity may be effective in increasing the stability of an unfermented frozen dough. Experiments by another researcher (Zaehringer *et al.* 1951) confirm this observation. On the other hand, several researchers prefer the compressed form of yeast for frozen doughs because of the absence of significant quantities of dead yeast cells which weaken the dough (Anon. 1963C; Kline and Sugihara 1967).

Flour.—A high-quality medium-strong, either winter or spring wheat, patent flour is recommended for frozen doughs. Some laboratories suggest a bromated-type flour, while others suggest unbromated types. A high-protein quality is important; the level is not critical.

Yeast Food.—With either bromated or unbromated flour the normal level of bromate-type yeast food required in conventional baking, about $\frac{1}{2}$% of the flour weight, is satisfactory.

Salt.—Since salt retards yeast activity as well as serving as a flavor enhancer, the suggested level is 1.5 to 2.0%.

Sugar.—Sugar levels at 5 to 10% of the flour weight are recommended; for bread the usual range is 5 to 7%. The higher levels increase proofing time. Sucrose and dextrose perform equally well.

Shortening.—Good quality lard or shortening at a 5% level is recommended for fine grain quality and tender texture. An emulsifier of the mono-diglyceride type at about 3% of the shortening level benefits volume and crumb quality.

Milk.—Nonfat dry milk at levels of 2 to 4% enhances the crust color but has little effect on the internal characteristics of the crumb. Merritt (1960) suggests substituting dried sweet dairy whey for the nonfat dry milk because its high lactose content contributes to crust color, but it is not utilized by the yeast.

**Absorption.**—This seems to run in the 52 to 64% range, depending on the flour proteins. The 60% level is a good starting point. The goal is a dough slightly stiffer than the conventional, in order to facilitate handling and machining.

## Mixing

The straight dough procedure seems to be the one in general use in making frozen bread dough. Rollag and Enochian (Anon. 1967G) reported that of the 26 producers they interviewed, 23 were using this method, and two were using the sponge and dough procedure, while one gave no answer. The majority of researchers report satisfactory results with straight dough procedures. From the producer's standpoint straight dough equipment involves a smaller investment than does continuous mix equipment. The American Baking Institute (Anon. 1964) reported that in their study frozen doughs with the best storage life were made by the continuous mix method. However, the required proof times as presented in their report are not realistic for the average point-of-sale baker or for the home baker.

Several steps in the mixing procedure should be emphasized:

(1) Use a high-speed dough mixer with a refrigerating jacket to keep the dough temperature at about 65° to 70°F. (18°–21°C.). This inhibits fermentation, produces a plastic dough that handles easily, and induces faster freezing.

(2) Mix the dough to full development. Undermixed doughs result in a sticky product with ingredients unevenly dispersed and gluten inadequately developed. The result is poor volume and quality, coarse grain in the baked product. Overmixed doughs are difficult to handle; they are sticky and runny in character; they yield a baked product with essentially the same faults as the undermixed doughs. Several factors influence the optimum time of mixing: flour strength, dough temperature, ingredients, and speed of mixing. Mixing to the "clean-up stage" is a good rule-of-thumb. At this point, the dough pulls away from the mixer wall, forms a continuous mass and becomes elastic, smooth, and stiff. Weaker flours generally require dumping at this stage while stronger flours may require mixing a little beyond this point.

(3) For doughs which are to be frozen with no previous fermentation, allow just enough floor time to recover from mixing before machining, about 15 min.

(4) Divide and round, using conventional equipment; give minimum overhead proof; mold.

Fermentation

There seem to be two schools of conviction on the advisability of fermenting a dough before freezing. Several researchers (Godkin and Cathcart 1949; Merritt 1960; Zaehringer et al. 1951; Meyer et al. 1956; McPherson and Lamb 1948; Kline and Sugihara 1967) demonstrated experimentally that frozen unfermented doughs when properly formulated, mixed, frozen, and stored, performed very satisfactorily with respect to proof time and specific volume after storage periods ranging from 12 weeks to one year. Merritt (1960) demonstrated that doughs using his formulation, Table 51,

Table 51

Merritt's Experimental Dough Formula

| Formula | Parts by Weight | Procedure |
|---|---|---|
| Flour | 100 | Combine all ingredients in |
| Water | 65 | a high-speed dough mixer |
| Dry yeast | 4 | with a refrigerating jacket. |
| Yeast food, bromate type | 0.5 | Mix to full development. |
| Salt | 1.75 | Dough temperature should be |
| Dextrose sugar | 7 | 65° to 70°F. (18° to |
| Shortening | 9 | 21°C.). |
| Dairy sweet whey | 5 | |

Source: Merritt (1960).

properly mixed, with no fermentation other than 10 to 15 min. during make-up, frozen at −25°F. (−32°C.) and stored below +10°F. (−12°C.) until used, had a shelf-life or stability period of about one year. Slabs of dough, 16 to 20 oz., have good performance after 16 months of storage under these same conditions.

Merritt fermented portions of the above-mentioned doughs 30 to 45 min. before processing. The processing, with the exception of the fermentation period prior to freezing in this case, was identical with that given the unfermented dough. All frozen samples, when removed from the freezer, were proofed at 95°F. (35°C.) with 80% R.H. They were baked at 425°F. (218°C.) for 17 min. Specific volume was calculated (volume in cc. divided by weight in gm.). A specific volume for good rolls is 4.5. When it drops to 4.0 or less, the roll is compact and heavy, the eating characteristics are unpleasant. The fermented rolls had a normal proof time and specific volume through eight weeks of storage. After that the required proofing time increased and the quality rapidly deteriorated. After 21 days of storage the baked rolls were unacceptable. The proofing period was over three hours, the specific volume low, the crumb dark, and the cell structure broken down. By contrast, the rolls baked from the dough frozen without previous fermentation not only developed a fermentation flavor during the proofing period, but continued to perform satisfactorily with respect to proof time and specific volume. Flavor, grain, and volume remained at a high-quality level during the extended storage period. Table 52 demonstrates the required proofing period and specific volume of the unfermented doughs through nine months of storage. Merritt warns that fermentation of the

#### Table 52

#### Effect of Storage on Performance

(Unfermented Dough)

| Storage at —25°F. (—32°C.), months | 1 | 6 | 9 |
|---|---|---|---|
| Proof time at 95°F. (35°C.) and 80% R.H., min. | 70 | 80 | 85 |
| Specific volume, volume/weight | 4.6 | 4.3 | 4.2 |

Source: Merritt (1960).

dough before freezing has more effect on stability and required proofing time than any other single factor. He demonstrated that the stability of a frozen dough is inversely related to the amount of fermentation before freezing. With more than one hour fermentation, the stability during frozen storage was reduced to a few weeks. With a half-hour, the stability might be satisfactory for 3 to 4 months. When no fermentation was given, the dough was stable up to 12 months, provided proper formulation, mixing, freezing, packaging, and storage practices were carefully observed. Merritt's findings confirm those of Godkin and Cathcart (1949) and Fenton et al. (1947), who demonstrated that unfermented doughs were more stable than fermented doughs at sub-freezing storage temperature; Kline also confirmed this in 1967.

In contrast to the conclusions and recommendations reached by the above-mentioned researchers, the American Institute of Baking, the Pillsbury Laboratories, and several others recommend a full or, at the least, a partial period of fermentation before make-up and freezing of doughs (Anon. 1964; Pillsbury Co. 1966B). In order to resolve seeming contradictions, one must take into account the quality desired in the baked product, the intended storage period, ultimate handling, and the probable temperature abuses the dough may undergo before bake-off. There is no argument that during the fermentation process certain physical and chemical changes occur in the dough which result in dough maturity and mellowness. Flavor precursors are developed which are emitted as enticing aromas during the bake-off, and account for the delightful, though transient, flavor in the freshly baked rolls and bread. The key problems are the limitation of storage stability of fermented doughs and the unreasonable proofing periods required after several weeks of frozen storage. Those who recommend the fermentation step also advise a limit of 10 to 12 weeks of storage. The American Institute of Baking summarized the effect of storage periods on proof-times of their frozen dough experiments (Anon. 1964). They more or less speak for themselves. After one week of storage both the straight and the continuous mix doughs with proof temperature: 80° to 85°F. (27° –29°C.) and R.H.: 75%, required proof time of 3 hr., 15 min. after 11 weeks, 4 hr., 15 min. for straight doughs and 7 hr., 30 min. for continuous mix doughs were required. Pillsbury Co. (1966B) states that frozen fermented bread dough when stored at 0°F. ( − 18°C.) will maintain its quality in storage for 10 to 12 weeks. Beyond that, noticeable losses in volume occur. They make no mention of the proof periods required. The choice of method must be resolved by the ultimate disposition of the frozen dough. Where bake-off at a point-of-sale outlet in supermarket, retail bakery, or food service institution is the goal after short storage of a week or two, and all handling is done by personnel trained in the temperature limitations of the product, there is no problem. If the retail frozen food cabinet is the ultimate channel of distribution, the producer can anticipate some temperature abuse during transportation and handling, and no control whatsoever over the duration or temperature of storage once the product reaches the hands of the customer.

The problems involving flavor, texture, stability, and proof-time requirements in bread doughs earmarked for distribution to the homemaker via the frozen food cabinets in retail markets may be resolving itself by the increasing popularity of "brown 'n serve" breads. The dough preparation follows the guidelines for normal bread dough procedure. The sponge is given a full 4½ hr. fermentation at 76° to 77°F. (24°–25°C.). The slightly stiff dough is fully developed during the remix with the dough temperature at 78°F. (25°C.). After floor time of 15 to 20 min. the dough is machined through standard make-up equipment and panned in perforated foil trays. Normal handling at the molder, panner, oven, depanner, and cooler is achieved by placing the foil tray in metal bread trays slightly larger than the foil tray. The loaves are given a normal bake for 10 min. at 450°F. (232°C.). Oven temperature is then reduced to 250° to 300°F. (121°–149°C.) and baking continued until loaves are completely baked, but not browned. Some bakers prefer a steady temperature of 250°F. (121°C.) throughout the bake-off. The cooled bread is packed in polyethylene bags, 2 per bag for 13-oz. loaves, 1 per bag for the 18-oz. loaf. The homemaker has only to remove the polyethylene bag, bring the loaf to room temperature in its foil tray and bake in a preheated 400°F. (204°C.) oven until browned (about 14 min.). This product offers fully developed flavor in the baked loaf as well as stability during frozen storage. The plus bonus is the minimum preparation required of the homemaker.

The Foremost Foods Co. markets a whey-cysteine-bromate product (Reddi-Sponge) which brings about development and maturity in a dough independent of yeast fermentation mechanisms. That organization has kindly furnished the following information and formula, Table 53, to the author for reprint in this chapter.

Table 53

Use of "Reddi-Sponge"

| | Formula | |
|---|---|---|
| Ingredients | Parts by Weight | Procedure |
| Flour | 100.0 | (1) Mix all ingredients on low speed and |
| Water | 62.0 | then high speed to full development. |
| Yeast | 4.0 | If longer than 12 min. hold yeast |
| Yeast food | 0.5 | and add during last 4–5 min. of |
| Sugar | 8.0 | mixing. |
| Salt | 2.0 | (2) Adjust water and jacket temperature |
| Shortening | 3.0 | to give final dough temperature of |
| Emulsifier (mono- | | 70°–75°F. (21°–24°C.). |
| diglyceride | 0.4 | (3) Relax 10 min. |
| Reddi, sponge | 3.0 | (4) Divide, round, give minimum overhead |
| Total oxidant | — | proof, and mold. |
| 70–80 p.p.m. | | (5) Freeze in blast freezer at —10°F. |
| | | (—24°C.) or lower. |

**Whey / Cysteine / Bromate in Frozen Dough**[5]—It is evident from the literature that a critical factor in frozen doughs is short storage stability of the yeast cell. Proof times of the dough increase rapidly after 6 weeks and become too long after 12 weeks to make bread which satisfies the housewife.

In our studies, the proof time varied directly with the amount of activation of the yeast cell prior to freezing. Activation by fermenting in a brew or sponge step before mixing the dough or by a straight step after mixing, gave poor shelf-life; and the longer the fermentation, the poorer the shelf-life. Since these fermentation steps are used to provide other essential dough and bread properties, their elimination made it difficult to prepare acceptable bread.

The use of a whey / cysteine / bromate product (Reddi-Sponge) to provide the optimum mixing, machining, and maturing properties by means of direct biochemical action on the flour protein molecules not only doubled shelf-life through elimination of fermentation steps, but also allowed reduction of dough outlet temperature to 65° to 70°F. (18°–21°C.).

[5] Contributed by R. G. Henika, Foremost Foods Co., Research and Development Center, Dublin, Calif.

The best procedure was to mix all ingredients in minimum time at 70°F. (21°C.), allow the dough to relax five minutes, and then divide, round, overhead, mold, and freeze as rapidly as possible.

Commercial use of this product and process has proved that frozen doughs can be made and merchandised successfully when teamed with proper distribution and marketing techniques.

### Freezing

Freezing involves a phase change from liquid or semi-liquid to the solid state. Low temperatures and rapid freezing minimize crystal size. Small crystals are less damaging to cell structure than large crystals. They thaw more rapidly. Fast freezing at low temperature is recommended. A blast freezer is economical and freezes rapidly. Doughs should be covered during the freezing period with polyethylene film or bag to prevent surface moisture loss and crusting. The liquid nitrogen flash or jet systems require the least floor space and offer the fastest rate of freeze of any system in present use. Gelber (1966) describes such a system in use at a large frozen dough plant:

"The finished dough is cut, shaped, and packed in foil containers. These are placed on in-feed conveyer to freezing tunnel. The product is cooled by nitrogen gas in the precooler section of tunnel, then passes under a spray of liquid nitrogen for final freezing at −320°F. (−195°C.). The total tunnel exposure involves six minutes."

Whatever the system, variable speed adjustments are advisable for automatic conveyor systems through the freezing tunnel in order to accommodate differences in unit size of products.

Godkin and Cathcart (1949) state:

"The freezing rate of the doughs was shown to influence the preservation of the biological activity of the yeast incorporated therein. It is possible that when yeast dough is frozen at a slow rate, the yeast cells are subjected to a prolonged critical temperature at the freezing point of the dough, and although the cells are not destroyed during this time they are weakened and gradually destroyed during subfreezing storage."

### Packaging

Doughs may be packaged before or after freezing, depending upon the size of product, type of container, system and rate of freezing available. Packaging after freezing should be accomplished quickly and under conditions which will prevent surface thawing. Thin slabs of dough, one inch, or less in thickness, freeze and thaw more quickly. They should be packaged individually in plastic or other material which will prevent sticking when thawed. Two essential properties of the package are moistureproofness and migrant-odor barrier.

## Storage Temperature

A storage temperature of 0°F. (−18°C.) after quick-freezing will keep dough frozen and the yeast essentially inert biologically. Many producers are using −10°F. (−23°C.) as insurance against mishandling and temperature fluctuations which may be encountered during transportation and distribution. Temperature fluctuations during storage or distribution can seriously impair the quality of the dough and result in an unacceptable baked product.

## Thawing and Proofing

Thawing is a long and often frustrating step. Many suggestions are offered; probably the simplest and safest for the consumer is to thaw frozen dough overnight in a refrigerator. Other consumer directions should include:

Place frozen or thawed dough loaf in a well greased bread pan of the proper size to accommodate the loaf. Pan size is important and should be specified on the package.

Brush top lightly with melted shortening or butter.

Cover pan with dampened cloth to prevent surface drying and crusting.

Place in warm place, out of drafts, to rise, preferably at a temperature of 80° to 85°F. (27°–29°C.).

Let rise until dough is about one inch above pan. (At this step proper pan size is important.) Approximate rise time should be given as guidance for the novice baker.

The in-store bake-off facility has several choices for thawing frozen doughs. Many use just room temperature, others use retard boxes. Avoid loading the retard box with both large and small units at any one time . . . the load should be uniform in unit size. The most efficient means at this time for large-scale thawing of frozen doughs is microwave energy, which does the job in minutes.

When a proof box is loaded with thawed dough at low temperature, the temperature of the box is lowered and proofing delayed. A box with thermostatically controlled temperature of 85°F. (29°C.) and relative humidity at about 70% will minimize proof time. One enterprising baker (Anon. 1967H) solicited the cooperation of a freezer manufacturer to engineer from a basic freezer a unit that could be operated as either a sub-zero freezer, a retarder, or a proof box by merely switching a dial . . . or be set to cycle automatically from freezer to retarder to proofer over given periods.

This device has made possible a shorter work day. The idea offers many time-saving and convenience possibilities for in-store bake-off of frozen dough products.

Procedures for bake-off and cooling thawed dough products are normal.

## Conclusion

After considering the pros and cons of the various recommendations offered by several laboratories for the formulation, preparation, storage, and handling of frozen doughs, the author is inclined toward the conclusions offered by Merritt (1960), "The most important factor for successful marketing of frozen dough is stability." A stable frozen dough retains its ability to ferment, rise, and expand after thawing and baking. Research at the Western Regional Laboratory of the U.S. Dept. of Agr. (Kline 1967) confirms Merritt's findings that fermentation prior to freezing diminishes yeast stability in a frozen dough. Guidelines for personnel responsible for dough handling from mixer to freezer might well stress the importance of conditions which keep yeast in a dormant state and discourage any activity and budding. The channels from freezer, down through packing, storage, transportation, and distribution should be streamlined to provide maximum protection from temperature fluctuations. Retail market managers and personnel, in particular, require thorough indoctrination in the perishability of frozen doughs and in the quality control measures imperative during handling and storage. Especially do they require information on storage period and temperature tolerance. Dating frozen dough products to guard against quality losses resulting from prolonged storage is highly recommended. The consumer is entitled to complete package information describing the temperature and storage requirements of the product as well as detailed directions for proofing and baking the product.

Persistent research may eventually develop a strain of yeast with high tolerance to prolonged low-temperature storage in dough products. Any innovation which results in quality improvement and a decrease in proof-time requirements will encourage market expansion and acceptance of frozen doughs.

### BIBLIOGRAPHY

## Batters

Anon.   1955. Bakers sift new techniques. Food Eng. 27, No. 4, 113, 117, 159, 160.
Fenton, F., and Darfler, J.   1946. Foods from the freezer precooked or prepared. Cornell Extens. Bull. 692.
Glabau, C. A.   1956. Behavior of unbaked frozen cake batters in aluminum foil pans. Part 14, Bakers Weekly 169, No. 7, 38–40.

Graul, L. S., and Lowe, B. 1947. How storage affects frozen cakes and batters. Food Inds. *19*, 330–332.

Joslin, R. P., and Ziemke, J. O. 1955. New leavener triggered by heat. Food Eng. *27*, No. 9, 59–61, 184.

Mackey, A. O. 1955. Microscopic structure of frozen batter. Food Technol. *9*, 261–263.

Mackey, A. O., Jones, P., and Dunn, J. 1952. The effect of ingredient variations on the quality of white and chocolate cake batters baked prior to freezing or baked from frozen batters. Food Research *17*, 216–224.

Meyer, M., Buckley, R., and Moore, R. Research shows differences in frozen butter cakes and sponge cakes. Refrig. Eng. *57*, 340–342, 338, 392.

Miller, C., and Beattie, I. E. 1949. On freezing and frozen storage of cake. J. Home Econ. *41*, 463–464.

Moore, R., Meyer, B., and Buckley, R. 1954. The effect of freezer storage temperature on cake quality and on carbon dioxide content of cake batters. Food Research *6*, 590–596.

Owen, R. F., and Van Duyne, F. O. 1950. Comparison of the quality of freshly baked cakes, thawed, frozen baked cakes, and cakes prepared from batters which had been frozen. Food Research *15*, 169–178.

Paul, P., Batcher, O. M., and Fulde, L. 1954. Dry mix and frozen baked products. J. Home Econ. *46*, 249–253.

Pickens, O. 1955. The freezing of cake batters. Baker's Dig. *29*, 181–185.

Pillsbury Co. 1966. Frozen bakery foods. Baking Ind. *126*, No. 1594, 45–47; No. 1597, 33–35.

Rollag, N. L., and Enochian, R. V. 1964. The freezing of commercial bakery products; current practices, problems, and prospects. U.S. Dept. Agr., Marketing Research Rept. *674*.

Sharka, D. M., and Van Duyne, F. O. 1955. Effect of freezing and freezer storage on cake quality. II. Variation in batter treatment before and after freezer storage. Food Research *20*, 282–288.

Sunderlin, G. L., Collins, O. D., and Acheson, M. 1940. Frozen batters and doughs. J. Home Econ. *32*, 381–382.

Zaehringer, M. A., and Mayfield, H. L. 1951. The effect of leavening and shortening combinations on the frozen storage of cakes and batters prepared at high altitudes. Food Technol. *5*, 151–154.

## Doughs

Anon. 1955. Bakers sift new techniques. Food Eng. *27*, No. 4, 113–160.

Anon. 1963A. Fast rising frozen bread dough industry challenges prebaked and "fresh" market. Quick Frozen Foods *26*, No. 2, 71–74.

Anon. 1963B. Freezing permits "staff-of-life" to make sentimental journey home. Quick Frozen Foods *26*, No. 3, 147–150.

Anon. 1963C. Frozen unbaked bread. Technical Service Dept., Tech. Serv. Bull. *306*, Fleischmann Div., Standard Brands Sales Co.

Anon. 1963D. Frozen dough with Reddi-Sponge. Foremost Foods Co. Ind. Div., Technical Service Letter *22*.

Anon. 1964. Frozen bread dough. American Inst. Baking Bull. *108*.

Anon. 1965. Frozen dough; variety bread; effect of bromate level on white bread. American Inst. Baking Bull. *112*.

Anon. 1967A. A.S.B.E. Report, Baking Ind. *127*, No. 1608, 78, 82, 84, 88, 90.

Anon. 1967B. Bakers convention. Baking Ind. *127*, No. 1608, 58–64.

Anon. 1967C. Breakthrough in continuous mix dough processing improves bread sales. Bakery Prod. & Market. *2*, No. 1, 22–28.

Anon. 1967D. Country maid bakery thrives right next door to a supermarket with fresh-frozen bakery dept. Bakery Prod. & Market. *2*, No. 4, 31–35.

Anon. 1967E. Horst Denk talks bread automation, fermentation, quality and costs. Bakery Prod. and Market *2*, No. 2, 20–24.

Anon. 1967F. How national food is planned for frozen bake-off. Bakers Review *133*, No. 1, 12–13.

Anon. 1967G. Potentials for frozen dough. Economic Research Service, U.S. Dept. Agr. Bull. *787*.

Anon. 1967H New freezer-retarder-proofer helps shorten Bon Ton Bakery's work day. Bakery Prod. and Market *2*, No. 2, 32–34.

Anon. 1967I. Whatever happened to frozen bread dough? Quick Frozen Foods *29*, No. 10, 87–92.

Baeuerlen, R. J. 1964. Latest developments in freezing. Bakers Weekly *201*, No. 11, 79–81.

Beattie, H. G., Edelmann, E. G., and Cathcart, W. H. 1949. Keeping quality of frozen bakery products. Food Technol. *3*, 160–162.

Charles, V. R., and Van Duyne, F. O. 1953. Effect of freezing and freezer storage upon the quality of baked rolls, brown-and-serve rolls, and shaped roll dough. Food Technol. *7*, 208–211.

Cotton, R. H. 1960. Recent trends in American baking technology. Bakers Dig. *34*, No. 6, 34–41.

Davis, R. E. 1965. Freezing; Performance and Problems. Baking Ind. *124*, No. 1575, 27–30, 40–42.

Dibble, W. E. 1967. Cases for batch process. Baking Ind. *127*, No. 1609, 29, 31, 44.

Doll, F. A. 1967. What's ahead for retail bakers? Bakers Review *133*, No. 5, 22–23.

Fenton, F. 1946. Unknown factors upset precooked foods quality control. Food Freezing *1*, 163–165, 188, 189.

Fenton, F. 1947. Frozen cooked foods. Refrig. Eng. *53*, No. 2, 107–111.

Gelber P. 1966. LIN freezing, shipping keep freshness in "to-be-baked" goods. Food Processing and Market *27*, No. 12, 32–34, 64.

Glabau, C. A. 1955. Behavior of unbaked frozen doughs when aluminum foil pans are used. Part 1 Bakers Weekly *168*, No. 6, 42–46; Part 2. *Ibid. 168*, No. 7, 54–56; part 3. *Ibid. 168*, No. 8, 44–46.

Godkin, W. J.,and Cathcart, W. H. 1949. Fermentation activity and survival of yeast in frozen fermented and unfermented doughs. Food Technol. *3*, 139–146.

Henika, R. G., Hoyer, W. H., and Walsh, H. S. 1966. Low dough temperature and short brews with whey-cysteine in continuous-mix bread and buns. Cereal Science Today *11*, 387–392, 427.

Henika, R. G., and Rodgers, N. E. 1965. Reactions of cysteine, bromate, and whey in a rapid breadmaking process. Cereal Chem. *42*, 397–408.

Kamman, P. 1967A. Cases for continuous process. Baking Ind. *127*, No. 1609, 29, 30, 40, 42.

Kamman, P. 1967B. The case for continuous process bread. Bakery Prod. and Market. *2*, No. 3, 26–30, 40, 44, 45.

Kilborn, R. H. 1967. Minor ingredients as a factor in bread properties. Bakers Dig. *41*, No. 2, 24–27, 30, 33.

Kline, L., and Sugihara, T. F. 1967. Western Regional Research Laboratory, U.S. Dept Agr., Agricultural Research Service, Albany, Calif., Private communications.

Koren, P. M. 1967. Shortening, continual research perfects baking ingredients. Baking Ind. 127, No. 1604, 33–36.

Lehault, B. 1967. Fundamentals of mechanized sweet goods production. Bakers Dig. 41, No. 2, 38–42, 86.

Lorenz, K., and Bechtel, W. H. 1964. Frozen bread dough. Bakers Dig. 38, No.6, 59–63.

Lorenz, K. 1965. Frozen dough, and bake-off. Baking Ind. 124, No. 1575, 30, 40.

McPherson C., and Lamb, M. W. 1948. Improved bread made from frozen dough. Food Inds. 20, 1289–1291, 1407, 1408.

Merritt, P. P. 1960. The effect of preparation on the stability and performance of frozen, unbaked, yeast-leavened doughs. Bakers Dig. 34, No. 4, 57–58.

Meyer, B., Moore, R., and Buckley, R. 1956. Gas production and yeast roll quality after freezer storage of fermented and unfermented doughs. Food Technol. 10, 165–168.

Ogren, K. E. 1964. The economics of a loaf of bread; from the farm to the consumer. Address before the Third National Wheat Utilization Research Conference. U.S. Dept. Agr., Economic Research Service.

Peppler, H. J. 1960. In Bakery Technology and Engineering, S. A. Matz (Editor). Avi Publishing Co., Westport, Conn.

Pillsbury Co. 1966A. Frozen baked foods, the view today. Special Circ., Minneapolis, Minn.

Pillsbury Co. 1966B. Quality maintenance of frozen baked goods. Baking Ind. 126, No. 1597, 33–35.

Pyler, E. J. 1952. Baking Science and Technology, Vols. 1 and 2, Siebel Publishing Co., Chicago, Ill.

Reed, G. 1966. Yeast, what it does and how. Am. Soc. Bakery Eng. Proc. 42nd Annual Meeting, Chicago, Ill., 126–130.

Schiller, G. D. 1967. Flour requirements for continuous breadmaking. Bakers Digest 41, No. 2, 44–46, 87.

Shukis, A. I. 1965. Frozen bread dough and brown and serve bread. Bakers Weekly 208, No. 11, 44–45.

Shukis, A. I. 1966. Formula adjustments for frozen bakery foods. Bakers Weekly 209, No. 8, 26, 27, 55, 56.

Stadt, R. 1965. History, research, and economics, freezing finished baked products, frozen dough and bake-off. Baking Ind. 124, No. 1575, 28–30, 40, 42.

Sunderlin, G. L., and Collins, O. P. 1941. And now quick frozen pies, cookies, cakes and biscuits. Quick Frozen Foods 3, No. 7, 13, 44.

Thorn, J. A., and Ross, J. W. 1960. Determination of yeast growth in doughs. Cereal Chem. 37, 415–421.

Wakershauser, K. W. 1967A. Questions flow fast at bakery engineer meeting in Chicago, Bakers Review 133, No. 4, 22–24.

Wakershauser, K. W. 1967B. Tomorrow's bakery today. Bakers Review 133, No. 5, 8–10.

Zaehringer, M. V., Mayfield, H. L., and Odland, L. M. 1951. The effect of certain variations in fat, yeast, and liquid on the frozen storage of yeast doughs. Food Research 16, 353–359.

## CHAPTER 18

J. W. Pence | **Bread and Rolls**

## INTRODUCTION

Freshly baked bread and rolls are very perishable and more sensitive to variations in freezing, storage, and defrosting practices than the richer bakery items more often frozen. The most attractive features of the freshly baked bread-type products decline rapidly from the time they are taken from the oven. Within a very few hours their attractiveness declines seriously. The only known method to arrest or significantly retard these undesirable changes is by freezing. Low unit value and large production volume are major factors that have deterred a wider use of freezing for breads in general and white bread in particular.

Bread and rolls have been preserved by freezing for a great many years in northern climates (Carlin 1965), but commercial practice in the United States has only become significant in the past decade or so. Work reported as early as 1925 (Berg and Morrison 1925; Glabau and Pirie 1925; Marx 1932; Katz 1934) established that the freezing of commercial bread could be conducted successfully. Until the mid-fifties the commercial freezing of bread and rolls was largely confined to the United States, but more recently the practice has gradually been extended to most Western European countries (Belderok and Wiebols 1964). Recent studies have evaluated economic factors concerned with bread freezing (Enochian 1960; Rasmussen and Prouty 1966A, B, C) and have surveyed the practices, problems, and prospects (Rollag and Enochian 1964).

## PRESENT STATUS IN INDUSTRY

Continually rising costs of production have caused the baking industry to examine carefully the possible benefits that can arise from use of freezing, particularly those that may reduce costs of production or distribution. In 1961, nearly 40% of all bakers froze at least part of their production, according to Rollag and Enochian (1964), and the practice has grown at the rate of 4 to 5% per year in recent years. A contributing factor also cited by these authors is that the growing expansion in sales of frozen bakery products, plus an apparent increase in the home-freezing of bakery goods, indicate a growing acceptance of frozen bakery products by consumers.

J. W. Pence is Chief, Cereals Laboratory, Western Utilization Research and Development Division, Agricultural Research Service, U.S. Dept. Agr., Albany, Calif.

The several potential advantages for the commercial freezing of bakery products were recently summarized (Rasmussen and Prouty 1966A, B, C) to include the following points listed here in brief form: (1) to take care of overs and unders in production and to adjust to unforeseen peaks and slumps in demand; (2) to more nearly equalize baking schedules throughout the week; (3) to increase hourly output by elimination of or reduction in setup and changeover time; (4) to expand product line by adding new items; (5) to build new and larger bakeries that can serve the increasingly extended distribution areas demanded by industry trends; (6) to improve product quality at point of sale; (7) to reduce handling of special ingredients; (8) to reduce chances for errors inherent in production of many small batches; (9) to improve inventory control; and (10) to reduce bookkeeping and accounting costs.

### Extent of Freezing by Wholesale Companies

From results of an industry-wide survey Rollag and Enochian (1964) report that 27% of the single unit wholesale bakeries made use of freezing, whereas only 12% of the larger multiunit wholesale bakeries did so. In contrast, 38% of the grocery chain bakeries used freezing. Within these categories, however, only 20% of those bakeries producing only bread and rolls made use of freezing. In contrast, 44% of those whose production of bread and rolls was more than half, but not all, of their total, used freezing. The group producing only bread and rolls consisted mostly of large-scale wholesale bakeries. The authors suggested that most bakeries of this type may not be able to make a significant reduction in their production costs by having a frozen inventory for later sale. Freezing, however, may serve to reduce losses when anticipated demand does not develop or they may find frozen distribution a means of expanding their sales area and reducing distribution costs. Bakeries in the 51 to 99% bread and roll class of production were mostly retail or small wholesale bakeries that produced a large number of products. How much of the freezing involved bread and rolls was not determined. Approximately half of all bakeries surveyed froze 10% or less of their production, and this would surely include most of those specializing in bread and rolls.

On the other hand a number of wholesale firms have featured the freezing of bread and rolls. The products are distributed widely in frozen form and are sold either as the frozen product or after defrosting. The practice has allowed these firms to reach much wider markets than they otherwise could.

As separate classes in the wholesale category, 39% of the bakeries specializing in home service and 35% of those catering to institutional segments of the market were reported to be using freezing (Rollag and Enochian 1964). The latter seem more likely to deliver products in the frozen state than the former.

### Extent of Freezing by Retail Bakeries

The survey by Rollag and Enochian (1964) indicated that use of freezing was most prevalent among multiunit retail bakeries, being used by 56%. Single unit retail bakeries had a comparable figure of 46%. The authors suggest that a possible reason for the greater use of freezing in the retail trade is that they produce a larger number of different items in relatively small quantities and have larger daily sales variation than other types of bakeries. Most of the bakers reported that they could benefit by making larger batches of each product for a frozen inventory, which could subsequently be defrosted as needed for sale. Although no figures were given for the extent to which bread and bread-type rolls were frozen, one may well suppose that rolls were frozen to greater extent than bread and that except for variety breads, only a small percentage of the weekly production of the latter was frozen.

### QUALITY FACTORS AFFECTED BY FREEZING

Because the objective of freezing bread is to preserve freshness beyond its normal duration, the effect of freezing, storage, and defrosting on the features that characterize fresh bread become of primary concern. As noted earlier bread declines steadily in quality from the time that it is baked. The soft, silky, resiliency that characterizes the crumb gives way to a gradually developing firmness and harshness. The crisp, relatively dry crust becomes more moist and tough, a condition often spoken of as leathery. Apart from these physical changes, the taste and aroma of the fresh loaf change markedly and fairly rapidly. The sum of these changes is correctly termed staling, although the term is frequently misused by reference to the physical changes only—possibly because the changes in firmness can be measured with a fairly good degree of objectivity, and because the consumer generally judges the freshness of wrapped bread at the time of purchase by squeezing it.

### Changes in Crumb Firmness

The fact that crumb firming is temperature dependent was reported many years ago (Katz 1928) and has since been amply confirmed by many workers. Katz (1928) reported that firming was most rapid at 27° to 29°F. ($-2.8°$ to $-1.7°$C.), and that the rate decreased as the temperature was raised or lowered. This is exemplified by Figure 60 showing the curve obtained by Pence and Standridge (1955). Below 18° to 20°F. ($-7.8°$ to $-$

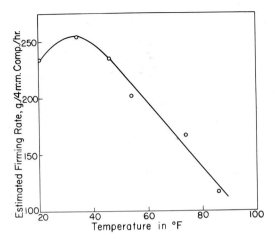

Courtesy of Western Utilization Research and Development Division, U.S.
Department of Agriculture

Fig. 60.    Effect of temperature on the firming rate
of commercial white bread.

6.7°C.) or other ostensible freezing point for bread, firming rate declines rapidly. At 0°F. (−18°C.) it was scarcely measurable after seven weeks of storage, although the superimposed effect of freezing and thawing on the total change disturbed the accuracy of the determination in one study (Pence *et al.* 1955C).

In conjunction with loss of softness and resiliency during staling, bread crumb becomes harsher, crumblier, and dry-seeming. These changes are not dependent on loss of moisture from the crumb (Bradley and Thompson 1950; Bechtel *et al.* 1953), although any moisture loss aggravates the condition. The changes, however, appear to be caused by retrogradation of starch as the crumb ages, leading to more rigid and brittle structures. The consequent increasing crystallinity was noted by workers following changes in X-ray diffraction patterns and solubility (Katz 1928, 1936). Schoch and French (1947) indicate that retrogradation of the linear segments of the branches on amylopectin molecules are more likely to be involved in the observed changes than the amylose molecules. The term normally is applied only to the latter. Senti and Dimler (1960) point out, also, that the continuity of the networks involved may be more important than the abundance or extent of crystalline regions. They further comment that transfer of moisture between components in the crumb has at most a minor effect.

The virtual arrest of firmness changes in bread held at 0°F. (−18°C.) or lower, presumably stems from immobilization of starch molecules in the frozen crumb, although only about 70% of the water in bread is in the form of ice at 0°F. (−18°C.) (Mannheim *et al.* 1957).

### Flavor Retention

Existing knowledge of the chemistry of bread flavor and its deterioration after baking is still fragmentary. Compounds contributing to taste and odor, however, emanate chiefly from fermentation and crust browning (the Maillard reaction), both leading to formation of volatile or quite reactive compounds. Maillard browning may also continue at sensible rates after the cessation of baking. Thus, flavor could change or diminish by way of loss of important compounds through volatilization or changes due to oxidation, condensation, or other chemical reactions. All changes, however, would be greatly slowed at the temperature of frozen bread.

For these reasons flavor retention in frozen bread and rolls should be excellent. Commercial and private experience has more than amply confirmed this expectation.

### Moisture Distribution

During the staling of bread, migration of moisture within the loaf is appreciable, particularly into the crumb and the outer half-inch or so of crumb from the central core of more-moist crumb (Bradley and Thompson 1950). Such migration can account for an important part of the staling changes that occur (Bechtel and Meisner 1954), although measurements of crumb firmness and compressibility do not reflect this as well as sensory evaluations (Bechtel et al. 1953).

Subsequent detailed study of the distribution of moisture within frozen bread and frozen-and-defrosted bread, however, showed them to retain essentially the moisture distribution pattern of the freshly baked bread that had not been frozen (Pence et al. 1956B). Moreover, a fluctuating storage temperature caused no important movement of moisture within frozen bread. Microwave defrosting caused no change in the moisture distribution of bread, despite the fact that the center core of the loaf increased in temperature faster than the crust region.

Significant losses of moisture during the freezing of bread and rolls is unlikely because the surface of the product is cooled very rapidly with a resultant decrease in the tendency of water to evaporate. For example, Pence et al. (1955A) found that freshly baked, unsliced 22.5-oz. loaves lost only 4 gm. of moisture in 5 hr. exposure to air at $-20°F.$ ($-28.9°C.$) and flowing at 1,200 linear f.p.m.

### IMPORTANCE OF FREEZING RATES

Because the rates at which breads become firm during staling are temperature-dependent, the rate at which the temperature of bread crumb is reduced to satisfactory low levels during freezing affects greatly the final apparent freshness of the defrosted product. Most breads and rolls exhibit a deflection in cooling curves between 14° and 22°F. ($-10°$ and $-5.6°$C.) which may be considered a freezing point or freezing zone. Firming rates are low enough in this temperature range that subsequent cooling to the more desirable storage temperatures of 0°F. ($-18°$C.) or lower can be conducted safely at slower, less costly rates (Cauble and Murdough 1956). Careful consideration therefore must be given to relationships among costs of freezing at different rates for different products, tolerable decrease in

Courtesy of Liquid Carbonic Division of General Dynamics Corporation

Fig. 61.   Over-all view of Cryotransfer liquid nitrogen freezing system.

Courtesy of Air Products and Chemicals, Inc.

Fig. 62.   The Cryo-quick liquid nitrogen freezing system.

quality, freezer capacity, power costs, and other related factors. This is particularly true for the newly developed freezers that use liquid nitrogen to achieve very rapid freezing rates (Shukis 1966; Newton 1966; Breyer *et al.* 1965; and McIntyre 1965).

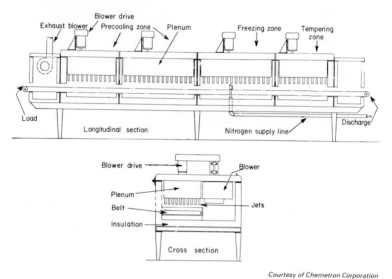

*Courtesy of Chemetron Corporation*

Fig. 63.  Diagram of the Ultra-freeze liquid nitrogen freezer system.

## White Bread

A rather comprehensive study by the U.S. Dept. of Agr. determined the effects of a wide variety of conditions on the rate at which commercial white bread will freeze in a blast freezer (Pence *et al.* 1955A).

**Wrapped Bread.**—Freezer temperature was the variable with greatest effect on freezing rate of wrapped bread. Whether or not the bread was sliced made little difference, nor was loaf weight of much consequence, presumably because all dimensions except length were the same for the loaves compared. Air velocity had a small but consistent effect on freezing rate, but there would appear to be little advantage to using more than moderate air velocities. The effect of air temperature is shown in Fig. 64 and that of air velocity in Fig. 65.

Composition of wrapping material was found to have no significant effects on freezing rates (Pence 1955), but the snugness with which the bread is wrapped is important. The air space between the loaf and the wrapper is apparently of greater insulating importance than wrapper composition or the porosity of the crumb. Breads wrapped in waxed paper, Cellophane, or

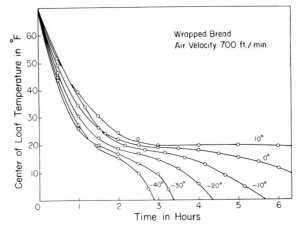

Courtesy of Western Utilization Research and Development Division, U.S. Department
of Agriculture

Fig. 64.  Effect of freezer temperature at an intermediate
air velocity on rate of freezing of wrapped white bread.

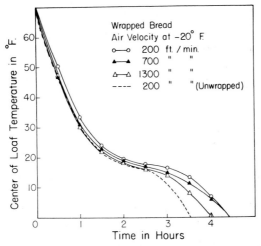

Courtesy of Western Utilization Research and Development Division, U.S.
Department of Agriculture

Fig. 65.  Effect of air velocity at low temperature
on rate of freezing of wrapped white bread.

aluminum foil all froze at closely similar rates, whereas loosely wrapped
loaves froze significantly slower than either normal or snugly wrapped
loaves (Pence 1955). As a further example of the insulating effect of dead
air spaces within packages, freezing rates were enormously slowed for

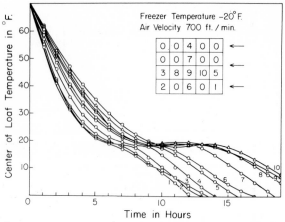

Fig. 66. Rate of freezing of wrapped white bread, packed in a pasteboard delivery carton, at low temperature and intermediate air velocity.

bread packed in delivery cartons (Pence *et al*. 1955A). The effect of position within the carton is illustrated in Fig. 66.

**Unwrapped Bread.**—Without the insulating effect of wrappers, the freezing rate of bread responds to differences in air velocity and to orientation of the loaf in the air stream, as well as to freezer temperature (Pence *et al*. 1955A). The potential advantage of the considerably faster freezing rates possible with unwrapped bread is offset by the awkwardness, if not the practical impossibility, of freezing unwrapped sliced bread. Slicing the bread after freezing may well be possible, but it would involve most certainly some significant modification of slicing machinery and perhaps would require operation of wrapping machines in a refrigerated room.

**Effects on Crumb Firmness.**—There seems little question that bread should be frozen as soon after baking as practically possible in order to retain the maximum of fresh quality. Direct demonstration of differences during the first few hours after baking is difficult, but results become quite discernible within 8 to 12 hr. after baking (Kirk 1963; Pence *et al*. 1955C). Rate of freezing is also very important, as shown by the following data (Pence *et al*. 1955C).

| Freezing Time Hr. | Average Increases in Firmness as Gm. / 4Mm.Compression |
|---|---|
| 0.5 | 16 |
| 1.5 | 32 |
| 3.0 | 57 |
| 7.0 | 71 |

Studies by Anderson (1954), by Pence and Standridge (1955), and by Kirk (1963) indicate clearly that freezing, if properly conducted, need not shorten the shelf-life of bread. A freezing time of about 90 min., attainable with freezing at −20°F. (−28.9°C.) and moderate air velocity, will adequately meet the requirements. The very rapid freezing rates attainable by use of liquid nitrogen may therefore not be applicable to any significant extent with such a large-volume, relatively low-cost product as ordinary white bread.

## Variety Breads

Most of the factors involved in the freezing of white bread will apply quite similarly to the freezing of variety breads. The latter, however, tend to be denser and produced in smaller, less economical batches. Both of these factors encourage the freezing of variety breads. Because raisin bread, whole wheat bread, oatmeal bread, and similar compact loaves are smaller per unit weight than ordinary white bread, they occupy less space in holding freezers and can be handled more economically. Also, because they generally are produced at less than a daily frequency and in small batches, there is greater economic incentive to maintain a frozen inventory from which to meet daily sales needs.

Although many variety breads are more dense and of smaller dimensions than ordinary white bread, freezing times may not differ significantly. For example, Pence et al. (1955A) found that whole wheat bread froze at virtually the same rate as ordinary white bread despite a considerable difference in crumb density—1,965 ml. average volume for the one-pound loaf of whole wheat and 2,375 ml. for the white. On the other hand raisin bread cooled faster, not only to an ostensible freezing range near 15°F. (−9.4°C.) but also to a core temperature of 0°F. (−18°C.). Sour French bread with its lean formula froze at a more rapid rate and showed a freezing range near 22°F. (−5.6°C.). For such reasons as these, anyone undertaking the commercial freezing of variety breads should determine carefully how each kind of bread performs in the facilities available.

## Rolls and Sweet Yeast Goods

Rather considerable quantities of rolls of various kinds are frozen by retail bakeries and by the wholesale bakeries who specialize in frozen products (Arnold 1956). The higher unit value and the smaller unit size of these products make them well suited for frozen preservation. A frozen inventory of items, such as hamburger or hot-dog buns, subject to unexpected fluctuations in demand is particularly helpful to smooth out weekly operations by allowing the operator to draw on it to meet sudden increases or to divert overages to it to meet decreases in demand. Other advantages are cited by Rollag and Enochian (1964) and Rasmussen and Prouty (1966A).

Lean products with compositions similar to that of ordinary white bread require rapid freezing rates and attendant precautions to retain optimum freshness, but richer products are more tolerant to variations in conditions. Products containing generous levels of shortening, sugar, eggs, etc., freeze very well and are handled satisfactorily under a rather wide variety of conditions.

**Bread-type Rolls.**—Although baked rolls have been frozen rather generally in recent years, little published information is available on effects of variations in freezing times and related factors on quality retention. Cathcart (1956), Beattie *et al.* (1949), and Charles and Van Duyne (1953) report that bread-type rolls freeze well in moving air at temperatures ranging from −10°F. (−23.3°C.) down to −25°F. (−31.7°C.). Additional information was later provided by Kulp and Bechtel (1958) who investigated the effects of air velocity, freezer temperature, and Cellophane wrapping on the freezing rates of soft dinner rolls. Figure 67 summarizes some of their results. Arnold (1956) describes the freezing of dinner rolls on a large scale.

Kulp and Bechtel (1958) found dinner rolls to behave generally like white bread in the sense that the cooling curves showed a freezing plateau,

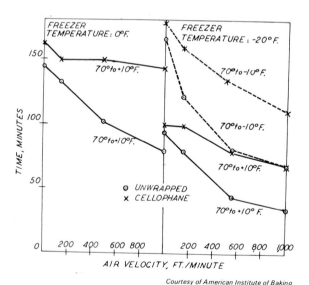

Fig. 67. Effect of packaging on cooling times of dinner rolls at freezer temperatures of 0° and −20°F. (−18° and −29°C.) and various air velocities.

so that high air velocity and low temperature were necessary to reduce the duration of the freezing zone. The effect of air velocity on the freezing rate of unwrapped rolls was large enough to suggest serious consideration of packaging rolls after freezing. Kulp and Bechtel (1960) found 8-oz. units (9 rolls, 7 × 7 × 1½ in.) of unwrapped dinner rolls to lose only 0.2 to 0.8% of their initial weight during freezing conditions including high air velocity (1,000 linear f.p.m) and a temperature of −20°F. (−29°C.). Prompt packaging after freezing to forestall subsequent moisture loss would therefore be entirely feasible.

**Sweet Rolls.**—As a class of yeast-raised rolls intermediate in richness between lean bread-type rolls and the very rich Danish-type rolls, items such as cinnamon rolls and hot cross buns exhibit behavior during freezing that is likewise intermediate. For example, Kulp and Bechtel (1958) found cinnamon rolls to show no freezing zone deflection in cooling curves, although there was some evidence of a freezing zone between 5° and 10°F. (−15° and −12.2°C.). As a result, freezing times were generally shorter than with dinner rolls of less rich composition (compare Figs. 67 and 68). On the other hand, rate of freezing and defrosting had a greater effect on the freshness rating (taste panel) of cinnamon rolls than on the ratings of dinner rolls (Kulp and Bechtel 1960). With either product the loss in freshness was distinctly less than for freshly baked rolls allowed to stand 24 hr. at room temperature (70°F.) (21.1°C.). A clear advantage for the freezing of

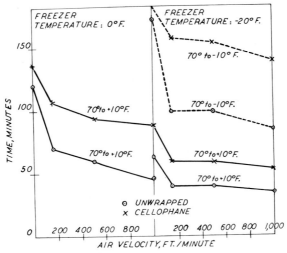

Courtesy of American Institute of Baking

Fig. 68. Effect of packaging on cooling times of cinnamon rolls at freezer temperatures of 0° and −20°F. (−18° and −29°C.) and various air velocities.

cinnamon rolls was demonstrated, unless they were to be consumed on the same day they were baked.

**Danish Pastry.**—Although rich yeast-raised pastries and coffee cakes have been frozen for many years with generally good results, little published information exists on effects of freezing conditions on quality aspects of the products. Kulp and Bechtel (1961) measured freezing times for three sizes of Danish pastry (rolls, snails, braided coffee cake) under a variety of blast freezer conditions. As with other products, freezing time was substantially lower with unwrapped products, and moisture losses were negligible. With packaged products, freezer temperature had the most influence on freezing time; there was no advantage in using air above 500 linear f.p.m. In contrast to results with products of less rich composition, freezing time had no significant effect on taste panel judgment of product freshness. The frozen products after defrosting were rated only slightly below freshly baked products, whereas unfrozen products stored 24 hr. at room temperature had staled quite perceptibly.

These observations suggest that the very fast freezing times for Danish pastry cited by McIntyre (1965), Breyer *et al.* (1965), Shukis (1966), and Newton (1966) would not be required for preservation of quality in rich items such as Danish pastry. Such a use of liquid nitrogen freezing would more likely be justified on the basis of rate of throughput or other factors.

## STORAGE CONSIDERATIONS AND EFFECTS

Although bread and related products are subject to considerable change in quality, chiefly firmness, during the process of freezing, they are rather stable during frozen storage if it is properly conducted. Time and temperature effects during storage are interrelated so that attention to both is required. Rollag and Enochian (1964) found that more than two-thirds of commercial bakers stored frozen products less than a week, but some reported that certain products were stored indefinitely. Most stored products at temperatures between 5° and −15°F. (−15.0° and −26°C.). Storage in home freezers frequently is for many weeks and even months, but in all likelihood different criteria for quality evaluation and acceptance are also used.

### Influence of Storage Temperature and Duration

Earlier literature references on the storage of frozen bread were reviewed by Cathcart and Luber (1939) who also reported that bread could be stored at −7.6°F. (−22°C.) for up to six weeks before odor changes decreased salability. Later work by Cathcart (1941) indicated that bread could be successfully stored for a year or so at −30°F. (−34.4°C.) if protected from oxygen by vacuum packaging. Reports from commercial practice (Weberpals

1953 and Arnold 1956) indicate that bread and rolls can be stored for many weeks at a variety of temperatures down to −35°F. (−37.2°C.).

Results showing effects of storage times and temperatures on crumb firmness of ordinary white bread were reported by Pence (1955), Pence *et al.* (1955B), and Pence *et al.* (1955C) as follows:

| Storage Temperature | | Length of Storage, | Average Increases in Firmness as |
|---|---|---|---|
| °F. | °C. | Days | Gm. / 4Mm.Compression |
| 72 | 22.2 | 1.2 | 27 |
| 15 | − 9.4 | 28 | 63 |
| 10 | −12.2 | 28 | 26 |
| 0 | −17.8 | 28 | 6 |
| −10 | −23.3 | 24 | 0 |

Kulp and Bechtel (1960) found that soft dinner rolls and cinnamon rolls could be stored at 0° and −20°F. (−18° and −29°C.) for at least two months without critical increases in firmness or decreases in freshness as judged by a taste panel. Rapid firming and loss of freshness occurred during storage at 10°F. (−12°C.) above, however.

Similar results were obtained with Danish pastries (Kulp and Bechtel 1961). At 0°F. (−18°C.) or below, no significant change in freshness or firmness occurred within eight weeks. At 10°F. (−12°C.) considerable firming and a significant loss of freshness occurred within seven days, making 10°F. (−12°C.) an unsuitable temperature at which to store this type of product.

The necessity to store frozen bread and rolls at 0°F. (−18°C.) or below in order to retain original freshness adequately over practically useful intervals is thus confirmed by both experimental work and commercial experience.

## Moisture Changes in Stored Products

Although losses of moisture during the freezing of unwrapped breads and rolls are negligible (see above), serious losses can occur during prolonged storage; and significant shifts of moisture can occur within products containing fruit pieces or other hygroscopic materials.

**Losses from Products.**—Pence *et al.* (1955A) found that freshly baked unsliced bread (22.5-oz. loaves) lost moisture steadily when stored unwrapped at 0°F. (−18°C.). Average loss at the end of 14 days was 1 oz. per loaf (4%). Similarly, Kulp and Bechtel (1960, 1961) advise against storing soft dinner rolls, cinnamon rolls, and Danish pastry without wrappers to prevent significant losses of moisture.

General industrial experience indicates that the common types of wrapping materials are quite adequate to prevent loss of moisture from frozen products into the atmosphere of the frozen storage space. Moisture from the product will condense and freeze on inner surfaces of wrappers, however, as accumulations of frost. Variations in storeroom temperature will aggravate this accumulation because of the well known propensity of moisture to move to surfaces having the lowest temperature. These frost accumulations seldom are troublesome unless storage is for more than a week or so, and they are slower to form, the lower the storage temperature. They are difficult to avoid because of the pronounced shrinkage of bread when it is frozen. Thus, even snugly wrapped loaves contract enough to create space between product and wrapper for the accumulation of frost. Upon prolonged storage, surfaces of the frozen product will exhibit the dry, whitish appearance characteristic of the freezer burn shown by most frozen products when dehydrated in frozen storage.

**Redistribution within Products.**—The progressive redistribution of moisture within freshly baked bread as it ages appears to be halted by freezing. Pence *et al.* (1956B) showed frozen bread to have essentially the same distribution of moisture as freshly baked unfrozen bread for at least seven weeks of storage at 0° or 20°F. ($-18°$ or $-7.0°C.$). However, a small but significant drying of the crust region of the loaves occurred during storage at a temperature cycled between 0° and 20°F. ($-18°$ or $-7.0°C.$).

A curious phenomenon occasionally encountered in frozen bread (Walker 1957) is a narrow whitish band or ring occurring a half an inch or so beneath the crust. According to Pence *et al.* (1958), the rings result from the slow sublimation of moisture from the moist inner core of the frozen loaf into the drier crust region. The initial occurrence of white rings and their subsequent rate of inward growth were related to storage temperature. At 15°F. ($-9.4°C.$) the rings began to appear as early as two weeks after the bread was placed in storage; at 10°F. ($-12°C.$) about five weeks were required; and at 0°F. ($-18°C.$) ten weeks or more were necessary. The width of the rings is an indication of the extent of moisture migration from the affected zone, and the distance within the loaf that the ring begins indicates how fresh the bread was when it was frozen—the fresher the bread the closer to the crust will be the outer edge of the ring.

Movement of moisture from frozen crumb into the raisins in cinnamon rolls was reported by Kulp and Bechtel (1960). The consequent drying of crumb in the region of the raisins was felt to contribute significantly to a lesser stability of this product during frozen storage than might be anticipated. This would also presumably be true for products such as hot cross buns or any other containing hygroscopic fruit pieces or ingredients.

### DEFROSTING PRACTICES AND PRECAUTIONS

Although rate of defrosting was found by Pence *et al.* (1955C) to be less influential than rate of freezing on crumb firmness, defrosting should be conducted with all due care. Improper defrosting can easily destroy any gains in quality preservation obtained by strict adherence to good freezing and storage practices. A broad discussion of factors affecting defrosting rates has been provided by Barta (1958).

## Effect of Relative Humidity

In contrast with freezing operations, the gain or loss of moisture by the product during defrosting can be substantial and serious. Depending upon duration of exposure, temperature differences, and relative humidity unwrapped frozen products can either gain or lose moisture so as to deteriorate in quality. Wrapping materials also can be damaged, especially by copious deposits of moisture during early stages of defrosting.

Slightly faster defrosting can be obtained at a given temperature by use of high relative humidity air because of the higher heat content of the air, but most students of defrosting have recommended humidities ranging between 40 and 60% (Pence et al. 1956A; Barta 1958; Belderok and Wiebols 1964). The advantage with wrapped products is probably not enough to offset possible damage to gloss and brightness of the packaging material, so that a relative humidity of around 50% would be most desirable. However, close control of humidity is very important with unwrapped products.

Belderok and Wiebols (1964) obtained good results at 122°, 140°, and 158°F. (50°, 60°, and 70°C.) with both 60 and 70% R.H. and an air velocity of about 500 f.p.m. Defrosting was continued only until the center temperature of the loaves reached about 32°F. (0°C.) after which they were allowed to stand another hour at room temperature. Under these conditions the crusts were crisp and short, closely resembling those of freshly baked bread. Nearly equally good results and a considerably greater tolerance were obtained with wrapped bread, although temperatures higher than 140°F. (60°C.) were not recommended because of damage to some types of wrappers.

## Effect of Air Temperature

As shown in Fig. 69, air temperature has a considerable effect on the rate of defrosting of wrapped bread. Effects of variations in defrosting times on quality characteristics, however, are not as large as might be expected. Results on crumb firmness obtained by Pence et al. (1955C.) are as follows:

| Defrosting Time Hr. | Average Increases in Firmness as Gm. / 4 Mm.Compression |
|---|---|
| 2.3 | 13 |
| 5.5 | 32 |
| 10.8 | 31 |

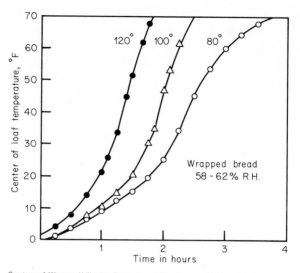

Fig. 69.    Effect of air temperature on rate of defrosting
wrapped white bread at an intermediate relative humidity
and low air velocity (150 f.p.m.).

The rather modest increases in firmness that occur in crumb when bread
is defrosted at room temperature (4 to 5 hr.) would appear to be quite tolerable in practice. Pence and Standridge (1955) observed that bread frozen
in 90 min. and defrosted at room temperature would not suffer a dimin-
ished shelf-life under commercial conditions. Belderok and Wiebols (1964)
reached somewhat similar conclusions.

Kulp and Bechtel (1960) found only small differences in freshness and
firmness of soft dinner and cinnamon rolls due to variations in freezing and
defrosting conditions. Even less effect was found for Danish pastry (Kulp
and Bechtel 1961).

Rollag and Enochian (1964) found that over ¾ of U.S. bakers who
defrosted baked products did so at room temperature with no special
equipment. Others used fans to blow air over the products, placed the
products in or near the oven where the warmer air would hasten the defrosting, or, to prevent loss of moisture, used closed containers for defrosting.

Use of warmed air for defrosting has two principal advantages to recommend it. One is faster defrosting and the other is reduction in relative humidity to minimize problems with condensation of moisture on products
and packages. Bakers who have invested time, money, and skill in the production of high-quality frozen products should protect their investment by

careful attention to the principles and precautions of the simple process of defrosting.

## Microwave Defrosting

The very rapid rates of defrosting possible with high-frequency capacitative and / or inductive heating equipment (Spooner 1957; Hansen 1959) have been of considerable potential application to frozen bakery products for several years, but high equipment costs have prevented use of the method on any significant scale. Pence *et al.* (1956A) were unable to achieve complete reversal of the firming of frozen bread by defrosting with microwave energy, although the freshly defrosted crumb was quite attractive. Somewhat similar results had been obtained much earlier by Cathcart *et al.* (1947) who also pointed out the utility of high-frequency heating for inhibition of mold growth within sealed packages of bread or other baked products.

The rapidity with which the defrosting of large quantities of frozen products can be accomplished and the freedom from hazards of excessive moisture condensation are among advantages that may eventually offset the high initial cost of this equipment, so that the potential of this method of defrosting may be realized.

### FORMULATION

The widely held opinion that richer products are more tolerant to variations in freezing, storing, and defrosting practices appears to be supported by available experimental information that bears directly upon the point (Kulp and Bechtel 1960, 1961). On the other hand, there is no question that even the leanest breads or rolls can be frozen quite satisfactorily by use of methods and equipment well within the reach of all bakers. Thus, no particular changes in formulation are required for successful freezing, although better results might be obtained more easily by even modest increases in shortening, sugar, or eggs in bread and roll formulas.

### PACKAGING

The heavy preponderance of products to be frozen are packaged before freezing, as reported by Rollag and Enochian (1964). This was true both for products sold or distributed frozen and for products that were defrosted before being sold or distributed. A partial explanation, according to these authors, may be that in large mechanized bakeries, operations through slicing and wrapping are completely mechanized, but operations connected with freezing frequently are not. Thus, in these bakeries, interruption of operations to freeze the product before wrapping would result in higher costs. Products to be sold unfrozen in retail shops generally are frozen unwrapped.

Moisture-transmission resistance of the films widely used for bread wrap appears to be satisfactory, although some films are better than others in this regard. Some are also better for preventing the pickup of foreign odors and flavors by baked products during freezing, storage, or defrosting. Rollag and Enochian (1964) report that polyethylene film was the most commonly used packaging material for packaging frozen bread products.

## BIBLIOGRAPHY

Anderson, D. 1954. Evaluation of the shelf-life and taste depreciation of bread, soft rolls, coffee cakes, and doughnuts as affected by freezing. Proc. 30th Annual Meeting Am. Soc. Bakery Engrs. *1954*, 89–95.

Arnold, P. D. 1956. Two years of handling frozen bread and rolls. Proc. 32nd Annual Meeting Am. Soc. Bakery Engrs. *1956*, 165–168.

Barta, E. J. 1958. Principles of the defrosting of frozen bakery products. Bakers Dig. *32*, No. 4, 50–52.

Beattie, H. G., Edelman, E. C., and Cathcart, W. H. 1949. Keeping quality of frozen bakery products. Food Technol. *3*, 160–162.

Bechtel, W. G., and Meisner, D. F. 1954. Staling studies made with flour fractions. III. Effect of crumb moisture and of tailings starch. Cereal Chem. *31*, 176–181.

Bechtel, W. G., Meisner, D. F., and Bradley, W. B. 1953. The effect of crust on staling of bread. Cereal Chem. *30*, 160–168.

Belderok, B., and Wiebols, W. H. G. 1964. Studies on the defrosting of frozen bread. Food Technol. *18*, 1813–1818.

Berg, I. A., and Morrison, C. B. 1925. Temperature and quality. Some studies of the effect of holding baked products at freezing and below. Baking Technol. *4*, 83–85.

Bradley, W. B., and Thompson, J. B. 1950. The effect of crust on changes in crumbliness and compressibility of bread crumb during staling. Cereal Chem. *27*, 331–335.

Breyer, F. L., Wagner, R. L., and Ryan, J. P. 1965. Application of liquid nitrogen freezing to bakery products. Bakers Dig. *39*, No. 6, 56–63.

Carlin, G. T. 1965. History of freezing in the baking industry. Baking Ind. *124*, No. 1575, 28.

Cathcart, W. H. 1941. Further studies on the retardation of the staling of bread by freezing. Cereal Chem. *18*, 771–777.

Cathcart, W. H. 1956. What can we expect from frozen bakery products? Cereal Sci. Today *1*, 8–15.

Cathcart, W. H., and Luber, S. V. 1939. Freezing as a means of retarding bread staling. Ind. Eng. Chem. *31*, 362–368.

Cathcart, W. H., Parker, J. J., and Beattie, H. G. 1947. Treatment of packaged bread with high frequency heat. Food Technol. *1*, 174–177.

Cauble, J. L., and Murdough, R. S. 1956. Freezing baked goods automatically. Bakers Dig. *30*, No. 2, 56–58, 72.

Charles, V. R., and Van Duyne, F. O. 1953. Effect of freezing and freezer storage upon quality of baked rolls, brown-and-serve rolls, and shaped roll dough. Food Technol. *7*, 208–211.

Enochian, R. V. 1960. Marketing frozen bread: A preliminary report. U.S. Dept. Agr. Pamphlet *AMS-395*.

Glabau, C. A., and Pirie, P. G.   1925.  Effect of climate on stale returns.  Bakers Weekly 46, No. 1, 57–59.

Hansen, C. C.   1959.  Advanced techniques in the freezing and defrosting of baked products.  Proc. 35th Annual Meeting Am. Soc. Bakery Engrs. 1959, 96–103.

Katz, J. R.   1928.  Gelatinization and retrogradation of starch in relation to the problem of bread staling.  In A Comprehensive Survey of Starch Chemistry, Vol. 1, R. P. Walton (Editor).  Chemical Catalog Co., New York.

Katz, J. R.   1934:  The staling of bread.  Bakers Weekly 81, No. 3, 43.

Katz, J. R.   1936.  X-ray investigation of gelatinization and retrogradation of starch in its importance for bread research.  Bakers Weekly 81, No. 12, 34–37, 46.

Kirk, D. J.   1963.  How fresh is frozen bread?  Bakers Dig. 37, No. 1, 58–60, 65.

Kulp, K, and Bechtel, W. G.   1958.  The effect of temperature and air velocity on the freezing and defrosting rates of some bakery products 1.  Dinner rolls and cinnamon rolls.  Cereal Chem. 35, 276–289.

Kulp, K., and Bechtel, W. G.   1960.  Effect of freezing, defrosting, and storage conditions on the freshness of dinner rolls and cinnamon rolls.  Cereal Chem. 37, 170–179.

Kulp, K., and Bechtel, W. G.   1961.  Effect of freezing and frozen storage on the freshness and firmness of Danish pastry.  Food Technol. 15, 273–275.

Mannheim, H. C., Steinberg, M. P., Nelson, A. I., and Kendall, T. W.   1957.  The heat content of bread.  Food Technol. 11, 384–388.

Marx, V. E.   1932.  Freezing bread to preserve it.  Bakers Helper 57, 1074–1075.

McIntyre, D. L.   1965.  Liquid nitrogen freezing—comparative economics and practices with other freezing methods.  Bakers Weekly 206, No. 1, 23–29.

Newton, E. L.   1966.  Nitrogen.  Bakers Weekly 209, No. 3, 38–43.

Pence, J. W.   1955.  The freezing, storage, and defrosting of commercial bread.  Proc. 31st Annual Meeting Am. Soc. Bakery Engrs. 1955, 106–114.

Pence, J. W., Lubisich, T. M., Mecham, D. K., and Smith, G. S.   1955A. Effects of temperature and air velocity on rate of freezing of commercial bread.  Food Technol 9, 342–346.

Pence, J. W., Lubisich, T. M., Standridge, N. N., and Mecham, D. K.   1955B. A progress report on freezing, storage, and defrosting of bread.  U.S. Dept. Agr. Mimeo Circ. ARS 74-4.

Pence, J. W., and Standridge, N. N.   1955.  Effects of storage temperature and freezing on the firming of a commercial bread.  Cereal Chem. 32, 519–526.

Pence, J. W., Standridge, N. N., Black, D. R., and Jones, F. T.   1958.  White rings in frozen bread.  Cereal Chem. 35, 15–26.

Pence, J. W., Standridge, N. N., and Copley, M. J.   1956A.  Effect of temperature and relative humidity on the rate of defrosting of commercial bread.  Food Technol. 10, 492–495.

Pence, J. W., Standridge, N. N., Lubisich, T. M., Mecham, D. K. and Olcott, H. S.   1955C.  Studies on the preservation of bread by freezing.  Food Technol. 9, 495–499.

Pence, J. W., Standridge, N. N., Mecham, D. K., Lubisich, T. M., and Olcott, H. S.   1956B.  Moisture distribution in fresh, frozen, and frozen-defrosted bread.  Food Technol. 10, 76–79.

Rasmussen, C. L., and Prouty, W.   1966A.  An evaluation of freezing:  Advantages, techniques, and cost factors.  Part I.  Bakers Weekly 212, No. 6, 37–38.

Rasmussen, C. L., and Prouty, W.   1966B.  An evaluation of freezing:  Advantages, techniques, and cost factors.  Part II.  Bakers Weekly 212, No. 9, 23–26.

Rasmussen, C. L., and Prouty, W. 1966C. An evaluation of freezing: Advantages, techniques, and cost factors. Part III. Bakers Weekly, *212*, No. 10, 24, 26–27.

Rollag, N. L., and Enochian, R. V. 1964. The freezing of commercial bakery products: Current practices, problems, and prospects. U.S. Dept. Agr. Marketing Research Rept. *674*.

Schoch, T. J., and French, D. 1947. Studies on bread staling. I. The role of starch. Cereal Chem. *24*; 231–249.

Senti, F. R., and Dimler, R. J. 1960. Changes in starch and gluten during aging of bread. Bakers Dig. *34*, No. 1, 28–32, 70–71.

Shukis, A. J. 1966. Liquid nitrogen: Equipment and techniques for freezing bakery products. Bakery Weekly *210*, No. 7, 22–26.

Spooner, T. F. 1957. Freezing, holding, and thawing of frozen baked foods—equipment and procedures. Proc. 33rd Annual Meeting Am. Soc. Bakery Engrs. 1957, 173–181.

Walker, N. H. 1957. Success story in freezing. Baking Ind. 107, No. 8, 54–56, 154–155.

Weberpals, F. 1953. How near is frozen bread? Bakers Weekly *160*, No. 11, 30–34.

## CHAPTER 19

Donald K. Tressler | Pies and Pie Crust

## INTRODUCTION

Most pies are little changed by freezing regardless of whether they have been baked or not. About the only exceptions are certain custard pies, which may exhibit considerable leakage on freezing and thawing.

Although baked pies freeze satisfactorily, the frozen unbaked product is usually preferred by the homemaker, since thawed prebaked pies are likely to be rather stale, if they are not reheated during the thawing process, and, if reheated, prebaked pies are likely to dry out and brown too much. On the other hand, in most cases, after baking, pies, which have been frozen before baking, cannot be distinguished from pies which have never been frozen. Many housewives buy many kinds of frozen unbaked pies, even though they must be baked before serving, since it enables them to serve delicious freshly baked pies without the trouble of making the crust and filling.

A large assortment of various frozen pastry doughs is on the market, including packaged frozen pastry dough in brick form, rolled and "pre-paired" pie crust pastry dough, folded French puff pastry, rolled and "pre-paired" French puff pastry, rolled and shaped oval casserole toppings, preformed tartlet shells, and other unbaked pastry products. A large assortment of frozen unbaked pies is available including the following: Five-inch fruit pies—apple, Boysenberry, cherry, peach, and pineapple, pumpkin, raisin, raspberry, rhubarb, and strawberry; cream pies—blackbottom, chocolate, coconut, lemon strawberry, and pineapple; deep dish pies—apple, cherry, and blueberry. Frozen pizza pies are also popular (see p. 356).

Cook and his students (Anon. 1964) have made a survey of the sale of frozen pies to consumers and found that apple and cherry pies are favorites, followed by blueberry, peach, and mince. The standard 8-in. pie was the size preferred by an overwhelming majority of consumers. More pies are purchased in the autumn than at any other season. Fruit pies are much more popular than cream pies. Of the cream pies, chocolate is the favorite, followed by banana, neapolitan, lemon, and strawberry. See Chapter 3.

## WHAT CONSTITUTES A GOOD PIE

Carlin *et al.* (1953) have indicated that a good pie should have a crisp, tender, rich, and fragile crust, of golden color mottled with brown; it

Donald K. Tressler is a consultant and President, Avi Publishing Co., Westport, Conn.

should break short, and not be tough nor should it be pasty. The filling, if fruit, should be clear and brilliant, not viscous; it should be oozing, and not gelatinous nor gummy. The flavor should be the true flavor of the fruit involved, and not the flavor of water and starch.

## PROBLEMS ENCOUNTERED IN FREEZING

### Fruit Pies

Four of the principal problems encountered in freezing pies are the following:  (1) the prevention of oxidation and resultant darkening of the fruit; (2) use of a jelling agent which will retain the proper consistency and clarity of filling during freezing and subsequent thawing; (3) the prevention of the filling soaking into the bottom crust, which may make it soggy; (4) obtaining uniform browning of the top and bottom crusts.

Oxidation and the resultant darkening of the fruit, which may occur during the storage and thawing of the unbaked pie, is particularly troublesome in the case of apple, apricot, banana cream, sweet cherry, and peach pies. As a rule, the problem is solved by the use of frozen fruits which have been treated to inactivate enzymes during preparation for freezing. Treatments which may be employed during preparation for freezing to inactivate fruit enzymes include sulfuring, blanching, or other heat treatment, and addition of ascorbic acid (see Chapter 3, Volume 3). If fresh apples, apricots, bananas, sweet cherries, and peaches are used in making unbaked pies for freezing, some means of controlling enzyme actions must be used by the pie maker, or otherwise the flavor and color of the product will deteriorate undesirably during preparation, storage, and thawing. Means of controlling enzyme actions are indicated in the directions for making these fruit pies given farther on in this Chapter.

The selection of the thickening agent is of great importance. The thickening agent should not have a pronounced flavor; this rules out most flours. Further, the starch of flour exhibits a strong tendency to become insoluble and gel-like during the freezing and thawing process. Ordinary corn and wheat starches can be used, since they may be satisfactory from a flavor standpoint, but the resulting pie filling is not entirely satisfactory. When gels made with ordinary cornstarch are frozen and thawed, the amylose crystallizes and syneresis occurs (Anon. 1954A); further, the gel is not as clear as when either tapioca starch or waxy maize starch is used. When gels made from the latter are frozen and thawed, little or no syneresis occurs, and the clarity of the gel is retained. These starches are relatively high in amylopectin and low in amylose.

Solutions of the waxy starches undergo consistency changes on freezing and thawing, but this effect is largely reversed if the solution can be reheated above 122° to 140°F. (50°–60°C.). Waxy rice flour in particular has been recommeded for use in precooked frozen foods (Hanson, Campbell, and Lineweaver 1951; see also pp. 318 to 320). The best resistance to freezing is shown by waxy corn and sorghum starches which have been chemically modified to introduce cross-bonding within the granule. It should be realized that a solution of none of these products reconstitutes perfectly. With any starch, quick-freezing and rapid thawing are necessary, since maximum change occurs in the starch solution at or near the freezing point.

A mixture of waxy maize starch and Irish moss extract is also recommended as a thickener for fruit pie fillings. The Irish moss extract holds moisture very well and helps to prevent sogginess of the bottom crust.

Carlin et al. (1953) have indicated that "there are also a number of gums, etc., which can be staisfactorily used as additives. One is carboxymethyl cellulose, commonly known as C.M.C. It not only thickens well but also provides outstanding brilliance to the fruit and juice. Another is gum tragacanth which, when used in conjunction with starch, thickens well and provides clarity and brilliance. Locust bean gum will do the same thing. Pectin is also used with starch for thickening. A low-methoxyl pectin is the proper type to use. It will provide outstanding brilliance to the juice."

The difficulties with the bottom crust encountered in the case of two crust pies may be wholly or partially controlled in various ways. One method, patented by Hanau (1951) involves brushing on, or otherwise applying, to the unbaked crust a thin layer of an edible fat or shortening which prevents the filling from coming into direct contact with the crust. Another consideration is that, as a rule, when low protein, soft wheat flours (e.g., seven per cent protein) are used, a relatively low proportion of shortening will be required but the resulting crust will absorb the filling readily. On the other hand, higher grade, fairly strong, soft wheat flours containing 8.0 to 8.5% of protein will require a higher percentage of shortening (e.g., 55 to 65%) in the dough. However, this crust will be flaky, yet firm enough to withstand rough handling, and one which will not absorb so much filling, and, consequently, will not become soggy so readily. Another point of importance in reducing the absorption of the filling, is to cook the starch, or other thickener, then cool the filling before placing it on the pastry dough. A cool, partially jelled filling will not soak into the pastry dough as readily as a warm one. It is also important to hold, transport, and display fruit pies, which ordinarily have a high sugar content, and, consequently, a low softening point, at a uniformly low temperature, preferably −5°F. (−20°C.) or lower. If this is done, liquid will not separate from the filling and seep to the bottom of the pie. Often pies are badly damaged by allowing them to warm to +15° (−9°C.), or even +10°F. (−12°C.) during transportation.

If the bottom crust is moist, it may not brown properly during baking. Preparing, freezing, and handling the unbaked pies, so as to avoid the absorption of the filling by the pastry dough of the bottom crust, will do much to improve the baking of that crust. Thawing, or partial thawing, of the frozen pie prior to baking, is advisable in order to obtain a uniform baking of the top and bottom of the pie. If the pie is at 0°F. (−18°C.) when it is placed in the hot oven, the top crust is likely to turn to a golden brown color long before the interior of the pie is heated through. A shiny aluminum pie plate will reflect much of the radiant heat of the oven. A dull plate bottom will permit more heat to be absorbed by the bottom of the pie and consequently more rapid and uniform baking. If shiny aluminum foil plates are used as containers for frozen pies, the homemaker should be advised to place the pie on a dark baking tray or piece of sheet metal or a soapstone for baking.

Laura K. Track, Quick Frozen Foods home economist, has suggested (Anon. 1966) that imaginative flavoring of pie crusts might greatly increase the sale of all kinds of pies, just as the use of graham cracker crust has helped to boost the demand for cream pies. Recently, crusts flavored with pecans have been introduced and appear promising. She suggests a ginger snap crust for pumpkin pies; cloves in crust for peach pies; a cinnamon crust for blueberry pie, and a walnut crust for cranberry or pear pie. Other suggestions include grated orange and lemon rinds in crusts for both lemon and orange pies; cinnamon and nutmeg crust for apple pie, and mixed nuts crust for many fruit and potpies. Another suggestion which should be popular is the use of cookie crumbs for frozen dessert pies.

### Custard and Chiffon Pies

The pumpkin and chiffon pie fillings, of the types described on pp. 432–436, can be frozen and thawed without marked change in consistency and flavor. On the other hand, many boiled custards and some chiffon pie fillings are partially coagulated on freezing and thawing, and consequently do not make entirely satisfactory frozen pies. Glabau (1952) observed less leakage from boiled custards and chiffon pie fillings made with ordinary cornstarch and eggs than from those made with either waxy maize starch and eggs, or tapioca starch and eggs. However, some seepage from the thawed filling was noted in nearly all cases.

Glabau also tried freezing of chiffon pies using either (1) a combination of eggs, starch, and gelatin or (2) gelatin and eggs as the thickening agent. When gelatin and eggs were used, no seepage was observed, regardless of the freezing temperature. When the mixture of eggs, starch, and gelatin was employed, fillings frozen at −20°F. (−29°C.) and then thawed, were superior to those frozen at a higher temperature. From these observations it may be concluded that chiffon pies should be made with gelatin and eggs (with little or no starch), and that they should be rapidly frozen.

A study of the storage life of unbaked fruit pies at various temperatures made at the Western Regional Research Laboratory of the U.S. Dept. of Agr. (Anon. 1963; Kulp and Bechtel 1962; Guadagni *et al*. 1963B) clearly indicates the importance of storing pies at 0°F. ( − 18°C.) or lower (Table 54).

The following are some conclusions of this study of the storage life of frozen apple, blueberry, boysenberry, cherry, and peach pies.

"Flavor of the fillings was the most important quality change during storage found in frozen apple, blueberry, boysenberry, cherry, and peach pies, in a recent study at the U.S. Dept. Agr. research laboratories in Albany, Calif. The pies were prepared in commercial establishments from frozen stock of known history. Freezing was by air-blast tunnels or plate freezers. The pies and dough from the same batch of pie crust were stored at 0, +10, +20, and +30°F. and then baked after from 4 weeks to 2 yr. storage.

"Special comments regarding the results of this study are:"

"**Flavor of Crust.**—Anti-oxidants in the shortening for the dough evidently retarded rancidity, as the dough kept 2 to 5 times longer than the fillings before flavor changes were noted.

**Flavor of Fillings.**—Better quality filling stock resulted in longer keeping quality of the pies. Apple pie fillings showed greater variation in keeping quality than other fillings. The sulfur dioxide treated apple slices, the more preferred procedure for blanching apples, made pies of better initial color and flavor and they were. much more stable than those prepared from water blanched slices."

Table 54

Good Quality Storage Life (in Weeks) of Frozen Fruit Pies

| | Temperatures, °F. (°C.) | | | |
|---|---|---|---|---|
| | 0° (−18°) | +10° (−12°) | +20° (−7°) | +30° (−1°) |
| Apple pie | | | | |
| Flavor | 30–72 | 20–52 | 6–12 | 1½–2½ |
| Color | 36–60 | 10–14 | 4–6 | 2–4 |
| Appearance | 36–52 | 12–17 | 6–9 | 2–3 |
| Blueberry pie | | | | |
| Flavor | 20–30 | 10–12 | 2–3 | ½–1½ |
| Color | 60–70 | 10–12 | 4–6 | 1–3 |
| Appearance | 18–22 | 8–12 | 4–6 | 1–3 |
| Boysenberry pie | | | | |
| Flavor | 36–72 | 17–40 | 6–7 | 2–3 |
| Color | 36–52 | 10–24 | 5–6 | 1–4 |
| Appearance | 28–36 | 12–17 | 7–8 | 1–2 |
| Cherry pie | | | | |
| Flavor | 60–78 | 36–40 | 8–9 | 2–2½ |
| Color | 52–60 | 20–24 | 4–6 | 1½–2½ |
| Appearance | 20–24 | 10–12 | 4–6 | 1½–2 |
| Peach pie | | | | |
| Flavor | 60–78 | 36–40 | 8–9 | 2 –2½ |
| Color | 52–60 | 20–24 | 4–6 | 1½–2½ |
| Appearance | 20–24 | 10–12 | 4–6 | 1½–2 |

## PIE CRUST

### Types of Crust

Carlin *et al.* (1953) have indicated that pie crusts are usually classified as: (1) *mealy*, if there is little or no flake at all; (2) *flaky*, if the crust has any semblance of flake whatsoever; (3) *extra-flaky*, if the flake is particularly elongated and has a puff pastry appearance when closely inspected. The mealy crust is used extensively because it is easy to make and has the good factors of tenderness and low shrinkage. However, it has poor crispness retention, no flaky character, is difficult to brown in the oven, and therefore has little or no color; consequently, it is not well suited for pies which are to be frozen. The flaky crust is characterized by a flaky texture of varying degrees; it is tender and retains its crispness. It browns well in the oven. Its disadvantages are that if it is not mixed properly, it shrinks during baking, also its preparation and use requires skilled workmanship and a more highly specialized type of flour and shortening. The extra-flaky, or the "roll-in" crust, is characterized by extreme flakiness. It has a large volume, puffs considerably, and, if used for shells, makes an extremely light crust. It is excellent for topping chicken (see p. 169), or meat pies (see p. 254), where a prebaked top is added. This crust requires a high proportion of shortening, approximately a pound of shortening to a pound of flour. It is subject to excess shrinkage unless made right.

The flaky crust is the type recommended for preparing pies for freezing. A formula and procedure for making this type of pie crust is given on pp. 414–417.

### Ingredients

**Flour.**—Although a good pie crust can be made from "all purpose" flour, for crusts of superior quality, unbleached soft wheat pastry flour of low protein content, preferably about eight per cent, should be used. In general, the higher the protein content, the higher the percentage of shortening required to make a light flaky crust. Therefore, if flours of high protein content are used, the proportion of shortening should be increased above that indicated in the formulas given on pp. 414 and 415.

**Shortening.**—Carlin *et al.* (1953) have indicated the following requirements for shortening and certain supplementary ingredients used in making pie crust:

"Almost any type, namely, hydrogenated, lard, margarin, butter—nearly all of the fats can be used in pie crust if proper adjustment and compensations are made to take advantage of the characteristics of each type. We believe, however, that the best pie dough, considering both finished crust and manipulation of the dough, is obtained with a shortening of superb plasticity. It must be plastic, which means that it must be workable over a very wide range of temperatures. It must be plastic and pliable at low temperatures because pie crust operation is best if it is at low temperature . . . A plastic shortening should be medium firm, not brittle, not oily, and it must hold that texture over a temperature range from around 55°F. (13°C.) low, to a high of about 90°F. (32°C.) . . . Pure lard is one of the most plastic shortenings available . . ., particularly if the pie crust ingredients are refrigerated. Pure lard is plastic at low temperatures. On the other hand, lard becomes soupy or oily at temperatures of 80°F. (26.5°C.) or above, unless it is especially processed for pie work. Special pie lards which have been plasticized to increase their melting point and to make them more satisfactory for use at temperatures of 80°F. (26.5°C.) and above are available from many sources. These products are also plastic at low temperatures. Most hydrogenated shortenings have a relatively short plastic range and are objectionable because of brittleness if held under refrigeration. Such shortening can be used satisfactorily in pie crusts at temperatures of 65° to 85°F. (18°–29.5°C.). Vegetable shortenings made especially for pie work with plasticity adjusted for a broader working temperature range are available in some of the larger marketing areas . . .

"The second property essential to pie crust shortening is a clean flavor. The flavor of any shortening must be absolutely perfect because baked pie crust contains from 35 to 40% shortening. It is even richer in fat than a doughnut. Any off-flavor in shortening will automatically be reflected and emphasized in the crust. Certain shortenings have a natural flavor, e.g., regular lard. The flavor of lard is looked on as complementary to the flavor of pie crust in many sections of the country. For that reason alone it is often preferred above all other shortenings in the manufacture of quality pies. Modern technology, however, has enabled the production of lards completely free from flavor which are finding increasing favor in those sections of the country where the lard flavor is not desired. Hydrogenated vegetable oil shortenings are usually flavorless; if not they are not suitable for pie work. There is another shortening known as 'high-ratio' or 'emulsifier' type of shortening commonly used for cakes. There is nothing wrong with its use in pies except that it is more expensive and it doesn't do anything for the pie crust that other shortenings won't do. There are some who have attempted to make pie crust with oils (salad oil) and it can be done. Oils are productive of a dough of extremely difficult handling properties and are therefore not recommended. Margarine and butter are sometimes blended with shortening for the sake of their flavor. Their use improves the flavor of crusts made with bland and tasteless shortening. It must be remembered margarine and butter contain about 20% salt and moisture and it is necessary to raise the shortening content accordingly to compensate for the moisture carried into the dough by these products.

**Supplementary Ingredients.**—"Milk powder or liquid milk is sometimes used in pie dough to enhance coloring properties. While both products will accomplish the desired result of improved crust color their use will be reflected in a lack of crispness retention . . .

"Both whole eggs and egg whites have been recommended as pie crust ingredients. Our studies indicate that either egg yolk or whole eggs will improve coloring characteristics but will reduce crispness retention after baking. No beneficial results have been obtained through the use of egg whites.

"Salt is used in pie crust for flavoring purposes. Approximately 2½ to 3% salt, based on total flour weight, represents a normal quantity of salt for this purpose.

"Sugar up to two per cent of the weight of the flour is sometimes used to enhance coloring properties. Of the various sugars obtainable for this purpose, corn sugar, or dextrose, will prove most satisfactory because of its good browning characteristics."

Corn syrup may be used in place of dextrose. Since corn syrup contains water (usually about 20%), one-fourth more of the syrup should be used and the amount of water reduced accordingly.

Approximately one per cent of baking powder may be used to prevent shrinkage in chiffon and other single crust pies for which previously baked pie shells are required.

### General Notes on Crust Preparation

To make a crust of good quality, all of the ingredients of the dough should be at 60°F. to 65°F. (15.5°–18.5°C.). The shortening, dry ingredients, and water (or milk) should be combined with a minimum of mixing and handling. The dough should be measured and rolled with the least possible handling and formed into pies in such a way as to have very little "scrap" left over.

In small pie shops, all of the ingredients of the pie crust should be put into a large cooler maintained at 55° to 60°F. (13°–15.5°C.) for 8 to 24 hr. in order to cool them to the proper temperature for use.

Larger scale operations, which involve the making of dough for 100 pies or more daily, should be carried out in air conditioned rooms maintained at 55° to 60°F. (13°–15.5°C.) large enough to permit both the preparaton of the dough and the storage of flour, shortening, and other ingredients. The water used should be chilled to 55°F. (13°C.) in a water cooler. The shortening should preferably be of a type that can be worked at 60°F. (15.5°C.). If shortening which is hard at 60°F. (15.5°C.) is used, it should not be stored in the air conditioned room, but should be held at a somewhat higher temperature and then brought into the air conditioned room shortly before use.

**Formulas.**—Either of the two following formulas will make excellent pie crust:

| Formula A | % | Lb. | Oz. |
|---|---|---|---|
| Unbleached soft wheat flour | | | |
| (8% protein) | 47.1 | 100 | 0 |
| Salt | 1.0 | 2 | 2 |
| Nonfat milk powder | 3.3 | 7 | 0 |
| Cerelose | 2.0 | 4 | 4 |
| Shortening, e.g., Covo | 32.8 | 69 | 10 |
| Water | 13.8 | 29 | 5 |

| Formula B | % | Lb. | Oz. |
|---|---|---|---|
| Unbleached soft wheat flour |  |  |  |
| (8% protein) | 48.1 | 100 | 0 |
| Salt | 1.0 | 2 | 0 |
| Nonfat milk powder | 3.3 | 6 | 14 |
| Cerelose | 2.0 | 4 | 0 |
| Shortening | 31.8 | 66 | 2 |
| Water | 13.8 | 28 | 11 |

If desired, fluid whole milk may be substituted for the water and dry milk. The amount of fluid whole milk used should be the same[1] as the sum of the weights given for water and dry whole milk in the formulas.

**Procedure**

*Small Shop.*—A sufficient quantity of flour for a single batch is sifted into large pans in which it is weighed out. The pans are then placed on a rack mounted on casters. The salt, shortening, sugar or corn syrup, and dry milk and water or fluid milk are weighed out and placed on the same rack. The rack is then wheeled into a room maintained between 55° and 60°F. (13° to 15.5°C.). In summer, when the weather is warm, the room should be kept near 55°F. (13°C.). In cool weather, a temperature of 60°F. (15.5°C.) will be satisfactory. The ingredients of the batch are allowed to stand overnight so that they attain the temperature of the cooler.

When pie dough is wanted, the rack is pushed alongside an Artofex Super Dough Mixer (see Fig. 70). The shortening is put in the mixing bowl first, then the flour and other dry ingredients[2] are added. The mixer is then started and allowed to operate for about five minutes or until the shortening is thoroughly mixed with the flour and other dry ingredients. From time to time, the edge of the bowl is scraped with a wooden paddle in order to mix in any ingredients which are not touched with the mixer arms. Then while the mixer is still operating, the water, or water solution of corn syrup and fluid milk (if used), are slowly added. Mixing is continued for about 90 sec. longer (45 "grabs" of the mixer arms).

The prepared dough mix is then transferred to pans which are returned to the cooler (55° to 60°F.; 13° to 15.5°C.) where the dough is allowed to stand at least four hours.

**Pie Making Operations.**—When needed for pie making, the pans of dough are wheeled alongside an automatic dough ball divider (e.g., a Colborne divider, Fig. 71). The dough is emptied into the hopper of the divider and is cut into dough balls, each of the proper size to make one bottom or one top crust. The dough balls are flattened slightly as they are put into shallow pans placed on racks mounted on casters.

The pans of dough balls are wheeled alongside the dough roller (Fig. 72). In a small pie shop, this will be mounted on a bench. The roller operator puts a dough ball through between the upper roller and then through the lower roller, which operates at right angles from the upper one. Anoth-

---

[1] The amount of milk solids in the whole fluid milk will be close, but not identical to the milk solids in the dry milk indicated.

[2] As an optional method, the salt and dextrose may be dissolved in the water instead of mixing it with the flour.

*Courtesy of Excelsior Industrial Corp.*
Fig. 70.    The Artofex mixer and kneader.

er operator then places the roller sheet of dough[3] in an aluminum or a special heat-resistant paper pie plate, and trims the dough to fit the plate. A measured amount of filling is then placed on the dough. The edge is then wet by atomizing with water. The upper crust is then put in place; the edge is pressed and scalloped, thus sealing the pie; the surplus dough is trimmed off. If desired, the top of the finished pie is brushed or atomized with milk. The pie is then placed on a portable rack on which it is frozen.

**Large Scale Operations.**—If the dough-making operations are carried out in an air conditioned room maintained at 55° to 60°F. (13° to 15.5°C.) in which all of the ingredients used are stored for at least 24 hr. prior to making into dough, they can be weighed directly into the Artofex bowl. As a rule, the shortening is weighed into the bowl, then the other ingredients

[3] In most pie shops, the rerolled scrap dough (trimmings) is generally used for the bottom crust.

*Courtesy of Colborne Mfg. Co.*

Fig. 71. Automatic dough ball divider. Dough in large chunks is placed
in the feed end of the machine, and is sheeted out by means of a roller
12 in. wide. The height of roller determines the weight of the dough.
The dough then travels along on the belt to the cutters which cut out
four dough balls at one time. It then continues out on to the takeoff
conveyor, where the dough balls can be placed in racks or on pans, or
on to conveyors which carry the dough balls up to the crust rollers.

are added. The method of making the dough is the same as that described
above under "*Small Shop.*" After the dough has been prepared, it is usually held for four hours or longer in the air conditioned room.

In some of the larger shops, the pies are made on rotary machines such
as those manufactured by the Colborne Manufacturing Co. (Fig. 73). In
making pies on a rotary pie machine, one girl, operating the crust roller,
rolls the bottom crust. A second operator places a pie plate in a holder and
puts the bottom crust on this plate. The lower crust is then moistened with
an atomizer. A third operator fills the pie with a measured amount of the
desired filling. As the pie passes the crust roller again, the top crust is
rolled by the first girl and placed on the pie by the second. Next, the pie is
trimmed and sealed. The pie is then brushed or atomized with milk, if desired, and the finished pie is then removed from the pie holder and placed
on portable racks.

### Freezing Pies

The racks of pies are pushed into an air-blast freezer, where they are frozen, preferably at $-20°F.$ ($-29°C.$) or below (Fig. 74, and 75). When the
interior of the pies has been cooled to $0°F.$ ($-18°C.$) or lower (about six
hours), the racks of pies are pushed out of the freezer into a cold room

Courtesy of Colborne Mfg. Co.

Fig. 72. High-speed crust roller with self-feeding dough ball conveyor. The dough balls are placed on the feed belt, which carries them into the first pair of rollers. The dough comes through the first pair of rollers oblong in shape and from the last pair round in shape. Finishing rollers are over 15 in. long and the machine is therefore suitable for any size of pie. Rollers are instantly adjustable to any thickness of crust.

maintained preferably at about 20°F. (−6.5°C.). Here the pies are packed in moisture-vapor-proof packages, which in turn are placed in corrugated fiberboard containers for shipment or storage.

Refrigerated plates, e.g., those made by the Dole Co., are also entirely satisfactory for freezing pies. However, considerably more labor may be required in handling the pies, since it is usually necessary to put the trays of pies on trucks which are then pushed alongside the plate freezers on which the pies are transferred.

When frozen, the trays of pies must be moved to tables for packing into cartons.

Some bakeries, which are located near commercial cold storages, may

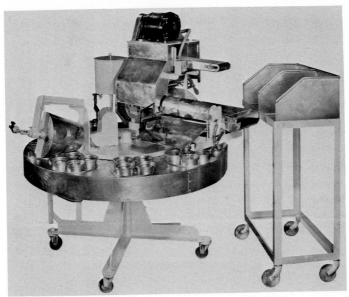

Fig. 73. Colborne rotary pie machine. High-speed crust roller with self-feeding dough ball conveyor and 17-in. finishing rollers is driven by a separate motor, making it possible to use the roller independently of the rest of the machine. Wetter brush moistens bottom crusts to make perfect seal. Rubber dockers located on opposite side of trimmer mold dough into pie plates. Trimmers seal the pie and at the same time cut off all excess dough. They can be quickly removed. Positive trimmer drive provides flexibility to the trimmer. Variable speed drive provides change of pace to suit production schedule. Casters make it easy to move the machine about the bakery. Plate holders are simply set upon the machine and are instantly removable. Rolled dough comes down the slide convenient for operator to pick it up. A separate dough cart with removable partition for top and bottom doughs is furnished. Self-feeding dough ball conveyor carries dough balls into machine automatically.

freeze their pies in the low-temperature rooms of the commercial storage, provided a temperature of −10°F. (−23°C.) or lower is maintained. Sufficiently rapid freezing may be obtained by placing a fan or blower in a position to circulate cold air over the pies which have been arranged on racks. As soon as the pies are solidly frozen, they should be removed from the racks and packed in moisture-vapor-proof cartons.

Almost all pies are high in sugar, and soften at relatively low temperatures. Because of this, storage should be at −5°F. (−20°C.) or lower, and the temperature should never be allowed to rise above 0°F. (−18°C.) at

*Courtesy of Greer Division, Joy Manufacturing Co.*

Fig. 74. After leaving the pie-filling machine, a Greer Diverter System separates flow into two streams to feed multiple loading stations.

any time during transportation or in the retailers' cabinets.

Many large bakeries use straight line units instead of the rotary machines. The units made by the Colborne Manufacturing Co. are built to operate at any speed between 1,000 and 1,800 large pies hourly.

At the lower speed, six girls can operate this unit. One girl places the pie plates in the holders; the next rolls the bottom crust, and the third places it on the pie plates as they move along on the conveyor. The crusts are automatically pushed down into the pie plates and the edges dampened by the machine. The fourth girl using a dipper fills the pies with the desired filling, and the fifth operator rolls the top crust. The sixth places it on top of the filled pies. The traveling conveyor moves the pies along to where they are trimmed and sealed automatically and also sprayed with milk, if desired. The pies are then placed on racks to be frozen.

*Courtesy of Greer Division of Joy Manufacturing Co.*

Fig. 75. Conveying pies to a Greer multi-tray freezer. The upper level of pies is on the way to a Greer air-blast freezer; the pies below are leaving the freezer for packaging.

### BLUEBERRY PIE

| Formula for Filling | Per 100 Eight-inch Pies | | |
|---|---|---|---|
| | % | Lb. | Oz. |
| Frozen blueberries (without sugar or syrup) | 53.86 | 53 | 14 |
| Sugar | 26.93 | 26 | 15 |
| Water, or juice | 16.16 | 16 | 3 |
| Waxy maize, or a specially modified starch | 2.69[4] | 2 | 11 |
| Salt | 0.36 | | 6 |
| | 100.00 | | |

[4] The amount of starch required will depend on the kind of starch used. Carboxymethyl cellulose may also be used as a thickener.

## Method

Place the starch in a large pan, stir in half of the water (cold) or blueberry juice, and continue stirring until the starch is all suspended. Put the remainder of the water in an aluminum or stainless steel steam-jacketed kettle, then stir in the starch suspension. Turn on the steam and heat the solution until it reaches 180°F. (82°C.).

**Procedure A.**—Cool the starch solution by running cold water in the outer jacket, when cooled down to 120°F. (49°C.) stir in the sugar and salt. Continue stirring and cooling until all of the sugar and salt have been dissolved and the temperature has been reduced to 70°F. (21°C.).

Allow the blueberries to thaw until they can be handled easily and the lumps broken up. To do this, a 30-lb. can should stand at room temperature (70°F.; 21°C. or higher) for 16 hr.; a 50-lb. can may require 24 hr.

The partially thawed blueberries should be carefully inspected and cleaned before being used. This can be accomplished either by passing them over an inspection belt or by putting them through a cleaner consisting of two inclined slatted trays one above the other. The upper slatted tray should permit the blueberries to fall through onto the lower tray, and should screen out lumps of blueberries (which should be broken up by hand) along with any twigs or large pieces of foreign matter. The lower tray should have the slats so close together that the berries will not fall through but the small pieces of foreign matter will drop through and be eliminated. Both of the slatted trays should vibrate.

Although a fair cleaning job can be done with a "cleaner," the use of an inspection belt is also recommended.

In making the pies, spread a weighed quantity (8¾ oz. to an 8-in. pie) of the thawed blueberries over a bottom crust in an aluminum or special heat-resistant paper pie plate. Add a measured quantity of the sugar-starch solution (7¼ oz. to an 8-in. pie). Cover with top rolled pastry dough. Seal tightly around the edge. Brush or atomize with milk. Cut hole in center of top crust and make a number of small gashes or pricks in crust with a two-tined fork.

**Procedure B** (Method commonly used in larger bakeries).—The proper quantity of cleaned partially thawed blueberries (see above) are added to the hot starch solution. The mixture is stirred well, then the sugar and salt are added and stirring is continued until all of the sugar has dissolved. Then the filling is placed in large pans which are held in a cooler until needed.

If the blueberries and cooked starch are combined in this way, 16 oz. of the prepared filling should be allowed for each 8-in. pie.

**Notes.**—A waxy maize starch, such as National Starch Products Company's "Clearjel" is an entirely satisfactory thickening agent. Tapioca starch may be used but it may produce a "stringy" filling; however it gives a clear gel. Ordinary cornstarch may not be satisfactory. A mixture of waxy maize and modified corn starches may also be used.

### APPLE PIE

## Choice of Apples

Frozen apple pies may be made from either fresh or frozen apples. In the late summer, autumn, and winter, fresh apples give the best pies. During the remainder of the year, frozen apples may be used advantageously.

In summer, the Gravenstein and Maiden Blush are usually superior to other varieties. In early autumn, Duchess, Snow, and Wealthy apples are very good for pies. In mid-September, the Rhode Island Greening, Cortland, and McIntosh are available. In autumn, the McIntosh makes very good pies, but in winter many other varieties are superior. Some of the better varieties for use in the winter are the Rhode Island Greening, Northwestern Greening, Northern Spy, Baldwin, Grimes Golden, Stayman Winesap, Spitzenberg, Rome Beauty, Russet, Jonathan, King, Wagner, and York Imperial. The McIntosh and Cortland are excellent in the autumn, but deteriorate rapidly in storage and consequently usually are relatively inferior after they have been in storage three months (see also Chapter 3, Volume 3).

There is a great variation in the quality of the frozen apples now on the market. Many of the packers treat the apple slices with sulfur dioxide or sulfites prior to freezing. This treatment stops browning and gives a product which may be completely thawed without darkening at all, but unfortunately most sulfured apples may have an unpleasant taste because of the presence of residual sulfur dioxide and sulfites (see also Chapter 3, Volume 3). Some persons are particularly sensitive to the flavor left by the sulfur dioxide treatment and find it extremely disagreeable even when present in very small quantities. For this reason, sulfured apples should not be purchased for pie stock unless the product has been carefully tested and determined to be substantially free from residual sulfur dioxide and sulfites.

Some apples are treated in salt brine with or without vacuum. This treatment usually produces a product that is too salty for use in pies.

Some packers treat their apples with salt brine and then freeze them with sugar. Apples treated in this way may be too salty and may also brown during thawing.

Apple slices may also be steamed during preparation for freezing. Steaming inactivates the oxidative enzymes and consequently prevents browning. However, great care must be used in timing the steaming operation (usually 90 sec. is the optimum period) and in rapidly cooling the steamed slices, or else the product will be too soft after freezing and thawing. Further, the apples must be of firm varieties and not too ripe or the product will be mushy.

Recently, a procedure of blanching (heating) apple slices in a hot ascorbic acid solution has been worked out. This treatment is superior to the steam-blanching procedure, since the temperature used is below 212°F. 100°C.) and, consequently, the apples are not softened greatly. This treatment, which involves 3 min. immersion in a 0.3 to 0.5% ascorbic acid solution maintained at 180°F. (82°C.) is recommended, since the apples are not changed in flavor and still do not discolor either during thawing or during storage of the pies.

Although most apples are packed for freezing in 30- or 50-lb. enamel-lined cans or lined fiberboard packages of similar size, apples packed in smaller packages are also available. The ideal package would contain just enough sliced apples for one pie. If packed in this way, the apple slices could be thawed quickly and then transferred to the pie without breaking any of the pieces. When sliced apples are frozen in large containers, 18 hr. or longer are required for thawing, and further it is difficult to remove the thawed apples from the container without crushing some of them.

### Preparation from Fresh Apples

Fresh apples of the varieties and maturity indicated in the preceding consideration, are peeled, cored, seed-cells removed, then sliced. If the apples cannot be treated immediately, they are held under a salt brine, prepared by dissolving three ounces of salt in five gallons of water. To treat the apple slices, they are placed in an aluminum or stainless steel basket made of perforated metal so that it will drain easily. Then the basket containing the sliced apples is immersed and agitated for 3 min. in an 0.3 to 0.5% ascorbic acid solution[5] maintained at 180°F. (82°C.). An aluminum or stainless steel steam-jacketed kettle is suitable for holding and heating the ascorbic acid solution. The apple slices are removed from the solution and spread in a thin layer to drain and cool. Cooling must be rapid, preferably in a refrigerated air blast, or the slices will become too soft.

Some of the ascorbic acid solution, in which the apple slices were heated, is cooled and combined with (stirred into) the starch. The starch-ascorbic acid solution mixture is then heated to 180°F. (82°C.) to cook the starch. The sugar, salt, and spices are then added to the cooked starch solution and the solution cooled.

### Apple Pie Filling

| Formula Using Fresh Apples | Per 100 Eight-inch Pies | | |
|---|---|---|---|
| | % | Lb. | Oz. |
| Sliced apples | 62.10 | 62 | 2 |
| Sugar | 19.20 | 19 | 3 |
| Waxy maize, or a specially modified starch | 1.40 | 1 | 6 |
| Salt | 0.10 | | 1½ |
| Cinnamon[6] | 0.15 | | 2½ |
| Nutmeg[6] | 0.05 | | ¾ |
| Ascorbic acid solution or juice[7] | 17.00 | | |
| | 100.00 | | |

[5] The strength of the ascorbic acid solution should be checked about every half hour by titration with 2–6 dichlorophenolindophenol dye and then the solution brought back to the original strength by addition of ascorbic acid.

[6] The amount and proportion of spice indicated will not please all purchasers. Some may prefer less, others more spice. The amounts indicated are considered to be those required for medium spicing. If a heavily spiced pie is desired, 0.3% of cinnamon and 0.05% nutmeg may be used. In a lightly spiced pie, the amount of cinnamon may be cut to 0.1%.

[7] If frozen apples are used, any liquid which drips from them as they are thawed may be used.

Some of the ascorbic acid solution, in which the apple slices were heated, is cooled and combined with (stirred into) the starch. The starch-ascorbic acid solution mixture is then heated to 180°F. (82°C.) to cook the starch. The sugar, salt, and spices are then added to the cooked starch solution and the solution cooled.

Ten ounces of the treated apples are spread onto an eight-inch pastry-lined pie plate. Six ounces of the cool starch-spice solution are then added. The top crust is then put in place, sealed around the edges, brushed or atomized with milk or with milk and egg, and perforated as described under "Blueberry pie" (p. 422).

### Preparation from Frozen Apples

In preparing pies from frozen apples, frozen sliced apples of the proper variety should be selected. They must have a good flavor. The slices are thawed only sufficiently to permit them to be broken apart. The starch-sugar-salt-spice solution is prepared and cooled as indicated above.

Ten ounces of the partially thawed sliced apples are spread on a crust-lined aluminum or special heat-resistant paper pie plate; six ounces of the prepared starch-sugar-salt-spice solution are added, and the pie is made as directed for fresh apples.

### Storage

If fresh apples are used and treated as directed, the resultant pies will retain color and flavor for at least a year in storage at 0°F. (−18°C.). If frozen apples are used, the storage qualities of the pies will depend on (1) the quality of the frozen apples, (2) the treatment used in preparing the apples for freezing, (3) the length of storage which the apple slices have been held, and (4) the storage temperature. Further, if the purchaser thaws the pies before baking, the color and flavor of the apple slices will not be greatly changed, provided the apple slices have been properly treated.

Apple and all other pies should be stored at −5°F. (−20.5°C.) or lower, and should not be permitted to warm above 0°F. (−18°C.) during transportation and exhibition in the retailer's cabinet.

### CHERRY PIE

### Method

Place the starch in a large pan, stir in half of the water (cold) or cherry juice, and continue stirring until the starch is all suspended. Put the remainder of the water or cherry juice in an aluminum or stainless steel steam-jacketed kettle, then stir in the starch suspension. Turn on the steam and heat the solution until it reaches 180°F. (82°C.). The sugar, salt, and pectin are combined and mixed thoroughly and are then added and dissolved in the cooked starch.

| Formula for Filling | Per 100 Eight-inch Pies | | |
|---|---|---|---|
|  | % | Lb. | Oz. |
| Cherries[8] frozen (5 plus 1) | 71.67 | 87 | 6 |
| Waxy maize, or a specially modified starch | 2.86[9] | 3 | 8 |
| Sugar | 11.40 | 13 | 14 |
| Pectin (100 grade) | 0.36 |  | 7 |
| Salt | 0.10 |  | 2 |
| Cherry juice[10] or water | 13.61 | 16 | 10 |
|  | 100.00 | | |

The usual process of preparing the pies is to combine the warm (170°F.; 76.5°C.) sugar-starch-pectin solution with the partially thawed cherries, mixing thoroughly in the pan in which the starch solution was cooked. The addition of the cold cherries to the sweetening-thickening preparation cools it quickly. When thoroughly mixed, the prepared filling is transferred to large pans which are moved into a refrigerated room until needed. When the pies are filled, 19½ oz. of the filling are measured into each unbaked pie crust in an 8-in. paper or aluminum plate. Then the top cust is put in place, sealed, and trimmed.

An alternate procedure, sometimes used in small bakeries, is to cool the starch-sugar-pectin solution down to 80°F. (26.5°C.) or lower by running water in the outer jacket of the kettle. When cool, the thickening-sweetening solution is transferred to large pans and held in a cooler until needed. By this second method, 14 oz. of partly thawed cherries are placed on each unbaked crust in a paper pie plate, then 5½ oz. of the thickening solution is poured over the cherries and the top crust put in place, sealed, and trimmed.

Careful handling of the cherries is important. The cherries leak or drain considerably if completely defrosted when used. As a result, the cherries lose their plumpness, and furthermore the juice presents an added problem. Therefore, the cherries should be defrosted or softened only to the point where they may be broken apart, but should not be defrosted so much that there is much leakage.

Use of Fresh Cherries.—Where fresh cherries are used in making a frozen cherry pie, the cherries are pitted and then incorporated into the pie by either of the above methods. However, it is necessary to use additional sugar, 23% instead of the 11.4% needed when frozen cherries are used.

---

[8] Montmorency and English Morello varieties best.

[9] The exact amount will depend upon the kind of starch used.

[10] Cherry juice may be obtained by thawing a portion of the cherries completely (at least 36 hr. will be required) and then pressing the thawed fruit, preferably in a hydraulic press. Or frozen cherry juice may be purchased, and then thawed for use.

## RHUBARB PIE

Either fresh or frozen rhubarb will make a good frozen pie.

| Formula for Filling | Per 100 Eight-inch Pies | | |
|---|---|---|---|
| | % | Lb. | Oz. |
| Rhubarb[11] (either fresh or dry frozen) | 55.15 | 55 | 3 |
| Dehydrated whole egg | 3.67 | 3 | 11 |
| Sugar | 29.41 | 29 | 7 |
| Waxy maize, of a specially modified starch | 1.66[12] | 1 | 11 |
| Water | 10.11 | 10 | 2 |
| | 100.00 | | |

### Method Using Fresh Rhubarb

The starch is placed in a large pan. Half of the water (cold) is stirred in and stirring is continued until all of the starch is in suspension. The remainder of the water is put in an aluminum or stainless steel steam-jacketed kettle, then the starch suspension is stirred in. The steam is turned on to heat the solution until it reaches 180°F. (82°C.). The dehydrated eggs are sifted, then the sugar is mixed with the eggs.[13] The starch solution is cooled to 120°F. (49°C.) or lower, and the sugar-egg mixture slowly added; stirring is continued until the egg is all dissolved and the solution is smooth. From here on, either of two methods may be followed: (1) The rhubarb is cut in one-inch lengths; 8¾ oz. of the rhubarb are placed on an unbaked pie shell in an 8-in. plate and 7¼ oz. of the cold sugar-starch-egg solution added. The top crust is put in place and trimmed. (2) The starch-sugar-egg solution is cooled and then the washed and cut rhubarb is mixed with it. Sixteen ounces of this filling is placed on an unbaked pie crust in an eight-inch pie plate, then the top crust is put in place and sealed, brushed or atomized with milk, or a solution of egg and milk, and perforated as described under "*Blueberry pie*" (p. 422).

Procedure No. 1 requires two filling operations but it insures the proper proportion of rhubarb and other components.

**Note.**—Fresh eggs may be used in place of the dehydrated product, but the use of fresh eggs makes the preparation of the starch solution more difficult, since the quantity of water used must be reduced to allow for the amount of water in the fresh eggs. Fresh eggs are approximately 73% water and 27% egg solids.

### Method Using Frozen Rhubarb

Rhubarb is frozen both with and without added sugar and with and without blanching; sometimes it is frozen in syrup. Dry-packed frozen rhubarb, which has not been blanched, is easier to use than that which has

---

[11] If rhubarb is frozen with sugar, allowance must be made for the sugar, i.e., less sugar is added at the time the pies are made, and more rhubarb must be used.

[12] The amount of the starch will depend upon the kind of starch selected.

[13] The use of dehydrated egg as a thickening agent is advantageous since it produces a much richer pie, which has an especially desirable body and flavor which cannot be obtained when starch is substituted; further, it reduces the sharp acidity given by the oxalic acid of the rhubarb.

been blanched in preparation for freezing or that frozen in syrup. Therefore, it is suggested that the dry-packed product frozen either with or without sugar, but without blanching, be used.

The frozen rhubarb is allowed to defrost just enough so that it can be broken apart, then it is used just as directed for fresh rhubarb. If the rhubarb has been frozen with sugar, it will be necessary to reduce the amount of sugar in the formula accordingly, and, of course, it will be necessary to use more of the frozen rhubarb.

### Freezing Rhubarb Pies

No special technique need be used in freezing rhubarb pies. They should be placed on a portable rack, which when filled should be pushed into an air-blast freezer, where they are frozen preferably at −20°F. (−29°C.) or lower.

### PEACH PIE

| Formula Using Fresh Peaches | Per 100 Eight-inch Pies | | |
|---|---|---|---|
| | % | Lb. | Oz. |
| Fresh sliced peaches | 77.83 | 77 | 14 |
| Sugar | 19.45 | 19 | 8 |
| Waxy maize, or a specially modified starch | 2.59 | 2 | 10 |
| Ascorbic acid | 0.13 | | 2 |
| | 100.00 | | |

Fully ripe (soft) yellow freestone peaches of good flavor, and also preferably of a variety which does not brown readily, should be used. J. H Hale, Halehaven, South Haven, Veefreeze, and Rio Oso Gem are among the best for pies; however, the common Elberta, although it browns readily, will give a satisfactory product.

The best results will be obtained by treating the peaches with a mixture of ascorbic acid and sugar in order to draw out some of the juice and obtain some penetration of the ascorbic acid and the sugar. Consequently, the following procedure is recommended:

The peaches are sorted over and the soft-ripe ones selected for making pies on the day in question. The remainder are allowed to stand at room temperature for a day or two longer to ripen. The peaches selected are then peeled. Since hand peeling with a knife is laborious, the peaches are usually blanched, or treated with lye, before peeling. The details of the peeling procedures are presented in Chapter 3, Volume 3.

Then the peaches are sliced. In small scale operations, slicing is done by hand; in larger scale operations the slicing is carried out by machines. The peach slices are next weighed out and placed in containers made of corrosion-resistant materials (stainless steel or aluminum). The slices are next mixed with one-fourth of their weight of sugar containing 0.6% of ascorbic acid and allowed to stand 2 to 3 hr. At the end of this period, the juice that has formed is drained off. This juice or syrup is then slowly stirred into the starch, in the proportion of 3 lb. 6 oz. of starch per juice from each 100 lb. of sliced peaches. When a smooth suspension of the starch in the syrup has been obtained, the mixture is heated in a steam-jacketed kettle or a double boiler with constant stirring until a temperature of 180°F. (82°C.) is reached. The starch solution is then cooled to room temperature, and mixed with the peaches from which the juice has been drawn. Sixteen ounces of this filling are then placed on an unbaked pie crust in an eight-inch aluminum or heat-resistant paper plate, and the top crust put in place, trimmed, and sealed, etc., and frozen according to the procedure described previously for other fruit pies.

Another procedure which eliminates the necessity of allowing the peaches to stand for the formation of the syrup, involves the making of some peach purée and its use in the preparation of the starch solution. This method may be briefly described as follows:

A mixture of granulated sugar and ascorbic acid containing 0.6% of ascorbic acid is prepared. Then peaches are peeled and sliced by either of the procedures described on p. 194. The sliced peaches are mixed with one-fourth of their weight of this sugar-ascorbic acid mixture. One-fourth of the sliced peaches-sugar-ascorbic acid mixture is converted into a purée by putting it through a Chisholm-Ryder tapered-screw purée machine (American Utensil type). This purée is slowly stirred into one-tenth of its weight of starch and stirring continued until a smooth mixture has been obtained. The mixture is then heated in a steam-jacketed kettle or a double boiler until 180°F. (82°C.) has been reached. The solution is cooled to room temperature and mixed with the remainder of the sliced peaches-sugar-ascorbic acid mixture. The filling is then ready for use in making pies.

### Method Using Frozen Peaches

Peaches are usually frozen as sliced peaches in a heavy syrup in the proportion of three parts of peach slices to one part of the heavy syrup (usually a 60% solution of granulated sugar). The proportions of sugar and peaches used must take into consideration the amount and concentration of sugar syrup used in freezing the peaches.

Procedure A.—The peaches are almost completely defrosted and then drained. In order to thaw peaches without serious darkening and marked change of flavor, it is necessary to use frozen peaches to which ascorbic acid has been added during the process of preparation for freezing (usually the ascorbic acid is added to the syrup used on the peaches). The starch is placed in a pan and the syrup drained from the peaches is slowly stirred in; stirring is continued until a smooth suspension of the starch is obtained. The mixture is then placed in a steam-jacketed kettle or in a double boiler and heated until its temperature reaches 180°F. (82°C.). The solution is then cooled to room temperature or below. As the solution cools, the salt and lemon powder are stirred in. When the mixture reaches room temperature, the thawed drained peaches are stirred in, and the filling is ready for use.

Procedure B.—A somewhat better pie filling may be obtained by dissolving the starch in peach purée prepared from a portion of the frozen peaches (after thawing, of course). This procedure eliminates the necessity of completely thawing the peaches; it is only necessary to thaw them sufficiently so that they can be broken up.

In preparing peach pie filling by Procedure B, approximately one-eighth of the peaches used are thawed completely, then converted into a purée in a Chisholm-Ryder (American Utensil) purée machine. This purée is slowly stirred into the starch until a smooth suspension is obtained. The starch-purée mixture is then heated in a small steam-jacketed kettle or a double boiler until it reaches 180°F. (82°C.). During cooling, the salt and lemon powder are stirred in. When the starch-purée mixture reaches room temperature, the remainder of the sliced peaches which have been partially thawed are broken up and mixed with the starch-purée mixture. The filling is then ready for use.

**Formula Using Frozen Peaches and Purée**

| | Per 100 Eight-inch Pies | | |
|---|---|---|---|
| | % | Lb. | Oz. |
| Frozen peaches (3 parts sliced fruit plus 1 part 60% syrup) | 85.14 | 85 | 3 |
| Peach purée (prepared from frozen peaches having composition given above) | 12.48 | 12 | 8 |
| Waxy maize, or specially modified starch | 2.07 | 2 | 1½ |
| Salt | 0.21 | | 3 |
| Dehydrated lemon juice | 0.10 | | 1½ |
| | 100.00 | | |

**Filling and Freezing Pies**

Regardless of the method used in making the peach pie filling, 16 oz. of the cool filling should be placed in each 8-in. pie. The method to be used in filling, covering, sealing, and freezing the peach pies is the same as that described for other pies.

Peach pies must be frozen and stored at a low temperature, otherwise the yellow color of the peaches may darken.

## MINCE PIE

**Method**

Firm, tart, high-quality apples should be chosen. The apples are peeled, cored, then weighed and chopped.

Use raw, lean beef of high quality, of cuts such as neck, chuck, or shoulder, that has been previously State or Federal inspected. The meat is cut into half-pound chunks, then cooked under steam pressure (15 p.s.i.) for 30 min. If pressure cooking equipment is not available, the meat should be simmered for 6 to 8 hr. After the beef has been cooked and cooled, it is ground, using a meat grinder.

| Formula for Mince-Meat | Per 100 Eight-inch Pies | | |
|---|---|---|---|
| | % | Lb. | Oz. |
| Apples, chopped | 35.05 | 39 | 7 |
| Beef | 12.54 | 14 | 2 |
| Suet | 2.51 | 2 | 13 |
| Raisins | 7.84 | 8 | 13 |
| Currants[14] | 3.85 | 4 | 5 |
| Citron, candied | 1.54 | 1 | 12 |
| Brown sugar | 11.59 | 13 | 1 |
| Orange (fresh, whole) | 6.94 | 7 | 13 |
| Lemon (fresh, whole) | 3.85 | 4 | 5 |
| Apple juice | 13.51 | 15 | 3 |
| Cinnamon | 0.12 | | 2 |
| Cloves, ground | 0.06 | | 1 |
| Mace | 0.04 | | $\frac{3}{4}$ |
| Pepper | 0.01 | | $\frac{1}{4}$ |
| Nutmeg | 0.06 | | 1 |
| Ginger | 0.02 | | $\frac{1}{3}$ |
| Allspice | 0.09 | | $1\frac{1}{2}$ |
| Salt | 0.38 | | 7 |
| | 100.00 | | |

Fresh, sweet, beef suet must be used. It hould be refrigerated at all times to keep it firm during grinding and mixing. The salt should be added to the suet just before the suet is combined with the other ingredients. The candied citron should be chopped.

There are several forms in which lemon and orange may be used, and, consequently, there are several factors that must be taken into consideration. If fresh oranges and lemons are used, they are cut, the seeds removed, and then ground. The ground fruit is covered with water in an open kettle and is boiled slowly for one hour. During this procedure, most of the water boils away, leaving the chopped peels practically dry. They are then added to the mincemeat.

Candied orange and lemon peels may be used. However, it is necessary to reduce the amount of peel by making the following adjustment. Candied orange peel (3.85%) and candied lemon peel (2.70%) are used, and additional apple juice (4.24%) to compensate for the difference between the candied and fresh oranges and lemons.

Orange marmalade may likewise be used in place of fresh oranges or candied orange peels. If marmalade is used, add 3.85% orange marmalade and 3.09% extra apple juice.

For those who like a wine flavor in mince pie, sherry wine may be added to the above mincemeat by substituting 1.93% sherry wine for that quantity of apple juice.

In choosing spices, high grade, pure spices should be selected for most satisfactory results.

**Mixing and Handling.**—The chopped apples and apple juice are placed in an adequate container. To this is added the chopped suet and salt, the

---

[14] If currants are not available, raisins may be substituted.

chopped meat, raisins, currants, citron, orange and lemon peel, sugar, and spices. The small amount of liquid remaining in the kettle after the beef has been cooked under pressure should be included in the mix. If the meat is simmered, the liquid is *not* included. The ingredients are mixed thoroughly and the mincemeat is placed in relatively small containers. e.g., 30-lb. tins, and stored in a refrigerator for 12 to 24 hr. to prevent fermentation and permit the blending of the flavors and the soaking of the peels, raisins, and currants. An 8-in. pie with two crusts requires 1 lb. 2 oz. of mincemeat filling.

### PUMPKIN PIE

| Formula for Filling | Per 100 Eight-inch Pies | | |
|---|---|---|---|
| | % | Lb. | Oz. |
| Pumpkin (strained) | 41.40 | 51 | 12 |
| Milk (dehydrated, nonfat) | 3.20 | 4 | |
| Eggs (dehydrated whole) | 4.20 | 5 | 4 |
| Sugar, granulated | 6.21 | 7 | 12 |
| Sugar, brown | 6.21 | 7 | 12 |
| Salt | 0.82 | 1 | |
| Water | 37.30 | 46 | 10 |
| Cinnamon | 0.42 | | 8½ |
| Ginger | 0.16 | | 3¼ |
| Nutmeg | 0.08 | | 1½ |
| | 100.00 | | |

This pie is considered to be one of medium spicing. If higher spicing is desired in a pumpkin pie, the spices may be increased in the same ratio.

### Method Using Fresh Eggs

Fresh or canned pumpkin may be used with similar results. However, the fresh pumpkin gives a slightly better product. If fresh pumpkin is used, the pumpkin is cut and the seeds removed. The pumpkin slices are then steamed under pressure for 15 to 20 min. at 15 lb. If a pressure steamer is not available, it may be steamed in a large kettle on racks at atmospheric pressure for 45 min. The pumpkin is then scraped from the rind, if the hard-rind variety is used. If the soft-rind varieties are used, the pumpkins, without peeling, are run through a purée machine. The strained pumpkin is then ready for use.

Whole fluid egg and whole fluid milk may be used in place of the dehydrated products, if more readily available, although the dehydrated milk and eggs give equally satisfactory results. If fluid eggs and milk are used, the ingredients and proportions are as follows:

| Formula Using Fresh Eggs | Per 100 Eight-inch Pies | | |
|---|---|---|---|
| | % | Lb. | Oz. |
| Pumpkin (strained) | 41.40 | 51 | 12 |
| Milk (whole fluid) | 30.76 | 38 | 7 |
| Egg (whole fluid) | 13.94 | 17 | 7 |
| Sugar, brown | 6.21 | 7 | 12 |
| Sugar, granulated | 6.21 | 7 | 12 |
| Salt | 0.82 | 1 | |
| Cinnamon | 0.42 | | 8½ |
| Ginger | 0.16 | | 3¼ |
| Nutmeg | 0.08 | | 1½ |
| | 100.00 | | |

Brown or white sugar may be used. However, when white sugar is used the color of the pie is rather yellow, and when brown sugar is used, the pie is dark brown in color. The formulas given combine brown and white sugar in equal proportions. The pie was judged to have a pleasing appearance.

## Preparation Using Dehydrated Products

If dehydrated pumpkin and dehydrated eggs and milk are used, the water lost during dehydration must be replaced and the dextrose and corn-starch used in dehydrating the pumpkin must be taken into consideration.

### SQUASH PIE

There seems to be little difference between a pie made from high-quality winter squash and one made from high-quality pie pumpkin, except that the squash pie is slightly more yellow than the pumpkin pie. The pumpkin pie formula may be used.

### THE MAKING AND FREEZING OF CHIFFON PIES

A chiffon pie is a one-crust pie filled with a light, fluffy mixture. In mak-ing the pies for freezing, the pie shell is first baked and cooled, then filled. When used by the housewife, the chiffon pies need thawing only, since the filling has been cooked and the crust baked. Thawing requires holding the pies for about two hours on the kitchen counter; it may be accomplished in about an hour by the use of a fan. Thawing in the oven is not recommend-ed, since the filling is likely to become fluid.

Topping with whipped cream prior to freezing is not advisable because of the fragility of the cream topping. However, the housewife may top the pies with whipped cream before serving.

**Chocolate Chiffon Pie**

| Formula Using Dehydrated Eggs | Per 100 Eight-inch Pies | | |
|---|---|---|---|
| | % | Lb. | Oz. |
| Gelatin (powdered) | 1.25 | | 15 |
| Unsweetened chocolate | 10.00 | 6 | 3½ |
| Granulated sugar | 31.25 | 19 | 8½ |
| Salt | 0.18 | | 1½ |
| Dehydrated egg white | 3.57 | 2 | 3½ |
| Dehydrated egg yolk | 2.68 | 1 | 10 |
| Vanilla extract | 0.18 | | 1½ |
| Water | 50.89 | 31 | 12½ |
| | 100.00 | 62 | 8 |

**Procedure.**—Small Bakery (100 pies per batch).

The powdered gelatin is stirred into 6 lb. 4 oz. of cold water (in an eight-quart pan) and allowed to soak. The dehydrated egg white is slowly stirred into 12 lb. 8 oz. of lukewarm water 100°F. (38°C.) (in a 12-quart pan), and allowed to stand for 30 min., stirring occasionally. The remainder (12 lb. 13½ oz.) of the water is heated to boiling with the chocolate (using an eight-quart pan), stirring until an emulsion is obtained. The chocolate water mixture is cooled to 150°F. (65.5°C.). The dehydrated egg yolk is mixed with 13 lb. of the granulated sugar in a 10-gal. steam-jacketed kettle, then slowly the chocolate-water mixture is stirred in, the salt and vanilla extract are added; the product is cooked until thick (temperature 180° F. (82°C.) with constant stirring.

The gelatin solution is stirred in; the solution is then cooled to 70°F. (21°C.) by running water in jacket or by transferring to a pan which is put in a refrigerator.

The egg white solution is beaten until stiff, and the remainder of the sugar is slowly added; beating is continued until stiff. The beaten egg whites are added to the chilled chocolate gelatin "custard" while the mixture is being stirred slowly with a mechanical agitator.

Ten ounces of the pie filling is placed in each eight-inch previously baked pie shell. The pies are placed on a rack to freeze in an air-blast freezer.

Chocolate chiffon pies for freezing can be prepared using frozen egg yolk and frozen egg white, instead of dehydrated eggs, using the formula and same general procedure just described. However, the amount of the frozen egg yolk and white must be sufficient to provide the same amount of egg solids.

*Courtesy of Quick Frozen Foods*

Fig. 76.   Thawed chocolate chiffon pie ready for serving.

**Pineapple Chiffon Pie**

Per 100 Eight-inch Pies

| Formula Using Dehydrated Eggs | % | Lb. | Oz. |
|---|---|---|---|
| Gelatin (powdered) | 1.43 | | 11½ |
| Granulated sugar | 25.51 | 12 | 12 |
| Dehydrated egg yolk | 3.06 | 1 | 8 |
| Dehydrated egg white | 4.08 | 2 | ½ |
| Pineapple juice, canned (unsweetened) | 30.61 | 15 | 5 |
| Salt | 0.41 | | 3½ |
| Water | 34.90 | 17 | 7½ |
| | 100.00 | 50 | |

**Procedure.**—(100 pies per batch).—the powdered gelatin is stirred into six pounds of cold water and allowed to soak. The dehydrated egg white is slowly stirred into the remainder (11 lb. 7½ oz.) of the water which has been warmed to about 100°F. (38°C.) The egg white solution is allowed to stand for about one-half hour with occasional stirring.

The dehydrated egg yolk is mixed with ten pounds of the granulated sugar and the salt, and then placed in a ten-gallon steam-jacketed kettle. The pineapple juice is stirred in and the solution heated with constant stirring until it is thick and smooth (about 180°F.; 82°C.). The gelatin solution is then stirred in. The mixture is then cooled to 70°F. (21°C.) by running cold water in the jacket or by transferring to a pan which is put in a refrigerator.

The egg white solution is beaten until stiff, then the remainder of the sugar is beaten in, and the beating continued until the egg white is very stiff. The stiff egg white is then slowly stirred into the previously cooled egg-yolk-pineapple juice-gelatin "custard."

Eight ounces of the pie filling are placed in each eight-inch previously baked pie shell. The filled pies are put on a rack and frozen in an air-blast freezer.

## Method Using Frozen Eggs

Pineapple chiffon pies for freezing can be prepared using frozen egg yolk and frozen egg white, instead of dehydrated eggs, using the same general procedure just described. However, the amount of frozen egg yolk and white must be sufficient to provide the same amount of egg solids.

**Lemon Chiffon Pie**

Per 100 Eight-inch Pies

| Formula Using Dehydrated Eggs | % | Lb. | Oz. |
|---|---|---|---|
| Powdered gelatin | 1.32 | | 10½ |
| Granulated sugar | 23.52 | 11 | 12 |
| Dehydrated egg yolk | 5.65 | 2 | 13 |
| Dehydrated egg white | 2.83 | 1 | 6½ |
| Dehydrated lemon juice | 10.55 | 5 | 4½ |
| Salt | 0.38 | | 3 |
| Water | 55.75 | 27 | 14½ |
| | 100.00 | 50 | |

**Procedure.**—The powdered gelatin is stirred into four pounds of cold water and allowed to soak. The dehydrated egg white is slowly stirred into eight pounds of water which has been heated to 100°F. (38°C.), then allowed to soak, stirring occasionally.

The dehydrated egg yolk is mixed with 12 lb. of the granulated sugar, the dehydrated lemon juice and the salt, and then placed in a 10-gal., steam-jacketed kettle. The remainder of the water (9 lb. 1 oz.) is slowly stirred in. The mixture is slowly heated, with constant stirring, until it becomes smooth and thick (180°C.). The gelatin solution is then slowly stirred in, the stirring is continued until all of the gelatin has dissolved. The "custard" (lemon juice-egg yolk-gelatin solution) is then cooled to 70°F. (21°C.) either by circulating cold water in the jacket or by transferring to a pan which is then put in a refrigerator. The egg white solution is beaten until stiff, then the remainder of the granulated sugar is beaten in and the beating continued until the whites become very stiff. The beaten egg whites are then slowly stirred into the cooled "custard."

Eight ounces of the filling are put in each previously baked eight-inch shell. The pies are placed on racks and frozen in an air-blast freezer.

Lemon chiffon pies for freezing can be prepared using frozen egg yolk and frozen egg white, instead of dehydrated eggs, following the same general procedure just described. However, the amount of frozen egg yolk and white must be sufficient to provide the same amount of egg solids.

## DEEP DISH PIES

### Apple Pies

#### Formula for Filling

| | Lb. |
|---|---|
| Waxy maize or specially modified starch | 100.0 |
| Sugar, granulated | 710.0 |
| Salt | 4.5 |
| Ground nutmeg | 6.5 |
| Ground cinnamon | 6.5 |
| Water | 730.0 |
| | 1557.5 |

#### Method

Enough water is placed in a stainless steel, steam-jacketed kettle, equipped with an agitator, to fill the outlet pipe down to the valve, then the starch is added and the remainder of the water is slowly run in, while the agitator is moving at high speed. When the starch is all in suspension, steam is turned into the jacket. Heating is continued until the temperature reaches 175° to 180°F. (79.5°–82°C.) then a mixture of the sugar, salt, and spices is slowly stirred in. This addition cools the solution, so it is necessary to continue the heating and stirring to bring the temperature up to 155° to 160°F. (68.5°–71°C.) at which point the steam is shut off, and the filling of the pies begun.

#### Preparation of the Pies

Nine ounces of either freshly blanched apple slices, prepared as described on p. 424, or that weight of thawed slices, are weighed into a small aluminum foil container suitable for deep dish apple pies (e.g., a Reynold's "Traypak") which is then placed on a conveyor belt and moved to a filling machine where five ounces of the filling are added. The filled "dishes" are moved on a conveyor belt in front of workers, who place a piece of freshly rolled pastry dough (prepared as described on pp. 414 to 417), of the proper size to cover the filling. The pastry dough is pricked (perforated). The pies then move to an automatic, or semiautomatic, machine where the covers are put in place and crimped on. The covered pies are then placed on trays, which are in turn put on racks mounted on casters. When filled, the racks of pies are moved into a freezer, and frozen in an air blast, preferably at $-20°$F. ($-29°$C.) or lower. When frozen, the pies are removed from the air-blast freezer and packed in fiberboard shipping cases.

### Cherry Pies

**Formula for Filling**

| | Per 1,000 16-oz. Pies | |
|---|---|---|
| | % | Lb. |
| Frozen cheeries (5 plus 1) | 56.0 | 510 |
| Waxy maize or specially modified starch | 3.5 | 31.5 |
| Sugar | 17.0 | 153.0 |
| Pectin (150-grade) | 0.6 | 5.4 |
| Salt | 0.2 | 1.8 |
| Water | 22.7 | 204.3 |
| | 100.0 | 906.0 |

### Method

Enough water is placed in a stainless steel, steam-jacketed kettle to fill the outlet pipe down to the valve, then the starch is put in the kettle and the agitator started at high speed and the water slowly added. When the starch is all suspension, the juice that has drained from the previously thawed cherries (17 30-lb. cans per 1,000 16-oz. pies), is added, and the steam turned on. Heating and agitation is continued until the temperature reaches $180°$ to $185°$F. ($82°$ to $85°$C.), then an intimate mixture of the sugar, salt, and pectin is slowly stirred in. It should be noted that the pectin must be thoroughly mixed with the sugar and salt or it will not dissolve. Then the drained cherries are added slowly with constant agitation. When thoroughly mixed, and at a temperature of $130°$F. ($54.5°$C.), the pie filling is run into the hopper of the filling machine. Each aluminum pie dish (e.g., Reynold's "Traypack") is filled with 14.25 oz. of the filling; then 1.75 oz. of pastry dough, rolled and cut to the proper size and shape to cover the filling, is added. The dough is perforated, then the "dishes" are covered and frozen as has been described above for *Deep Dish Apple Pies*.

### BIBLIOGRAPHY

Anon. 1950. Frozen pies. Refrigeration Research Foundation Information Bull. *50–4*, 2–3.

Anon. 1954A. Modern Methods For Freezing Baked Products. Bakers Weekly, New York and Chicago.

Anon. 1954B. A New Treatise on Pies. Tech. Service Dept. American Maize-Products Co., New York.

Anon. 1955. Storage of frozen bakery products. Commodity Storage Manual, Refrigeration Research Foundation, Colorado Springs, Colo.

Anon. 1963. Good quality keeping time of frozen fruit pies. Refrigeration Research Foundation Information Bull. 63, No. 8, 2–3.

Anon. 1964. Frozen fruit, cream pies. A consumer survey. Quick Frozen Foods 26, No. 8, 83–86.

Anon. 1966. Flavoring crusts for dessert and pot pies could open potential for special market. Quick Frozen Foods 29, No. 3, 147–148.

Beattie, H. G., Edelmann, E. C., and Cathcart, W. H. 1949. Keeping quality of frozen bakery products. Food Technol. 3, 160–162.

Carlin, G. T., Allsen, L. A., Becker, J. A., Logan, P. P., and Ruffley, J., Jr. 1953. Pies, how to make, bake, fill, freeze, and serve. Nat'l. Restaurant Assoc. Tech. Bull. 121.

Fenton, F. 1947. Frozen cooked foods. Refrig. Eng. 53, 107–111.

Glabau, C. A. 1952. How bakery products react to low-temperature freezing. Part 13. Effects of freezing upon boiled custard pie fillings, pointing out the results obtained with the three starches employed (cornstarch, waxy maize, and tapioca. Bakers Weekly 156, No. 13, 52–54. Part 14. Relationship of seepage to liquid in boiled custard pie fillings when they are frozen. Ibid. 156, No. 14, 56–58. Series turns from a study of the conventional boiled custard to a similar analysis of chiffon pie fillings. Ibid. 156, No. 15, 38–40. Freezing chiffon pies, this time using a freezing range from −10°F. to −20°F. Ibid. 156, No. 16, 42–43.

Glabau, C. A. 1956. Behavior of unbaked frozen pies in aluminum foil pans. Part 15. Bakers Weekly 169, No. 8, 40–42.

Guadagni, D. G., Harris, J., and Eremia, K. M. 1963A. Factors affecting quality of pies prepared from frozen bulk-pack red sour pitted cherries. Food Technol. 17, No. 2, 103–106.

Guadagni, D. C., Harris, J., and Okano, J. 1963B. Stability of commercially prepared frozen fruit pies. Food Technol. 17, No. 7, 114–118.

Hanau, N. A. 1951. Pastry products and preparation thereof. U.S. Pat. 2,547,206. Apr. 3.

Hanson, H., Campbell, A., and Lineweaver, H. 1951. Preparation of stable frozen sauces and gravies. Food Technol. 5, 432–440.

Hollinger, M. E., and McCartney, G. 1947. How to give frozen pies a "homemade" touch. Western Canner and Packer 39, No. 11, 81.

Inglis, W. 1947. Factors in successful production of frozen pies. Western Canner and Packer 39, No. 10, 73.

Kulp, K., and Bechtel, W. G. 1962. Frozen fruit pies. Food Technol. 16, No. 7, 104–106.

Meyer, B. 1955. Home freezing of prepared and precooked foods. J. Home Econ. 47, 603–606.

Meyer, B., Buckley, R., and Moore, R. 1952. Breads, cakes, and pastries from the home freezer. Univ. Tenn. Agr. Extens. Service Publ. 342 (Tenn. Agr. Expt. Sta. Bull. 223 Rev.).

Morris, E. 1953. Calcium firming summer apples. Okla. Agr. Expt. Sta. Bull. B-396.

Nicholas, J. E., Ruth, D., and Swanson, M. E. 1947. Crystallization behavior in the freezing of fresh fruit pies. Frozen Food Industry 3, No. 7, 8–9, 31–34.

Olson, G., Nicholas, J. E., and Ruth, D. 1948. Factors in crispness of the lower crust of some frozen fruit pies. Quick Frozen Foods 11, No. 1, 67–69.

Overman, A.   1947. Antioxidant effect of soy bean flour in frozen pastry. Food Research *12*, 365–371.

Pratt, D.   1955. The place of frozen pies in to-day's trend towards convenience foods. Bakers Weekly *166*, No. 1, 45–47.

Schulman, G. S.   1962. Frozen Hawaiian pineapples for pies. Quick Frozen Foods *24*, No. 10, 53, 159.

Sunderlin, G.   1945. Into the freezer instead of the oven. Quick Frozen Foods *7*, No. 8, 88–89.

Tressler, D. K.   1947A. General directions for making pies for freezing. Special Rept. to Frozen Food Foundation (unpublished).

Tressler, D. K.   1947B. Discussion on freezing pies. Bakers Weekly *134*, No. 2, 47–48.

Tressler, D. K.   1948. Frozen pie filling. Locker Operator 9, No. 13, 24.

## CHAPTER 20

Donald K. Tressler

# Cakes, Cookies, Muffins, Shortcakes, and Waffles

## CAKES

Cakes of almost all kinds can be frozen and thawed without notable change. As has already been indicated in Chapter 16 (pp. 360 to 369), research workers differ in their opinions as to which freeze and store with less change: batters or the prebaked cakes. If the product is to be stored for not longer than three or four weeks, most bakers favor freezing batters rather than baking and freezing the cakes, since the warm cakes baked from batters, which have been in storage for a short time only, have the attractive aroma and flavor of cakes just out of the oven. On the other hand, few batters produce cakes of good volume, texture, and flavor when baked after storage for six months, even at temperatures well below 0°F. ( −18°C.); whereas, as will be seen from the discussion which follows, many kinds of cakes retain their acceptability almost perfectly during storage for this period or even longer.

Although several workers report that cakes made from frozen batters are somewhat superior to thawed cakes which were baked before freezing, the freezing and use of frozen batters have two distinct disadvantages: (1) As has been pointed out above, most frozen batters have a relatively short storage life, and (2) they require baking, and in some instances both thawing and baking.

### Changes Which Occur in Cakes During Freezing and Storage

**Loss of Volume.**—Miller and Beattie (1949) studied the freezing of chocolate cakes and cake batters. They noted no noticeable difference in the average scores of freshly baked cakes and freshly thawed cakes after 14 weeks' storage. However, they observed a marked loss of volume occurring during freezing and storage, a large proportion of which took place during the first two weeks. Graul and Lowe (1947) compared the quality of frozen cakes made with (1) butter, and (2) hydrogenated lard. In each instance there was a volume loss of approximately ten per cent in four months and a somewhat greater loss after eight months' storage. Skarha and Van Duyne

---

Donald K. Tressler is a consultant and President of the Avi Publishing Co., Westport, Conn.

(1955A) reported a 10% loss in 16 weeks, and a 20% loss of volume in spice cakes in 32 weeks.

Other research workers have observed no such great loss of volume. Zaehringer and Mayfield (1951), who studied the effect of freezing and storage of plain shortened cakes, found little if any decrease in volume even after four months' storage at −10°F. (−23°C.) (only 0 to 5%). The slight differences in volume lost on freezing noted by these workers appeared to be due to the shortening used. Cakes made with butter did not lose volume. Those made with lard lost about 3.5%, and those with hydrogenated vegetable shortening lost approximately 5.0%. Owen and Van Duyne (1950) also studied the effect of freezing and storage on plain shortened cake and reported a loss in volume varying from 0% in 4 weeks to about 5% after 16 weeks' storage. Meyer et al. (1949) compared the effects of freezing and cold storage on shortened cakes and sponge cakes. They reported small losses (0 to 5%) in volume of both types of cakes during the first three months' storage, and somewhat larger but unaccountably irregular losses during longer storage periods.

Pence and Heid (1960) and Pence (1961) did not observe marked loss in volume during freezing and storage of yellow layer cakes, chocolate layer cakes, chiffon cakes, angel-food, or pound cakes.

From the above review of the literature on shrinkage of shortened cakes during freezing and storage, it may be concluded that there is likely to be some shrinkage of the cake, and that the longer the storage period, the greater the shrinkage may be. It is probable that the formula used, especially the kind and amount of shortening used, and the procedure followed in making the batter and baking the cake, affect the extent and rate of loss of volume which occurs during freezing and storage.

Sponge and angel-food cakes do not ordinarily shrink in volume as do shortened cakes (Anon. 1954B); often an actual increase of volume is noted.

**Softness or Compressibility.**—Freezing and subsequent storage makes shortened yellow and pound cakes a little less easily compressible (a little firmer). Freezing affects the compressibility of chocolate and devil's-food cakes very little. On the other hand, freezing apparently improves the compressibility or softness of sponge and angel-food cakes (Anon. 1954B).

**Crumbliness.**—Devil's-food cake becomes somewhat more crumbly on freezing and thawing. Glabau (1954) reported that a less crumbly devil's-food cake was obtained if the cake was frozen at −15°F. (−26°C.) rather than at a higher temperature.

**Tenderness.**—If resistance to shearing force, as measured by a modified[1] MacMichael viscosimeter, is used as an index, the tenderness of pound, yellow layer, and chocolate layer cake decreases somewhat (the cake exerts greater resistance to shearing force).

More recently, Pence and Heid (1960) made a careful study of changes in texture of yellow layer, chocolate layer, chiffon, angel-food, and pound cakes during freezing and subsequent storage at various temperatures, and concluded that most of the changes in texture occurred during storage, and further that the higher the storage temperature the more rapidly the changes occurred.

Pence and Heid conclude:

"Texture changes in the frozen cakes were generally detected before changes in flavor. Principal texture changes were loss of original crumb resiliency and increases in crumbliness and harshness. Each type of cake exhibited texture changes of a somewhat different characteristic nature . . ."

"Yellow and chocolate layer cakes exhibited relatively good stability at 10°F. ($-12$°C.) and greatly improved stability at 0°F. ($-18$°C.). However, little gain in stability was obtained at $-10$°F. ($-23$°C.) and $-30$°F. ($-34.5$°C.). Layer cakes seemed to soften and become more moist at 0°F. ($-18$°C.) or below. This apparent softening eventually deteriorated into an unacceptable gumminess or pastiness. Layer cakes were by far the most stable of the cakes studied."

"Pound cakes, at temperatures of 0°F. ($-18$°C.) and below, very rapidly developed differences in texture, but the initial loss of resiliency and increased firmness later appeared to become overshadowed by increased tenderness, as the cake became more crumbly."

"All types of cake showed significant differences from freshly baked cakes within four weeks at 0°F. ($-18$°C.). Even after significant changes had occurred in the frozen cakes, however, their quality was still good. In all cases, they were superior to day-old unfrozen cakes."

## Storage Life of Frozen Cakes

**Cake Scores.**—In general, the consensus is that, if examined within two weeks after freezing, the scores of the thawed cakes are not much different from those of comparable freshly baked cakes.

---

[1]Glabau (1952) modified a MacMichael viscosimeter so as to obtain a shearing test which could be used as a measure of tenderness. His description of the modified instrument and method of use follows:

"A prong or fork is attached to the hexagonal nut that is screwed onto the end of the spindle, thus holding the wire inside in place. A slice of cake is placed into the large cup, the spindle suspended by the wire at the top of the instrument, and the fork inserted into the cake. The cup with the cake is then slowly rotated by means of a motor and the fork gradually shears it. The resistance offered is read off on the dial at the other end of the spindle. Note that the cake becomes somewhat tougher as the freezing temperature goes downward, for the control cake which was not frozen offered a resistance of 485° MacMichael; cake No. 2,580°; No. 3, 600°; No. 4, 625°, and cake No. 5, 615°," (Anon. 1954B).

**Scores After Storage.**—Few bakers want to store frozen cakes for more than a short time. However, if a company attempts national distribution of frozen bakery products, then storage life becomes of considerable importance.

Pence (1961) concluded that

"all types of cakes studied (yellow layer, chocolate layer, chiffon, angel-food, and pound) showed reliably detectable changes after four weeks at 0°F. (−18°C.). Even after such changes had occurred, however, the quality was quite high and in all cases they were superior to day-old unfrozen cakes."

Pence did not study the storage of cakes for longer than an eight-week storage period. The conclusions of others who have studied deterioration in storage for longer periods follow: Paul *et al.* (1954) and Meyer *et al.* (1953) found that the scores for appearance, color, flavor, tenderness, and texture do not drop greatly during a 6 or 7 months' storage period. Graul and Lowe (1947), however, found that when cakes were stored at −10°F. (−23°C.), they retained color, aroma, and flavor of "plain cakes" far better than at the usual 0°F. (−18°C.) storage temperature. They also noted that cakes containing "synthetic vanilla" did not keep their palatability nearly as long in storage as comparable products flavored with vanilla extract. Zaehringer and Mayfield (1951) compared the storage life of frozen cakes made with (1) hydrogenated vegetable oil, (2) butter, and (3) lard. Those made with either hydrogenated vegetable oil or butter retained their palatability well for four months, but those made with lard were definitely of inferior flavor immediately after freezing and deteriorated further during storage. Similarly, Meyer *et al.* (1953) reported (Table 55) that plain yellow cakes, shortened with either butter or hydrogenated vegetable oil, retained their palatability for nine months at −5°F. (−20°C.).

Table 55

Flavor Scores [1] of Frozen Baked Cakes

| Length of Freezer Storage at 0°F. (−18°C.) | Egg-White Sponge Cakes Baked before Freezing | Whole-Egg Sponge Cakes Baked before Freezing | Egg-Yolk Sponge Cakes Baked before Freezing | Length of Freezer Storage | Shortened Cakes Baked before Freezing | |
|---|---|---|---|---|---|---|
| | | | | | Butter | H.V.O.[2] |
| None | 39 | 40 | 38 | None | 40 | 39 |
| 2 weeks | 39 | 39 | 34 | 2½ weeks | 40 | 39 |
| 1 month | 39 | 39 | 33 | 1 month | 39 | 39 |
| 2 months | 39 | 38 | 31 | 2 months | 40 | 39 |
| 4 months | 38 | 37 | 24 | 6 months | 39 | 39 |
| 6 months | 38 | 37 | 11 | 9 months | 38 | 36 |

Source: Meyer, Moore, and Buckley (1953).
[1] Maximum score, 40. Average of five judges' scores.
[2] Hydrogenated vegetable oil.

**Storage Life of Spice Cakes.**—Skarha and Van Duyne (1955A), who studied the effect of freezing and freezing storage on the quality of spice cakes, found that the flavor and other qualities were well retained for four weeks at 12.4°F. (−11°C.) (average score for frozen cake 89 compared with 96 for a freshly baked cake, out of a possible 100 points). After that the scores of the frozen product declined rapidly. Their results are summarized in Table 56. In considering these results it should be noted that the spice cakes were stored at 12.4°F. (−11°C.) and not at the usual frozen food storage temperature of 0°F. (−18°C.). Further, spice cakes were studied, and it is highly probable that spice cakes do not retain their palatability as well as either plain white or yellow cakes. This conclusion has been substantiated in the laboratory of one of the authors.

**Sponge Cakes.**—Meyer et al. (1953) have shown that while egg-white sponge cakes retain their palatability almost perfectly for six months, egg-yolk sponge cakes developed a bad off-flavor in about two months. Sponge cakes made with whole eggs retained their palatability almost as well as those made with egg whites and shortened cakes (see Table 55, p. 443). The probable cause of the objectionable off-flavor which developed during storage of the cakes made with egg yolks is the oxidation of the liquids of the egg yolk.

A summary of data indicating the storage life of cakes of various kinds is presented in Table 67, p. 530.

## Frosted (Iced) Cakes

Freezing, per se, has no deleterious effects on either the flat or the fondant type of icings. Proper packaging is of great importance to retard drying, and consequent hardening of the icing during freezing and storage, and to prevent the condensation of moisture on the cake during thawing. The lower the temperature of the cake at the time it is brought from the freezer, the greater the amount of moisture that will be condensed on the cake, other conditions being the same. If the weather is warm and humid, some means should be used to prevent the condensation of too much moisture on the cake. One simple means is to dehumidify the air in which the cakes are to be defrosted. Another is to bring the cakes from the freezer and permit them to stand in a cool room 32° to 40°F. (0°–5°C.) of relatively low humidity before bringing them into a warm room. A third means of preventing excess condensation is to use fans to blow warm air over the cakes while they are thawing.

## Packaging

Cakes, both plain and iced, should be packaged in moisture-vapor-proof sheeting prior to freezing. Waxed paper, of the type commonly used by

Table 56

Effect of Freezing and Freezer Storage at 12°F. (−11°C.) on Palatability of Spice Cake

| | Number of Cakes Rated | Weeks of Freezer Storage | Number of Ratings | Shape | Surface | Volume | Texture | Grain | Color | Flavor | Freshness | Mean Total Palatability Scores and Standard Deviations of the Mean |
|---|---|---|---|---|---|---|---|---|---|---|---|---|
| | | | | | | Mean Values for Scores of Characteristics of Cakes | | | | | | |
| Maximum scores | — | — | — | 10 | 10 | 10 | 20 | 10 | 10 | 20 | 10 | 100 |
| Standard 1 cakes[1] | 6 | — | 24 | 10 | 8 | 10 | 20 | 8 | 10 | 20 | 10 | 96 ± 0.3 |
| Standard 2 cakes[2] | 6 | — | 24 | 10 | 8 | 10 | 20 | 8 | 10 | 20 | 10 | 96 ± 0.5 |
| Thawed frozen baked cakes | 6 | 1 | 24 | 9 | 7 | 9 | 17 | 8 | 10 | 19 | 10 | 89 ± 0.9[3,4] |
| Standard 1 cakes[1] | 6 | — | 24 | 10 | 8 | 10 | 20 | 8 | 10 | 20 | 10 | 96 ± 0.3 |
| Standard 2 cakes[2] | 6 | — | 23 | 9 | 8 | 10 | 19 | 8 | 10 | 20 | 10 | 92 ± 1.0[3] |
| Thawed frozen baked cakes | 6 | 4 | 24 | 9 | 7 | 9 | 18 | 8 | 10 | 18 | 9 | 87 ± 1.2[3,4] |
| Standard 1 cakes[1] | 6 | — | 24 | 10 | 8 | 10 | 20 | 8 | 10 | 20 | 10 | 96 ± 0.2 |
| Standard 2 cakes[2] | 6 | — | 24 | 9 | 8 | 10 | 19 | 8 | 10 | 19 | 9 | 91 ± 1.1[3] |
| Thawed frozen baked cakes | 6 | 8 | 24 | 9 | 6 | 8 | 16 | 7 | 8 | 16 | 8 | 80 ± 1.5[3,4] |
| Standard 1 cakes[1] | 6 | — | 24 | 10 | 8 | 10 | 19 | 8 | 10 | 20 | 10 | 95 ± 0.5 |
| Standard 2 cakes[2] | 5 | — | 20 | 9 | 8 | 10 | 19 | 8 | 10 | 20 | 10 | 92 ± 1.0 |
| Thawed frozen baked cakes | 6 | 16 | 24 | 9 | 6 | 9 | 16 | 8 | 8 | 16 | 8 | 80 ± 1.1[3,4] |
| Standard 1 cakes[1] | 6 | — | 24 | 10 | 8 | 10 | 20 | 8 | 10 | 20 | 10 | 96 ± 0.4 |
| Standard 2 cakes[2] | 6 | — | 21 | 10 | 8 | 10 | 19 | 8 | 10 | 19 | 10 | 93 ± 0.9[3] |
| Thawed frozen baked cakes | 5 | 24 | 18 | 7 | 6 | 7 | 11 | 6 | 8 | 12 | 6 | 63 ± 1.6[3,4] |
| Standard 1 cakes[1] | 6 | — | 24 | 10 | 8 | 10 | 20 | 8 | 10 | 20 | 10 | 95 ± 0.4 |
| Standard 2 cakes[2] | 6 | — | 24 | 10 | 8 | 10 | 19 | 8 | 10 | 20 | 10 | 94 ± 0.7 |
| Thawed frozen baked cakes | 6 | 32 | 24 | 6 | 5 | 6 | 9 | 6 | 7 | 12 | 4 | 55 ± 1.9[3,4] |

Source: Skarha and Van Duyne (1955A).
[1] Standard 1 cakes baked on days cakes and batters were frozen.
[2] Standard 2 cakes baked on days frozen cakes and batters were tested.
[3] Significantly different from standard 1 cakes.
[4] Significantly different from standard 2 cakes.

bakers, is not very satisfactory as it is not moisture-vapor-proof. Moisture-proof Cellophane, polyethylene, and Pliofilm sheetings are satisfactory (see Chapter 4 of this volume, also Chapter 12 of Volume 2). After wrapping, the sheeting should be heat-sealed, and the cake either placed directly on a tray, or the wrapped cake put into a bleached sulfite carton. In either case, the wrapped, or wrapped and packaged cakes, are placed on trays on a wheeled rack, which is pushed into an air-blast freezer for freezing at 0°F. (−18°C.) or below.

Dressel (1955) recommends wrapping cakes in polyethylene, packaging in sulfite boxes, and freezing at +5°F. (−14.5°C.). Freezing at lower temperatures did not produce a better product and caused trouble from moisture condensation when the cakes were removed from storage.

### Freezing Rates

One might assume that wrapping would materially retard the freezing of devil's-food cake, but this does not appear to be the case since the curves in Fig. 77 show that the wrapped cake required only one-half hour longer to freeze than the cake which had not been wrapped.

From Fig. 78 it will be seen that the temperature of a two-layer sponge cake drops to 10°F. (−12°C.) in about three hours, whereas it requires approximately twice this time to reduce bread to this temperature. The apparent reason for the lesser time required to freeze cake is the relatively low moisture content (22.16%) of the cake compared to that of the bread (6.77%). The curves indicating the freezing rates of cheese cake and chiffon cake (Fig. 79) seem to prove that the percentage of moisture in a baked product is a very important factor in determining the freezing rate. It is evident that the higher the moisture content, the longer the time required to freeze baked goods, other conditions remaining the same.

### COOKIES

Most cookies contain so little moisture that they may be frozen and thawed several times without noticeably affecting their quality. Since freezing and holding at a low temperature keeps them from becoming stale, the frozen cookie business should eventually become of importance. In 1955, eight companies packed frozen cookies for sale at retail. Two companies packed frozen brownies in that year. It is probable that many more bakeries froze cookies as a means of holding them for sale later, after thawing, to groceries and supermarkets.

In general, the freezing of cookies offers few problems. As in the case of cakes, it is of great importance to package them in moisture-vapor-proof packages so that they will not dry out during storage, and also will not lose their crispness because of condensation during thawing.

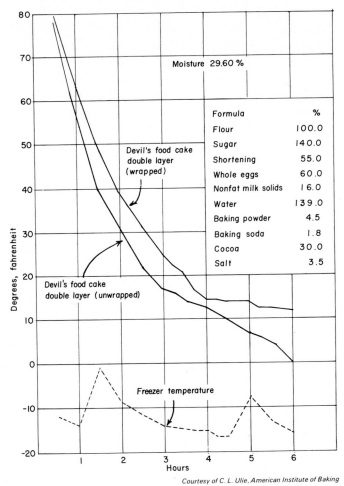

Courtesy of C. L. Ulie, American Institute of Baking

Fig. 77. Cooling and freezing curves for wrapped and unwrapped devil's-food cake. The cakes were frozen in a Sta-Kold vertical freezer. The devil's-food cakes weighed 24 oz. each.

Nearly all cookies retain their freshness almost perfectly for long storage periods, if held at a sufficiently low temperature. Beattie *et al.* (1949) reported that Christmas tree cookies, coconut molasses cookies, small bridge cookies, almond macaroons, and chocolate chip cookies retained their acceptability for 14 months when stored at −15°F. (−26°C.).

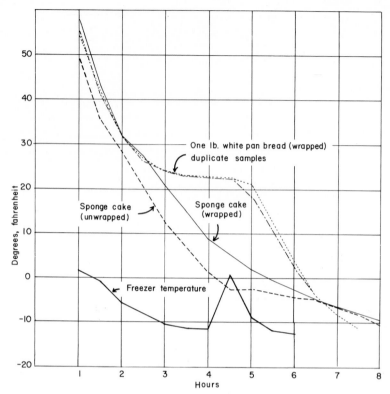

Courtesy of C. L. Ulie, American Institute of Baking

Fig. 78.   Comparison of the freezing rates of sponge cakes and bread. The products were frozen in a Sta-Kold vertical freezer. The sponge cakes weighed eight ounces each.

Sponge Cake Formula

|                          | %     |
| ------------------------ | ----- |
| Flour                    | 100.0 |
| Eggs, whole, fortified   | 175.0 |
| Sugar                    | 151.0 |
| Salt                     | 3.0   |
| Vanilla flavor           | 0.5   |
| Vegetable oil            | 40.0  |

The samples of sponge cake contained 22.16% of moisture. All samples were placed in the freezer one hour out of oven.

## MUFFINS

Paul *et al.* (1954) studied the freezing and storage of muffins. They wrapped cooled muffins in moisture-proof Cellophane, froze the wrapped product at −20°F. (−29°C.) and stored them at 0°F. (−18°C.). The frozen muffins retained their acceptability almost perfectly for six months, after

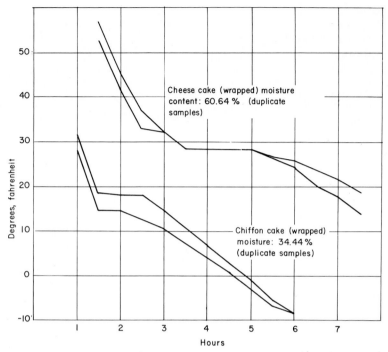

*Courtesy of C. L. Ulie, American Institute of Baking*

Fig. 79.   Comparison of freezing rates of wrapped cheese and chiffon cakes.

| Cheese Cake Formula | | Chiffon Cake Formula | |
|---|---|---|---|
| | % | | % |
| Bakers' cheese | 44.00 | Flour | 100.00 |
| Patent flour | 2.80 | Baking powder | 5.00 |
| Corn starch | 1.40 | Salt | 2.00 |
| Granulated sugar | 6.90 | Granulated sugar | 137.00 |
| Whole eggs | 5.50 | Salad oil | 52.00 |
| Salt | .34 | Egg yolks | 52.00 |
| Emulsified shortening | 1.40 | Water | 60.00 |
| Vanilla | .34 | Vanilla | 4.00 |
| Sour cream | 8.27 | Egg whites | 104.00 |
| Fresh milk | 11.00 | Cream of tartar | 1.00 |
| Egg white | 11.00 | | |
| Sugar | 6.90 | | |

which they deteriorated rapidly. Some loss in volume was noted. They recommended thawing and reheating the muffins in the wrapper in an oven at 300°F. (149°C.).

The simplest way of carrying out a muffin freezing operation is to prepare a dry muffin mix, such as that which can be made using the following formula and procedure:

| Ingredients | % |
|---|---|
| Pastry flour | 65.75 |
| Dehydrated whole egg | 2.00 |
| Dextrose | 10.00 |
| Granulated sugar | 5.00 |
| Nonfat milk powder | 3.00 |
| Baking powder | 3.25 |
| Shortening, hydrogenated vegetable | 10.00 |
| Salt | 1.00 |
| | 100.00 |

## Method

**Large Scale.**—All the ingredients except the shortening are mixed, then sifted. The shortening is melted, then sprayed on to the mixture. After cooling, the mixture is put through a Fitzpatrick mill or an Entoleter, and again sifted.

**Small Scale.**—The shortening is placed in the mixer bowl. With the mixer operating at medium speed, the dextrose and sugar are added and "creamed." The milk powder, flour, dehydrated egg, baking powder, and salt are sifted together, and then slowly added to the creamed shortening while the mixer is operating at medium speed. When thoroughly mixed, the mix is put through a Fitzpatrick mill or an Entoleter.

## Preparation of Muffins

The muffin mix is placed in a mixer bowl and the mixer operated at slow speed. One gallon of water is added for each 12 lb. mix. Mixing is continued at medium speed until the batter is smooth. The batter is filled into muffin tins. Baking should be at 375°F. (191°C.).

## Packaging and Freezing

After cooling, the muffins are placed in cartons, preferably of aluminum foil, so that they may be reheated without removal from the container. The lid is crimped on and the product frozen in an air-blast freezer after which the cartons are packed in a fiberboard container for shipment or storage.

**Kinds of Muffins.**—The formula presented above produces plain muffins. With the addition of blueberries to the batter, blueberry muffins are produced. With proper modifications of the formula, whole wheat, bran, and corn muffins can be produced for freezing.

## WAFFLES

Frozen waffles were introduced in 1949. They are now packed by five different companies in the United States.

The simplest way of running a waffle freezing operation is to prepare a dry mix in advance. A suitable formula and method of preparing a dry mix follows:

| Ingredients | % |
|---|---|
| All purpose flour | 78.0 |
| Nonfat milk powder | 5.7 |
| Dehydrated whole egg | 3.7 |
| Granulated sugar | 2.6 |
| Baking powder | 1.5 |
| Soda | 0.5 |
| Salt | 0.8 |
| Shortening, hydrogenated vegetable | 7.2 |
|  | 100.0 |

### Method

**Large Scale.**—All the ingredients except the shortening are mixed, then sifted. The vegetable shortening is melted, then sprayed on to the mixture. After cooling, the mixture is put through a Fitzpatrick mill and again sifted.

**Small Scale.**—With the mixer operating at medium speed, the shortening and sugar are "creamed." The flour, milk powder, dehydrated eggs, baking powder, soda, and salt are sifted together, and then slowly added to the creamed shortening while the mixer is operating at medium speed. When thoroughly mixed, the mix is put through a Fitzpatrick mill or an Entoleter.

### Batter Preparation

The waffle mix is placed in a mixer bowl, and the mixer operated at slow speed. One gallon of water is added for each six pounds of mix. Mixing is continued at a medium speed until the batter is smooth.

The prepared batter is allowed to stand for a few minutes, after which the waffles are baked on thermostatically controlled waffle irons. The type of waffle baking equipment will depend upon the size of the business.

The hot waffles are allowed to cool on trays and then slipped into transparent bags made of moisture-proof Cellophane, polyethylene, or other moisture-vapor-proof sheeting, two waffles to the bag. The bags may be imprinted or printed labels may be placed in each bag. The trays of packages of waffles should be frozen at below zero temperature. After freezing, they should be packed in corrugated fiberboard shipping containers. Storage should be at 0°F. ($-18$°C.) or lower. If made with a freshly prepared mix, with either freshly dehydrated dried eggs or strictly fresh eggs, and held at a temperature not higher than 0°F. ($-18$°C.) the frozen waffles will retain their acceptability for a year or even longer.

**Use.**—Frozen waffles are easy to prepare for the table. The housewife merely drops them into a household toaster, in which they become hot and ready to eat in about a minute.

### PANCAKES

One of the surprising recent developments in the precooked frozen food field is the introduction and success of frozen pancakes (Anon. 1954A). The method described for preparing the mix, the batter, and freezing and packaging waffles may be used in preparing, packaging, and freezing pancakes.

Of course a pancake formula should be used to make the batter, and the cakes must be baked on hot griddles and not on waffle irons.

## SHORTCAKES

Frozen strawberry shortcake was introduced in 1949. The product is excellent but it must be held at a uniformly low temperature, preferably *not higher than 0°F. (−18°C.)* for freezing, storage, and marketing, if high quality is to be maintained.

### Preparation of Cakes

Shortcakes are of two general types. In one, the cake is a true cake, either the sponge type (angel-food, an egg-white sponge, or regular sponge, made with egg yolk or whole eggs) or a shortened cake, made with whole eggs. In the other, a rich biscuit dough is the "cake."

If sponge or shortened cakes are used, ordinary baker's cakes of good quality made according to standard bakery practice (Anon. 1954B) may be cut to fit the container selected for the frozen products.

If a rich biscuit dough is used as the cake, this can be prepared according to the following procedure and formula:

| Ingredients | % |
|---|---|
| Patent flour | 100.0 |
| Baking powder | 2.5 |
| Salt | 0.5 |
| Granulated sugar | 8.0 |
| Hydrogenated vegetable shortening | 25.0 |
| Frozen whole eggs | 10.5 |
| Whole fresh milk | 18.0 |
| Total | 164.5 |

The flour, baking powder, salt, and sugar are sifted together and placed in a mixer. The shortening is cut in, then the thawed egg is mixed in, and the milk is added, with just enough mixing to produce a dough which can easily be handled. The dough is placed in shallow baking pans and baked at 450°F. (232°C.) for 15 to 20 min.

### Strawberry Filling

An excellent strawberry filling is prepared by thickening thawed sliced strawberries with a waxy maize starch (such as "Clearjel") according to the following formula and procedure:

A 30-lb. can of frozen sliced strawberries is thawed and the juice is drained. Then two pounds of "Clearjel" or other modified starch is placed in a steam-jacketed kettle equipped with agitator, six pounds of cold water are stirred in, then the juice drained from the berries is added and the mixture heated slowly with agitation until the temperature reaches 180°F. (82°C.) and a smooth starch solution has been obtained; five pounds of granulated sugar are added, then the heating is discontinued. The berries are slowly stirred in. The mixture is cooled by running cold water through the jacket. Enough concentrated strawberry flavor is added to give the product a noticeable aroma.

**Whip Toppings.**—See Chapter 14, pp. 320 to 323.

### Packaging and Freezing the Shortcake

The shortcakes can be conveniently packaged in rectangular tray-type, aluminum-foil packages. If a total weight of 12 oz. is packed in each package 6¾ oz. of cake may be placed in the aluminum-foil tray, then 5 oz. of the strawberry filling, and finally ½ oz. or slightly less of the whip topping. The covers are crimped on the containers by machine, after which they are placed on trays on wheeled racks for freezing in an air blast at −10°F. (−23°C.) or lower.

### DANISH PASTRY

Kulp and Bechtel (1961) of the American Institute of Baking have studied the effect of freezing and storage on the freshness and firmness of Danish pastry. The formula and procedure of making the pastry used by them are shown in Table 57. Kulp and Bechtel froze the Danish pastry,

Table 57

Formula and Procedure for Danish Pastry

| Part | Ingredient | Parts per 100 Parts Flour | Procedure |
|------|------------|---------------------------|-----------|
| I | Sugar | 22.7 | Cream together the |
| | Shortening | 14.3 | ingredients in I. Add |
| | Salt | 1.5 | II and cream, using |
| | Nonfat dry milk | 2.9 | Hobart mixer with |
| II | Whole eggs | 22.7 | paddle. Add III and |
| | Water | 38.7 | mix with dough hook. |
| III | Yeast | 6.7 | Roll IV into the dough. |
| | Bread flour | 77.5 | Ferment 16 hr. at 40°F. |
| | Cake flour | 22.5 | (4°C.). Roll out, and |
| IV | Margarine | 37.0 | cut to shape. |

both rolls and coffee cakes (1) in still air, and (2) in an air blast at (a) 150, (b) 500, and (c) 1000 linear f.p.m. at 0°, −10°, and −20°F. (−18°, −23.3°, and −29°C.). Defrosting was carried out at (1) 75°F. (24°C.), (2) 95°F. (35°C.), and 115°F. (46°C.) at 0, 150, 500, and 1,000 f.p.m. air velocity.

### Effect of Temperature of storage

The data obtained by Kulp and Bechtel (1961) on the freshness, and firmness of Danish pastry during storage at various temperatures for various periods are summarized in Table 58. For comparison, values are also included for the freshly baked product and for the product stored one day at

Table 58

Effect of Storage Time and Temperature on Freshness and Firmness of Packaged
Danish Pastry

| Days Storage | Temperature of Storage, °F. (°C.) | | | | |
|---|---|---|---|---|---|
| | 70 (21) | 20 (—6.5) | 10 (—12) | 0 (—18) | —20 (—29) |
| | Freshness[1] | | | | |
| 0 | 6.8 | 6.8 | 6.8 | 6.8 | 6.8 |
| 1 | 5.6 | — | — | 6.5 | — |
| 7 | — | 3.8 | 5.1 | 6.2 | 6.0 |
| 14 | — | 3.3 | 4.5 | 6.0 | 6.1 |
| 21 | — | 3.1 | 4.3 | 6.1 | 6.1 |
| 56 | — | — | — | 6.3 | — |
| | Firmness[2] | | | | |
| 0 | 16 | 16 | 16 | 16 | 16 |
| 1 | 29 | — | — | 28 | — |
| 7 | — | 55 | 43 | 30 | 24 |
| 14 | — | 55 | 62 | 24 | 23 |
| 21 | — | — | 79 | 31 | 29 |
| 56 | — | — | — | 29 | — |

Source: Kulp and Bechtel (1961).
[1] Minimum significant difference at 5% level = 0.8.
[2] Grams per sq. in.; minimum significant difference at 5% level = 9.7.

70°F. (21°C.). These data indicate that freshness is lost rapidly during storage at both 20° and 10°F. (—6.5° and —12°C.). In contrast, at 0°F. (—18°C.) there was no significant loss in freshness during the entire eight weeks of storage. The only increase in firmness was that caused by freezing and defrosting.

## DOUGHNUTS

**Cake-Type.**—Bechtel and Kulp (1960) have carried out comprehensive studies on the freezing, storage, and defrosting of doughnuts. The formulas for the doughnuts used in their studies are shown in Table 59.

Both cake and yeast-raised doughnuts freeze equally well provided they are handled properly. Care must be taken in thawing sugar-coated and glazed doughnuts.

The doughnuts were frozen both unwrapped and packaged at 0°, —10°, and —20°F. (—18°, —23°, and —29°C.) in still air and air blasts at 150, 500, and 1,000 linear f.p.m. Defrosting was carried out at (1) 75°F. (24°C.), 95°F. (35°C.), and 115°F. (46°C.) in still air and in air blasts at 150, 500, and 1,000 linear f.p.m.

Doughnuts and small cakes freeze in a relatively short time (Fig. 80), if they are spread out on a conveyor and frozen in an air blast at a low temperature.

Table 59

Formulas for Doughnuts

| Ingredients | Parts by Weight | |
| | Cake Doughnuts | Yeast-Raised Doughnuts[1] |
| --- | --- | --- |
| Flour | 100 | 100 |
| Water | 42 | 52 |
| Yeast | — | 6 |
| Salt | 1.5 | 2.3 |
| Sugar | 37.5 | 16 |
| Baking powder | 3. | — |
| Nonfat dry milk | 6.3 | 5 |
| Shortening | 6.3 | 16 |
| Whole eggs, frozen | — | 16 |
| Egg yolk solids | 7.8 | — |

Source: Bechtel and Kulp (1960).
[1] Fermentation time, 30 min. at 76°F. (24°C.).

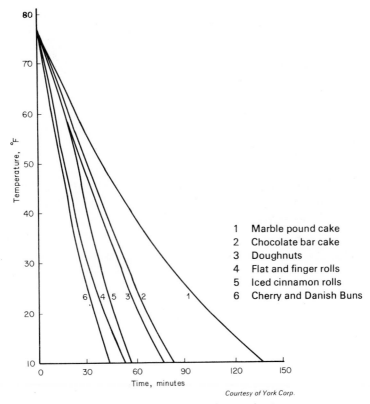

1   Marble pound cake
2   Chocolate bar cake
3   Doughnuts
4   Flat and finger rolls
5   Iced cinnamon rolls
6   Cherry and Danish Buns

Courtesy of York Corp.

Fig. 80.   Freezing rates of wrapped doughnuts, cinnamon rolls, and other specialties in a York-Union continuous freezer at −30°F. (−34°C.).

## Storage Studies

Bechtel and Kulp (1960) studied the changes in freshness and firmness of packaged doughnuts made according to the formula given in Table 59 and frozen at −20°F. (−29°C.) in an air blast at 1,000 linear f.p.m. Data obtained during storage of cake doughnuts are given in Table 60. Freshly

Table 60

Effect of Storage Time and Temperature on the Freshness and
Firmness of Cake Doughnuts

| Days in Storage | Temperature of Storage, °F. (°C.) | | | | |
|---|---|---|---|---|---|
| | 70 (21) | 20 (—6.5) | 10 (—12) | 0 (—18) | —20 (—29) |
| | Freshness Rating[1] | | | | |
| 0 | 6.9 | 6.9 | 6.9 | 6.9 | 6.0 |
| 1 | 5.5 | — | — | 6.2 | — |
| 7 | — | 5.9 | 5.8 | 6.0 | 6.0 |
| 14 | — | 5.1 | 5.3 | 5.8 | 5.6 |
| 21 | — | 4.6 | 4.6 | 5.3 | 5.5 |
| 56 | — | — | — | 4.6 | — |
| | Firmness, Grams per Square Inch[2] | | | | |
| 0 | 45 | 45 | 45 | 45 | 45 |
| 1 | 92 | — | — | 49 | — |
| 7 | — | 79 | 78 | 52 | 52 |
| 14 | — | 125 | 87 | 55 | 51 |
| 21 | — | 106 | 89 | 49 | 46 |
| 56 | — | — | — | 73 | — |

Source: Bechtel and Kulp (1960).
[1] Minimum significant difference at 5% level = 0.6.
[2] Minimum significant difference at 5% level = 13.6.

fried cake doughnuts were rated fresh (6.9) by the panel and their firmness was 45 gm. per sq. in.

Bechtel and Kulp conclude

"Freezing and defrosting lowered the freshness of doughnuts, but had far less effect than standing at room temperature for 24 hr. Within the limits employed, differences in freezing and defrosting time had only minor effects on freshness or firmness of doughnuts. If speed of freezing is of major importance, doughnuts may be frozen unwrapped with little moisture loss. Appreciable moisture loss occurs during defrosting of unwrapped doughnuts and this practice is not recommended. For frozen storage, the temperature of 0°F. (−18°C.) appears adequately low. Above this temperature doughnuts become stale and firm rather rapidly."

### OTHER FROZEN PASTRY PRODUCTS

## French Pastry

Cream puffs, chocolate éclairs, and most other French pastries can be *quick-frozen* without marked change, provided they are held at a uniformly low temperature. Rapid freezing, immediately after filling, is important as otherwise the shells may be soggy. Since the fillings of many French pastries have such a high sugar content, they partially thaw when a temperature above 5°F. is reached. Consequently, if the storage temperature fluctuates, e.g., from 0° to 5°F. ( −18° to −15°C.) a portion of the moisture thaws each time the temperature rises to 5°F. This partial thawing and refreezing repeated over and over again often causes a change in texture of the filling. For these reasons, many bakers freeze the pastry shells, and fill them after thawing (Dressel 1956).

## Cheese Cake

Most cheese cakes can be frozen and thawed without noticeable change in texture or flavor. A uniform storage temperature of 0°F. ( −18°C.) or below is also desirable for this product.

*Courtesy of Quick Frozen Foods*

Fig. 81.   Frozen cheesecake in aluminum foil container with lift-out tabs for easy removal.

### BIBLIOGRAPHY

Anon.   1954A. Quaker Oats unveils frozen pancakes. Quick Frozen Foods *17*, No. 2, 148.
Anon.   1954B. Modern Methods for Freezing Baker Products. Bakers Weekly, New York and Chicago.
Anon.   1955A. Bakers sift new techniques. Food Eng. *27*, No. 4, 113, 117, 159–160.
Anon.   1955B. Storage of frozen bakery products. Commodity Storage Manual, Refrigeration Research Foundation, Washington, D.C.
Anon.   1955C. A practical guide to cake doughnut production. Bakers Weekly *168*, No. 5, 28–31.
Anon.   1956. Making cheese cake. Food Eng. *28*, No. 1, 174.
Anon.   1964. Increasing number of cost conscious bakers discover merits of freezing. Quick Frozen Foods *27*, No. 4, 86–88.

Anon.   1966. Flexibility, economics, quality "plus" of freezing baked goods opens new vistas. Quick Frozen Foods 28, No. 8, 72–73.

Anon.   1967. Frozen cream pie sales may rise 20% via added variety plus better quality. Quick Frozen Foods 29, No. 12, 101–103.

Barta, E. J.   1958. Principles of the defrosting of frozen bakery products. Bakers Dig. 32, No. 4, 50–52.

Beattie, H. G., Edelman, E. C., and Cathcart, W. H.   1949. Keeping quality of frozen bakery products. Food Technol. 3, 160–162.

Bechtel, W. G., and Kulp, K.   1960. Freezing defrosting, and frozen preservation of cake doughnuts and yeast-raised doughnuts. Food Technol. 14, 391–394.

Cathcart, W. H.   1956. What can we expect from frozen bakery products? Cereal Science Today 1, 8.

Cathcart, W. H., and Beattie, H. G.   1947. Freezing preservation and the baking industry. Western Canner and Packer 39, No. 3, 82–83.

Copell, D. F.   1956. To freeze or not to freeze? Bakers Weekly 170, No. 8, 36.

Dressel, H.   1955. What are the possibilities for frozen cakes? Bakers Weekly 168, No. 5, 46–47.

Dressel, H. J.   1956. How to freeze bakery goods in hot humid areas. Bakers Weekly 170, No. 1, 33–34.

Fenton, F.   1951. Foods from the freezer, precooked and prepared. Cornell Extens. Bull. 692 Rev.

Glabau, C. A.   1952. How bakery products react to low-temperature freezing. Part III. The freezing of pound cake. Bakers Weekly 155, No. 13, 44–45, 48.

Glabau, C. A.   1954. Freezing and thawing cakes of different flour-sugar relationship. Bakers Weekly 163, No. 13, 54–56.

Graul, L. S., and Lowe, B.   1947. How storage affects frozen cakes and batters. Food Inds. 19, 330–332.

Kulp, K., and Bechtel, W. G.   1958. The effect of temperature and air velocity on the freezing and defrosting rates of some bakery products. I. Dinner rolls and cinnamon rolls. Cereal Chem. 35, 276–289.

Kulp, K., and Bechtel, W. G.   1960. Effect of freezing, defrosting, and storage conditions on the freshness of dinner rolls and cinnamon rolls. Cereal Chem. 37, 170–179.

Kulp, K., and Bechtel, W. G.   1961. Effect of freezing and frozen storage on the freshness and firmness of Danish pastry. Food Technol. 15, 273–275.

Kulp, K., Ponti, J. G., Jr., and Bechtel, W. G.   1959. Some factors that affect the staling of white and yellow layer cakes. Cereal Chem. 36, 228.

Mackey, A. O., Jones, P., and Dunn, J.   1952. The effect of ingredient variations on the quality of white and chocolate cakes baked prior to freezing or baked from frozen batters. Food Research 17, 216–224.

Meyer, B.   1955. Home freezing of prepared and precooked foods. J. Home Econ. 47, 603–606.

Meyer, B., Buckley, R., and Moore, R.   1949. Research shows differences in frozen butter cake and sponge cake. Refrig. Eng. 57, 340–342, 388, 392.

Meyer, B., Buckley, R., and Moore, R.   1952. Breads, cakes, and pastries from the home freezer. Univ. Tenn. Agr. Expt. Sta., Sta. Bull. 223 Rev.

Meyer, B., Moore, R., and Buckley, R.   1953. Flavor deterioration in frozen cake batters. Food Research 18, 70–75.

Miller, C., and Beattie, I. E.   1949. On the freezing and frozen storage of cakes. J. Home Econ. 41, 463–464.

Owen, R. F., Chase, J. T., and Van Duyne, F. O.   1951.  Freezing cooked and prepared foods. Univ. Ill. Agr. Extens. Service Circ. *618.*
Owen, R. F., and Van Duyne, F. O.   1950.  Comparison of the quality of freshly
baked cakes, thawed frozen baked cakes, and cakes prepared from batters which
had been frozen. Food Research *15,* 169–178.
Paul, P., Batcher, O. M., and Fulde, L.   1954.  Dry mix and frozen baked products.
I. Dry mix and frozen cakes. J. Home Econ. *46,* 249–253.
Paul, P., Batcher, O. M., and Gaffner, K.   1954.  Dry mix and frozen baked prod-
ucts. II. Dry mix and frozen muffins. J. Home Econ. *46,* 253–254.
Paul, P. Sween, E., and Bittner, B.   1955.  Dry mix and frozen baked products. III.
Dry mix and frozen gingerbread. J. Home Econ. *47,* 256–258.
Pence, J. W.   1961.  Research on freezing of bakery products. Bakers Dig. *35,* No.
6, 64–68.
Pence, J. W., and Hanamoto, M.   1959.  Studies on the freezing and defrosting of
cakes. Food Technol. *13,* 99–106.
Pence, J. W., and Heid, M.   1960.  Effect of temperature on stability of frozen
cakes. Food Technol. *14,* 80–83.
Pence, J. W., and Standridge, N. N.   1958.  Effects of storage temperature on firm-
ing of cake crumb. Cereal Chem. *35,* 57–65.
Skarha, D. M., and Van Duyne, F. O.   1955A.  Effect of freezing and freezer stor-
age on cake quality I. Baked spice cakes and cakes baked from frozen batters.
Food Research *20,* 273–281.
Skarha, D. M., and Van Duyne, F. O.   1955B.  Effect of freezing and freezer stor-
age on cake quality. II. Variation in batter treatment before and after freezer
storage. Food Research *20,* 282–288.
Steinberg, M.   1957.  Frozen fried food varieties. Proc. 33rd Ann. Meeting Am.
Soc. Bakery Engrs. 192–197.
Sunderlin, G. L.   1945.  Into the freezer instead of the oven. Quick Frozen Foods
*7,* No. 8, 88–89.
Sunderlin, G. L., and Collins, O. D. 1941.  And now—quick frozen pies, cookies,
cakes, and biscuits. Quick Frozen Foods *3.* No. 7, 13, 43–44.
Track, L.   1952.  How do to-day's waffles stand up? Quick Frozen Foods *14,* No. 9,
125, 130.
Tylor, J.   1953.  Freezing of sweet goods. Proc. 29th Ann. Meeting Am. Soc. Bak-
ery Engrs. 192–197.
Zaehringer, M. V., and Mayfield, H. L.   1951.  The effect of leavening and shortening combinations on the frozen storage of cakes and cake batters prepared at
high altitude. Food Technol. *5,* 151–154.
Ziemba, J. V.   1956.  Makes "gourmet" cakes by mass production. Food Eng. *28,*
No. 2, 55–57, 173.

## CHAPTER 21

W. S. Arbuckle

# Ice Cream and Other
# Frozen Dairy Foods

## HISTORY OF ICE CREAM MAKING

As early as 54 A.D. wines and fruit juices were cooled with ice and snow at the Court of Nero, Emperor of Rome. His slaves brought snow from the mountains and mixed it with fruit juice, pulp, and honey. Centuries later, a French cook of Charles I of England served the first ice cream at a banquet. Recipes for making cream ices are found in English cook books of the 18th century. Ice cream probably came to America with the early English colonists. A letter written in the year 1700 by a guest of Governor Bladen of Maryland reported that he had been served ice cream. The development of the ice cream industry including important processing methods, ingredient formulations, and merchandizing methods are given in the various chapters of the book *Ice Cream* by Arbuckle (1966).

The development of refrigeration, as covered in Chapter 1, of Volume 1, played an important part in ice cream making, as the cooling of wines and fruit juices led the way to the freezing of similar liquids and finally to the freezing of milk and cream.

## THE ICE CREAM INDUSTRY

The commercial production of frozen dairy foods in the United States is approximately a billion gallons and the consumption is about 22.6 qt. per capita. The production per capita for the different frozen dairy foods is approximately as follows: ice cream 15.3 qt., ice milk 4.5 qt., sherbet 0.9 qt., ices 0.7 qt., Mellorine type products 1.1 qt., and other frozen dairy products 0.1 qt. More than eight per cent of the total milk supply is utilized in the manufacture of frozen dairy foods.

The frozen dairy foods industry grew slowly in the United States until after 1900. The annual increase has been quite rapid since that date. During the past 25 years the number of plants manufacturing frozen dairy foods has decreased over 60% but the average production per plant has increased sixfold. The states in order of rank in the production of ice cream and related products are California, Pennsylvania, New York, Illinois, Ohio, Texas, Michigan, Indiana, Massachusetts, and Florida.

The International Association of Ice Cream Manufacturers has collected data on the relative distribution of the various ice cream flavors. Statistics indicate that more vanilla ice cream is sold than any other flavor and

W. S. Arbuckle is Professor of Dairy Manufacturing, University of Maryland, College Park, Md.

amounts to approximately 51%. The approximate consumption of the next five most important sellers is, chocolate, 12%; strawberry, 9%; variegated chocolate, 4%; cherry vanilla, 3%; and butter pecan, 3%. The remaining 18% is spread over 44 other flavors. A fairly good percentage of this is composed of fruit flavors.

## CLASSIFICATION OF ICE CREAMS

The general classification of frozen dairy foods includes ice cream, frozen custard or French ice cream, ice milk, sherbet, and water ices. These may include approximately 30 products depending on composition, processing methods, ingredients, flavoring, size or shape, and condition of the product when sold.

A classification based on regulatory requirements may include the following: (1) ice cream; (2) frozen custard including French ice cream; (3) ice milk; (4) sherbet; (5) water or fruit ice; (6) quiescently frozen dairy confections; (7) quiescently frozen confections; (8) artificially sweetened frozen dairy foods; and (9) imitation ice cream.

The legal definition of ice cream and related products is set forth in the Federal Standards of Identity for Frozen Desserts and includes a number of requirements. These requirements usually include those shown in Table 61.

Table 61

Composition Standards for Frozen Desserts

|  | Ice Cream | Bulky Flavor Ice Cream | Frozen Custard or French Ice Cream | | Ice Milk | Fruit Sherbet | Water Ices |
|---|---|---|---|---|---|---|---|
|  |  |  | Plain | Bulky Flavor |  |  |  |
| Minimum fat, % | 10 | 8 | 10 | 8 | 2 | 1 | — |
| Maximum fat, % | — | — | — | — | 7 | 2 | — |
| Minimum tms[1], % | 20 | 16 | 20 | 16 | 11 | 2 | — |
| Maximum tms[1], % | — | — | — | — | — | 5 | — |
| Minimum wt./gal., lb. | 4.5 | 4.5 | 4.5 | 4.5 | 4.5 | 6 | 6 |
| Minimum tfs[2] wt./gal., lb. | 1.6 | 1.6 | 1.6 | 1.6 | 1.3 | — | — |
| Maximum stabilizer, % | 0.5 | 0.5 | 0.5 | 0.5 | 0.5 | 0.5 | 0.5 |
| Maximum emulsifier, % | 0.2 | 0.2 | 0.2 | 0.2 | 0.2 | — | — |
| Maximum acidity, % | — | — | — | — | — | 0.35 | 0.35 |
| Total wt. egg yolk solids, not less than, % | — | — | 1.4 | 1.12 | — | — | — |

[1] TMS—total milk solids.
[2] TFS—total food solids.

Packaged ice cream usually refers to ice cream in containers of the kind and size in which it reaches the consumer. Bulk ice cream pertains to ice cream that is to be repackaged or dispensed in portions for the consumer.

In fruit and nut ice cream a reduction in the fat and milk solids resulting from the addition of flavoring material in fruit, nut, and chocolate flavoring material is usually allowed. This usually amounts to at least 2% fat and 4% milk solids.

BASIC INGREDIENTS

When commercial ice cream was being introduced in this country, the ingredients were cream, fluid milk, sugar, and stabilizer. Later condensed milk, nonfat dry milk, and butter became popular ice cream ingredients. Technological developments and changes in marketing and economic conditions have since encouraged the development and use of many other products.

A wide range of choice of ingredients for ice cream is now available from various sources. These ingredients may be grouped as (a) dairy products and (b) nondairy products. The dairy products group is most important as they furnish the basic ingredients of milkfat and milk-solids-not-fat (MSNF) which have essential roles in good ice cream. Some dairy products provide fat, other MSNF, others supply both fat and MSNF and still others supply bulk to the mix.

The nondairy product group includes sweetener solids, stabilizers and emulsifiers, egg products, flavors, special products, and water.

The basic ingredients in frozen dairy foods are milkfat, MSNF, sweetener solids, stabilizers, emulsifiers, and flavoring.

## Milkfat

The functional properties imparted by these different basic ingredients from which the mix is formulated are quite varied. Milkfat is an ingredient of major importance in ice cream. The use of the correct percentage is vitally essential not only to balance the mix properly, but also to satisfy legal standards. It contributes to the rich palatable flavor, imparts smoothness, improves body and texture, enhances color, and increases food value. Studies show that the fat particles concentrate toward the surface of the air cell during the freezing process in ice cream. Milkfat does not lower the freezing point. It tends to retard the rate of whipping. High fat content may limit consumption, will have a high caloric value, and will be an expensive ingredient. The fat content of commercial ice cream is usually 10 to 12%. The best source of milkfat is fresh cream. Other sources are frozen cream, plastic cream, butter, butteroil, and condensed milk blends. More recent sources of fat include the butterfat mix products, condensed sweetened cream, and specially treated milkfats.

Milk-solids-not-fat content varies inversely with fat percentage in order to maintain proper mix balance and insure proper body and texture and storage properties. Milk-solids-not-fat also enhance palatability, increase food value, and are economical. Excessive amounts may result in a salty or cooked flavor and a soggy or sandy texture defect. The amount of solids-not-fat usually add to the mix ranges from 10 to 12%. The best source of MSNF is fresh condensed skim milk or whole milk. Other sources are non-fat dry milk, superheated condensed skim milk, sweetened condensed whole or skim milk, dry whey solids, dry buttermilk solids, and special products.

## Sweetener Solids

The sweetener for ice cream may be cane sugar (sucrose) alone or may be cane sugar plus some corn product. A sweet ice cream is generally desired by the public. Sweetening should be used in moderation, not only for optimum palatability, but for handling properties as well. The sugar may be used in dry or liquid form. It is difficult to make a better ice cream than one made wholly from sucrose. Approximately 15% sugar is usually used. One-third to one-half or more of the cane sugar may be replaced by corn sugar for economy, handling, or storage reasons. Many good sugar blends are available. Much interest has been shown in the low-conversion corn syrup solids products in order to gain solids and maintain product properties and sweetness. Blends of sucrose with medium- or high-conversion corn solids have also been used advantageously.

The values sometimes used as a guide in estimating the relative sweetness of sucrose and corn syrup solids combinations are as follows: Sucrose-100, Dextrose-80, 62 D.E. (dextrose equivalent) -88, 52 D.E.-56, 42 D.E.-50, 36 D.E.-46, 32 D.E.-42, and 28 D.E.-38. A similar guide for freezing point depression is: Sucrose-1.00, Dextrose-2.00, 62 D.E.-1.14, 52 D.E.-0.96, 42 D.E.-0.78, 36 D.E.-0.67, 32 D.E.-0.61, and 28 D.E.-0.54.

Stabilizers extensively used in frozen dairy foods include: sodium and propylene glycol alginates; CMC (sodium carboxymethyl cellulose); guar gum; locust bean gum; carrageenan (Irish moss extract); gelatin; and pectin.

The alginates have an immediate stabilizing effect upon addition to mix. CMC produces a chewy characteristic in the finished product. Gelatin produces a thin mix and requires an aging period. Pectin is used in combination with the gums as a sherbet or ice stabilizer. The use of stabilizers (1) improves smoothness of body, (2) aids in preventing ice crystal formation in storage, (3) gives uniformity of product, (4) gives desired resistance to melting and improves handling properties. Limitations encountered in using excessive amounts of stabilizers include (1) undesirable melting characteristics, (2) resistance to melting, (3) soggy or heavy body.

Emulsifiers produce a smooth stiff finished product and aid in reducing the whipping time. Egg yolk solids produce similar results but usually not as pronounced effects and may be added to improve whipping and body

and texture. The emulsifiers used in frozen dairy foods may be either glyc-
erides or polysorbates.

Special products such as sodium caseinate, calcium sulfate, mineral salts,
and delactosed milk solids have various effects on the preparation of the
mix and the finished product.

## MANUFACTURE OF ICE CREAM

"Ice cream means the pure, clean, frozen products made from a combination of milk products, sugar, dextrose, corn syrup in dry or liquid form,
water, with or without egg or egg products, with harmless flavoring and
with or without harmless coloring, and with or without added stabilizer or
emulsifier composed of wholesome edible material. It shall contain not
more than 0.5% by weight of stabilizer and not more than 0.2% by weight
of emulsifier, not less than 10% by weight of milkfat and not less than 20%
by weight of total milk solids; except when fruit, nuts, cocoa, chocolate,
maple syrup, cakes, or confection are used for the purpose of flavoring,
then such reduction in milkfat and in total milk solids as is due to the addition of such flavors shall be permitted, but in no such case shall it contain
less than 8% by weight of milkfat, nor less than 16% by weight of total
milk solids. In no case shall any ice cream weigh less than 4.5 lb. per gal.
or contain less than 1.6 lb. of total food solids per gal."

The mix consists of all ingredients with the exception of flavors, fruits,
and nuts. The amount of ingredients needed is accurately calculated and is
carefully compounded to give the proper composition and balance of fat,
solids-not-fat, sugar, and stabilizer. Only the highest quality products
should be used. The use of inferior products will result in an inferior ice
cream and reduced sales.

The properties of the formulated mix should be such that it has the proper viscosity, stability, and handling properties and such that the finished ice
cream will meet the conditions which prevail in the plant where it is to be
produced.

A typical mix formula for 200 gal. of ice cream mix for a good average
composition mix of 12% butterfat, 11% MSNF, 15% sugar, 0.3% stabilizer
and 38.3% total solids might be as follows:

| | Lb. | Fat | MSNF | Sugar | Stabilizer | Total Solids |
|---|---|---|---|---|---|---|
| Cream 40% | 300.0 | 120.0 | 16.2 | | | 136.2 |
| Condensed skim milk (27%) | 247.6 | | 66.9 | | | 66.9 |
| Skim milk | 299.4 | | 26.9 | | | 26.9 |
| Sugar | 150.0 | | | 150.0 | | 150.0 |
| Stabilizer | 3.0 | | | | 3.0 | 3.0 |
| Total | 1000.0 | 120.0 | 110.0 | 150.0 | 3.0 | 383.0 |

The basic steps of production in manufacturing ice cream are composing and blending the mix, pasteurization, homogenization, cooking, ageing, flavoring, freezing, packaging, hardening, and storage.

The diagram shown in Fig. 82 presents a flow chart of the typical processes used in the manufacture of different frozen dairy foods. A typical ice cream plant layout is shown in Fig. 83.

The first step of processing is composing the mix. This procedure may range in scope from the small batch operation where each ingredient is weighed or measured and added, to the large pushbutton operation where many of the ingredients are metered into the batch. The common procedure is to: (a) add liquid materials (cream, milk, or other liquid milk products) to mix vat or pasteurizer, (b) apply heat (optional) and then add dry solids such as egg yolk, gelatin, etc. Mixing dry products with three parts of

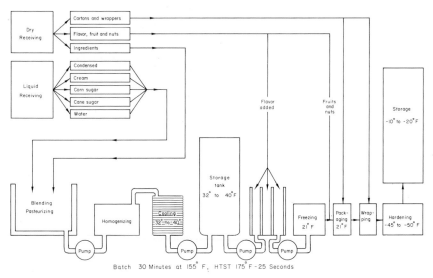

Fig. 82.   Flow chart for ice cream processing.

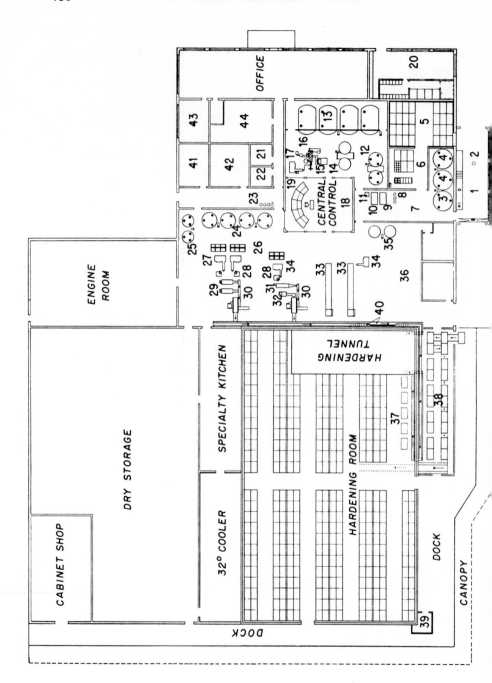

Fig. 83.   Ice cream plant layout.

1—receiving
2—tank truck manhole
3—corn syrup tank (500 gal.)
4—sugar syrup tank (500 gal.)
5—butter and plastic cream storage
6—melting room
7—storage
8—CIP tanks
9—nonfat dry milk hopper
10—cocoa hopper
11—stabilizer hopper
12—mix assembly tanks (1000 gal.)
13—raw products tanks (4000 gal.)
14—batch pasteurizing tanks (500 gal.)
15—homogenizer
16—UHT-HTST pasteurizer
17—mix cooler
18—laboratory
19—auto-control panel
20—drivers' room
21—air condition unit
22—cold water unit

23—CIP tanks
24—mix storage tanks (2,000 gal.)
25—mix storage tanks (1,000 gal.)
26—flavor tanks
27—freezers
28—fruit feeder
29—½-gal. fillers
30—Hayssen bundler
31—pint filler
32—cup filler
33—Vita freeze (500 doz.)
34—freezer
35—pop supply tank
36—chocolate bar and novelty area
37—palletizing area
38—palletizing room
39—receiving, shipping
40—belt conveyor
41—coffee lounge
42—men's locker room
43—women's locker room
44—conference room

sugar and adding to the mix will aid in their dispersion, (c) add sugar when the mix reaches approximately 120°F. (49°C.), (d) use caution to insure that all materials are dissolved before pasteurization temperature is reached.

The pasteurization process consists of heating products for approved temperature and time. This may be:

| | |
|---|---|
| Holding method | 160°F, (71°C.) for 30 min. |
| High temperature-short time | 175°F. (79°C.) for 25 sec. |
| Vacreation | 193°F. (90°C.) for instant-about 3 sec. |
| Ultra high temperature | 240°F. (115°C.) for instant |

Pasteurization (1) renders the mix free of harmful bacteria, (2) brings into solution and aids in blending the ingredients of the mix, (3) improves flavor, (4) improves keeping quality, and (5) produces a more uniform product. There is a trend toward the higher temperature processes.

When the batch pasteurization method is used the mix is pasteurized by heating to 155° or 160°F. (68° or 71°C.) and held at that temperature for 30 min., thus killing all pathogenic types of bacteria and all or nearly all other objectionable organisms. The required time and temperature of pasteurization varies in different localities depending on state and city laws and ordinances. For that reason, temperature of pasteurization is carefully controlled and recorded.

When the continuous method of pasteurization is used the high-temperature, short-time (HTST) treatment is used. Mix processing arrangements vary greatly with the HTST treatment and in some arrangements the hot mix is homogenized before pasteurization is accomplished. Immediately following pasteurization, the hot ice cream mix is passed through the high-pressure pump of the homogenizer at pressures that range from 1500 to 3000 p.s.i.; this machine breaks the particles of butter fat into very small globules (Fig. 84).

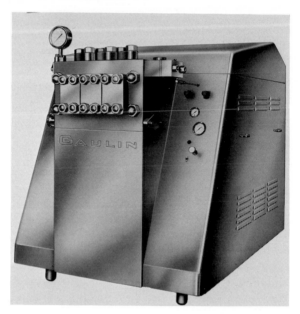

Fig. 84.   Manton-Gaulin homogenizer.

The purpose of homogenization is to produce a homogeneous mix. The hot mix is pumped from the pasteurizer through the homogenizer. The optimum homogenization temperature may range as high as 180°F. (82°C.). This process reduces the size of fat globules.

The advantages of homogenization are as follows:  (1) thoroughly blends the ingredients of the mix; (2) breaks up and disperses the fat globules, thus preventing churning of the fat during freezing; (3) improves the texture and palatability of the ice cream; (4) makes possible the use of different ingredients; (5) reduces ageing and aids in obtaining overrun; (6) produces a more uniform product.

Homogenization reduces the size of fat globules to less than two microns (one micron = $\frac{1}{25,000}$ in.). The homogenization pressures generally used are 1,500 to 3,500 lb. for the single stage machine. For the two stage homogenizer, pressures of 2,000 to 3,000 lb. are used on the first stage and 500 to 1,000 on the second stage. The correct amount of pressure to apply for a given mix is influenced by the following: type of homogenizer, temperature of mix (low temperature-lower pressure), acidity of mix (high acid-lower pressure), composition of mix (high fat, stabilizer, and solids require low pressure to prevent excessive viscosity).

The smooth mix then flows to a cooler (Fig. 85) where the product is cooled as rapidly as possible in order to prevent bacterial growth. The cooler chills the mix to a temperature of 40°F. (4°C.) or colder. After chilling,

*Courtesy of National Dairy Council*

Fig. 85.   Cooling the ice cream mix. Sanitary pipelines carry the hot, pasteurized, and homogenized mix to a cooler. Here the temperature of the mix is reduced rapidly to about 40°F. (4°C.) as the mix flows down over refrigerated tubes, then out to the holding tanks.

the mix may go directly to the freezers, or it may go to small flavor tanks where liquid flavorings like vanilla or chocolate are added, or it may go to so-called ageing tanks. These tanks, flavor or ageing, are insulated to maintain the temperature of the mix at 40°F. (4°C.) or lower. If the mix is aged, it is held from 4 to 24 hr. The ageing step is believed to be necessary if gelatin is used as the stabilizer. By ageing the mix, the gelatin has time to set and better accomplish the purpose for which it was added. Most authorities agree that a four-hour ageing is ample, but many plants prepare a mix one day and hold it overnight for freezing the next day. Most vegetable stabilizers set up immediately upon being cooled and if one of them is used, there appears to be less advantage in ageing.

Changes that take place during ageing include: (a) combination of stabilizer with water of the mix; (b) the fat solidifies; (c) the proteins may change slightly; (d) increase in viscosity; and (e) mix ingredients may become more stable.

Under present operating conditions, an ageing period of 3 or 4 hr. is satisfactory. Prolonged ageing beyond seven days may result in abnormal product properties.

Freezing the mix is one of the most important steps in the making of ice cream. The freezing process should be accomplished as rapidly as possible to insure small ice crystals and a smooth texture in either the batch freezer or the continuous freezer. The function of the freezing process is: (1) to freeze a portion of the water of the mix; (2) to incorporate air into the mix. There are four phases of the freezing process: (1) lowering the temperature from the ageing temperature (usually about 40°F.; 4°C.) to the freezing point of the mix; (2) freezing a portion of the water of the mix; (3) incorporating air into the mix; (4) hardening the ice cream after it is drawn from the freezer.

Freezing involves refrigerating the mix in a freezer cylinder which is surrounded by sub-zero ammonia or brine, as today most plants use the continuous freezer (Fig. 86). The cylindrical freezer is provided with blades which scrape the freezing mix from the refrigerated metal walls of the machine. During the whipping, air is forced into the mix increasing the volume of the frozen ice cream. Without this overrun, ice cream would be an almost inedible hard frozen mass.

The temperatures at which the mix starts to freeze varies with the per cent total solids, but for the average formula that temperature is approximately 27°F. (−2.8°C.). When the ice cream is drawn from the freezer, its temperature will usually range from 25° to 20°F. (−3.7° to −6.7°C.).

The freezing time and temperature is affected by the type of freezer used. When the batch freezer is used, the freezing time to 90% overrun approximate is about seven minutes and the drawing temperature is about

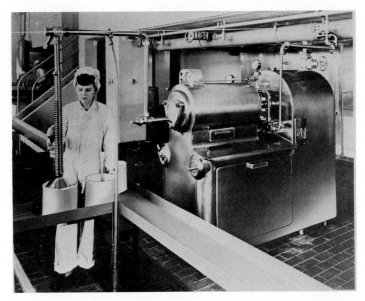

Fig. 86. Continuous ice cream freezer. The soft ice cream which emerges from the freezer is run through another machine called a flavor feeder where fruits are added prior to packaging.

24° to 26°F. (−4° to −3°C.) continuous freezer, the freezing time to 90% overrun approximate is about 24 sec. and the drawing temperature is about 21° to 22°F. (−6° to −5.6°C.); counter freezer, the freezing time to 90% overrun approximate is about 10 min. and the drawing temperature is about 26°F. (−3°C.) and for the soft serve freezer, the freezing time to 90% overrun approximate is about 3 min. and the drawing temperature is about 18° to 20°F. (−8° to −7°C.). About half the water of the mix is frozen in the freezer and most of the remaining water is frozen in the hardening room.

If fruit is to be added to the mix, the soft ice cream coming out of the freezer is run through a flavor feeder machine which adds the fruit. The soft ice cream then goes to a packaging machine where it may be packed in bulk containers or small packages (Fig. 87) for retail sale. From the packaging machine, the product goes to the hardening room, where the freezing process is completed. In the hardening room (Fig. 88), the packaged soft ice cream becomes firm within 24 hr. Hardening rooms are maintained at a temperature of −10° to −30°F. (−23° to −34°C.) either with or without forced air circulation. The ice cream is now ready for storage or delivery.

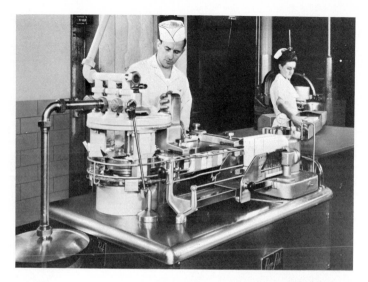

Fig. 87.   Packaging ice cream. A packaging machine opens flat paraf-
fined packages, fills them with ice cream and closes each package. This
machine packages 4,000 pints per hour.

Fig. 88.   Ice cream hardening room. In the hardening room, the soft
ice cream from the freezers becomes firm within 24 hr. Unit air cooler
and ducts are shown which maintain this room at a temperature of
−20°F. (−29°C.).

## SOFT SERVE PRODUCTS

Soft serve products are those sold as drawn from the freezer without hardening. The product is drawn from the freezer at a temperature of about 18° to 20°F. ($-8°$ to $-7°$C.). The mix composition of soft serve is usually lower in sweetener solids and total solids, in order to meet desired dryness and stiffness characteristics. The overrun on soft serve products usually ranges from 35 to 45%.

There is a marked demand for soft serve products and a high percentage of these products meet the standards for ice milk. As the soft serve products became commercially important, freezing equipment was developed which would dispense, at all times, a soft freshly frozen product. Batch and semi-continuous type freezers are available. Most retail sales establishments selling soft serve products do not attempt to produce their own mix, but buy the mix and freeze it in the soft serve freezers. Refrigerated storage space for the mix is provided.

## VANILLA AND CHOCOLATE ICE CREAM

The flavor materials should be used in sufficient amounts, and they should be of the best quality. Careful selection of fine natural flavoring materials will do much to eliminate the "unnatural flavor" criticism so often directed at the finished product.

The types of vanilla used are numerous. There are liquid and powder types. Pure vanilla, reinforced vanilla with vanillin, and imitation vanilla are available at various strengths. Concentration ranges from single strength (extracted from 13.35 gm. of vanilla beans per gallon extract) to concentrated (tenfold, or $10\times$ single strength).

The amount of vanilla used depends on mix composition. Four to six ounces of single strength vanilla per 5 gal. of 12% fat mix may be preferred. The lower the butterfat content the more vanilla is required. As the serum solids are increased, more vanilla is required. The sugar level also plays an important role. A low sugar level requires a higher vanilla level. At a high sugar level the amount of vanilla makes little difference in consumer preference.

Chocolate products for flavoring ice cream are cocoa (20–25% cocoa fat), chocolate liquor (50–53% cocoa fat), cocoa liquor blends (36–40% cocoa fat), and chocolate syrups. The use of 3% cocoa and $1\frac{1}{2}$% chocolate liquor is very acceptable.

The best chocolate ice cream is made by compounding and processing a chocolate mix of 10% fat, 10% MSNF, 18% sugar, 3% cocoa, $1\frac{1}{2}$% chocolate liquor, 0.2% stabilizer to 42–43% total solids. This is a typical formula.

Fresh fruit and frozen fruit are most desirable as fruit flavoring materials. Three to four parts of berries to one part sugar used at the rate of 15 to 20% produces good results.

Fruit particle size in ice cream is important. It is difficult to get smoothness in large fruit portions. Very small particles result in good texture but poor flavor appeal.

The amount of fruit, nuts, and candy flavoring material may vary depending on the flavor being made. This range for the fruit may be from 12–30%, for nuts from 4 to 8%, and for candy from 5 to 8%.

In fruit ice cream a reduction in the fat content up to 2% fat and up to 4% MSNF is permitted resulting from the addition of flavoring material. The importance of fresh and frozen fruits in frozen dairy foods merits further attention to this subject.

## FRUIT FLAVORS

Fruit flavors may be obtained from four sources: synthetic, canned fruit, fresh fruit, and frozen fruit.

Although synthetic fruit flavors have long been used in the making of so-called fruit ice cream, and even to this day are being used in a limited way by some manufacturers in their cheaper grades, they are far from being true fruit flavors. They are usually composed of one or more chemical substances that by analysis may be found in the fresh fruit, or are chemicals that resemble the flavor of the fruit in question. In no case are the flavors genuine, and experienced tasters can usually detect synthetic flavors; likewise, the buying public can usually detect them, and only buys ice cream made from them either because of the lack of a better product or because of low price.

Since the beginning of the canning preservation of fruits, canned fruits have been used for the flavoring of fruit ice cream. In most cases, the resulting product is far superior to one made with synthetic flavors. However, it has all of the disadvantages that the canned fruit itself has, namely, poor color, flavor, and texture.

Fruit ice cream made with fresh fruit usually excels in natural color and flavor that made with either synthetic flavors or canned fruit. Its main disadvantage is its seasonal nature. A disadvantage in its use is that the fruit itself contains so much water in its composition, that in freezing, it freezes harder than the ice cream itself, the resulting product being a smooth velvety ice cream containing hard chunks of frozen fruit.

Frozen fruit, when properly packed and frozen, is used in the making of fruit ice cream, and its use offers all of the advantages of the fresh fruit, with none of its disadvantages. A considerable number of research workers have all reported satisfactory results in the making of fruit ice cream with frozen fruit.

Frozen fruits are packed with and without sugar; with few exceptions, those packed with sugar are superior to those packed without sugar (see also Volume 3, Chapter 3). It has been found that fruits packed with sugar are best for use in the making of ice cream because the fruit takes up a high concentration of sugar and does not freeze any harder than the ice cream.

PROCEDURES AND RECIPES

## Strawberry Ice Cream

The adaptability of the varieties and the various methods of freezing strawberries have been discussed in Volume 3, Chapter 3. Fabricius (1931) did a great deal of experimenting on the use of strawberries for ice cream manufacture. He found that variety was a deciding factor influencing the quality of flavor. Maturity was the second significant factor since berries picked when fully ripe gave a superior flavor over berries which had been picked for shipment. Fabricius (1931) experiments also proved cold-packed strawberries to be superior to canned berries and that both gave products that were superior to those packed using strawberry extracts for flavoring. In the same test, Fabricius froze strawberries with and without sugar. Those frozen with sugar at $-20°F.$ $(-29°C.)$ gave the best flavored and best-textured ice cream. Hening and Dahlberg (1933) also found that ice creams in which sugar packed berries were used gave the best products in flavor, appearance, and texture. They used sliced strawberries packed in 80% cane sugar syrup which had been stored at $0°F.$ $(-18°C.)$. The strawberries were mixed into the ice cream after it was drawn. The only objection to the product was the hardness of the sliced pieces of fruit. This was overcome by allowing the frozen berries to thaw and stand in their syrup overnight.

Strawberries frozen for use in ice cream should be packed in $2 + 1$, $2\frac{1}{2} + 1$, or $3 + 1$ ratio with sugar, or in a 40 to 50% sugar syrup; this was suggested by Mack and Fellers (1932). These workers also found that the percentage of fruit used affects the rate of freezing, the body and texture of ice cream, as well as the flavor and appearance. In making ice cream using from 6 to 20% of fruit, they noted that the product became progressively better flavored up to 15%. Higher percentages increased the fruit flavor only slightly and decreased the desirability of texture and body. These defects caused the product to deteriorate more rapidly in storage and so indirectly contributed to the factor of poorer flavor.

Hening and Dahlberg (1933) suggested the following directions for making strawberry ice cream:

"A strawberry variety that has been found to give good results in freezing tests should be used. The berries should be sliced. A ratio of berries to sugar of 2 to 1 or the use of a 75% sugar solution (2.5 lb. of berries to 1.6 lb. of syrup) will give good results. It is desirable to freeze the fruit quickly to 0°F. (−18°C.) and to hold it at 0°F. (−18°C.) or below to retain the maximum flavor. Small containers, such as the 30-lb. tin single service container, can be more readily frozen and handled than barrels and proper proportions of berries to syrup can be secured more easily. Before using the berries, they should be thawed at a temperature not exceeding 40°F. (4°C.) and soaked in their syrup for 12 to 24 hr. to soften them.

It is desirable to make a special mix for fruit ice creams in which the fat content is about 2% higher and the serum solids 1.5% higher than in regular vanilla ice cream to make allowance for the diluting effect of the syrup. The sugar content of the mix should be about 2% below that of vanilla ice cream, as 5 to 6% sugar is added in the fruit juice. The use of 20% of fruit gives a very desirable, evident flavor and plenty of visible fruit. The syrup should be drained off the berries and the berries alone placed in the hardening room for about a half hour to chill well. The syrup and color should be added to the mix in the freezer. The berries can be readily mixed by hand with the frozen ice cream. A hopper is desirable, but a large can, such as a 10-gal. tin container, may be used for this purpose. It is essential to prechill the utensils and the berries to avoid increasing the temperature of the ice cream, thereby lessening the degree of smoothness and creaminess of the finished product."

It is perhaps regrettable that over the past 20 odd years, no investigator has made as comprehensive or as detailed a study on the use of frozen fruits in ice cream as did Mack and Fellers (1932) and Hening and Dahlberg (1933). Surely there is a need for such a study in view of the many new varieties that have come into existence and are now being used in commercially frozen packs.

Arbuckle (1952) reports that a 3 + 1, berry-sugar ratio pack is the best for use in ice cream. If fruit particles in ice cream are icy the product will not have good consumer acceptance. For fruit to have the same consistency as the ice cream when served, he states that the sugar content in the fruit should be at least 21%, which conditions can be held with a 3 + 1 berry-sugar ratio. Arbuckle also advises that there seem to be two schools of thought in regard to the appearance of strawberry ice cream. One group believes that the berries should be completely broken up so that only the seeds show. The other group believes that the berries should appear in large portions. He believes that both groups can be satisfied and suggests that one half the berries be pulped and added to the flavor vat and that the remainder be added through the fruit feeder.

According to Struble (1951) the ice cream industry might use greater quantities of the frozen fruits (primarily strawberries) if the quality of the frozen fruit pack was improved. In reporting on an examination of a number of samples, Struble commented on the variation in the berry-sugar ratio. The lot in question was labeled 3 + 1 berry-sugar ratio yet there were containers, the contents of which analyzed as high as 12 + 1. Obviously, variation of that nature would make it next to impossible to prepare a high-quality ice cream where the balanced ratio of butterfat to solids other than fat, is so important. Another instance of poor quality was noted in the above examination was the amount of undissolved sugar in the bottom of some containers in which the berries were packed; also too much extraneous matter was present, such as caps, weeds, and insects. In addition, Struble (1951) expressed the thought that the use of frozen fruits in ice cream manufacture would be materially increased if packers avoid varieties that do not have good berry flavor.

Struble (1952) repeated his suggestion to the packers that there be sufficient mixing of the sugar and berries so that there is never any trace of undissolved sugar in the tin. He recommended additional mixing beyond that necessary to dissolve the sugar. Struble also repeated his plea for better quality cold-packed fruit.

A report of Guadagni (1956) seems to minimize the importance of adding sugar to berries when packed for use in ice cream. He summarizes his report as follows:

"It is increasingly apparent that the most important single factor affecting the flavor quality of strawberry ice cream is the selection of highly flavored varieties which are harvested at optimum maturity and promptly frozen. With high-quality berries, such factors as freezing rate, fruit-to-sugar ratio, 'sugar curing,' and stabilization seem to offer little or no advantage in the flavor quality of the finished ice cream.

This suggests that strawberry ice cream could be satisfactorily flavored by simply adding the proper amount of high-quality unsugared strawberry purée."

In part, the above summary is in agreement with Tressler (1946) who said:

"For some unexplained reason, crushed and puréed fruits hold their flavor and color better than fruits which have not been crushed prior to freezing."

However, Tressler (1946) did not recommend packing unsugared strawberry purée for use in ice cream. He said:

"For many purposes, the addition of sugar to the purée is desirable. The addition of sugar helps to hold the flavor and color and also retards oxidation."

### Raspberry Ice Cream

The recipe quoted for strawberries is adaptable to this fruit and yields a good flavored, full-bodied ice cream.

Hening and Dahlberg (1933) found that a 20 to 25% quantity of raspberries produced an excellent flavored ice cream. The whole berry, which had been packed in 80% cane sugar syrup and stored at 0°F. ($-18$°C.) was mixed into the ice cream after it was drawn from the freezer. The syrup in which the berries was packed was added to the mix in the freezer. They noted that raspberry ice cream stored at 15°F. ($-10$°C.) for six months was of poorer flavor and texture than the same lot stored at 0°F. ($-18$°C.) for the same length of time.

Mack and Fellers (1932) reported that less fruit was necessary to make a desirable flavored ice cream of raspberries than any other fruit flavor. They used 12 to 15% of raspberry purée from which 75% of the seeds had been removed. This gave a superior product in flavor, but still somewhat seedy in texture. After reducing the purée to 10% and combining with commercial extract, a product of equally good flavor and better texture was produced.

A marked difference in the desirability of different varieties was found. Preferred in order were Cuthbert, Herbert, and St. Regis. The varieties Newman, Latham, and Ontario gave decidedly poorer products and deteriorated in storage more quickly. Raspberries of the first three varieties yielded better flavored ice creams when they had been packed in 3 + 1 ratios with cane sugar syrups. The ratio of 2 + 1 was also acceptable, but not superior in flavor or texture.

### Peach Ice Cream

The adaptability of different varieties of peaches to freezing has been discussed in Volume 3, Chapter 3. Early Crawford was the only variety used by Hening and Dahlberg (1933) in their studies. Mack and Fellers (1932) noted that good flavored peach ice cream could be made with Hiley, J. H. Hale, Elberta, Champion, and Crawford.

It was found that pulped peach skin would greatly increase the flavor of peach ice cream. Also in the same studies, Hening and Dahlberg found that peaches packed in the ratio of 5 + 1 of cane sugar and kept at 0°F. ($-18$°C.) produced a good textured and flavored ice cream if 25 to 30% of fruit was used.

A slightly lower amount of fruit, 15 to 20% was suggested by Mack and Fellers and a ratio of 3 + 1 parts of fruit to sugar was considered by them to yield the best product.

They found that yellow-fleshed peaches gave a greater concentration of flavor than white, and since the fruit is firmer in texture, large shreds of the yellow peaches were evident in the ice cream. They did not find any variety to yield sufficient flavor unless a flavoring extract was added along with the fruit. By replacing one-third of the peaches with apricots, excellent results are claimed by some manufacturers. Pulped fruit was found to be easier to handle and yielded a more desirable flavor and appearance since shreds of the peaches were visible.

The following directions for the making of peach ice cream are given by Hening and Dahlberg (1933):

"Fresh, ripe peaches of a standard variety with a fairly pronounced flavor should be dipped in boiling water, skinned, and ground or very finely sliced. The pulp should be mixed with sugar at the rate of 5 to 1 and immediately frozen to and held at 0°F. (−18°C.) or below.

A day before using, the frozen peaches should be held at 40°F. (4°C.) to thaw. The color and the peaches may be added to the ice cream mix in the freezer as there is little advantage in endeavoring to retain pieces of peach in the ice cream due to the blending of color with the ice cream and to lack of a pronounced flavor. About 25% of peaches gave a recognizable, mild peach flavor. Peaches do not increase the moisture and sugar content of the ice cream as much as strawberries or raspberries, so they may be advantageously added to the regular vanilla mix, but the flavor will be best if the mix is rather rich.

As previously mentioned, approximately 20 to 30% of the fresh, ripe peaches may be skinned like an apple and, after grinding the skins finely and adding 20% of sugar, cooked for five minutes just below the boiling point. The cooked skins with pulp may then be frozen and used to increase the intensity of the peach flavor by replacing 5 to 10% of the peaches in the ice cream. The skins must be fine enough to avoid detection in the ice cream.

One per cent of apricot added to peach ice cream increased the intensity of the flavor noticeably. Although the flavor was characteristic of apricots, few persons recognized their presence."

## Cherry Ice Cream

Sour varieties of cherries were found to be superior to other kinds of cherries in the production of ice cream. Mack and Fellers (1932) list in the order of preference Montmorency, Early Richmond, and May Duke. The Morello variety is less desirable and none of these varieties gives as good a flavor as processed maraschino cherries. The addition of a good commercial cherry extract, or the use of a small amount of oil of bitter almonds, added to the thawed frozen fruit of any of the above varieties, will give a flavor of ice cream comparable to that made from maraschino cherries. For ten gallons of fruit it is necessary to add only 1 to 2 ml. of oil of bitter almonds or benzaldehyde. This must be thoroughly mixed through the fruit before adding to the ice cream mix.

The following recipe for cherry ice cream was developed by Hening (1935):

"Eleven pounds of Montmorency cherries packed in the ratio of 4 to 1 plus 2½ lb. of sugar were thawed and allowed to soak in their syrup for 20 hr. prior to their use in ice cream. It took the greater part of this time to dissolve the additional sugar. This total of 13½ lb. of cherries and syrup was added in the early part of the freezing period to the 31½ lb. of mix in the freezer. This mix contained 14% fat, 11% MSNF, 14% sugar, and 0.5% of a medium grade gelatin. The scraper and dasher broke up the cherries and after the ice cream was hardened, small pieces of cherry were attractively distributed through the ice cream. These pieces were not hard or icy and they increased the cherry flavor in the ice cream.

Thirty per cent of cherries and syrup may seem like an excessive amount, but since the cherry flavor is mild, this amount can be used to very good advantage. Cherry ice cream is very refreshing and was pronounced very good by everyone tasting it. The addition of a small amount of almond flavor or bitter almond oil produced an unusual and pleasing flavor. Experiments with cherries to which cherry extract had been added before freezing the cherries indicated that excellent flavor could be secured with a little less fruit, but the proportion of fruit in the ice cream needed to be high."

Arbuckle *et al.* (1961) used fruit concentrate and essence of seven different fruits including peach, apple, strawberry, blueberry, grape, red raspberry, and cherry to flavor ice cream, sherbets, ices, ice milk, and variegated ice cream. Many of the fruit concentrates and essences studied proved to be valuable and economical means of improving the flavor of fruit ice cream and related products, either when used to supplement the use of fruit, or in some cases, when used as the only source of fruit flavor.

### Pineapple Ice Cream

Frozen pineapple was not available for the work done by Mack and Fellers in 1932 but it is believed that considering the excellent product that can be obtained in the freezing of pineapple, they could have produced equally satisfactory results with frozen pineapple in place of the heat-preserved fruit they used. Their work showed that from 12 to 15% fruit gave the most desirable flavor and texture to ice cream. In a comparison of pineapples packed in Hawaii and Puerto Rico by crushing and canning, the flavor imparted by the Hawaiian packs was noticeably stronger and better. They also had the advantages of firmer flesh, less syrup, and better color.

### Other Fruit Ice Creams

Mack and Fellers (1932) made studies of fruit ice creams and fruit ices using less common flavors. In such fruits as wild and Evergreen blackberries, cranberries, Damson plums, red currants, rhubarb, and nectarines, they attained surprising results.

In using blackberries of both wild and Evergreen varieties, the products were only of fair quality since the good natural flavor was offset by a decidedly inferior appearance. This was also true when red currants, Damson plums, and rhubarb were added to the ice cream mix. These same fruits gave good quality products when made into frozen ices.

Nectarines imparted a flavor not unlike peaches when used in ice cream, but the frozen product was unattractive in appearance after storage.

In ice cream, cranberries lost their characteristic flavor. In frozen ices, the pulped fruit gave a product superior to the fruit packed whole or sliced. Cranberry pulp or sliced cranberries were scored the best packs in appearance and flavor when they were frozen with sugar in a ratio of 1 + 1. Regardless of the method of freezing, the fruit kept perfectly in storage.

Apricot ice cream was produced by Hening and Dahlberg (1933) using a ratio of 4 lb. of fruit to 1 lb. of sugar. The pulp was preheated to 180° to 190°F. (82° to 88°C.) and held for five minutes before freezing. When the fruit was stirred into the ice cream after it was drawn from the freezer, the skins of the apricot were much less noticeable than when they were added to the mix in the freezer. The flavor was satisfactory and the color and texture acceptable.

Hening (1949) in developing a new method of producing apple juice found that the resulting product could be used to add apple flavor to ices and ice cream. In making juice he found it advantageous to add ascorbic acid in apple juice solution during or immediately after milling and before pressing. Thirty-five per cent of this apple juice was blended with an ice cream mix that contained 14% milkfat, 10% MSNF and 15% sugar. While this ice cream was a delicious product, the mix appeared diluted. Later experiments indicated that 29% of the 37% soluble solids apple juice concentrate resulted in an excellent product, when an additional 5% sugar was added to the apple juice concentrate.

## Variegated Ice Cream

This is an ice cream that has become especially popular. When this product first appeared on the market it was a vanilla ice cream with chocolate ribboned through it. The appearance of the product gave it such names as ripple, ribbon, ribbonnette, wave, marble, and zig-zag ice cream. As the popularity of the product increased, other combinations of flavors have appeared on the market and among these are the fruit purées that have been covered in Chapter 4 of Volume 3.

Dahle (1941) describes the methods for the manufacture of variegated ice cream as follows:

"Many types of pumps, fillers, etc., are available for use with the continuous freezers which give a nice "waviness" of flavor to the ice cream, and more uniformity than with some of the apparatus used for batch freezers. Some of the equipment used for incorporating the flavor with the batch freezer is far from sanitary, but it works fairly well. The pressure tank apparatus requires two operators for best results.

"Some small manufacturers using batch freezers have done a good job by pouring in the flavor from the measuring can as the ice cream is coming from the freezer. This takes two operators, one to pour and the other to throttle the gate of the freezer. The one who pours has the pouring lip of a two quart container against the stream of ice cream coming from the batch freezer. Brick ice cream can be made from batch ice cream by merely pouring the flavor on layers of vanilla ice cream in the tray. This is a clumsy way to operate, but it is being practiced by many small manufacturers using batch freezers."

Today, variegated ice cream is an important product as it is believed to rank fourth behind vanilla, chocolate, and strawberry in sales across the country. Variegator machines are available that make possible precise control of the amount of the variegating desired in packages ranging from pints to half-gallons.

## Frozen Custard

Frozen custard includes French ice cream and French custard ice cream, and under Federal Standards has composition requirements similar to those for ice cream, but must contain a minimum of 1.4% egg yolk solids. If bulky flavors are used, frozen custard may contain 1.12% egg yolk solids.

"Frozen custard is a clean, wholesome product made from a combination of two or more of the following ingredients: milk products, sugar, dextrose, corn syrup in dry or liquid form, water, with egg or egg products, with harmless flavoring and with or without harmless coloring, and with or without added stabilizer or emulsifier composed of wholesome edible material. It shall contain not more than $\frac{1}{2}\%$ by weight of stabilizer, and not more than $\frac{1}{5}\%$ by weight of emulsifier, not less than 10% by weight of milkfat, not less than 20% by weight of total milk solids, not less than 1.4% by weight of egg yolk solids, except when it shall contain fruits or nuts, cocoa, chocolate, maple syrup, cakes, or confection used for the purpose of flavoring, then such reduction in milkfat, total milk solids, and egg yolk solids as is due to the addition of such fruits and nuts shall be permitted, but in no case shall it contain less than 8% by weight of milkfat nor less than 16% by weight of total milk solids and 1.12% by weight of egg yolk solids. In no case shall any frozen custard weigh less than $4\frac{1}{2}$ lb. per gallon and contain less than 1.6 lb. of total food solids per gallon."

An example of a formula for custard or French ice cream may be as follows:

| Ingredient | Solids, % |
|---|---|
| Milkfat | 10.1 |
| Milk solids-not-fat | 11.0 |
| Egg yolk solids | 1.5 |
| Sweetener solids | 16.0 |
| Stabilizer-emulsifier | 0.4 |
| Total solids | 39.0 |

## Ice Milk

Ice milk is a product similar to ice cream but less milkfat and food solids. "It shall contain not more than ½% by weight of stabilizer, not more than ⅕% by weight of emulsifier, not less than 2%, nor more than 7% by weight of milkfat, and not less than 11% by weight of total milk solids. In no case shall any ice milk weigh less than 4½ lb. per gallon and contain less than 1.3 lb. of total food solids per gallon."

An example of ice milk formula is as follows:

| Ingredient | Solids, % |
|---|---|
| Milkfat | 4.0 |
| Milk solids-not-fat | 13.0 |
| Sweetener solids | 13.0 |
| Stabilizer-emulsifier | 0.5 |
| Total solids | 30.5 |

## Fruit Sherbets

"Sherbet is a pure, clean, frozen product made from milk products, sugar, dextrose, corn syrup in dry or liquid form, water, with or without egg or egg products and harmless fruit or fruit juice flavoring and with or without harmless coloring with not less than 0.35% with fruit acid, as determined by titrating with standard alkali and expressed as lactic acid, and with or without added stabilizer or emulsifier composed of wholesome edible material. It shall contain not less than 3% nor more than 5% by weight of total milk solids and weigh not less than 6 lb. per gallon."

Day et al. (1959) presented formulas involving corn sweeteners for sherbets which had melting points similar to that of ice cream. A formula for a medium smooth, medium firm body and texture was listed as follows:

| Ingredient | Lb. |
|---|---|
| Cane sugar | 11.0 |
| Corn syrup solids (30 D.E.) | 10.0 |
| Ice cream mix (12% fat, 11% MSNF, 15% sugar) | 17.5 |
| Stabilizer | 0.4 |
| Fruit purée (5 + 1) | 15.0 |
| Water and 10¾ oz. 50% citric acid solution and color | 46.1 |
| | 100.0 |

Ross (1963) outlines numerous formulas suitable for commercial use.

## Water or Fruit Ice

Water ice or fruit ice is a pure, clean frozen product made from sugar, dextrose, corn syrup in dry or liquid form, water and harmless fruit or fruit

juices flavoring with or without harmless coloring, with not less than 0.35%
of fruit acid, as determined by titrating with standard alkali and expressed
as lactic acid and with or without added stabilizer or emulsifier composed
of wholesome edible material, It shall contain no milk solids and weigh not
less than 6 lb. per gallon.

Fruit ices differ from ice cream in body and texture and are usually
somewhat more tart in flavor. Water replaces the cream, while for sherbets
whole milk is used. A satisfactory base for fruit ices can be made (Mack
and Fellers, 1932) from:

| Ingredient | Lb. |
|---|---|
| Water | 33 |
| Cane sugar | 9 |
| Fruit | 8 to 10 |
| Corn syrup solids | 3 |
| Gelatin | 0.5% |
| Citric acid or tartaric acid (50%) | |
| enough to produce an acidity of 0.7% | |

"Freeze to a firm consistency in the freezer. An overrun of 30 to 35% can be expected when the ice is drawn. Sherbets can be made by the same formula, substituting whole milk for water."

Satisfactory fruit pulps to use for ices include puréed raspberries, peaches, strawberries, plums, and pineapples. Rhubarb packed in a ratio of 1 +
1 with cane sugar; blackberry pulp packed 2 + 1; currants; and cranberries
frozen 2 + 1 with sugar; all yield products possessing characteristic flavors.

Hening (1949) reported that a pleasing milk flavored apple ice was produced by using 79.2% apple juice and 20% sugar.

## Miscellaneous Products

Other products not covered in the standards of identity, but regulated by
some states are as follows:

"Quiescently frozen dairy confections mean a clean and wholesome frozen product made from water, milk products, and sugar, with added pure or imitation flavoring, with or without added harmless coloring, with or without added stabilizer
and with or without added emulsifier; and in the manufacture of which freezing
has not been accompanied by stirring or agitation. It contains not less than 13% by
weight of total milk solids, not less than 33% by weight of total food solids, not
more than ½% by weight of stabilizer, and not more than ⅕% of weight by
emulsifier. Stabilizer and emulsifier must be composed of wholesome edible material.

"This confection must be manufactured in the form of servings, individually
packaged, bagged, or otherwise wrapped, properly labeled and purveyed to the
consumer in its original factory-filled package.

"In the production of these quiescently frozen confections, no processing or mixing prior to quiescent freezing shall be used that develops in the finished confection mix any physical expansion in excess of ten per cent.

"Quiescently frozen confections mean a clean and wholesome frozen, sweetened, flavored product in the manufacture of which freezing has not been accompanied by stirring or agitation. This confection may be acidulated with harmless organic acid, may contain milk solids, may be made with or without added harmless pure or imitation flavoring, with or without added harmless coloring. The finished product may contain not more than ½% by weight of stabilizer or emulsifier composed of wholesome edible material. The finished product shall contain not less than 17% by weight of total food solids."

"This confection must be manufactured in the form of servings, individually packaged, bagged or otherwise wrapped, properly labeled, and purveyed to the consumer in its original factory-filled package."

"Artificially sweetened ice cream means the pure, clean, frozen product made from a combination of milk products, sorbitol, calcium cyclamate, a nonnutritive artificial sweetener for use only by persons who must restrict their intake of ordinary sweets, with or without egg or egg products, with harmless flavoring and with or without harmless coloring, and with or without added stabilizer or emulsifier composed of wholesome edible material. It shall contain not more than ½% by weight of stabilizer and not more than ⅕% by weight of emulsifier, not less than 10% by weight of milkfat, and not less than 20% by weight of total milk solids; except when fruit, nuts, cocoa, chocolate, maple syrup, cakes, or confection are used for the purpose of flavoring, said flavoring shall be sweetened only with an artificial sweetener, then such reduction in milkfat and in total milk solids as is due to the addition of such flavors shall be permitted, but in no such case shall it contain less than 8% by weight of milkfat, nor less than 16% by weight of total milk solids. In no case shall any artificial sweetened ice cream weigh less than 4½ lb. per gallon and contain less than 1.6 lb. of total food solids per gallon."

"Imitation ice cream is any frozen substance, mixture, or compound regardless of the name under which it is represented, which is made in imitation or semblance of ice cream, or is prepared or frozen as ice cream is customarily prepared or frozen, and which is not ice cream, ice milk, frozen custard, sherbet, water ice, or fruit ice or quiescently frozen confections and quiescently frozen dairy confections as they are defined in this section."

**Mellorine.**—Mellorine is similar to ice cream or ice milk except that milkfat is replaced with a vegetable or animal fat. Willingham (1967) suggests the following formula for a good quality vegetable fat frozen dessert which can be marketed as mellorine.

| Ingredient | % |
|---|---|
| Vegetable fat | 12 |
| MSNF | 10.5 |
| Sweetener (in using corn sweetener or corn products, it may be possible to go as high as 17–18%) | 15–18 |
| Stabilizer | 0.3–0.4 |
| Emulsifier, if used | 0.05–0.1 |

It appears that the Federal Standards of Identity for ice cream will be that the product must contain at least 10% butterfat, but where a lower fat content is legal, a high-quality mellorine can be made using 8% vegetable fat, 10% MSNF, 15 to 18% sugar, 0.3 to 0.4% stabilizer, and an emulsifier may be used if desired.

In 1955, the U.S. Food and Drug Administration issued the following statement of general policy or interpretation (Federal Register, April 22):

"Use of Vegetable Fat in Products which are Imitations of Ice Cream.

"Under the authority vested in the Secretary of Health, Education and Welfare, by the provisions of the Federal Food and Drug and Cosmetic Act (sec. 701, 52 Stat. 1055; 21 U.S.C. 371) and delegated to the Commissioner of Food and Drugs by the Secretary (20 F.R. 1966), and pursuant to the provisions of the Administrative Procedure Act (sec. 3, 60 Stat. 237, 238; 5 U.S.C. 1002), the statement of interpretation contained in Section 3.18 *Use of vegetable fat in ice cream*, published in the FEDERAL REGISTER April 12, 1950 (15 F.R. 2082) is hereby revoked and the following statement of interpretation is hereby issued:

"Section 3.39 *Use of vegetable fat in products which are imitations of ice cream*. There is currently being marketed in interstate commerce a frozen product made in semblance of ice cream, but containing vegetable fats in complete or partial substitution for milkfat. In some cases the product is marketed under a fanciful designation. Such a product is not regarded as an imitation of ice cream, and thus amenable to the provision of the Federal Food, Drug and Cosmetic Act requiring the label to bear the name 'Imitation Ice Cream' with all these words in type of uniform size and prominence, regardless of whether a fanciful designation is used."

The following procedure, as reported by Reitz (1954) is the one most generally used.

Water (softened) is weighed and run into a mixing tank. It is then recirculated through the dry mixer where the nonfat milk solids, emulsifiers, stabilizers, and powdered eggs are weighed and blended. This homogeneous mixture is then pumped into a pasteurizing vat. Liquid sugar, corn syrup, and vegetable fat or oil are automatically measured into the mix. The vegetable fat used may be cottonseed, soybean (Rich 1953), or coconut oil. The fat is hydrogenated to a melting point of 94° to 98°F. (34° to 37°C.). The vegetable fats do not contain cholesterols and lack vitamin A. However, this vitamin can be added in controlled amounts. The mix is pasteurized at 165°F. (74°C.) for 15 min., is then homogenized and passed through the plate cooler to reduce the temperature to 38°F. (4°C.). The mix goes to a refrigerated tank where strawberries or vanilla are added. Chocolate is a special mix and the flavoring is added before pasteurization. The mix is pumped to a continuous freezer that discharges the product directly into filling and packaging machines.

## OTHER IMITATIONS OF DAIRY PRODUCTS

There are several formulations for vegetable dairy systems which can be frozen (Palmer 1967). Some of these with an explanation of the manufacturing steps are as follows:

## Imitation Milk

| Ingredient | % |
|---|---|
| Water | 87.25 |
| Nonfat milk solids | 9.00 |
| Durkee's Paramount C | 3.50 |
| Durkee's SGF 187 | 0.25 |
| Total | 100.00 |

**Procedure.**—Add nonfat milk solids to water and mix well to dissolve. Heat to 120°F. and add Paramount C and SGF 187. Heat mix to 160°F. (71°C.) for 30 min. and homogenize at 2,000 and 500 p.s.i. through two stage homogenizer. Cool product as rapidly as possible to 40°F. (4°C.). Product can be frozen and defrosted before use.

## Frozen Imitation Coffee Cream

| Ingredient | % |
|---|---|
| Low D.E. corn syrup solids | 10.00 |
| Paramount C or X | 10.00 |
| Sodium caseinate | 1.75 |
| SGF 187 | 0.40 |
| Carrageenan | 0.15 |
| Di-potassium phosphate | 0.30 |
| Water | 77.40 |
| Total | 100.00 |

**Procedure.**—Melt together Paramount and SGF 187. Dry mix corn syrup solids, sodium caseinate, stabilizer, and tetrasodium pyrophosphate. Add to water and heat to 105°F. (41°C.) while mixing. Add melted fat to water mixture and pasteurize at 160°F. (71°C.). Homogenize at 2,500 and 500 p.s.i. through two-stage homogenizer. Cool to 40°F. (4°C.), package, and freeze. Defrost at 40°F. (4°C.) before use.

## Concentrated Vegetable Fat Milk (Freeze-Thaw Stable)

| Ingredient | % |
|---|---|
| Nonfat milk solids | 36.00 |
| Water | 49.00 |
| Durkee's Paramount C with lecithin | 14.00 |
| Durkee's SGF 187 | 1.00 |
| Total | 100.00 |

**Procedure.**—Add nonfat milk solids to water. Mix well to disperse solids. Add Paramount C and SGF 187 and heat mix to 160°F. (71°C.) for 30 min. Homogenize mix at 2,000 and 500 p.s.i. through two-stage homogenizer. Cool mix as rapidly as possible to 40°F. (4°C.). Mix may be frozen. Defrost at 40°F. (4°C.) before use. To prepare combine 1 part mix with 3 parts cold water.

## BIBLIOGRAPHY

Anon. 1948. Ice-cream-mix. Natl. Military Estab. Specifications *JAN -1-705*, Dec. 8.

Anon. 1950. Ice-cream-mix. Natl. Military Estab. Specifications *JAN-1-705*, Amendment-1, April 21.

Anon. 1953. Ice cream: sherbets and ices. Federal Specification *EE-1-116b*, May 29.

Anon. 1954. Sales of "imitation ice cream" more than double in year. Quick Frozen Foods *17*, No. 1, 52.

Anon. 1955. Dairy products—general. Dairy Industry Supply Assoc. Trade and Tech. Bull. *622*.

Anon. 1960. Federal Standards for frozen desserts-Definition and Standards of Identity under Federal Food, Drug and Cosmetic Act, Part 20, Title 21, Code of Federal Regulations, Federal Register, 25, No. 145, July 27.

Anon. 1965. Production index of ice cream and related products. Special Bull. *110*, IAICM, Washington, D.C.

Arbuckle, W. S. 1952. Stabilized fruits for ice cream. Ice Cream Trade J. *48*, No. 5, 34, 36, 86.

Arbuckle, W. S. 1955. Potentials for flavor improvement. Ice Cream Field *66*, No. 5, 64, 66.

Arbuckle, W. S. 1966. Ice Cream, Avi Publishing Co., Westport, Conn.

Arbuckle, W. S., *et al.* 1961. The technology of utilizing concentrated fruit juices and essences in ice cream and related products. Md. Agr. Expt. Sta. Bull. A-118.

Bassett, H G. 1958. Ice cream emulsifiers. Ice Cream Review *42*, No. 2, 34, 36, 48–50.

Beavens, E. A. 1949. New frozen citrus purées and their use. Ice Cream Trade J. *45*, No. 10, 58, 96.

Bedford, C. L. 1946. The use of fruit purées in ice cream. Ice Cream Trade J. *42*, No. 5, 44, 80.

Bell, C. J. 1948. Manufacture of ice cream. Refrig. Eng. 55, No. 1, Refrig. Eng. Application Data Section 41.

Bendixen, H. A. 1948. Ice cream shrinkage. Ice Cream Trade J. *44*, No. 2, 46–47, 90–95.

Bird, E. W., Ross, O. E., Iverson, C. A., Ause, O. R., and Willingham, J. J. 1938. Oxidized flavors in strawberry ice cream. Iowa S. Coll. Agr. Res. Bull. *230*.

Bitter, H. 1947. Fast-freezing tunnels. Ice Cream Trade J. *43*, No. 3, 50; J. Dairy Sci, *30*, 97–98.

Bitting, H. W. 1955. Frozen food use in preserves, pies and ice cream. Quick Frozen Foods *17*, No. 10, 129–131.

Cane, R. F. 1949. Frozen fruits in ice cream. Ice Cream Field *53*, No. 6, 77.

Carvel, T. 1949. Frozen custard. Sou. Dairy Prod. J. *45*, No. 4, 60, No. 6, 96.

Culpepper, C. W., Caldwell, J. S., and Wright, R. C. 1928. Preservation of peaches for use in the manufacture of ice cream. U.S. Dept. Agr. Tech. Bull. *84*.

Dahlberg, A. C. 1956. The influence of ice milk and Mellorine on ice cream volume. Ice Cream Trade J. *52*, No. 2, 64–66, 113–115.

Dahle, C. D. 1930. Ice cream improved by quick-freezing. Food Inds. *2*, 178–179.

Dahle, C. D. 1941. Variegated ice cream. Ice Cream World *37*, No. 4, 14, 86.

Dahle, C. D. 1945. Commercial ice cream manufacture. Penna. State Coll. Agr. Expt. Sta. Circ. *277*.

Dahle, C. D.  1956. Composition of ice cream—functions and sources of principal constituents. Can. Dairy and Ice Cream J. 35, No. 8, 46–47.

Davis, J. G., Hanson, H. L., and Lineweaver, H.  1952. Characterization of the effect of freezing on cooked egg white. Food Research 17, 393–401.

Day, E. A., Arbuckle, W. S., and Seely, D. J.  1959. The manufacture of improved quality sherbets. Ice Cream Field 73, No. 2, 28, 30, 78–79.

Deck, E. M.  1952. Vegetable fat frozen desserts. Ice Cream Review 36, No. 4, 4, 78–79.

Deck, E. M.  1953. Tips on the manufacture of Mellorine. Ice Cream Review 36, No. 12, 106–108.

Decker, C. W.  1951. Strawberry ice cream. Ice Cream Review 34, No. 11, 146, 148, 150.

Eckles, C. H., Combs, W. B., and Macy, H.  1951. Milk and Milk Products, 4th Edition, McGraw-Hill Book Co., New York.

Fabricius, N. E.  1931. Strawberries for ice cream manufacture. Iowa Agr. Expt. Sta. Circ. 132.

Fouts, E. L., and Freeman, T. R.  1948. Dairy Manufacturing Processes. J. Wiley and Sons, New York.

Frandsen, J. H.  1958. Dairy Handbook and Dictionary. J. H. Frandsen, Amherst, Mass.

Frandsen, J. H., and Nelson, P. H.  1950. Ice Creams and Other Frozen Desserts, J. H Frandsen, Amherst, Mass.

Gelpi, A. J.  1955. Effect of antioxidants in the control of oxidized flavor development in stored ice cream. J. Dairy Sci. 38, 197–201.

Gemmill, A. V.  1953. One-floor straight-line operation. Food Eng. 25, No. 2, 51–55, 186–187.

Glabe, E. F., Goldman, P. F., Anderson, P. W., and Finn, L. A.  1956. Uses of Gelsoy in prepared food products. Food Technol. 10, 51–56.

Guadagni, D. G.  1956. Some quality factors in strawberries for ice cream. Quick Frozen Foods 18, No. 7, 211–212.

Guadagni, D. G., Walker, L. H., Talburt, W. F., and Farris, R.  1952. New apple sherbet flavor. Ice Cream Field 59, No. 3, 26, 72, 74.

Haire, R., and O'Meara, J.  1956. "Regimenting" ice cream in and out of tunnel gets faster, better hardening. Food Eng. 28, No. 9, 80, 189.

Halberstadt, M.  1952. Fast-freeze wind tunnels (for hardening ice cream). Intl. Assoc. Ice Cream Mfg. Proc. 48th Ann. Conv., 2, 49–51.

Hanson, H. L.  1954. Freezing of cooked poultry and egg products. Frosted Food Field 19, No. 1, 20–21.

Hanson, H. L., Nishita, K. D., and Lineweaver, H.  1953. Preparation of stable frozen puddings. Food Technol. 7, 462–465.

Hening, J. C.  1935. Using frozen cherries in cherry ice cream. Ice Cream Trade J. 31, No. 11, 16.

Hening, J. C.  1949. Apple ice and apple ice cream. Fruit Products J. 28, 365, 381.

Hening, J. C.  1950. Apple ice and apple ice cream possible by use of apple juice concentrate. Food in Canada 10, No. 4, 28–30.

Hening, J. C., and Dahlberg, A. C.  1933. Frozen fruits for ice cream, N. Y. S. Agr. Expt. Sta. Bull. 634.

Hibben, R. C.  1951. Ice cream—a century of progress. Southern Dairy Products J. 50, No. 6, 54–56.

Hoover, W. J. 1961. Experimental design to measure flavor differences with special reference to clingstone peaches. Presented at Ann. Mtg. Inst. of Food Technologists, New York.

Illes, G. M. 1955. Good sherbets. Ice Cream Field 65, No. 5, 50–52, 54–56.

Jacobson, R. E., and Bartlett, R. W. 1963. The ice cream and frozen dessert industry. Univ. Ill. Bull. 694.

Keeney, P. G. 1965. Commercial ice cream and other frozen desserts. Penna. S. Univ. Circ. 525.

Kiser, W. R. 1951. Production problems in fruit and nut ice cream. Southern Dairy Products J. 49, No. 6, 32, 134–136.

Krienke, W. A. 1956. Injection Method for fruit ice cream. Ice Cream Trade J. 52, No. 1, 38, 40, 90–92.

Leach, H. S. 1953. Good fruit ice cream. Ice Cream Field 61, No. 3, 20, 24, 26, 78, 80, 82.

Lehner, E. C. 1951. Method of making variegated ice cream. U.S. Pat. 2,576,842, Nov. 27.

Mack, M. J., and Fellers, C. R. 1932. Frozen fruits and their utilization in frozen dairy products. Mass. Agr. Expt. Sta. Bull. 287.

Mackenzie, P. K. 1955. Refrigeration equipment in the ice cream industry. Ice Cream Indus. Yearbook 1954–1955, 97–99, 106–108.

Masurovsky, B. I. 1946. The peach family of fruits in ice cream. Ice Cream Trade J. 42, No. 3, 62, 88.

Merory, J. 1960. Food Flavorings. Composition, Manufacture, Use. Avi Publishing Co., Westport, Conn.

Nickerson, T. A. 1954. Lactose crystallization in ice cream. I. Control of crystal size by seeding. J. Dairy Sci. 37, 1099–1105.

Palmer, H. H. 1967. Private Communication. Albany, Calif.

Pearson, A. M. 1963. Liquid nitrogen immersion for ice cream hardening. Ice Cream World 69, No. 10, 20, 34.

Price, S. D. 1955. Freezing of fruits for ice cream. Ice Cream Trade J. 51, No. 5, 36, 38, 110–114.

Reitz, A. J. 1954. New plant tailored to vegetable-oil "ice cream." Food Eng. 26, No. 7, 90–92.

Rich, R. E. 1953. The vegetable fat story. Quick Frozen Foods 16, No. 1, 116, 118.

Ross, O. E. 1950. Sherbets and ices. Ice Cream Trade J. 46, No. 7, 44–45, 86–92.

Ross, O. E. 1955. Sherbets. Wash. S. Coll. Inst. Dairying Proc. 24, 81–88.

Ross, O. E. 1963. Sherbets for tomorrow's markets. Ice Cream Field 81, No. 4.

Simfendorfer, S., and Martin, W. H. 1964. Effect of corn syrup solids on quality and properties of ice milk. Food Technol. 18, No. 3, 99–101.

Smith, R. L. 1963. Low temperature ice cream freezing. Food Eng. 35, No. 3, 81.

Sorber, D. G. 1947. Frozen fruit in ice cream. Ice Cream Field 49, No. 4, 24, 61–62. Southern Dairy Products J. 41, No. 4, 29, 36–40.

Sorber, D. G. 1950. Use of frozen fruit purées. Ice Cream Review 34, No. 3, 52, 77–78, 80.

Standard, H. W., and Tracy, P. H. 1954. Ice cream for a nation. National Dairy Council, Chicago, Ill.

Stein, C. M., Barnes, J., and Hedrick, T. I. 1963. Contact hardening of ice cream between vertical refrigerated plates. Food Technol. 17, No. 8, 105–107.

Struble, E. B.   1951. How the ice cream industry uses frozen fruits. Quick Frozen Foods *13*, No. 9, 72–73.

Struble, E. B.   1952. Improving the quality of fruits for ice cream use. Quick Frozen Foods *14*, No. 8, 121–122, 316, 318.

Taylor, J. C.   1961. Ice cream manufacturing plants in the Midwest—Methods, equipment and layout. Mktg. Res. Rept. 477, U.S. Dept. Agr. Mktg. Service, Washington, D.C., and Purdue Univ. Agr. Expt. Sta., W. Lafayette, Ind.

Tracy, P. H.   1946. Principles of ice cream making. Ice Cream Trade J. *42*, No. 7, 34, 67–69, No. 8, 62, 64, 78–81, No. 9, 36, 71–74, No. 10, 142, 192, No. 12, 36, 56–57.

Tracy, P. H., Sheuring, J. J., and Dorsey, M. J.   1947. Comparison of sucrose, high conversion corn syrup and dextrose in the preservation of peaches by the frozen pack method for use in ice cream. J. Dairy Sci. *30*, No. 3, 129–136.

Tressler, D. K.   1942. Using fruit purees to get new flavors in ribbon ice cream. Foods Inds. *14*, No. 9, 49–51, 99.

Tressler, D. K.   1946. Frozen fruit purees in ice cream. Ice Cream Field *47*, No. 1, 32, 60–61.

Turnbow, G. D., Tracy, P. H., and Raffetto, L. A.   1947. The Ice Cream Industry, 2nd Edition, John Wiley and Sons, New York.

Vetz, F. E.   1949. Sanitary technology in the ice cream industry. J. Milk and Food Technol. *12*, 41–47.

Willingham, J. J.   1963. Imitation frozen desserts. Ice Cream Field *82*, No. 1, 12, 56, 58.

Willingham, J. J.   1967. Mellorine—what, why, how. American Dairy Review *29*, No. 2, 42, 97–99, 101.

## CHAPTER 22

Jasper Guy Woodroof

# Freezing Candies

## INTRODUCTION

Candies have been frozen in increasing quantities for more than 20 yr. Since frozen candy is reported among miscellaneous items rather than as food, the exact quantity in storage is not known. However, refrigerated warehousemen have established rates for handling, freezing, and storing candies. Incomplete records show that individual warehouses store as much as 27,000,000 lb. in one year, about half of which is frozen. The quantity of both refrigerated and frozen candies is on the increase.

Since the manufacture and packaging of candies is a highly technical science, combined with art, executed under strictly sanitary conditions, the engineering problems are increased by freezing. Therefore, freezing storage is usually by those engaged in commercial warehousing.

Furthermore, since candy is a product of relatively high economic value, which is very sensitive to sudden changes in temperature and humidity, it is usually frozen and stored in a separate room. This is the reason certain refrigerated warehouses "specialize" in storage of candies and related products, while others do not store them.

Technically, candy is an ideal product for preservation by freezing storage (see Fig. 89). Among the qualities in favor of freezing candies are: (1) the lack of enzymes to cause breakdown in colors, flavors, proteins, and fats; (2) lack of natural cell walls which when broken by ice crystals, result in leakage when thawed; (3) low moisture content resulting in minimum change due to ice formation; (4) high concentration of sugars which stabilize the flavor and texture; and (5) ingredients (except fats) are stable even at common storage temperatures, and when frozen remain little changed for many years.

Candies have similarities to other products which have been highly successful as frozen products, and are in the fastest growing category of frozen foods. Among these items are fruit pies, fruit crisps, cream pies, sweet rolls, nut rolls, fruit cakes, ice cream, sherbets, and concentrated fruit juices. In fact, differentiation of certain frozen candies and high sugar bakery products is often difficult.

The stigma associated with frozen candies up to about 1950 no longer exists. On the contrary, freezing of candies has been so successful that more

Jasper Guy Woodroof is Distinguished Alumni Professor of Food Science, University of Georgia, Experiment, Ga.

Fig. 89. Some of more than 300 varieties of candies that have been successfully frozen. These include "summer candies"; chocolate bars; nut bars; dark and light chocolate covered creams,. nuts, and fruit centers; as well as some that are wrapped in Cellophane, foil, or glassine.

than 300 varieties are being frozen, and a number of formulas have been developed for candies which are intended to be frozen and eaten in the frozen state.

Candy technologists report that candies formulated specifically for freezing have more flavor and aroma, are higher in moisture, and have better mouthing qualities than candies made from regular formulas.

### Advantages of Freezing Candies

Candies are frozen to extend the shelf-life beyond that when no refrigeration, or common refrigeration, is used. Advantages in freezing are not in freezing as such, but in the low storage temperature used. In fact, candies containing a large amount of invert syrup, as cordial cherries, require a temperature of about $-10°F.$ ($-23°C.$) for freezing to occur. With freezing, assorted candies may be made throughout the year and held without change from seasons of low sales to periods of high demand, such as Christmas, Valentine's, Mother's Day, and Easter. Economic advantages are that regular production pay rates may be maintained rather than variations from periods of idleness to that of double pay. Many fine candies are manufactured out of season, stored or shipped in the frozen state, then thawed and successfully sold many months later as "fresh candies." Others are made according to special formulas, packaged especially as frozen foods, and sold as "frozen candies."

Specific advantages in freezing candies are: (1) difficult-to-store candies containing nuts, or as high as 20% butter, may be held for six months without staleness of rancidity; (2) chocolate candies may be held for ten months without change; (3) some candies as bonbons, Easter eggs, fudge, jellies, divinity, or creams which become dry and crusty, may be "freshened" by freezing and thawing; (4) soft candies may be handled frozen without crushing or sticking; (5) inversion of sugars in cordial cherries and similar candies may be postponed almost indefinitely by freezing.

### WHY FREEZE CANDIES

Candies are semiperishable. Experience has shown that the finest candies or candy ingredients may be ruined by a few weeks of improper storage. This includes many candy bars, packaged candies, and some choice bulk candies, especially those chocolate coated. Unless refrigeration is provided, from the time of manufacture through retail outlet, the types of candies offered for sale must be greatly reduced in the summer.

Benefits from refrigerated storage of candies, especially during the summer are: (1) insects are rendered inactive at temperatures below $48°F.$ ($9°$ C.); (2) the tendency to become stale or rancid is reduced as the temperature is reduced; (3) candies remain firm as an insurance against sticking to the wrapper or becoming mashed; (4) loss of colors, aromas, and flavors is reduced as the temperature is reduced; and (5) candies can be manufactured the year around, and accumulated for periods of heavy sales.

The need and economic justification for freezing candies are the same as for freezing other foods—better preservation for a longer time. This method of preservation is suitable for those candies: (1) in which very high-quality standards must be maintained; (2) in which a longer shelf-life is desired than is accomplished from other methods of storage; (3) which are normally manufactured from 6 to 9 months in advance of consumption; and (4) which are especially suitable for retailing as frozen items.

One of the chief reasons for freezing candies is to hold them in an un-

Table 62

Expected Storage Life

| Candy | | | Storage | | | |
|---|---|---|---|---|---|---|
| | Moisture Content % | Relative Humidity % | Temperatures, °F. (°C.) | | | |
| Name | | | 68 (20) | 48 (9) | 32 (0) | 0 (−18) |
| | | | Months | Months | Months | Months |
| Sweet chocolate | 0.36 | 40 | 3 | 6 | 9 | 12 |
| Milk chocolate | 0.52 | 40 | 2 | 4 | 6 | 8 |
| Lemon drops | 0.76 | 40 | 2 | 4 | 9 | 12 |
| Chocolate covered peanuts | 0.91 | 40–45 | 2 | 4 | 6 | 8 |
| Peanut brittle | 1.58 | 40 | 1 | 1½ | 3 | 6 |
| Coated nut roll | 5.16 | 45–50 | 1½ | 3 | 6 | 9 |
| Uncoated peanut roll | 5.89 | 45–50 | 1 | 2 | 3 | 6 |
| Nougat bar | 6.14 | 50 | 1½ | 3 | 6 | 9 |
| Hard creams | 6.56 | 50 | 3 | 6 | 12 | 12 |
| Sugar bonbons | 7.53 | 50 | 3 | 6 | 12 | 12 |
| Coconut squares | 7.70 | 50 | 2 | 3 | 6 | 9 |
| Peanut butter taffy kisses | 8.00 | 40 | 2 | 3 | 5 | 10 |
| Chocolate covered creams | 8.09 | 50 | 1 | 3 | 6 | 9 |
| Chocolate covered soft creams | 8.22 | 50 | 1½ | 3 | 5 | 9 |
| Plain caramels | 9.04 | 50 | 3 | 6 | 9 | 12 |
| Fudge | 10.21 | 65 | 2½ | 5 | 12 | 12 |
| Gum drops | 15.11 | 65 | 3 | 6 | 12 | 12 |
| Marshmallows | 16.00 | 65 | 2 | 3 | 6 | 9 |

changed condition for as long as nine months, then thaw and sell them as fresh candies. Experience shows that this is not only possible, but practical. The conditions that render such a procedure economical are: (1) freeze only those candies that would lose quality when held at a higher temperature; (2) eliminate the few kinds that crack during freezing; (3) package the candies in moisture-proof containers as is done with other frozen foods; (4) thaw the candies in the unopened packages to avoid condensation of moisture on the surface.

### CONDITIONS FOR SUCCESSFUL FREEZING

Following are prerequisites for successful freezing of candies:

(1) The candy must have high initial quality. That is, each ingredient and the formulation must be of high quality. There is a tendency for all except hard candies, cordial cherries and a few others, to lose flavor and other qualities from the time they are made. The primary requirement for successful freezing storage is to check early stages of staleness and rancidity. Candies requiring ageing should be allowed to do so before freezing.

(2) Candies of similar storage qualities would be segregated. In general, high fat and nut candies have a shorter storage life than those with low fat and without nuts, and these should therefore be separated in storage. There

is a gradual migration of moisture within a package from candies high in moisture to those low in moisture, which is undesirable. For this reason, low moisture sweet chocolate (0.36%), chocolate-covered peanuts (0.91%), and peanut brittle (1.5%) should not be packaged with high moisture soft creams (8.2%), caramels (9.1%), or jellies (15%).

(3) Candies must have moisture-proof packages. As with other frozen foods, packages suitable for frozen candies must have a moisture barrier. This is to prevent loss or gain of moisture during storage, on removal from storage. Candies are manufactured with a fairly definite moisture content and either gain or loss of one per cent moisture may seriously lower the quality.

The moisture barrier in boxed candies may be (1) an individual foil wrapper over each piece of candy, (2) a closely fitted moisture-proof inner liner for each box, or (3) a sealed vapor-proof overwrap for each box.

(4) The storage temperature should be constant. There is no critical temperature at which candies must be frozen or stored. However, the lower the temperature and the more constant it is held, the longer will be the storage life of candies. Fluctuating storage temperatures produce alternating vapor pressure, which in turn cause a "pumping action." This action, when repeated many times, results in irreversible loss of moisture and flavor from candies.

(5) Temper candies when removed from freezing storage. Frozen candies are brittle and excessive handling may result in breakage. A rise of temperature in steps of about 15°F. (8°C.) each is one means of defrosting slowly by tempering. However, the greatest need for tempering is to reduce condensation on the package. In no case should condensed moisture be allowed to collect on the candies. One of the surest ways to prevent this is to allow the candy to reach room temperature before opening the package. Moisture on the surface of chocolate candies dissolves sugars, which when dried, cause "sugar bloom."

### CANDIES SUITABLE FOR FREEZING

Since candies vary widely in texture and composition, one contemplating freezing them should first consider their general suitability, and then test-freeze a sample of each kind to be frozen. Most of the physical changes due to freezing occur within 48 hr. and any changes during thawing occur during a similar period; therefore, preliminary testing may be relatively simple.

On the basis of five years' research on freezing more than 300 varieties of candies, Woodroof (1955) classified candies as (1) those unchanged by freezing, storing for three months and thawing, (2) those improved by freezing, and (3) those injured or damaged by freezing.

Candies unchanged by freezing include most candies. More than 75% of all the types of candies which were frozen experimentally had identical appearance, texture, and flavor after being frozen and thawed, as those that were not frozen. This is on the condition that the candies were packaged to prevent drying out and thawed in a manner to prevent moisture from condensing on the surface. Candies which were unchanged in finish, texture, and structure by freezing included all chocolate-covered candies with soft or semisoft centers, hard candies of all kinds (except bars of pulled candies), panned candies, French creams, glazed creams, crystallized hard creams, and most brittles and spun candies. Candies individually wrapped in foil, Cellophane, or glassine were generally unchanged by freezing.

Some candies were improved by freezing and thawing. Included in this group were high-moisture candies without protective coating or individual wrapping, especially those candies ordinarily subjected to surface drying. This is particularly true with coated or uncoated coconut candies such as coconut bonbons. Other types of cream candies such as marshmallows or Easter eggs are improved in texture by freezing, particularly if they have a dry surface. Freezing tends to equalize the moisture and give them a smooth texture. About ten per cent of the candies included in experiments have been definitely improved by freezing.

Candies improved in freshness, mellowness, and / or smoothness when frozen and subsequently properly warmed included almond toffee, Brazil caramels, butter bonbons, caramel-coated coconut, caramel-coated English toffee, caramel nougats, coconut bonbons, coconut fruit loaf, coconut macaroons, creamed almonds, divinity, divinity with nuts (almonds, pecans, walnuts), Easter eggs (panned), filbert truffles, fudge, fudge with nuts (almonds, pecans, walnuts), hard cream fruit centers, jellies (gum drops, jelly bars, butterscotch, and fruit flavors), jelly marsh, nut rolls (soft centers, with Brazil nuts, pecans, walnuts), Opera cream caramels, orange jelly slices, almond caramels, nut clusters (Brazil nuts, peanuts, pecans), puffs, soft cream drops, caramel-covered English toffee, fudge bars, malted milk balls, marshmallows, nuts (almonds, Brazil nuts, peanuts, pecans, walnuts), soft cream mints.

Confections harmed by freezing include the spun types, chips (especially those with fine holes and thin cell walls), chocolate coated hard candies and Brazil nuts, and caramels.

They ranged in moisture content from 16 to 18% in a few varieties, 10 to 12% in moisture in most chocolate covered soft candies, 1 to 2% in brittles and hard candies. Since injury was not related to moisture content it was decided that cracking or splitting of pieces was due more to differential expansion of different layers than to the formation of ice crystals.

When only the chocolate coating fractures, the cracks seem to close on

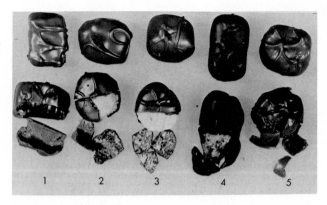

Fig. 90. Five of the less than five per cent of the varieties that cracked on being frozen. Upper normal. Lower cracked due to freezing.

Fig. 91. Damaged candies sometimes, erroneously, associated with freezing. Upper left, sugar bloom and desiccation; lower left fat bloom; right, same candies with normal finish.

thawing and warming. In some cases the cracks in the chocolate coating extended to the center of the pieces, as with mellow thins. But in most cases the cracks went only through the chocolate coating.

In a few instances, the bond between the chocolate coating and the layer beneath was not broken, as with orange-pineapple creams and peanut

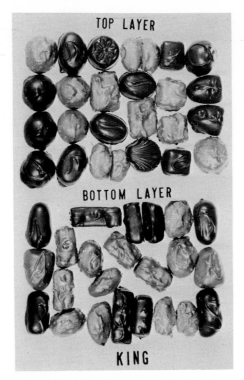

Fig. 92. The position of pieces of candies in a typical variety box with all packaging materials removed. Both moisture and flavors are frequently transferred from one piece to another.

puffs. Generally where the chocolate was directly on a hard surface, the bond was broken and the chocolate peeled off.

In each of these surface injuries due to freezing, the size of the cracks decreased as the candy thawed, and after remaining at room temperature about 12 hr. the cracks (with the exception of those in the specific spun candy and chips) were detected only with difficulty. Butter almond toffee was severely cracked while frozen, but after 12 hr. at room temperature no cracks were noted, even with a hand lens.

In one instance, chocolate-coated soft creams became more "runny" due to possible breaking of the emulsion on freezing. In another case, peanut butter spun bars increased in stickiness. And in a third case nut and fruit Easter eggs apparently had an off-flavor.

Injury due to cracking was reflected in shorter shelf-life. Individual cracked pieces dried on the inside and became stale or rancid quite rapidly,

Fig. 93. Honey Comb Chips. This is the only variety of candy found that "should not be frozen" due to its tendency to crumble.

depending on the severity of the surface injury. Often, the shelf-life was reduced to one-half by the cracks in the chocolate coating.

Candies injured, when subjected to the freezing techniques, included: almond puffs, almonds in caramel, caramel Brazils, chocolate plain Brazils, mellow mints, nut toffee, twin almonds, and vanilla caramels.

### PACKAGING CANDIES FOR FREEZING

Packages for candies serve many purposes, one of the most important of which is to protect the candy. The amount of protection needed varies with the kind of candy, the moisture content, the fat content, the amount of handling expected, the environment during storage, and the expected time between manufacture and consumption.

A well-manufactured piece of candy is an extremely delicate food item. It has a definite amount of sugars, moisture, fat, colors, and other ingredients—blended so as to produce a desired aroma, structure, texture, and appearance. Each of these qualities must be protected individually and collectively until the piece of candy is placed in the mouth of the consumer. The fact that a box of assorted candies may contain from 1 to 3 dozen kinds increases the problem of protecting the candies from one another as well as from conditions outside the box.

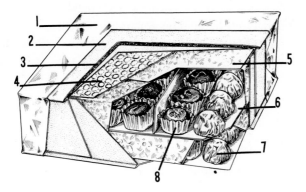

Fig. 94. The essential features of a package for protection of assorted candies from sugar-bloom. (1) Overwrap,
with sealed edges, which protects box and contents
against loss or gain of moisture; (2) chipboard box, telescope style, with extended edges, protects the candy from
mechanical injury during handling; (3) cushion in lid which
protects box and candy from injury and adds insulation;
(4) padding tissue, with high moisture-absorbing properties, protects candy from condensation; (5) inner liner,
with both end and side folds, protects candy against moisture change, but is not needed if suitable overwrap is
used; (6) divider which separates layers of candy; (7) individual wrapper which prevents losses of moisture and flavors from candies; (8) candy cup which protects individual
pieces of candy from rubbing together.

It is estimated that 25% of all candies spend some time in storage. This
figure is much higher for assorted boxed candies, and the trend is for it to
become even higher under present manufacturing conditions. Therefore, it
is assumed that the candies will be stored for a period.

One of the purposes of packaging candies is to retain, in so far as possible the fine qualities they have when manufactured. To accomplish this the
packages must do the following.

### Protect from Moisture Change

Possibly, the biggest problem in holding frozen candies is maintaining
their proper moisture content. This was found to be solved best by proper
packaging. Candies are made with a fairly definite moisture content, and
many of the most desirable qualities are lost when deviations from it occur.

Loss of moisture may occur in all except hard candies, but it is most likely to occur in high-moisture candies such as marshmallows, fudge, cara-

mels, starch jellies, cordial fruits, divinity, and soft creams. The results are loss of weight, graining, hardening, collapsing, or cracking. On the other hand, low-moisture candies, or those high in reducing sugars, such as hard candies, taffy, hard creams, and panned candies, are likely to absorb moisture, causing them to become soft, sticky, or runny when thawed.

### Protect from Flavor Changes

Experiments showed that retention of flavor in frozen candies depended mainly upon temperatures, but the manner of packaging controlled the flavors in three ways: (1) By retention of volatile flavors; (2) by prevention of transfer of flavors from one piece to another in the same package; and (3) by prevention of absorption of outside flavors. Unless frozen: (1) loss of flavor occurs in most fruit and nut candies, and the more delicate the flavor the more readily the loss is detected; (2) transfer of flavors is noticeable when strong-flavored candies, such as peppermint, are placed close to candies high in fat, such as those with nuts, butter, or cream; (3) absorption of foreign flavors occurs when high-fat candies are held in an atmosphere with pronounced odors.

### Protect from Oxidation

Oxidation manifested itself mainly in causing the fats to become stale or rancid, but it also caused fruits to darken and lose flavor.

### Protect from Sudden Changes in Temperature

This is particularly important during transportation and handling, since it is usually at this time that conditions occur that cause fat-bloom (graying or whitening of candies) and sugar-bloom (formation of sugar crystals on the surface).

Protective packaging includes some materials for insulation against brief exposure to temperatures about 32°F. (0°C.), and for providing moisture-absorbing materials close to the candy which functions when the candy is moved from the freezer to a warmer room. This is to prevent sweating (moisture condensation on the candies) and resulting sugar-bloom or stickiness.

### Protect from Crushing, Scarring, or Otherwise
### Marring the Original Finish

This is best accomplished when each piece of candy is individually wrapped. Individual cups or a carton with dividers between each piece are also good.

Protective packaging of candies consists essentially of providing one or more barriers (Fig. 94, p. 503), the nature of which depends upon the type

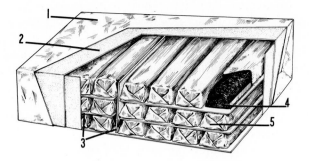

Fig. 95. The essential features of a package for protection of candy bars from condensation and sugar-bloom. (1)
Overwrap with sealed edges, which protects box and contents against gain or loss of moisture; (2) chipboard box,
telescope style, protects the candy from mechanical injury
during handling; (3) dividers which separate candy in sections of box, and absorb moisture which might condense
on the candy; (4) individual bar of candy; (5) individual
wrapper for candy bars to protect against change in moisture, act as a cushion to prevent mechanical injury, and
absorb moisture which might condense on the candy
bars.

of candy and kind of protection needed. Beginning with an individual
piece of candy the following may serve as protective barriers.

Coatings.—There are four types of coatings—chocolate, crystallized, fondant, and hard butter or "summer"—all of which protect the centers, to
some extent, from mechanical injury, oxidation, drying, migration of fats,
and loss of flavors. Heavy coatings are of more protection than light coatings.

Individual Wrappers—Many kinds of assorted boxed candies, candy
bars, and semibulk candies are individually wrapped to good advantage.
These include taffy kisses, cut caramels, fudge blocks, chocolate coated
pieces of a wide description, and most candy bars. Individual wrappings
are the most effective means of protecting candies. Individual wrapping
provided a cushion against crushing or scarring; prevented fat-bloom and
sugar-bloom under rather severe conditions; practically eliminated loss or
gain of moisture, oxidation, or migration of fats, and protected candies
against unsanitary conditions.

Individual wrappers protected candies where protection was generally
needed most—on the surface of the pieces. The amount of protection is in
proportion to the effectiveness of the material as a barrier and to the snugness of application. Sealing or gluing is not necessary when the wrapper fitted closely without air spaces between the wrapper and candy.

Individual wrapping with aluminum foil, Cellophane, Saran or similar material, was especially advantageous in: (1) preventing uncoated caramels and fudge blocks from drying; (2) preventing the flavor of peppermint and other strong flavors of candies from being taken up by those containing nuts or other fats; (3) reducing fat bloom on chocolate-coated candies temporarily exposed to temperatures about 32°F. (0°C.); (4) preventing sugar-bloom on candies exposed to dampness for a short time; (5) preventing candies high in invert sugar, as taffy kisses, from becoming sticky.

**Liners for Boxes.**—Lining boxes with moisture-proof materials so that the sheet surrounds the candy and is double folded over the top, is of some protection to the candies that are not individually wrapped. The protection thus afforded is far less than that provided by wrapping the individual pieces.

The overall benefits from innerlining boxes are limited by (1) lack of sealing of the edges of the liners so as to form complete water vapor barriers, (2) lack of actual contact with the candies, and (3) condensation which collects on the liner and is absorbed by the box, thus tending to weaken it.

**Overwraps for Boxes.**—As is the case with inner-liners for boxes, over-wraps are beneficial only to the candies that were not individually wrapped. In one experiment in which similar boxes of assorted (individually wrapped) candies were wrapped and unwrapped, and frozen for seven months; there was no difference in candies in boxes that were wrapped and unwrapped.

In numerous other experiments in which boxes of candies (unwrapped) were removed directly from 0°F. (−18°C.) to 70° (21°C.) and 75% R.H., there was severe condensation and sugar bloom on candies in the boxes that were not wrapped, as well as in boxes that were wrapped with materials that were semi-permeable to moisture. Boxes of candy wrapped in materials that were "excellent" moisture-barriers had no moisture condensation, either on the boxes or candies, when removed directly from 0° to 75°F. (−18°C. to +24°C.) with 95% R.H. When "very good," "good," or "fair" materials were used there was progressively more moisture condensation on the candy.

From these experiments it may be concluded that condensation and sugar-bloom may be controlled by overwrapping boxes of candy with moisture vaporproof material before being frozen, and by allowing them to reach room temperature before being opened.

**Paper Cups, Liners, Dividers, and Pads.**—These are components of the package for boxed candies usually made of glassine, untreated board, or tissue. Experiments have shown that these materials served many useful purposes in packaging candies, in that they acted as cushions, prevented the pieces from rubbing together, insulated the candy from sudden changes in temperature, and stabilized the moisture.

Protection from fat-bloom by these materials was indicated by the fact that pieces of candy that protruded above the edges of the cups bloomed much worse than those that did not; that pieces along the edges, and in the corners, of the box were worse than those near the center; and pieces on the top layer were more severely fat-bloomed than those on the bottom layer.

### TEMPERATURE OF FREEZING

Little effect on texture was traceable to temperature of freezing. Whether candies were frozen at $-10°$ ($-23°C.$) or at $-170°F.$ ($-112°C.$) produced small difference on quality. Most candies in the test were those which previous experiments had shown to be either improved or injured by freezing at $-10°F.$ ($-23°C.$). All except spun-candy chips behaved similarly.

Temperatures recorded by Mantey[1] in centers of cream candies placed in the middle and in the corners of one-pound boxes showed a smooth curve from $70°$ to $-33°F.$ ($+21°$ to $-36°C.$) indicating no definite "freezing point." He found that tempering frozen candies at $40°F.$ ($+5°C.$) to prevent condensation was unnecessary if one-pound boxes were overwrapped with vaporproof material and allowed to remain unopened at room temperature for two hours or longer.

It was also found that no serious effects on appearance or other change resulted when the candy was allowed to warm up to $70°F.$ ($21°C.$) for six hours and then was re-frozen at $0°F.$ ($-18°C.$).

The same investigator learned that butterscotch candies could be held in excellent condition for 241 days at $0°F.$ ($-18°C.$) while those containing nuts were good for more than six months without appreciable deterioration.

### NATURAL CANDY FLAVORS ARE STABLE IN FROZEN CANDY

These products consist of extracts, essences, pastes, and oils derived from a variety of plants and parts thereof. All of them appear to hold up well during freezing and thawing.

The flavor manufacturer separates the flavoring principles from the extraneous matter by expression, maceration, percolation, and distillation. Among the flavors are vanilla extract from vanilla beans; maple concentrates, "usually made by desugaring maple syrup to an extent where the maple flavor becomes the predominant factor instead of sweetness;" coffee concentrates, "prepared by extracting ground coffee with a menstrum and concentration of the extract by distillation under vacuum;" licorice extract, "made by percolating coarsely ground licorice root with boiling distilled

[1] Unpublished data by R. N. Mantey, commercial air-conditioning engineer, Dayton, Ohio.

Table 63

Effect of −10°F. (−23°C.) Freezing of Candies Compared
with −170°F. (−112°C.) Dry Ice Freezing

| Candy Items | Condition of Thawed Candies after Freezing at | |
|---|---|---|
| | −10°F. (−23°C.) | −170°F. (−112°C.) |
| Almond butter toffee | no change | no change |
| Almond toffee | no change | no change |
| Brazil caramel (slightly tough) | freshened, softer, mellowed | same as at −10°F. |
| Butter bon-bons | freshened | same as at −10°F. |
| Butterscotch jellies (slightly crusty) | freshened, mellowed less crusty | same as at −10°F. |
| Caramels (cellowrapped) | no change | no change |
| Caramel, chocolate almond (slightly hard) | freshened, softer | same as at −10°F. |
| Caramel covered coconut (slightly dry) | freshened, softer, more moist | same as at −10°F. |
| Caramel covered English toffee | freshened, mellowed | same as at −10°F. |
| Caramel covered English toffee, chocolate coated (slightly tough) | freshened, softer, more tender | same as at −10°F. |
| Caramel nougats (slightly dry) | freshened, softer, mellowed | same as at −10°F. |
| Caramel opera creams (slightly tough) | freshened, more tender | same as at −10°F. |
| Chocolate coated almonds | no change | no change |
| Chocolate coated coconut center with almond | no change | no change |
| Chocolate coated nougat (peanuts, caramel) | no change | no change |
| Chocolate fudge with walnuts (foil-wrapped) | no change | no change |
| Creamed almonds (very hard, brittle) | mellowed, softer | same as at −10°F. |
| Filbert truffles (slightly tough) | freshened, softer, more tender | same as at −10°F. |
| Fruit-flavored jellies (slightly crusty) | freshened, softer | same as at −10°F. |
| Hard cream, fruit centers | freshened | same as at −10°F. |
| Jelly bars (quite dry, crusty surface) | no change | freshened, softer, more moist |

water until the root is exhausted. The percolate is then concentrated to about one-half of its original volume by boiling under normal atmospheric pressure and then filtered. After filtration the water content of the filtrate is evaporated until the residue does not contain more than 17% of water; malt extract, "prepared by infusing malt with water at 140°F. (60°C.), concentrating the expressed liquid at a temperature not exceeding 140°F. (60° C.) and adding 10% glycerin by weight;" fruit pastes or purées "made by comminuting fruit to a paste with addition of sugar in the ratio of 3 to 5 parts of fruit to one part of sugar;" fruit flavor concentrates, "essentially fruit juices whose moisture content has been largely eliminated and

Table 63 (continued)

| Candy Items | Condition of Thawed Candies after Freezing at | |
| --- | --- | --- |
| | −10°F. (−23°C.) | −170°F. (−112°C.) |
| Jelly marsh (slightly hard) | freshened, softer, more mellow | freshened |
| Nougat, chewy, nut and fruit | no change | no change |
| Pecan nut rolls, fruit center (cellowrapped) | no change | no change |
| Peanut butter spun bar (butter cream) | no change | no change |
| Peanut butter spun bar (hard cream) | no change | no change |
| Peanut butter spun bar (chocolate coated) | no change | slightly gummy |
| Peanut butter spun bar (dark-chocolate coated) | no change | no change |
| Spun candy chips | | |
| Molasses (coarse holes, dark-chocolate coated) | no change | no change |
| Molasses (fairly coarse holes, dark-chocolate coated) | few cracked on inside | cracked throughout, shattered |
| Molasses (very fine holes, dark-chocolate | cracked throughout, shattered | cracked throughout, shattered |
| Peppermint (fairly coarse holes, milk-chocolate coated) | few cracked on inside | cracked throughout, shattered |
| Peppermint (very fine holes, dark-chocolate coated) | cracked throughout, shattered | cracked throughout, shattered |
| Uncoated spun chips (fine holes) | slightly grainy and cracked | slightly grainy and cracked |
| Toffee drops | no change | no change |

partly replaced by alcohol and / or sugar. This elimination is done either by distillation under high vacuum or, in the case of fruit sensitive to heat, by freezing out the water and separating the concentrated juice from the ice particles by centrifuging;" and concentrated citrus oils, expressed from the peel of oranges, lemons, and grapefruit (Adams 1952).

## RETAILING "FROZEN CANDIES"

The advantages of freezing candies are being realized by major confectioners, and from time to time another candy manufacturer enters the field of distributing candies in the frozen state. On three separate occasions (1949, 1952, and 1960) attempts were made by seven companies to establish a permanent frozen candy market, with little success. In 1966, at least three enterprising firms simultaneously ventured into the area. Each was teamed with a special promotional approach designed to spur repeat sales, while expanding the base interest in merchandising frozen candy, especially chocolate (Anon. 1966).

Andes Candies are now available frozen in 105 chocolate shops in Miami. The line consists of a choice group of chocolates, selected as best sellers from hundreds of the firms' varieties. The packages are in several sizes and varieties and the cartons have been sealed to protect the contents from moisture or other changes. Some of the items are featured in window packages. A special package has been designed to fit into the retailers' frozen food display cabinet.

Andes has developed a special freezer case for its line which is reported to be very successful in "creating an atmosphere of a fine candy shop." The case consists of a display area and a super-structure which shows the chocolates as they would be featured in a candy store window The frozen candies are also delivered by Western Union as Candy Grams with the in-

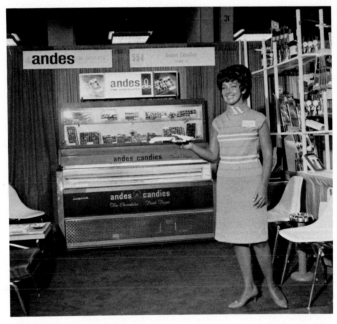

*Courtesy of Andes Candies*

Fig. 96. A cabinet specially designed to hold and display frozen candies. More than a dozen varieties of candies are displayed. Three companies in more than 25 cities are marketing frozen candies in a unique service with Western Union.

struction to hold for two hours before opening the box. (This is to prevent moisture condensation and possible stickiness.)

## QUESTIONS

(1) Does freezing cause candies to crack? Research has determined that candies which were injured by freezing included mostly spun candy chips, especially those with fine holes and thin cell walls, and chocolate-coated hard candies, Brazil nuts, and almonds. They ranged in moisture content from 16 to 18% in a few varieties, 10 to 12% in most chocolate covered soft candies, to 1 to 2% in brittles and hard candies. Since injury was not related to moisture content it was decided that cracking or splitting of pieces was due more to differential expansion of different layers than to the formation of ice crystals. Specific kinds of candies that crack are very few and should not be frozen. Of more than 400 kinds of candies that were frozen experimentally, not more than four kinds cracked.

(2) Does freezing cause candies or nuts to deteriorate rapidly after thawing? There is a slow rate of deterioration in both nuts and candies at any temperature. Refrigerating and freezing reduces the rate of deterioration for the length of time that they are exposed to low temperatures. When returned to high temperatures, deterioration continues at the same rate it would have if refrigeration had not been used.

(3) How should candies be thawed? Frozen candies should be thawed slowly and before the package is opened. Should outside air strike the candy when it is 10°F. (−12°C.) or more colder than the air, condensation will occur. Condensation dissolves sugar near the surface, causing the candies to become sticky. When the candy becomes dry again the sugar crystallizes on the surface as "sugar bloom."

(4) Can thawed candies be refrozen? Those candies which are known to be undamaged by freezing and thawing can be frozen and thawed a second time without damage. It is important to determine in advance which candies (and more than 80% of boxed candies fall into this class) can be frozen and thawed without injury.

(5) Does freezing cause "freezer burn" of candies or.nuts? Freezer burn is the result of excessive drying out of the surface and occurs only when the candies or nuts are improperly packaged. If the package is provided with a moisture-proof barrier, there should be no problem on this score.

(6) How long may frozen candies be kept? The storage life depends upon: (a) the ingredients used; (b) the storage temperature; (c) adequacy of packaging; and (d) formulation. In general, the storage life of high-quality candies should be 1 to 2 months at 68°F. (20°C.) in an air-conditioned room; 4 to 6 months at 48°F. (9°C.), or in cool storage; 6 to 9 months at 32°F. (0°C.) or in cold storage; or 9 to 12 months at 0°F. (−18°C.). Candies

low in dairy cream, butter, or nuts should keep almost twice as long as shown above; and the time of storage can be further increased by the use of antioxidants or vacuum packaging.

(7) Are there candies specially for freezing? Some candies are prepared especially for freezing. These are made of low melting point fat, have more flavor and softer texture than most candies, and should be eaten while cold. Preservation by freezing enables manufacturers to make candies by special formulas during seasons when sales are slack, to be sold during busy seasons or for special days such as Thanksgiving, Christmas, Valentine's Day, Easter, and Mother's Day. This is true with mail order companies and chain stores which stockpile candies and sell on highly competitive markets. Candies frozen and handled in this manner are carefully thawed in the unopened packages and sold at retail as fresh candies.

A more recent development is that of retailing frozen candies from low-temperature cabinets in candy shops and specialty food stores. While most candies may be handled in this manner, divinity, soft creams, and chocolate-coated candies with soft centers are especially suitable for handling frozen from the manufacturer to consumer. The quality of these kinds of candies is maintained perfectly if they are frozen in the factory and maintained continuously under refrigeration.

(8) What are points to remember in buying frozen candy? Frozen candies should be selected with the same care as that used in buying other frozen foods. Select only the packages that are neat, free of stains, tears, or dents, and do not show evidence of having been thawed or damaged in any way.

(9) Do frozen candies require special packages? Experiments showed that candies for freezing required more protection than those for common storage, because the storage period was usually longer and there was a greater tendency for condensation upon removal. A single layer of moisture-proof material—aluminum foil, polyethylene, Saran, Mylar, polypropylene, Cellophane, glassine, or laminations including one of these—afforded adequate protection. Candies not fully protected from desiccation grained, became hard and lost flavor.

Most protection is provided when the moisture barrier is in contact with the candy in the form of a sealed, individual wrapper. Inner liners for the boxes protected candy, provided they were sealed (which was difficult and seldom accomplished). The usual manner of applying moisture barriers was as overwraps for the boxes chiefly because these were easiest to apply and seal by machines. Overwraps for boxes provided less protection than wraps for individual pieces of candy because of the relatively large amount of air enclosed within the former. For the same reason, boxes with extended edges offered less protection than did those without extended edges.

## BIBLIOGRAPHY

Adams, P. 1952. Natural candy flavors. Am. Perf. & Ess. Oil Rev. *60*, 130.

Anon. 1966. Three companies seriously enter marketing of frozen candy. Quick Frozen Foods *28*, No. 7, 129–132.

Woodroof, J. G. 1955. Age-old candy problems solved by freezing. Food Eng. *27*, No. 6, 74–77, 225.

Woodroof, J. G. 1956. Protective packaging of candies. Packaging Eng. *1*, No. 5, 5 pages.

Woodroof, J. G. 1964A. Should candy be frozen? Quick Frozen Foods *27*, No. 1, 33–34, 48.

Woodroof, J. G. 1964B. Year-round quality of pecans improved by refrigeration. Peanut J. Nut World *43*, No. 9, 38–39.

## CHAPTER 23

Donald K. Tressler | Complete Meals

## INTRODUCTION

Most people think that frozen complete meals on a plate or platter are a recent innovation, forgetting that Maxson introduced the idea in 1945. In that year, the Maxson Food Systems, Inc. produced 18 different "Strato-Plates," designed primarily for the feeding of airplane passengers. The Maxson Co. also devised a "Whirlwind" oven, designed especially for reheating these sky plates on board airplanes. The list of "Strato-Plates" offered by that company follows:

French toast, glazed apples, potato puffs.
Macaroni au gratin, peas in butter sauce, carrots Vichy.
Vegetable meal—string beans in butter sauce, carrots Vichy, Mexican corn, French-fried potatoes.
Spaghetti and sauce, spinach-pimiento, French-fried potatoes.
Veal paprika and rice, gravy, carrots Vichy, string beans in butter sauce.
Potted roast veal, dressing, gravy, mashed sweet potato, green peas in butter sauce.
Filet of sole, creamed spinach, French-fried potatoes.
Roast turkey, dressing, gravy, peas in butter sauce, mashed sweet potato.
Pot roast of veal with gravy, carrots Vichy, potato patty.
Egg omelet, Canadian bacon, French-fried potatoes.
Beef patty, string beans in butter sauce, French-fried potatoes.
Beef goulash, gravy, peas in butter sauce, potato patty.
Hamburger and mushroom sauce, green beans in butter sauce, French-fried potatoes.
Pot roast of beef, gravy, Mexican corn, potato patty.
Chicken country style, spinach pimiento, mashed sweet potato.
Roast lamb, gravy, lima beans in butter sauce, potato patty.
Swiss steak, gravy, lima beans in butter sauce, potato Boulangere.
Tenderloin steak, sauce Bercy, green beans in butter sauce, French-fried potatoes.

Most of these meals were quite satisfactory, although the texture of the omelet was not good, the color of the Canadian bacon soon faded in storage, and its flavor soon became undesirable. As a consequence, the French toast, glazed apples, and potato puff was the only satisfactory breakfast menu.

The value of frozen dinners packed annually in the United States is far greater than that of any other precooked specialty. According to Quick Frozen Foods (Anon. 1966), it was $336 million in 1965, surpassing by more

Donald K. Tressler is a consultant and President of the Avi Publishing Co., Westport, Conn.

than $100 million that of frozen baked goods which was valued at $213 million.

As previously indicated meals on a platter were originally used to feed airplane passengers and crew. During the last few years, the chicken, turkey, seafood, and some of the other dinners have become very popular with the public. Recently, there has been a trend toward frozen entrées (the main course of dinners). When these are used by the homemaker, she has the opportunity of providing her own favorite vegetables (Anon. 1956). Leading restaurants that have gone into the frozen food business have had outstanding success in merchandizing frozen entrées.

A debate is now in progress as to whether entrées or platters possess the greater sales potential. The leading packers of meals on a plate or platter feel that these dinners offer the ultimate in convenience and that the complete tray dinner, which normally carries potatoes and a vegetable, along with the entrée, has greater attraction than the entrée alone. Recently, many packers of the frozen tray dinners have put out a line of popular entrées. These men believe that the meals on a platter will always sell well, but that there is also a big market for the frozen entrées (Anon. 1956) for the following reasons:

(1) Any person who dislikes mashed potatoes or peas is disqualified as a customer for most dinners.

(2) Fifteen to 40 min. of hot oven isn't very convenient—especially in the summer.

(3) Many chains are putting in vegetables under their own labels and we (the packers of frozen precooked foods) want to place ourselves in the market as an adjunct to the chains' own efforts.

(4) Vegetables take only eight minutes to cook, and an entrée that doesn't take much longer has in some ways greater convenience than the platter.

(5) Several packers of entrées lay great stress on the 'fact' that platters are not a 'company' dish. One of them puts it this way: 'Would you think of inviting company to the house and plunking a dinner in a compartmentalized tray, similar to those used by roadside diners, in front of him?' "

## PROBLEMS

One of the most difficult problems in producing meals on a platter is to work out a system of preparing, cooling, freezing, packaging, and reheating the products so that the meal will taste freshly cooked and not like warmed-up leftovers. Certain products, such as ordinary ham and Canadian bacon, when sliced, cooked, and frozen on a platter, quickly lose color and flavor (p. 38). Scrambled eggs and most omelets markedly change in texture and often also in flavor (see p. 36). Cooked sausage can be frozen without noticeable change in texture or flavor, but the frozen product may become rancid and develop other off-flavors during even a short storage period (p. 37). Since ham, Canadian bacon, sausage, and eggs are the principal items on many breakfast menus, the number of entirely satisfactory frozen breakfast menus now available is not large.

Potatoes, especially whipped or mashed potatoes, are likely to give trouble, as they often change in texture, becoming rather soggy, and take on a flavor resembling the warmed-over product. French-fried, au gratin potatoes, and potato puffs are less changed by freezing and reheating (see p. 225). However, it is difficult to reheat French-fried potatoes on a platter and obtain a product which tastes like a freshly fried potato.

It is not easy to produce frozen precooked green vegetables (e.g., peas, green beans, and spinach) of the same bright color and fresh flavor as those prepared in the home by cooking frozen blanched vegetables. One of the reasons for this is the difficulty of cooking, cooling, and freezing the vegetables rapidly enough to prevent marked loss of green color and fresh flavor. If vegetables are cooked in boiling water in lots larger than a few pounds, special equipment will be required to effect rapid cooking followed by fast cooling. However, rapid cooking can be effected by the use of steam under pressure, e.g., in a speed cooker, but this equipment does not handle more than a few pounds of product. Vegetables can be quickly cooled if they are spread out in a shallow layer in an aluminum pan, but this exposes the product to air which rapidly oxidizes the warm product with loss of color and vitamin C.

Fenton and Gleim (1948) have indicated some of the more difficult problems encountered in their study of frozen meals carried out for the U.S. Navy:

Courtesy of Quick Frozen Foods

Fig. 97. An attractive turkey dinner. A compartmentalized tray of sliced turkey with gravy, green peas and mashed potatoes ready for serving.

"First, it was necessary to choose single food items that had been successfully re-heated for serving after freezer storage. Then it was important to combine them in such a way that the food was not only satisfactory in nutritive value, color, shape, texture, and flavor, but was uniformly hot. Otherwise, one food on the plate was overcooked and another still had ice in the center. The rate of heat penetration depends mainly on the nature of the food, the amount, and the shape. In some plates, it was found that by the time the meat was hot enough for serving, the vegetable was overdone. Heat penetrates protein foods relatively slowly. It was found also that the fairly solid mass of a mashed vegetable required a longer time for reheating than did a 'loose' vegetable such as broccoli. Therefore, broccoli was only scalded before freezing, and its cooking was finished when the plate was reheated (15 to 25 min.).

Meats and poultry tended to dry out unless covered with a gravy or sauce of some kind . . .

Rapid chilling of the cooked food before freezing is necessary to keep bacterial growth to a minimum. The gravy was made very thick, and then chilled quickly by adding ice cubes in an amount equal to the omitted water . . .

During storage, some items on each plate lost quality sooner than did others. Hence it is important to use the meal before the items that have the shortest storage life begin to lose quality, or to use foods that have about the same storage life."

Spitz and Derby (1947), in reviewing the development of the Maxson "Strato-Plates," also indicate the importance of using sauces and gravies on cooked foods which are to be frozen on a plate, and state:

"Advantages result from the use of sauces in cooked frozen foods. In the first place, they provide products with an ideal protective coating. Dehydration and oxidation are minimized. Secondly, they facilitate molding, and the removal of the frozen products from the molds. Thirdly, they enhance flavor characteristics, since each sauce is prepared for a specific product. Sauces, however, are extremely difficult to freeze, since they may separate or gel. Separation or gelling was overcome after the sauce ingredients and methods of preparation were carefully investigated."

Since it is very important to protect as many as possible of the foods frozen on plates and platters by a covering of gravy or sauce, special consideration must be given to the starch, flour, or other thickener used, as otherwise the sauce or gravy may curdle or separate during thawing and reheating. Separation and curdling is of much more serious consequence in sauces and gravies used on meals on a plate or platter, than it is in separately packaged products which are removed from the package prior to reheating. In the latter case, the sauce or gravy, or product containing it, is usually stirred occasionally during reheating, thus mixing the sauce or gravy and restoring its normal appearance. Information concerning the best thickeners for use and mode of preparation of cream sauces and gravies is presented in Chapter 14.

## PRODUCTS WHICH FREEZE AND STORE WELL

As Fenton and Gleim have indicated (p. 514), it is of great importance to select only those items, to be included in plate dinner menus, which retain their flavor, texture, color, and appearance well during freezing, storage, and reheating. Since the problems encountered in selecting, preparing, and cooking foods for freezing have been covered previously in considerable detail in this chapter (p. 512-515), and in Chapter 2, there is no need to review them again. However, it may be well to point out which precooked foods have been found to be best for freezing on a plate or platter. Beef, lamb, veal, and poultry are considered to be wholly satisfactory. Pork tenderloin and fresh ham freeze perfectly but have a relatively short storage life. Ground and cured pork products are usually not considered satisfactory because of a very short storage life, even at 0°F. ($-18$°C.). Potato puffs and croquettes or patties, scalloped potatoes, potatoes au gratin, and French-fried potatoes are usually found to be best, although whipped and mashed potatoes are included in many of the menus. Many precooked vegetables freeze well (provided they are slightly undercooked before being placed on the plate or platter; see p. 232). The list of vegetables includes asparagus tips, broccoli, carrots, cauliflower, green lima beans, green snap beans, mixed vegetables, onions, spinach, and sweet corn. Most precooked lean fish and fish sticks freeze well. Salmon is satisfactory provided the meals are not be held in storage for very long. As a rule, crab, lobster, and shrimp dishes are quite satisfactory, but they may have relatively short storage life. Waffles and pancakes freeze well but special care should be taken in reheating them (see p. 450-452).

## VARIETIES OF MENUS PACKED

The various kinds of frozen meals are usually classified according to the entrée provided: thus there are chicken, turkey, fish, fish stick, ham, lamb, poultry, seafood, sparerib, Swiss steak, stuffed pepper, and veal meals. In addition, they are grouped by the method of cooking employed, e.g., Chinese, Mexican, Spanish, Hungarian, Italian, and Kosher.

A great variety of menus is frozen for sale to the public. It includes poultry, beef and veal, pork, ham, and shellfish meals. Numerous foreign dinners are offered (see Chapter 16).

## WHO EATS FROZEN DINNERS

In 1963, Prof. George C. Cook and his students made a survey, interviewing nearly a thousand housewives, in an effort to learn who is eating frozen dinners and what the consumers thought of them (Anon. 1965A). They found that in a considerable number of families the dinners were eaten principally by children. About 60% of those purchasing dinners regularly preferred chicken, 40% turkey, 32.6% beef, and only 15% the fish dinners. Most of those serving dinners accompanied the dinner with one or more side dishes such as a salad and a beverage. Many complained that the size of the portions was too small; in fact, this was the most common comment concerning the meals (see Chap. 3, p. 99).

### MEALS SERVED BY AIRLINES

Airline catering has become big business. The Pan American airline freezes a large proportion of its meals. (Anon. 1967).

Pan Am freezes all its own products and is able to buy in season at the lowest prices in the best markets (Anon. 1967). Frozen foods make it possible to offer a wider choice; cut down on waste and maintain consistently high quality. Pan Am production centers are located in New York, San Francisco, and Paris. The New York plant supplies 1.5 million meals a year to South America, Africa, the Caribbean, and part of Europe. San Francisco supplies a million meals to the Pacific area; Paris furnishes one-half million meals to Europe and the Middle East. The frozen meals are stored in flight kitchens strategically located in Mexico, Spain, Africa, etc., where the local staff prepares snacks, salads, and any other fresh additives. The frozen meals are reheated in specially designed, fast heating ovens.

### MENUS OFFERED BY AIRLINES

#### Lunch or Dinner

Many different meals are frozen for serving on board airplanes. The following list of meals (Colato 1954) is representative of the variety served on Canadian airplanes:

Braised chicken, mashed potatoes, mixed vegetables.
Breaded veal cutlets, peas, scalloped potatoes.
Braised sliced beef, French-cut green beans and scalloped potatoes.
Roast turkey, dressing, peas, and croquette potatoes.
Sliced roast veal, mixed vegetables, and scalloped potatoes.
Pork chops with apple sauce, scalloped potatoes, French-cut green beans.
Filet mignon, croquette potatoes, asparagus tips.
Veal scallopini, mashed potatoes, cauliflower au gratin.
Roast breast of chicken, croquette potatoes, peas.
Roast turkey and cranberry jelly, mashed potatoes, and French-cut green beans.
Roast lamb, mint jelly, scalloped potatoes and peas.
Mixed grill with potato balls and French-cut green beans.
Roast turkey, giblet gravy, dressing, mashed potatoes, peas.
Pot roast of beef, gravy, mashed potatoes, peas.
Chopped beef (Salisbury steak), gravy, mashed potatoes, mixed vegetables.
Swiss steak, gravy, mashed potatoes, peas.
Sirloin steak, au gratin potatoes, green peas.

## Breakfasts

Waffle, pork sausage, glazed apples.
Omelet, Spanish sauce, sausage patty, sweet roll.

### USE BY U.S. AIR FORCE

On many long flights, the U.S. Air Force uses precooked frozen meals (Bollman 1952; Anon. 1965B) which are reheated in a B-4 electric oven. The meal is put in an expendable aluminum tray or casserole and covered with a sheet of aluminum foil which is crimped under the protruding lip. The only preparation required is placing the trays in the B-4 oven which heats primarily by conduction, rather than by convection as do conventional ovens.

The five menus listed in Military Specification, MIL-M-13966C (Dec. 30, 1964) are described in Table 64.

Table 64

Description of Menus Purchased by the Department of Defense

| Menus | Net Weight |
|---|---|
| Menu No. 1—Turkey with dressing and gravy | |
| Turkey | 3 oz. |
| Dressing | 2 oz. |
| Gravy | 2 oz. |
| Mixed vegetables | 2½ oz. |
| Butter | 1 pat |
| Mashed sweet potatoes | 3 oz. |
| Butter | 1 pat |
| Total | 12½ oz. |
| Menu No. 2—Swiss steak with gravy | |
| Swiss steak | 4 oz. |
| Gravy | 2 oz. |
| Peas | 2½ oz. |
| Butter | 1 pat |
| Au gratin potatoes | 3½ oz. |
| Total | 12 oz. |
| Menu No. 3—Beef Steak | |
| Beef Steak | 4 oz. |
| Corn | 2½ oz. |
| Butter | 1 pat |
| Mashed potatoes | 3 oz. |
| Butter | 1 pat |
| Total | 9½ oz. |
| Menu No. 4—Beef pot roast with gravy | |
| Beef pot roast | 4 oz. |
| Gravy | 2 oz. |
| Green beans | 2½ oz. |
| Butter | 1 pat |
| Mashed potatoes | 3 oz. |
| Butter | 1 pat |
| Total | 11½ oz. |
| Menu No. 5—Waffles | Not less than 1½ oz. |
| Sausage links | 2 oz. |
| Applesauce | 3 oz. |
| Total | 6½ oz. |

Since the commercial methods employed in cooking foods preparatory to freezing have been presented in other sections of this book, they will not be considered in this chapter. It should be pointed out, however, that the preparation and cooking of a number of different foods for packing on trays or platters requires coordination of all of the preparation, cooking, cooling, packing, and freezing operations to an extraordinary degree. Each operation must be so timed and coordinated with every other operation that each of the products progresses steadily through the plant with a minimum of delay anywhere along the line. Otherwise, both the flavor and sanitary qualities of the frozen meals will be poor.

It should not be necessary to indicate that the plant must be well-equipped and well laid out. The meat cutting department must be arranged so that it receives the meat directly from a receiving ramp. This department should have a walk-in cooler (32° to 34°F.; 0°–1°C.), used solely for meat. If halves, quarters, or other wholesale cuts of meat are used, it should have an overhead track so that the meat can be hung and moved with a minimum of handling. If meals including a meat item are packed and shipped in interstate commerce, the plant must be operated under Federal Inspection; therefore, all facilities must meet Federal requirements for sanitation, etc.

The kitchens must have adequate cooking facilities and equipment, which will include a battery of kettles, ovens, steam cookers, grills, and deep-fat fryers. In addition, there must be a variety of specialized equipment such as meat and vegetable dicers, slicers, and comminuting machines, and also homogenizers, mixers, and blenders. Large walk-in coolers

*Courtesy of Quick Frozen Foods*

Fig. 98. The "Ekco Topper." This aluminum tray of food has been reheated on top of a saucepan of boiling water, thus converting an ordinary pan into a double boiler, and eliminating the nuisance of putting food into a double boiler, transferring it to a serving dish, and also making unnecessary the washing of a pan and a dish.

must be provided not only for fresh vegetables, fruits, milk, cream, butter, fish, shellfish, poultry, and other perishable items, but also to hold partially processed foods overnight and during short periods when certain processing equipment may be shut down for repairs, etc.

The assembly line where each of the items is placed on the tray or platter, must be especially well laid out or the labor cost of assembly will be entirely too high.

As a rule, each of the compartmentalized aluminum foil trays holding a meal is covered with lightweight aluminum foil. In some plants, each tray is then slipped into a shallow carton. The packages containing the meals on a tray are then automatically overwrapped and placed on shelves on a wheeled rack for easy movement into an air-blast freezer. In other plants, the foil covered trays are first frozen on shelves on a wheeled rack in an air blast, and when frozen, put into the cartons and overwrapped. Sufficient space should be left between the trays or cartons on the rack to permit air circulation around each carton during freezing.

## BIBLIOGRAPHY

Anon. 1952A. Precooked meals for small plants. Quick Frozen Foods 14, No. 12, 101–102.

Anon. 1952B. Launch frozen-meal service on Rock Island R.R. diners. Food Eng. 24, No. 3, 53, 151, 153.

Anon. 1955. Precooked dinners—Frozen meal-on-a-platter—Latest entry on best seller ranks. Quick Frozen Foods 17, No. 10, 83–85.

Anon. 1956. Frozen dinners debate—platters vs. entrées. Quick Frozen Foods 18, No. 10, 64, 178.

Anon. 1962A. Low priced frozen meals served hot at variety store snack counters. Quick Frozen Foods 24, No. 10, 113–116.

Anon. 1962B. New directions in frozen dinners. Quick Frozen Foods 25, No. 4, 109–111.

Anon. 1963A. Pat Boone Dine-O-Mat serves gourmet meals under a dollar out of vending machines. Quick Frozen Foods 25, No. 11, 95–97.

Anon. 1963B. Surveys show packers going in for large premium frozen "meals" on right track. Quick Frozen Foods 26, No. 4, 205–206–208–209.

Anon. 1964A. Military specification: Meal, precooked, frozen. MIL-M-13966C, 30 December 1964.

Anon. 1964B. Automation difficult objective in frozen dinner preparation. Quick Frozen Foods 26, No. 8, 194, 95.

Anon. 1965A. Who eats frozen dinners. Quick Frozen Foods 28, No. 3, 162–166.

Anon. 1965B. Interim amendment for Military specification: Meal, precooked frozen. MIL-M-13966C, Interim Amendment 1(GL) 15 December 1965.

Anon. 1965C. Texas packer scores with frozen convenience breakfast. Canner / Packer 134, No. 10, 30–31.

Anon. 1966. 1966 Frozen foods almanac. Quick Frozen Foods 29, No. 5, 199–222.

Anon. 1967. Mass airline switch to frozen meals inevitable; rate will accelerate. Quick Frozen Foods 29, Part 1, No. 9, 161–163; Part 2.

Bollman, M. C.   1952. Precooked frozen foods. Activities Report of Food and Container Research and Development Work of the Quartermaster Food and Container Institute for the Armed Forces 3 N.S., 160–163.

Colato, A. E.   1954. List of meals frozen by Aero Caterers Ltd., Winnipeg. Private communication. Supervisor of Catering, Trans-Canada Air Lines, Montreal, Que., Can.

Fenton, F., and Gleim, E.   1948. Dinners frozen right on the plate. Farm Research 14, No. 1, 5.

Fradelis, M. D.   1955. Convenience alone is not enough. Western Canner and Packer 47, No. 12, 40–42, 44.

Kennerly, A. B.   1965. Texas packer scores with frozen convenience breakfast. Canner / Packer 134, No. 12, 29–30.

Robertson, E. L.   1955. Precooked frozen food research in the Air Force in-flight feeding program. In precooked Frozen Foods—A Symposium. Surveys of Progress on Military Subsistence Problems Series 1, No. 7, 4–6. Quartermaster Food and Container Institute, Chicago, Ill.

Spitz, L., and Derby, T.   1947. Precooked frozen foods on a production line basis. Food Inds. 19, 930–932, 1032, 1034.

Vogel, S.   1956. 1955-A year of frozen food gains. Canner and Freezer 122, No. 2, 18, 21–22.

Ziemba, J. V.   1948. Frozen dinners-Though problems beset packers, a favorable future is seen. Food Inds. 20, 1434–1437.

## CHAPTER 24

Donald K. Tressler

# Storage of
# Precooked Frozen Foods

### INTRODUCTION

Of all the questions about production and handling of precooked frozen foods, the ones most frequently asked concern optimum storage conditions and permissible length of storage at various temperatures. This is not surprising since so little concerning the storage of precooked frozen foods has been published, and that to be found in the literature is often contradictory.

In order to understand the reason for these contradictions, it is necessary to know something about the more important factors affecting the storage life of these foods, which are the following.

### FACTORS AFFECTING STORAGE LIFE

#### (1) The Kind of Food Stored

Some, such as doughs, batters, frankfurters, ham, most white sauces and gravies thickened with wheat flour, and certain kinds of sandwiches, do not remain long in excellent condition under ordinary frozen storage conditions. Others, such as most soups, bread, and many meat dishes, hold their original quality remarkably well if the products are properly packaged and stored at 0°F. (−18°C.) or below.

#### (2) The Condition of the Product Entering Storage

(A) If the product is to be held for many months, it must be in excellent condition at the time it is frozen. Beef used in preparing products for freezing should not be aged longer than 7 or 10 days, otherwise the fat may not remain free from rancidity during long storage periods. Only strictly fresh fish and shellfish should be cooked for freezing. Fish sticks prepared from stale fish will deteriorate and become "salt fishy" in a few months even at 0°F. (−18°C.). Bread should be rapidly cooled and immediately placed in the freezer. Partly stale bread will become more stale during freezing and will not be appetizing.

(B) In the case of cooked fruits and vegetables, the variety of the fruit or vegetables is an important factor to be considered in estimating storage life. For example, in the case of cooked corn on the cob, the Barbecue variety will retain its high quality for at least 18 months at 0°F. (−18°C.); other

Donald K. Tressler is a consultant and President of the Avi Publishing Co., Westport, Conn.

varieties deteriorate at a far faster rate, e.g., Golden Cross Bantam is relatively poor after four months at 0°F. ( −18°C.).

(C) Another factor of major importance is the method of freezing employed. If products are packed in cases or large containers before freezing, they are frozen so slowly that they may not be of high quality when placed in storage; in other words, much or all of its commercial storage life may already have been exhausted (Guadagni 1961).

### (3) The Method of Cooking Employed

Stews will keep better than fried or broiled meats. Cream-style sweet corn will retain its flavor better than whole grain corn and far better than corn on the cob. Apple sauce can be stored longer than baked apples.

### (4) The Degree of Doneness.

In general, foods should be removed from the heat before they reach the well-done stage. Green vegetables, for example green beans, peas, spinach, Swiss chard, and broccoli, that are thoroughly cooked before freezing, gradually lose their bright green color during long storage. Berries should be given a minimum of heating, if they are to retain their bright colors during long storage.

### (5) Unstable Flavoring Ingredients Should Not Be Used

Spice cake and gingerbread deteriorate far faster than cakes which do not contain spices. The flavor of onion gradually fades during storage.

### (6) The Kind of Pack, Method of Packaging, and Packaging Materials Used, and Completeness of Fill

Whenever possible, the food should be solidly packed so that a large amount of surface is not exposed to the air. Meats should be covered with gravy or sauces. Vegetables should be covered with the liquid in which they were cooked. It is best to use air-tight, liquid-tight, moisture-vapor-proof packages which can be completely filled (see pp. 116–126, Chapter 4). Much of the deterioration of precooked foods is caused by oxidation (see Chapter 2), consequently the importance of packaging foods so as to exclude air cannot be over emphasized. The air must not only be eliminated at the time of packaging, but the packaging materials should be impermeable to oxygen. Packaging in an atmosphere of nitrogen retards oxidative deterioration, as is shown in Fig. 99 from Hanson (1960). Further, the packages should not permit desiccation, because the glaze of ice over the surface of the product helps to retard oxidation.

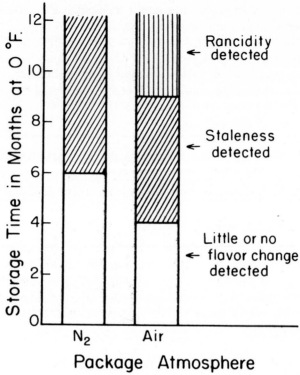

Fig. 99.    Effect of package atmosphere (air vs. nitrogen) on off-flavor development in fried chicken stored at 0°F. (−18°C.).

**(7) Last and Most Important of All of These is the Maintenance of a Uniformly Low Temperature Throughout the Storage Period**

In general, it can be said that the speed of chemical reactions is increased two and one half times when the temperature is raised 18°F. (10° C.). In the case of precooked foods, assuming that the products are held solidly frozen, most of the deterioration and change is caused by these chemical reactions. Conversely, when the temperature is raised 18°F. (10° C.), the permissible storage period is more than cut in two. Thus, if this chemical rule is assumed to hold for frozen foods, if a product retains its fresh quality for only two and one-half years at −36°F. (−38°C.), it can be kept for one year at 0°F. (−18°C.), and for only two months at +18°F. (−8°C.). Actually, the rate of deterioration about triples for every 18°F. (10° C.) rise in temperature (see also p. 39). It is safe to say that, if a food retains its fresh quality for three years at −18°F. (−28°C.) to −20°F. (−

29°C.), it can be held in good condition for one year at 0°F. (−18°C.), but only for six months at +10°F. (−12°C.).

Such generalizations can be applied only to temperatures at which foods remain substantially completely frozen. If the food contains a considerable percentage of sugar or other water-soluble solids, when the temperature is raised to the point where all or a portion of the food is liquid or semi-liquid, deterioration occurs at even a greater rate. For example, fruit pies containing a high percentage of sugar soften at 10° to 15°F. (−12° to −10°C.), and deteriorate rapidly at or above this temperature. Strawberry shortcake also has a short storage life at any temperature above +10°F. (−12°C.), whereas it will remain in good condition at 0°F. (−18°C.), for six months.

## DETERIORATION IS CUMULATIVE

In general, it can be said that the deterioration occurring during storage of frozen foods is cumulative. However, a food does not deteriorate *faster* at a higher temperature because it has previously been held at a lower temperature, and vice versa. Let us assume that food X has a storage life of 12 months at 0°F. (−18°C.), 6 months at 10°F. (−12°C.), and only 3 months at 15°F. (−10°C.). If this food is held 6 months at 0°F. (−18°C.), then 1 month at 10°F. (−12°C.), $\frac{2}{3}$ of its storage life would have been used up, i.e., $\frac{6}{12} + \frac{1}{6} = \frac{2}{3}$, and if the food were placed in a cabinet at 15°F. (−10°C.), it would become unacceptable in a single month (see also Guadagni 1961).

Further, it makes no difference whether the storage at higher temperature precedes or follows holding at the lower temperature or temperatures. Thus, if food "X," the storage characteristics of which have been described in the preceding paragraph is held first for 1 month at +10°F. (−12°C.), then for 6 months at 0°F. (−18°C.), $\frac{2}{3}$ of its storage life would have been used up, and if it were placed in a cabinet at 15°F. (−10°C.), it would become unacceptable in a single month (Anon. 1956B).

## EFFECT OF FLUCTUATING TEMPERATURES

When under fluctuating temperature, if the maximum temperature to which a frozen food is subjected is sufficiently low so that the product remains solidly frozen and no liquid separates, the rate of deterioration of many foods (excepting cream sauces and thickened gravies, Hanson *et al.* (1957), is approximately the same as that which occurs when the product is held uniformly at the mean temperature. Thus, if the temperature of a food fluctuates between −6° and +5°F. (−21° and −15°C.), the rate of deterioration is approximately the same as that which would occur if the food were held at a constant temperature of 0°F. (−18°C.) (Anon. 1956B).

On the other hand, if a chiffon pie of high sugar content were held at a temperature fluctuating between +5° and +15°F. (−15° and −9.4°C.), each time the temperature rose to +15°F. (−9.4°C.), it is probable that there would be some separation of liquid and that the amount of free liquid which appeared at +15°F. (−9.4°C.) would gradually increase, and the deterioration which occurred would be similar to that occurring at a constant +15°F. (−9.4°C.) temperature.

Fluctuating storage temperatures are considerably more detrimental to white sauces, thickened gravies, cornstarch, and custard puddings than a constant temperature, which is the mean of the maximum and minimum temperatures (see Fig. 100, also Hanson *et al.* 1957; Anon. 1956B). Fluctuating temperatures also accelerate the formation of frost and "cavity ice" inside packages.

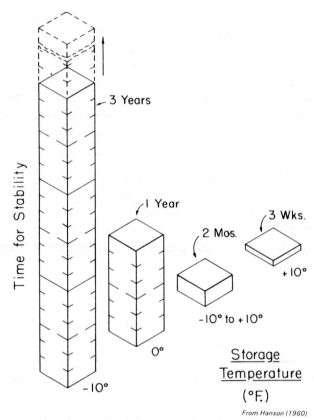

From Hanson (1960)

Fig. 100. Effect of constant and fluctuating storage temperatures on stability of frozen white sauce thickened with waxy rice flour.

## PRODUCTS WHICH HAVE SHORT STORAGE LIFE

Although the majority of precooked frozen foods and baked goods will remain in excellent condition for six months or longer, there are a few which have a very short storage life. In Table 65, the more important of these are listed.

Some of the reasons why these products deteriorate so rapidly follow: Ham, cured shoulder (picnic ham), Canadian bacon, frankfurters or wieners, bologna, and other cured pork products rapidly lose their red color, turn brown, and then gray, and change in flavor. These changes are caused principally by the oxidation of the pigment, nitric acid myochromogen (Watts 1954; see p. 38 of Chapter 2). Roll bread, and other yeast doughs, fermented for longer than 15 min. at 80°F. (27°C.), deteriorate rapidly because of the gradual death of yeast cells and loss of viability of those which remain (see pp. 370 to 382, Chapter 17). Batters and other unbaked goods containing baking powder have a relatively short storage life for two reasons: (1) The acid and soda of the baking powder slowly react (see also Chapter 17). (2) The carbon dioxide formed from this reaction gradually escapes from the batter, causing loss of leavening power. Spice cakes deterio-

Table 65

Precooked Products Which Have Short Storage Life

| Product | Maximum Storage Life at 0°F. ($-18$°C.) | Reference | Chapter in Which Storage of Product Is Considered |
|---|---|---|---|
| Bacon, Canadian[1] | 2 weeks | Tressler (1953) | 2, 11 |
| Batter, gingerbread | 3–4 months | Tressler (1947B) | 17 |
| Batter, muffin | 2 weeks | Fenton (1951) | 17 |
| Batter, spice | 1–2 months | Tressler (1947B) | 17 |
| Biscuits, baking powder | 1–2 months | Anon. (1954) | 18 |
| Bologna, sliced | 2 weeks | Anon. (1955A) | 5, 11 |
| Cake,[2] sponge, egg yolk | 2 months | Meyer, et al. | 20 |
| Cake, spice[2] | 2 months | Skarha and Van Duyne (1955) | 20 |
| Dough, roll | 1–2 months | Godkin and Cathcart (1949) | 17 |
| Frankfurters[1] | 2 weeks | Tressler (1953) | 2, 11 |
| Gravy[3] | 2 weeks | Hanson (1956) | 14 |
| Ham, sliced[1] | 2 weeks | Anon. (1955A) | 2, 5, 11 |
| Poultry giblets | 2 months | Czajkowski (1953) | 7 |
| Poultry livers | 2 months | Czajkowski (1953) | 7 |
| Sandwiches cheese ham bologna | 2 weeks | Fenton (1951) Anon. (1954) | 5 |
| Sauce, white[3] | 2 weeks | Hanson (1956) | 14 |
| Sausage[1] | 2 months | Tressler (1953) | 2, 11 |

[1] Special treatments may prolong storage life.
[2] See also Table 67.
[3] Thickened with ordinary wheat flour or corn starch.

rate rapidly (Skarha and Van Duyne 1955) because of loss and change of flavor of the spices. Sponge cakes, made with egg yolks cannot be kept in storage for long periods, because of undesirable changes in flavor of the egg yolk (Meyer *et al.* 1953). Strawberry shortcake, and other products in which the fruit is not immersed in syrup or other liquid, and, consequently, is exposed to the oxidative action of air, also have a short storage life even at 0°F. (−18°C.). The whites of hard cooked eggs are undesirably toughened by freezing, even though the storage period is very short (see p. 36).

Cream sauces and gravies thickened with wheat flour or ordinary cornstarch coagulate in a short time when stored at temperatures much above 0°F. (−18°C.) (Hanson *et al.* 1957; see also pp. 315 to 318.)

If these precooked foods and baked goods which have a short storage life at 0°F. (−18°C.) or higher are held at lower temperatures, their storage life will be increased somewhat, but still few of them will retain their original qualities for six months even though held at −20°F. (−29°C.).

### PRODUCTS WHICH HAVE STORAGE LIFE OF
### MEDIUM LENGTH

In Table 66, a considerable number of foods are listed which ordinarily will remain in good condition for 6 to 8 months at 0°F. (−18°C.). Some research workers will not agree that all of those listed should be included. However, the authors have evidence to indicate that if sufficient care is taken in the selection of the formulas used, the ingredients chosen, the method of cooking employed, and the packaging materials and method of packaging used, products of the kinds listed can be produced which will retain their fresh qualities at least as long as six months at 0°F. (−18°C.). However, it is dangerous to draw too sweeping generalizations concerning the probable storage life of any class of products. For instance, many fruit pies, e.g., prune, blueberry, and raisin, can be stored for a year or even longer without serious loss of quality.

On the other hand, peaches, fresh apricots, and apples must be specially prepared if the fresh quality is to be retained for as long as six months.

Some kinds of cakes retain their flavor, color, and texture during frozen storage better than others. This is shown in Table 67, in which the information, available in the literature on cake storage, is summarized.

Cooked lobster, crab, and shrimp meat toughen to a greater or lesser degree during freezing and storage, probably due to denaturation of proteins (see p. 36).

The fats of crabs and fish are highly unsaturated; therefore, they oxidize easily and change in flavor during long storage. Turkey fat also slowly changes in flavor during the cold storage of frozen turkey products.

Although the fats and oils in which potatoes are fried are composed prin-

Table 66
Precooked Products with Storage Life of Medium Length[1]

| Product | Reference | Chapter in Which Storage of Product Is Considered |
|---|---|---|
| Batter, devil's-food[3] | Tressler (1947B) | 17 |
| Batter, white cake[3] | Tressler (1947B) | 17 |
| Cakes,[2] various kinds[4] | Fenton (1951) | |
| | Meyer et al. (1953) | 20 |
| Chicken, fried[3] | Hanson 1954; Anon. (1956A and B) | 7 |
| Crab | Fitzgerald (1955) | 13 |
| Fish, fatty[1] | Tressler (1953) | 12 |
| Fruit purées | Johnson and Boggs (1947) | 8 |
| Ham, baked, whole[3] | Woodroof and Shelor (1955) | 11 |
| Lobster | Fitzgerald (1955) | 13 |
| Meals on a tray[1] | Gleim and Fenton (1949) | 23 |
| Meat balls | Anon. (1952) | 11 |
| | Owen et al. (1951) | |
| Meat loaf | Anon. (1952) | |
| | Owen et al. (1951) | 11 |
| Pies, chicken | Woodroof and Shelor (1955) | 7 |
| Pies, fruit, unbaked[4] | Tressler (1947A) | 19 |
| Pies, meat | Woodroof and Shelor (1955) | 11 |
| Potatoes, French-fried | Kirkpatrick et al. (1956) | 9 |
| Sandwiches | | |
| Roast beef | | |
| Various spreads | | |
| turkey | Anon. (1955A) | 5 |
| liverwurst | | |
| Soups[4] | Fenton (1951) | 6 |
| Shrimp | Lewis (1947) | 13 |
| Turkey[3] | Hanson et al. (1950) | 7 |

[1] Will remain in good condition at 0°F. (−18°C.) for 6 to 8 months.
[2] See also Table 67.
[3] Storage life 4 to 6 months; see Fig. 101.
[4] The storage life varies widely depending on the kind and also the flavoring or seasoning used. Many retain quality for a year or longer.

cipally of fats which are not highly unsaturated, still, since much of the fat on the French-fried potatoes is largely on the surface, and, consequently, in direct contact with the oxygen of the air, the storage life of the product is limited to about ten months at 0°F. (−18°C.). This same statement holds for other products fried in deep fat. If the fat used is not nearly saturated (from a chemical standpoint), or if it remains hot in the frybath for more than a few hours, foods fried therein may not remain free from rancidity for even eight months at 0°F. (−18°C.).

The storage life of meals on a plate depends largely on the components of the meal. If the meal includes sausage, ham, Canadian bacon, or any other food which deteriorates rapidly (see Table 65, P. 527) in frozen storage, the meal cannot be considered to be suitable for holding in zero stor-

Table 67

Length of Time Which Various Kinds of Cake Retain Their Acceptability

| Kind of Cake | Temperature of Storage | | Accept-ability Retained Months | Reference |
|---|---|---|---|---|
| | °F. | °C. | | |
| Angel food | −10° to 0° | −23° to −18° | 4 | Meyer *et al.* (1952) |
| Angel Food | −10° to 0° | −23° to −18° | 6+ | Meyer *et al.* (1953) |
| Cheese cake, French | −15° | −26° | 9+ | Beattie *et al.* (1949) |
| "Fathers Day" | −15° | −26° | 14 | Beattie *et al.* (1949) |
| Fruit cake | 0° | −18° | 12+ | Anon. (1955B) |
| Plain, yellow | 0° to −10° | −18° to −23° | 9+ | Meyer *et al.* (1953) |
| | −10° | −23° | 4+ | Zaehringer and May-field (1951) |
| | −10° | −23° | 8+ | Graul and Lowe (1947) |
| | 0° | −18° | 6+ | Paul *et al.* (1954) |
| Plain, white | 0° | −18° | 7+ | Paul *et al.* (1954) |
| Spice | +12° | −11° | 4 | Skarha and Van Duyne (1955) |
| Sponge (egg yolk) | −10° to 0° | −23° to −18° | 2 | Meyer *et al.* (1953) |
| Sponge (whole egg) | −10° to 0° | −23° to −18° | 6+ | Meyer *et al.* (1953) |

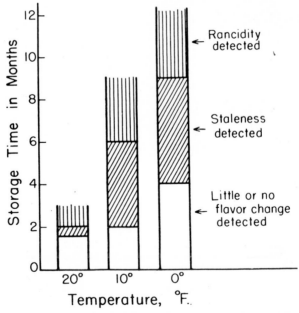

Fig. 101. Effect of storage temperature on off-flavor development in frozen fried chicken in retail packages stored at 0°, 10°, and 20°F. (−18°, −12°, and −6.7°C.).

age ($-18°C.$) for longer than four months. The placement of meals on a tray in the list of foods which will remain in good condition at $0°F.$ ($-18°C.$) for 6 to 8 months is, therefore, based on the assumption that no component listed in Table 65, (those which will not retain their fresh quality for longer than four months), is included. Since packaging of the foods on a tray is not such as to exclude contact with air, the storage life of the components is not as great as it would be if each were individually packaged in air-tight containers with little or no headspace.

### THE MORE STABLE PRECOOKED FOODS

In Table 68 are listed various food products which, if properly prepared and packaged, should remain in good condition at $0°F.$ ($-18°C.$) for at least 12 months. The list includes stews and sauces which can be solidly packed and thus eliminate air, and also the possibility of serious desiccation.

Table 68

Products Which Should Remain in Good Condition at $0°F.$ ($-18°C.$) for One Year or Longer

| Product | Reference | Chapter in Which Storage of Product Is Considered |
|---|---|---|
| Applesauce | Woodroof and Atkinson (1945) | 8 |
| Apples, baked | Rasmussen et al. (1948) | 8 |
| Bread | Cathcart (1941) | 18 |
| | Fenton (1951) | |
| Bread (rolls) | Fenton (1951) | 18 |
| Blackberries | Woodroof and Atkinson (1945) | 8 |
| Blueberries | Woodroof and Atkinson (1945) | 8 |
| Cake, fruit[1] | Woodroof and Shelor (1955) | 20 |
| Candies[2] | Woodroof (1951) | 22 |
| Cherries | Woodroof (1945) | 8 |
| Chicken, creamed[3] | Anon. (1956B) | 7 |
| | Kirkpatrick and Mountjoy (1948) | |
| Chicken à la king[3] | Kirkpatrick and Mountjoy (1948) | 7 |
| | Anon. (1956B) | |
| Cookies | Woodroof and Shelor (1955) | 20 |
| Doughs, cookie | Fenton (1951) | 17 |
| Fish, lean | | |
| Peanuts | Thompson et al. (1951) | 22 |
| Pecans | Woodroof and Heaton (1953) | 22 |
| Plums | Woodroof and Atkinson (1945) | 8 |
| Stew, beef | Woodroof and Shelor (1955) | 11 |
| Stew, veal | Woodroof and Shelor (1955) | 11 |
| Waffles | | 20 |

[1] See also Table 67.
[2] Some candies do not freeze well.
[3] If thickened with waxy rice flour.

The list also includes bread, rolls, and waffles, cereal products containing much air, which, however, are not particularly subject to oxidative deterioration.

This list cannot be considered as complete. Undoubtedly there are other cooked foods which are equally stable.

## BIBLIOGRAPHY

Agr. Research Service.    1960. Conference on frozen food quality. U.S. Dept. Agr. ARS-74-21, Albany, Calif.

Anon.    1952. Home freezing of baked goods. Home freezing of prepared and cooked foods. W. Va. Agr. Extens. Service, Unnumbered Circ.

Anon.    1954. Freezing cooked and prepared foods. Univ. Neb. Extens. Circ. 9979 Rev.

Anon.    1955A. Freezing of sandwiches to prevent deterioration. Termination Rept. Experimental Cookery Div. Quartermaster Food and Container Institute, Chicago, Ill.

Anon.    1955B. Storage of frozen bakery products. Commodity Storage Manual, Refrigeration Research Foundation, Colorado Springs, Colo.

Anon.    1956A. Frozen fried chicken storage limit six months, according to U.S. Dept. Agr. progress report. Quick Frozen Foods 18, No. 9, 175.

Anon.    1956B. Mimeo. News Release. U.S. Dept. Agr., Western Utilization Research Branch, Aug. 15.

Anon.    1959. Protect frozen foods from temperature damage. U.S. Dept. Agr., Agr. Research Service ARS-74-9.

Beattie, H. G., Edelmann, E. C., and Cathcart, W. H.    1949. Keeping quality of frozen bakery products. Food Technol. 3, 160–162.

Boggs, M. M., Sinott, C. E., Vasak, O. K., and Kester, E. B.    1951. Frozen cooked rice. Food Technol. 5, 230–232.

Boggs, M., Ward, A. C., Sinott, C. N., and Kester, E. B.    1952. Frozen cooked rice. II. Brown rice. Food Technol. 6, 53–54.

Cathcart, W. H.    1941. Further studies on the retardation of the staling of bread by freezing. Cereal Chem. 18, 771–777.

Charles, V. R., and Van Duyne, F. O.    1953. Effect of freezing and freezer storage upon quality of baked rolls, brown-and-serve rolls, and shaped roll dough. Food Technol. 7, 208–211.

Czajkowski, J. M.    1953. Guide to storage time for frozen foods. Univ. Conn. Extens. Service. Unnumbered. Published in March.

Fenton, F.    1951. Foods from the freezer: precooked and prepared. Cornell Extens. Bull. 692 Rev.

Fitzgerald, G. A.    1955. Private communication. Westport, Conn.

Gleim, E., and Fenton, F.    1949. Effect of 0°F. and 15°F. storage on the quality of frozen cooked foods. Food Technol. 3, 187–192.

Godkin, W. J., and Cathcart, W. H.    1949. Fermentation activity and survival of yeast in frozen fermented and unfermented doughs. Food Technol. 3, 139–146.

Graul, L. S., and Lowe, B.    1947. How storage affects frozen cakes and batters. Food Inds. 19, 330–332.

Guadagni, D. G.    1961. Integrated time-temperature experience as it relates to frozen food. ASHRAE J. 3, No. 4, 66–69, 83.

Hanson, H. L.  1960. Research on processing and preparation prepared frozen foods. J. Am. Dietet. Assoc. 36, 581–584.

Hanson, H. L., and Fletcher, L. R.  1958. Time-temperature-tolerance of frozen foods. XII. Turkey dinners and turkey pies. Food Technol. 12, 40–43.

Hanson, H. L., Fletcher, L. R., and Campbell, A. A.  1957. Texture stability of thickened precooked frozen foods as influenced by composition and storage conditions. Food Technol. 11, 339–343.

Hanson, H. L., Fletcher, L. R., and Lineweaver, H. 1959. Time-temperature-tolerance of frozen foods. XVII. Frozen fried chicken. Food Technol. 13, 221–224.

Hanson, H. L., Winegarden, H. M., Horton, M. B., and Lineweaver, H.  1950. Preparation and storage of frozen cooked poultry and vegetables. Food Technol. 4, 430–434.

Hucker, G. J., and David, E. R.  1957. The effect of alternate freezing and thawing on the total flora of frozen chicken pies. Food Technol. 11, 354–356.

Hutchings, B. L., and Evers, C. F.  1946. Research and quality control of precooked frozen foods. Refrig. Eng. 51, 26–29, 61, 78, 82.

Hutchings, B. L., and Evers, C. F.  1947. Problems in the production of precooked frozen foods. Food Technol. 1, 421–426.

Johnson, G., and Boggs, M. M.  1947. New fresh fruit spreads preserved by freezing. Food Inds. 9, 1491–1494, 1612–1613.

Kirkpatrick, M. E., Heinze, P. H., Craft, C. C., Mountjoy, B. M., and Falatko, C. E.  1956. French-frying quality of potatoes as influenced by cooking methods, storage conditions, and specific gravity of tubers. U.S. Dept. Agr. Tech. Bull. 1142.

Kirkpatrick, M. E., and Mountjoy, B. M.  1948. Keeping qualities of precooked chicken dishes studied. Frozen Food Industry 4, No. 5, 7, 32–33.

Kulp, K., and Bechtel, W. G.  1962. Frozen fruit pies. Food Technol. 16, 104–106.

Lewis, H.  1947. What effects do cooking time and packing have on frozen boiled shrimp? Food Freezing 1, No. 3, 48–49.

Lineweaver, H., Anderson, J. D., and Hanson, H. L.  1952. Effect of antioxidant on rancidity development in frozen creamed turkey. Food Technol. 6, 1–4.

Logan, P. P., Harp, C. H., and Dove, W. F.  1951. Keeping quality of frozen precooked chicken à la king, a bacteriological evaluation of hot and cold packs. Food Technol. 5, 193–198.

Meyer, B., Buckley, R., and Moore, R.  1949. Research shows differences in frozen butter cake and sponge cake. Refrig. Eng. 57, 340–342, 388, 392.

Meyer, B., Buckley, R., and Moore, R.  1952. Breads, cakes, and pastries from the home freezer. Univ. Tenn. Agr. Extens. Service Circ. 618.

Meyer, B., Moore, R., and Buckley, R.  1953. Flavor deterioration in frozen cake batters. Food Research 18, 70–75.

Miller, A. T., El-Bisi, H. M., Sawyer, F. M., and Eshbach, C. E.  1965. Care and handling of prepared frozen foods. Univ. Mass., Coop. Extension Service Food Management Leaflet 9.

Nickerson, J. T. R., and Karel, M.  1964. Preservation of food by freezing. In Food Processing Operations, Vol. 3, M. A. Joslyn, and J. L. Heid (Editors). Avi Publishing Co., Westport, Conn.

Owen, R. F., Chase, J. T., and Van Duyne, F. O.  1951. Freezing cooked and prepared foods. Ill. Coll. Agr. Extens. Service Circ. 618.

Paul, P., Batcher, O. M., and Fulde, L. 1954. Dry mix and frozen baked products. I. Dry mix and frozen cakes. J. Home Econ. 46, 249–253.

Pence, J. W., and Heid, M. 1960. Effect of storage temperatures on stability of frozen cakes. Food Technol. 14, No. 2, 80–83.

Pence, J. W., and Standridge, N. N. 1958. Effect of storage temperature on firming of cake crumb. Cereal Chem. 35, 57–65.

Rasmussen, C. L., Esselen, W. B., Jr., and Fellers, C. R. 1948. Canned and frozen baked McIntosh apples. Fruit Products J. 27, 228–229, 265.

Skarha, D. M., and Van Duyne, F. O. 1955. Effect of freezing and freezer storage on cake quality. I. Baked spice cake and cakes baked from frozen batters. Food Research 20, 273–281.

Stiebeling, H. K. 1952. Fluctuating temperatures in home freezers. In Report Chief Bureau Human Nutrition and Home Economics, Agr. Research Admin., U.S. Dept. Agr. 1952, 15.

Thompson, H., Cecil, S. R., and Woodroof, J. G. 1951. Storage of edible peanuts. Ga. Expt. Sta. Bull. 268.

Tressler, D. K. 1938. Bacteria, enzymes, and vitamins—indices of quality in frozen vegetables. Refrig. Eng. 36, 319–321.

Tressler, D. K. 1947A. General directions for making pies for freezing. Special Rept. prepared for Frozen Food Foundation (unpublished).

Tressler, D. K. 1947B. Preliminary experiments on the freezing of cake batters. Special Rept. prepared for Frozen Food Foundation (unpublished).

Tressler, D. K. 1953. What's new in frozen foods. J. Am. Dietet. Assoc. 29, 230–233. (A summary of a more comprehensive paper presented on Oct. 24, 1952, at the annual meeting of the Am. Dietetic Assoc. in Minneapolis, Minn.)

Van Arsdel, W. B. 1961. Alignment chart speeds computations of quality changes in frozen foods. Food Processing 22, No. 12.

Watts, B. M. 1954. Oxidative rancidity and discoloration in meat. Advances in Food Research 5, 1–52. Academic Press, New York.

Woodroof, J. G. 1951. Refrigerated candy keeps better. Ice and Refrig. 120, No. 4, 57–58, 60.

Woodroof, J. G. 1955. Freezing candies. Nat'l. Confectioners Assoc. Publ. 107.

Woodroof, J. G., and Atkinson, I. S. 1945. Freezing cooked foods. Food Inds. 17, 1041–1042, 1136, 1138.

Woodroof, J. G., and Cecil, S. R. 1951. Nuts: better kept—better candy. Food Eng. 23, No. 11, 129–131, 148, 150.

Woodroof, J. G., and Heaton, E. K. 1953. "Year 'round on pecans" by refrigerated storage. Food Eng. No. 5, 83–85, 141–142.

Woodroof, J. G., and Shelor, E. 1955. Keeping quality during storage of precooked frozen foods. In Precooked Frozen Foods—A Symposium—Surveys of Progress on Military Subsistence Problems Series 1, No. 7, 42–49. Quartermaster Food and Container Institute, Chicago, Ill.

Zaehringer, M. V., and Mayfield, H. L. 1951. The effect of leavening and shortening combinations on the frozen storage of cake batters prepared at high altitude. Food Technol. 5, 151–154.

## CHAPTER 25

# Handling and Use of
Donald K. Tressler

# Frozen Precooked Foods—
# Special Reheating Equipment

## INTRODUCTION

The procedures which should be used in freezing, warehousing, transporting, and handling precooked frozen foods are the same as those outlined for frozen foods which have not been cooked (see Chapters 12 of Volume 2 and 16 of Volume 3).

The need for maintaining uniformly low temperatures during the storage, transportation, and handling of frozen precooked foods have been considered in detail in the sections on Special Problems Encountered in Preparing, Freezing, Storing, Transporting, and Marketing Frozen Precooked Foods and Storage of Frozen Precooked Foods, Chapters 2 and 24, respectively, of this volume. In these chapters, it has been indicated that frozen desserts, such as fruit pies and shortcakes, which are high in sugar, are especially subject to damage by temperatures above 0°F. ($-18$°C.), and by temperatures which fluctuate much above 0°F. ($-18$°C.). Sauces and gravies, thickened with wheat flour or ordinary cornstarch, have also been shown to deteriorate rapidly when subjected to fluctuating storage temperatures (Chapter 14).

### GENERAL IMPORTANCE OF CAREFUL HANDLING
### OF PRECOOKED FROZEN FOODS

Guadagni (1961) has reported his studies on the hazards encountered by frozen foods during warehousing, transportation, retail delivery, and holding in a retail display cabinet. He concluded that if the products were not allowed to warm up during retail delivery to a temperature above 20°F. ($-7$°C.), the loss of "high quality storage life" was negligible (only 3 to 5%). Although this is undoubtedly true for boil-in-the-bag vegetables and many frozen fruits, it probably does not hold for a number of products which are damaged by widely fluctuating temperatures such as ice cream, sherbets, whipped toppings, sliced fruits in heavy syrups, and certain other products which become soft if warmed to 20°F. ($-7$°C.).

Moreover, there is little doubt that most prepared and precooked food products deteriorate at a greatly accelerated rate if they are permitted to warm to the point where they partially thaw. If frozen foods in display cases in groceries and supermarkets are piled so high that the top layer is above the level of refrigeration, thawing in the upper layer will occur if the

Donald K. Tressler is a consultant and President of the Avi Publishing Co., Westport, Conn.

535

foods are not sold quickly. The result is bound to be rapid deterioration of the partially thawed product, even though it is refrozen when the case is covered at night.

CLASSES OF PRECOOKED FROZEN FOODS

## Preparation for the Table

In general, precooked and prepared frozen foods may be divided into three general classes: (1) frozen desserts which are eaten in the frozen state, e.g., frozen eclairs, ice cream, ice cream cakes, sherbets, fruit in poly bags, and Velva Fruit; (2) foods which are eaten at ordinary room temperatures, e.g., cakes, most pies, cookies, candies, and confections, cold-processed jellies, fruit purées, and sauces, etc., and (3) foods which are served hot.

Serving Frozen Desserts.—As a rule, frozen desserts require no special preparation for the table except for allowing them to warm enough to soften them for eating. Care must be taken to keep them frozen at all times, especially during transportation to the retailer, and, after purchase, to the home. If Dry Ice is used as a refrigerant for the trip from the store to the home, the desserts are likely to be too firm for use unless they are permitted to warm to about 10°F. (−12°C.) prior to serving.

Defrosting Frozen Fruits.—Although fruits with the exception of apples are seldom cooked before freezing (unless they are made into pies, tarts, or puddings), it may not be out of place to indicate how they are best prepared for the table. If they are thawed slowly, or allowed to warm to room temperature, they lose flavor, color, and texture. They are best thawed rapidly in the unopened package and served when they are still quite cold. Fruits packaged in watertight, evacuated bags should be thawed in running cold water, or in a small pan of lukewarm water from which they should be removed while still cold.

Defrosting Baked Goods and Confections.—The importance of proper packaging and defrosting of confections, in order to avoid condensation on the product during thawing, has already been emphasized. As yet, much of the bread, cake, and other baked goods, and candy, nuts, and confections are defrosted before being sold at retail. Bread and rolls should be rapidly thawed and warmed to 70°F. (21°C.) or above, so as to keep to a minimum the time that the product remains in the zone 25° to 60°F. (−4° to +15.5° C.) in which staling occurs rapidly (see also pp. 401–403). A simple way of thawing bread rapidly is to put the loaves on a rack in rapidly circulating *heated* air. Most cakes do not stale so quickly, and, therefore, it is not so important to defrost them rapidly. However, care must be taken to prevent condensation of moisture thereon. Since the amount of moisture vapor held by warm air near the saturation point (close to 100% R.H.) is relatively large, condensation on cold packages of frozen products placed in a warm humid atmosphere will be great. Because of this, it is a bad practice to bring containers of frozen baked goods directly out of the freezer on a warm humid day, such as is often encountered in summer. A room of low relative humidity should be provided for defrosting bakery products at times when the humidity is high. The humidity of any room may be reduced to a satisfactorily low level by the use of a dehumidifier. Mechanical dehumidifiers, operated by electric motors, are generally useful, since they continue to condense moisture vapor as long as they operate and will not become saturated with water as do dehumidifiers which use chemicals for the absorption of the moisture.

**Defrosting Candies.**—Even greater care must be taken in the defrosting of candies and confections. Chocolates, and candies with chocolate coatings, should *not* be defrosted in rooms above 85°F. (29.4°C.) or the fat of the chocolate may soften, causing blooming; further, if the candies are individually wrapped, the wrappers may become discolored, and / or stick to the chocolates. Fine candies are often packed in fancy boxes. If the frozen product is moved into a humid room, even if the temperature of that room is 70°F. (21°C.), or somewhat lower, sufficient condensation may occur to damage the packages. This may be avoided in one of three ways; (1) reducing the humidity of the room in which the confections are defrosted to a point sufficiently low that condensation will not occur; (2) moving the containers of candies, first to a refrigerated room maintained at relatively low humidity and at a temperature midway between that of the storage and the ambient temperature, and allowing them to remain there until the temperature of the confection has risen to that of this "defrosting room;" (3) defrosting the confections in unopened shipping containers of a type impervious to moisture and moisture vapor. Such a container can be constructed of V-board. This type of board is dense and contains an asphalt barrier layer. Another way to make shipping containers impervious to moisture is to line them with a tough moisture-vapor-proof and moisture-proof liner such as polyethylene or Mylar.

If the frozen confections are defrosted in unopened shipping containers impervious to moisture and moisture vapor, the containers should not be compactly stacked, but should be spread out so as to permit ready access of air to each. Even if this is done, defrosting will be slow, because of the time required for the heat to pass into the center of the container.

## PROBLEMS ENCOUNTERED IN REHEATING FROZEN PRECOOKED FOODS

### Should Precooked Foods Be Thawed Prior to Reheating?

One of the most disputed questions concerning the reheating of pre-cooked foods is the desirability of thawing prior to reheating. Those who advocate thawing, or partial thawing, prior to reheating indicate that, by this procedure, more even heating is effected. The advocates of reheating without preliminary thawing, argue that permitting the food to thaw at room temperature gives the microorganisms present in the food a chance to multiply.

Causey and Fenton (1951) studied the bacterial content of frozen pre-cooked vegetables and meat dishes. They observed a fourfold increase in the bacterial plate count of baked stuffed potatoes during thawing (from 221 to 868 per gm.). However, the count in reheated thawed potatoes was not significantly different from that of the reheated frozen product (the numbers of bacteria found in the thawed potatoes after reheating, averaged 56 per gm., somewhat less than those found in the baked potatoes reheated without the thawing step). It should be noted that all of the precooked frozen vegetables used in the studies of Causey and Fenton contained very few microorganisms, having been prepared under highly sanitary conditions. If frozen precooked foods of relatively high bacterial content, e.g., one to two million per gram had been used and a fourfold increase in bacteria had occurred during thawing, the quality of the reheated food might have been open to question.

There are several products which, if placed in the solidly frozen condition directly over or under the heat, are likely to be overcooked on the outside before the internal temperature has reached serving temperature, e.g., 180°F. (82°C.). Products such as macaroni and cheese, pot pies, and tuna with noodles should preferably be partially thawed before reheating in an oven.

### Reheating Methods

Because of the great variety of frozen precooked foods and baked goods which are served warm, there is no *best* method of reheating all of them. Some products, e.g., soups, may be quickly and satisfactorily reheated in small pans over direct heat. Others, e.g., creamed poultry, may be better if they are brought up to serving temperature in a double boiler. If the pre-cooked products are packed in a tin can, vacuumized plastic bags, or other water-tight container, they may be quickly reheated in the original container simply by immersion in boiling water (see Fig. 107, p. 556). Products which have been deep-fat fried, such as fish sticks or French-fried potatoes, and casseroles dishes (pot pies, macaroni and cheese, etc.) may, perhaps, be reheated best in an oven. Where a golden brown surface color is desired, the reheating may be carried out under broiler heat. Another satisfactory way of reheating deep-fat fried products is to put them in a covered pan, containing one-half inch of hot fat, which has been placed over direct heat. The fastest methods of reheating precooked foods are (1) in a dielectric oven or "Radarange" (see p. 547) (Causey and Fenton 1951), and (2) in a pressure sauce pan or speed cooker (see p. 543). Causey and Fenton did not find the precooked foods which they reheated in the dielectric oven to be quite as palatable as when they were prepared by the other methods which they studied, viz., Maxon oven, household oven, double boiler, and direct immersion in boiling water. Pressure saucepans and other cookers, in which foods are reheated under 10 to 15 p.s.i. steam pressure, were found to be especially desirable for vegetables.

Some specialties, such as waffles and pancakes, may be simply and satisfactorily reheated in an ordinary household toaster. Complete meals on a tray may be reheated either in an ordinary household oven or some special type of oven such as a B-4 Whirlwind (see p. 543). Some meals on heavy foil trays may be satisfactorily reheated over direct heat.

Causey and Fenton (1951) have carried out two of the few studies reported in the literature in which various methods of reheating precooked frozen foods were compared. In their first study, they reheated six frozen precooked vegetables (cut green beans, Swiss chard, broccoli, carrots, beets, and baked stuffed potatoes) by five methods (dielectric, household and Maxon ovens, double boiler, and immersion boiler, and immersion in boiling water). They concluded:

"The least change of weight occurred in the double-boiler and household-oven methods. The greatest loss in weight was in the dielectric oven.

"Scores for palatability varied with the reheating methods, the particular vegetable concerned, and the characteristic being studied. All products were considered acceptable when reheated by any of the methods. No one reheating method was scored best for all quality characteristics of any one vegetable.

"Statistically significant differences in the palatability data were as follows: The characteristics that differed in the cut green beans and the preferred method for that characteristic were surface appearance, household oven; color, Maxon oven; texture, double boiler. Significant differences between reheating methods occurred in the flavor scores for Swiss chard, with the double boiler method preferred. The color of broccoli was best when it was reheated in the double boiler, and the aroma was best when reheating was done in the dielectric oven. The surface appearance of the diced carrots was best in those reheated in boiling water. This method was also best for the surface appearance and color of the shredded beets.

"No differences in ascorbic acid retention owing to reheating methods was observed . . .

"Bacterial counts were low before and after reheating."

In a second study concerned with a comparison of the reheating of meat dishes, in which the quality of creamed chicken on rice, chicken paprika with gravy, spaghetti and meat balls, and ham patties were compared after reheating by the same five methods used in their vegetable study, Causey and Fenton reached the following conclusions:

"The reheating times of the unthawed foods varied from 3¼ min. to 90 min. depending upon the product and the reheating method. The dielectric oven required the least time. The other methods in order of increasing time were: Maxon oven, boiling water, household oven, and double boiler. Thawing the individual servings had only a small effect on the reheating time.

"Least weight was lost during reheating in the household oven and the double boiler. The largest weight loss occurred during reheating in the dielectric oven. The products reheated in boiling water gained weight due to seepage of water through the Pliofilm bags.

"All of the products by the five methods were scored as acceptable, ranging in total palatability score from 6.5 to 8.4 out of a possible maximum of 10. The palatability scores were highest in products reheated in boiling water, and lowest for those reheated in the dielectric oven. The greatest differences were in surface appearance of all the products and in the tenderness and juiciness of the meat.

"Little loss of thiamine occurred from any of the products during any of the reheating methods . . .

"Low bacterial counts were observed after reheating the products by all of the methods. Initial counts were low, less than 2,000 per gram in all products. . ."

More recently, Vahlsing, Inc. has demonstrated that frozen vegetables, and many other products which have been packed in an aluminum foil tray, can be reheated by an ingeniously simple method (Anon. 1966). The housewife places the tray of frozen product in a deep skillet containing three-quarters of an inch of hot water (Fig. 102). The skillet is covered with

Courtesy of Vahlsing, Inc.

Fig. 102. This simple way of reheating on top of the range uses less heat and gives a better quality than reheating in oven.

a tight-fitting lid and the water brought to the boil, then the heat is lowered and the product permitted to steam for from 6 to 12 min., depending upon the product and the serving temperature preferred. This method provides the consumer with the same advantage offered by the boil-in-the-bag procedure inasmuch as there is no cleaning and washing of saucepans after cooking. An added advantage is that the foil tray can be used as a serving dish, which means one less dish is soiled. Obviously, this method retains the quality of the product just as does the double boiler method of reheating.

**The Boil-in-the-Bag Procedure.**—Many packers partially cook vegetables, add either a butter or cream sauce, and pack them in special evacuated and heat-sealed polyethylene bags (see Chapter 4, Volume 3). These products are reheated and the cooking completed by dropping the bags into a pan of boiling water, then thawing and cooking the product for ten or more minutes after the water has come to the boil the second time. As noted in Chap. 4 of Volume 3, this method yields a full-flavored product, because it is rapidly reheated without contact with air and without any loss of juice or sauce.

## Second-Stage Cooking of Frozen Partially Fried Potatoes

Kirkpatrick *et al.* (1956) have compared four procedures for second-stage cooking of parfried potatoes: (1) 10 min. in a 500°F. (260°C.) oven; (2) 5 min. in a broiler at 500°F. (260°C.); (3) 5 min. in a 500°F. (260°C.) oven, followed by 3 min. in a broiler at 500°F.; and (4) in deep-fat at 375°F. (190°C.) for 1½ min. In each test, the sample for deep-fat frying was thawed to room temperature. In the other tests, the samples were cooked both without thawing and after thawing for four hours at 72°F. (22°C.). A summary of the results of this work follows:

"All color scores were high, 4.4 or above, indicating that good color was obtained from all methods. Statistical analysis showed that no method was significantly better than another. The mean scores for uniformity-of-browning (4.6) for the unfrozen control samples fried off in deep fat were significantly higher than most of the scores for the other samples. Oven and oven-broiler methods gave the lowest scores for tenderness; with one exception the scores were significantly lower than those for the deep-fat-fried samples. Most tender were the samples cooked in deep fat. Crispness, mealiness, and flavor were significantly poorer for samples cooked in the broiler than by any other method. Differences among the other methods were not great enough for significance.

"The unfrozen control samples were judged to be significantly more oily than several lots of French-fries cooked by simplified methods, a result that was to be expected, since the controls were subjected to additional oil absorption in the second stage of cooking. Chemical analysis also showed that the simplified methods for second-stage cooking produced French-fries with an oil content (8.8 to 10.7%) that was considerably lower than the oil content (16.1%) of the French-fries prepared by the conventional method of frying in deep fat."

Since this study was carried out, it has been found that the housewife will get an excellent product if she reheats the parfried potatoes in a small amount of shortening in a covered skillet or frypan on top of her range. The quality of the reheated French-fries, prepared in this way, is comparable to that obtained when the potatoes are reheated in hot deep fat.

## REHEATING PROCEDURES RECOMMENDED

### In an Oven

Reheating in an oven is commonly recommended for more kinds of precooked frozen foods than any other method. The following is a partial list of products which are usually reheated in an oven: Baked apples, baked beans, barbecued beef, barbecued pork, beef roasts, chicken croquettes, chow mein, codfish cakes, crab Imperial, deep-fat fried shellfish (clams, crab cakes, crabmeat balls, oysters, scallops, and shrimp), deviled crabs, English muffins, fish cakes, fish sticks, fried chicken, fried eggplant, fried fish fillets, fruit cobblers, fruit pies, ham patties, liver and onions, macaroni and cheese, meals on a plate or tray, muffins, stuffed peppers, pork spareribs, pot pies (poultry, meat, tuna), potatoes (au gratin, French-fried, hash brown, patties, puffs, and whipped); rolls, spinach soufflé, and stuffed cabbage.

If fried foods are heated in an oven, the paper wrappers should be removed and the food left uncovered. The oven temperatures usually recommended for reheating precooked foods vary from 375° to 425°F. (190° –218°C.). For pizza pies, meals on aluminum plates, and some other products a higher temperature, e.g., 450°F. (232°C.) is recommended.

### In a Broiler

Many of the products on the list of those commonly reheated in an oven may be prepared for the table in a broiler. All products fried in deep fat may be reheated in a broiler, provided they are turned after the side under the heat has attained the desired color.

### On Top of the Range

Heating on top of the range should preferably be done in a heavy cast aluminum or copper-clad steel saucepan or frying pan. A few of the items which may be reheated in this way include the following: Apple and other fruit sauces, chicken à la king, chili con carne, creamed chicken, gravies, Hungarian goulash, soups, chowders, and gumbos, stews (beef, Brunswick, chicken, veal, kidney, oyster, etc.).

### In Shallow Fat in a Frying Pan

Most fried foods may be satisfactorily reheated in shallow fat in a frying pan on top of a range. These products include: fish fillets and portions, fish sticks, French-fried potatoes, fried clams, crab cakes, crabmeat balls, oysters, scallops, and shrimp, lobster cakes and cutlets, codfish cakes, eggplant, and ham patties.

### In a Toaster

The simplest way of reheating pancakes and waffles is by placing the frozen product directly in a *preheated* toaster.

### In Pressure Saucepan or "Speed Cooker"

Most vegetables including green beans, lima beans, broccoli, cauliflower, peas, sweet corn, spinach, and other greens, and mixed vegetables are excellent when thawed and reheated in a pressure saucepan or "Speed Cooker." The time required for reheating will vary from 1 to 4 min. depending upon the product and the quantity to be reheated.

### In Double Boiler

Heating in a double boiler is usually recommended for shrimp Creole, various sauces, thick gravies, Welsh rarebit, and other products which may scorch if reheated directly over a gas flame or electric unit.

### SPECIAL EQUIPMENT FOR REHEATING FROZEN PRECOOKED FOODS

### Special Ovens for Heating Meals

**The B4 Oven.**—During World War II, the W. L. Maxson Co. offered the Maxson Whirlwind ovens for use in reheating the Maxson frozen meals. The Maxson oven, which was used to reheat Maxson "Strato-Plates," warmed the frozen meals by means of rapidly circulating air heated by electric heaters. According to Chatham *et al.* (1951), the Maxson oven used by the U.S. Air Force had the following disadvantages:

"(a) excessive weight and bulk; (b) high power requirements; (c) short life and high maintenance requirements of the fan motor; (d) inefficient conduction of heat; and (e) excessive time required to heat cans of IF[1] meal components."

Because of these disadvantages, an effort was made to find an oven better suited to Air Force requirements. The Mansfield Aircraft Products Co.'s airline-type of food warming oven was modified by attaching an electric heating element to the bottom of each shelf, thus obtaining heating by

---

[1] Components of the In Flight Ration.

metal to metal conduction which proved practicable for reheating pre-cooked frozen meals on a tray. A thermostat, incorporated in the electric circuit, automatically makes and breaks the circuit to maintain the desired temperature after the initial heating phase. This oven, the B4 (Fig. 103),

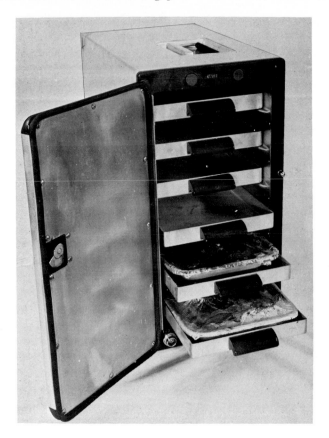

Fig. 103. The B-4 oven used on some planes of the U.S. Air Force to reheat precooked frozen meals. Heating elements are attached to the bottom of the shelves of the B-4 oven.

which is used by many bombers and other large planes of the U.S. Air Force, has six trays. It operates on 28 volts D.C., 120-volt single-phase A.C., and 208-volt, three-phase A.C. Oven dimensions are $15\frac{3}{4}$ in. high, $8\frac{1}{4}$ in. wide, and $16\frac{1}{4}$ in. deep; the weight is 22 lb. It has a capacity of six frozen meal plates, one on each shelf.

The time required for thawing and reheating of the frozen meals in this oven depends principally upon the following factors:

(1) the temperature of the food; (2) the weight of each serving of each product; (3) the latent heat of the product; (4) the specific heat of the product; (5) the conductivity of the product; (6) the material used in making the plates; (7) the area of the food in contact with the plate; (8) the area of the plate in contact with the shelf.

The meat and vegetable items usually reach 170°F. (77°C.) internal temperature in about 25 min. An item which conducts heat poorly, such as fairly dry cooked rice, may take as long as 40 min. to reach this temperature.

**The REF Whirlwind Oven.**—The REF Dynamics Corp. offers an improved type of oven (Fig. 104) in which reheating of plate meals is effected

*Courtesy of REF Dynamics Corporation*

Fig. 104. The REF dynamics whirlwind oven. This oven is used in reheating frozen meals on many of the U.S. Air Force planes. The thermostatic controls and rapid air circulation combine to produce uniformly heated products.

by rapidly circulating electrically heated air. This oven has a stainless steel inner body, insulated by Fiberglas from an aluminum outer body. Air from electric heaters located behind the rear baffle is constantly circulated by a high-speed, motor-driven fan which maintains a temperature of 400° ± 10°F. (205° ± 5°C.), and which is automatically controlled by a thermostat. The thermostat may also be set to allow selection of specific heat ranges. This oven has the following inner dimensions: 8⅞ in. deep, 14¾ wide, and 11 in. high. The basic model is supplied with racks, with a capacity of 12 meals. Other racks, each holding twelve small casseroles, allow a total capacity of 24 meals per cooking cycle. The heater elements require

3,250 watts, 115 / 200 volt, 400 cycle 3-phase current. The weight of the basic model is 55 lb.

## Other Special Reheating Equipment

The Flex-Seal Speed Cooker.—This equipment is used in restaurants for the rapid thawing and reheating or cooking of frozen vegetables and certain other foods. This cooker uses steam under pressure to reheat or cook vegetables in an extraordinarily short time. The method of operation may be briefly described as follows: A source of steam supplies steam at a pressure of 20 to 25 p.s.i. A mechanical timer operates a solenoid which allows the steam to enter the cooker at a pressure of 15 lb. p.s.i. As steam enters the cooker it drives out all air through a trap that closes when the cooker is filled with saturated steam (in about 30 sec.). In approximately one minute, the pressure reaches 15 p.s.i. (temperature 250°F.; 121°C.). When the product has been reheated or cooked (a 30-oz. package of frozen peas will cook without previous defrosting in 3½ min.), a solenoid shuts off and vents the steam in the cooker into the drain, allowing the pressure to drop in 30 sec. The door now opens automatically.

Electronic or High-Frequency Dielectric Equipment.—Normal oven cooking, as we now know it, is the application of heat to the surface of a food. The surface of the food heats up and the heat is then absorbed and conducted through the food until it is cooked to the desired degree of doneness.

Electronic cooking is the utilization of high-frequency radio waves to produce heat throughout the entire mass of food, hence giving faster cooking. What happens is that the energy passing back and forth very rapidly through the food causes a molecular action that generates heat. If this energy is applied at ultra-high frequency it is called microwaves.

The RadaRange Microwave Oven.—High-frequency dielectric ovens are used in some hotel and restaurant kitchens for the very rapid reheating and / or cooking of certain products. The RadaRange (Fig. 105) delivers 1,500 watts of microwave energy: which penetrates the food from all directions and creates instantaneous heat to a depth of 2½ to 3 in., defrosting and reheating the food with amazing speed. For example, cooked fish fillets or sticks can be reheated from the frozen state to serving temperature in 1½ min.

Reheating in an electronic or microwave oven has a distinct advantage in the preparation of precooked frozen foods for the table, for by the use of this equipment it is possible to thaw and bring the food to the proper temperature for serving without browning or heating the exterior above the desired temperature.

Fig. 105.  The Rada-range microwave oven model Mark VI-ten. This oven plugs into an ordinary 115-volt line. It is designed for heating precooked sandwiches, casseroles, and similar small or medium-sized food items. Time for heating a precooked hamburger to serving temperature is 35 sec. A hot turkey sandwich would be ready in 30 sec., and barbecued pork in 40 sec. Stews and casseroles run up to 80 sec., but baked goods need only 7 sec.

*The General Electric Electronic Oven.*—One of the earlier problems encountered in the development of the electronic oven was that although the food cooked uniformly throughout, there was no exterior browning. The exterior browning, on the other hand, is highly desirable for it improves the appearance and enhances the flavor of many products. To accomplish this browning, it is therefore necessary to apply external heat to the food. In the General Electric Electronic Oven (Fig. 106), this is done by utilizing Calrod heating elements in the same manner as in the standard oven. The result is ultra-high-speed cooking with the desired browning for flavor and appearance.

In reheating frozen foods which have been precooked to the proper degree of doneness, this oven should be used solely as an electronic oven, i.e., without turning on the Calrod heating elements, so that the food can be brought to the serving temperature without overheating or browning the exterior.

*Courtesy of General Electric Co.*

Fig. 106. The General Electric Co.'s Versatronic range. The use of this oven permits conventional cooking and microwave heating at the same time, or either system of cooking, depending on the chef's desires. In it a hard frozen 8-lb. turkey can be roasted in an hour.

The utensils used in an electronic oven should be made out of glass, porcelain, ceramics, certain plastics, or other nonmetallic materials, or plastic coated aluminum foil. Metal or foil containers which have not been coated with plastic should not be used because the microwaves will tend to arc and cause the food to burn. Bare metal acts as a shield. At the same time, the nonmetallic utensils used are not affected by the high-frequency because they are of different molecular structure than food. Therefore, when ultra-high frequency is used by itself, as for thawing frozen strawberries, the dish remains cool while the fruit thaws. In fact, when ultra-high frequency only is used, the oven walls and the air in the oven do not heat up—only the food is affected.

## BIBLIOGRAPHY

Anon. Undated. Handbook of operation and maintenance instruction for the REF Whirlwind oven. REF Mfg. Corp., Mineola, N Y.

Anon. 1946. Pan American Airways is initial airline to serve precooked frozen meals. Nat'l. Provisioner *114*, No. 15, 21.

Anon. 1961. Microwave oven makes bid to capture industrial market for mass feeding. Quick Frozen Foods 23, No. 8, 217–218.

Anon. 1966. Revolutionary method of heating vegetables on top of home range. Quick Frozen Foods 28, No. 10, 50–51.

Bartholomew, J. W. 1948. Utility of high frequency heating in the frozen food industry. Quick Frozen Foods 11, No. 4, 59–61.

Bollman, M. C. 1951. Precooked frozen foods. Activities Report of Food and Container Research and Development Work of the Quartermaster Food and Container Institute 3, N.S., 260–263.

Bollman, M. C., Brenner, S., Gordon, L. E., and Lambert, M. E. 1948. Application of electronic cooking to large-scale feeding. J. Am. Dietet. Assoc. 24, 1041–1048.

Causey, K., and Fenton, F. 1951. Effect of reheating on palatability, nutritive value, and bacterial count of frozen cooked foods. I. Vegetables, J. Am. Dietet. Assoc. 27, 390–395. II. Meat dishes. Ibid. 27, 491–495.

Chatham, J. D., Guy, B. L., and Dyme, H. C. 1951. Wright Air Development Center. Wright-Patterson AFB Memorandum Rept. WCRDF-691-5B.

Eickelberg, E. W. 1950. Electronic heating for frozen foods. Quick Frozen Foods 12, No. 12, 48–49.

Gleim, E., and Fenton, F. 1949. Effect of 0°F. and 15°F. storage on the quality of frozen cooked foods. Food Technol. 3, 187–192.

Guadagni, D. G. 1961. Integrated time temperature experience as it relates to frozen food quality. ASHRAE J. 3, No. 4, 66–69, 83.

Hanson, H. L. 1954. Research makes frozen cooked poultry products a reality. Part I. Poultry Processing and Marketing 60, No. 6, 12, 20. Part II. No. 8, 17, 28–30.

Hussemann, D. L. 1951. Effect of cooking on the bacteriologic flora of selected frozen precooked foods. J. Am. Dietet. Assoc. 27, 855–858.

Ice, R. M., Longree, K., Fenton, F., and Harris, K. W. 1952. Effect of holding on bacterial count and palatability of meat loaves before and after freezing and after reheating. J. Am. Dietetic Assoc. 28, 325–330.

Kirkpatrick, M. E., Heinze, P. H., Craft, C. C., Mountjoy, B. M., and Falatko, C. E. 1956. French frying quality of potatoes as influenced by cooking methods, storage conditions, and specific gravity of tubers. U.S. Dept. Agr. Tech. Bull. 1142.

Kolb, C. 1947. The use of quick-frozen fresh and precooked foods by transportation facilities. Quick Frozen Foods 9, No. 11, 72–73.

Longree, K. 1950. Quality problems in cooked frozen potatoes. Food Technol. 4, 98–104.

Meyer, B., Moore, R., and Buckley, R. 1956. Gas production and yeast roll quality after freezer storage of fermented and unfermented doughs. Food Technol. 10, 165–168.

Rayman, M. M., Anellis, A., and Cichon, C. J. 1956. Thawing rates of precooked frozen meals in commercial shipping containers. Paper presented before the 1956 Ann. Meeting Institute of Food Technologists.

Robertson, E. L. 1955. Precooked frozen food research in the Air Force in-flight feeding program. In Precooked Frozen Foods—A Symposium. Surveys of Progress on Military Subsistence Problems. Series 1, No. 7, 4–6. Quartermaster Food and Container Institute, Chicago, Ill.

Sayles, C. I., and MacLennan, H. A. 1965. Ready Foods. Cornell Hotel and Restaurant Administration Quarterly, Research Rept. *10*.

Singer, K. M. 1946. An improved method of reheating cooked frozen foods. Quick Frozen Foods *8*, No. 9, 84–85, 128.

Straka, R. P., and Combes, F. M. 1952. Survival and multiplication of *Micrococcus pyogenes* var. *aureus,* in creamed chicken under various holding, storage, and defrosting conditions. Food Research *17*, 448–455.

Tinklin, G. L., Deck, C., Kalen, J., and Vail, G. E. 1950. Swiss steaks into the freezer and out. J. Am. Dietetic Assoc. *26*, 30–33.

Tressler, D. K. 1945. Merchandising frozen cooked foods. Ice Cream Field *46*, No. 4, 68, 76.

Vail, G. E. 1955. Precooked frozen meat products. In Precooked Frozen Foods—A Symposium. Surveys of Progress on Military Subsistence Problems, Series 1, No. 7, 11–18. Quartermaster Food and Container Institute, Chicago, Ill.

## CHAPTER 26

# The Use of Frozen Prepared and Precooked Foods in Restaurants, Hotels, and Institutions

Donald K. Tressler

## INTRODUCTION

Since World War II, frozen precooked foods have come into regular use by many restaurants, hotels, cafeterias, hospitals, schools, and military establishments.

The preparation of frozen precooked meals on a compartmented tray or platter and their use by air lines, the military, and the general public are described in Chapter 23. The preparation and use of special frozen dietary foods in hospitals, infirmaries, and institutions is considered in Chapter 15. The methods employed in preparing, packaging, and freezing each kind of food are presented in various chapters in this book. A general consideration of the storage life and optimum conditions of storage of precooked frozen foods is given in Chapter 24.

In this chapter, the advantages of the use of frozen prepared and precooked foods in restaurants, hotels, institutions, and schools are outlined. Suggestions are given, and descriptions of methods presented which may be used or are currently employed for the packaging, freezing, and thawing of these frozen foods for use in public eating establishments. The present extent of the use of these frozen foods in public eating establishments and the extent to which these foods may be used in the future are also considered.

## USE OF SPECIAL FROZEN PRODUCTS

Practically all hotels, restaurants, "diners," and institutions regularly use one or more frozen precooked foods, but only a few (particularly the chains) cook and freeze their own products. Examples of special frozen precooked items in general use by a large number of public eating establishments are "French"- or "par"-fried potatoes, winter squash, and crab meat. The particular advantages to the hotel or restaurant of the use of these frozen precooked products are presented in the sections of this book where their production is considered.

Donald K. Tressler is a consultant and President of the Avi Publishing Co., Westport, Conn.

## ADVANTAGES OF THE USE OF PRECOOKED FROZEN FOODS
### IN RESTAURANTS AND HOTELS

### For a Single Restaurant or Hotel

Labor in hotel kitchens lacks flexibility because it is not possible to arrange work schedules to coincide with the day-to-day fluctuations in sales. If frozen precooked foods are used, much labor is saved because sufficient food can be prepared, packaged, and frozen at one time for a number of meals. In the case of a large restaurant these operations can be put on a large scale or "factory" basis.

Much waste is eliminated. If servings are individually packed, the food need not be reheated in advance, but can be quickly thawed and heated to serving temperature after the patron has given the waiter his order. Thus, even though a lesser number of meals are served than anticipated, there is no loss because of unsold food which will either have to be thrown away, or made into cheaper, less desirable dishes.

Seasonal foods can be purchased, prepared, and frozen when they are low in price, and served later when they are out of season and high in price.

A much larger and more pretentious menu can be offered. This is made possible by a stock of a considerable number of frozen items which can be offered on the menu, but need not be reheated until ordered. Further, because of the stock in the freezer, patrons who come in late will not be disappointed because the supply of a particular item on the menu has been exhausted.

### For a Chain of Hotels, Restaurants, or Motels

The preparation and use of prepared and precooked frozen foods by a chain of restaurants, cafeterias or other public eating establishments has been demonstrated to be especially advantageous and profitable. The reasons why this is so are not only those listed for single establishments, but also include the following:

The work of preparation, packaging, and freezing can be carried out in one large central kitchen employing factory methods and equipment. Such an arrangement and procedure is much more economical both of labor and of management. A single high-class chef can supervise the food preparation and cooking in this central kitchen. The individual restaurants in the chain will not require a high-priced chef or chefs. Ordinary cooks can do the thawing and reheating of the foods prepared in the central kitchen and can supervise the routine operations, such as preparing beverages, making toast, preparing eggs, and cooking chops and steaks. When the work of preparation, cooking, and freezing is done in a large central kitchen, effi-

cient, labor-saving methods and equipment can be employed which eliminate many of the time-consuming laborious procedures necessary in the
preparation of food in a relatively small kitchen.

The use of precooked frozen foods is especially advantageous to a large
chain of restaurants and motels where there is a wide fluctuation from day
to day in the number of patrons. Unless precooked frozen foods are used,
there is bound to be a great loss of food whenever bad weather or any
other circumstance causes a great reduction in the number of meals served.
If frozen precooked foods are used, it usually is not necessary to remove the
food from the freezer until after the customer has ordered.

In many instances, food costs will be less because of the larger purchasing power of the central kitchen. Further, all foods frozen can be purchased when they are relatively low in price.

Another special advantage enjoyed by a restaurant chain preparing foods
on a large scale in a central kitchen is that the quantity of food being frozen is great enough to justify the use of special quick freezing equipment
which will produce a truly high-class frozen product, difficult if not impossible to distinguish from the freshly cooked food.

### SAVINGS WHICH MAY BE MADE BY SERVING COMMERCIALLY PACKED FROZEN PRECOOKED FOODS

Christian (1965) made a one-year study of the relative cost of food and
labor of a modern transient hotel when (1) the food was prepared and
served by conventional methods, and (2) when commercial frozen precooked foods were served. His results are summarized in Table 69.

Christian's conclusions are quoted below:

"(1) Food cost as a percentage of food sales did not increase when pre-prepared
frozen entrees were used. Exhibit I presents a six-month comparison of food cost
using pre-prepared entrees with figures for the preceding year when all food was
conventionally prepared. This might be attributed to less food wastage caused by
over-production and cooking errors.

(2) Payroll expense was reduced. Exhibit 2 gives a six-month payroll expense average for the pre-prepared frozen program and shows a seven per cent average
monthly reduction in labor cost in relation to food sales.

(3) Food production and service were speedier.

(4) The menu was enlarged to provide guests with a wider variety of entrees
from which to choose.

(5) Food sales increased during the pre-prepared frozen entree program. Guest
complaints were fewer than during the previous year when food was prepared by
conventional methods.

(6) Employees handling the pre-prepared entrees needed only simple culinary
skills but detailed written instructions were required for the proper preparation and
service of each item. While a cook could handle the program with little difficulty, a
chef or other supervisor was needed to oversee proper reconstitution and food merchandising."

Table 69

Relative Cost of Food and Labor in Hotel Restaurant
When Conventional Food Was Served and When
Frozen "Pre-Prepared" Entrées Were Served

| Month | Food Cost Conventional Food Preparation % of Sales | Food Cost Pre-Prepared Entrées Utilized % of Sales |
|---|---|---|
| | EXHIBIT I | |
| 1 | 39.3 | 36.5 |
| 2 | 37.0 | 42.3 |
| 3 | 38.0 | 38.8 |
| 4 | 40.2 | 37.5 |
| 5 | 38.7 | 40.4 |
| 6 | 38.5 | 43.3 |
| Average | 38.6 | 39.8 |

EXHIBIT II

| Month | Labor Cost Conventional Food Preparation % of Sales | Labor Cost Pre-Prepared Entrées Utilized % of Sales |
|---|---|---|
| 1 | 40.4 | 35.6 |
| 2 | 41.5 | 31.4 |
| 3 | 44.0 | 37.1 |
| 4 | 45.3 | 37.0 |
| 5 | 47.5 | 37.0 |
| 6 | 39.6 | 38.1 |
| Average | 43.0 | 36.0 |

Source: Christian (1965).

## PRESENT IMPORTANCE OF USE IN RESTAURANTS

Since 1950, a number of large restaurants have gone into food freezing on a large scale, selling their products through their own "carry-out" department. These restaurants, now wholesale manufacturers of frozen cooked foods, include such companies as Bickfords, Horn and Hardart, Dutch Pantry, and Schrafft of the Boston-New York-Philadelphia area, the Hot Shoppes in the Washington, D.C. area, Stouffers, John R. Thompson, and Grace Smith of the Cleveland-Toledo-Chicago area, Lawry's and Manning Inc. in the far West, and Howard Johnsons which operates in nearly all sections of the country.

Many other restaurants are freezing cooked foods either for their own use or for sale to patrons in their stores. The large companies have processing plants well equipped with the most modern freezing and packaging machinery, and maintain both laboratory and test-panel control over production. All have the know-how and ability to produce an endless variety of highly acceptable cooked foods.

## OUTSTANDING FOOD FREEZING OPERATIONS
### BY RESTAURANTS

### Mannings, Inc.

Manning's chain of restaurants and cafeterias has been successful in cutting labor costs in its kitchens, by changing to the serving of a large line of frozen precooked foods (Heinen 1966). The frozen precooked items served by this chain include all soups, all stews, all "wet dishes" (chicken pies, chicken à la king, meat balls, beef Stroganoff, etc.), and all meat substitutes (macaroni and cheese, tamale pie, ham and lima beans, tuna and noodles, etc.). The cooks in the branch kitchens prepare only the "easy to cook" items such as roasts, fish, meat loaves, spare ribs, pork chops, steak, and liver, which are not frozen.

Manning's central kitchen and food freezing plant is in Eugene, Ore.; here about 25,000 lb. of food is frozen daily. The food is packaged in boilable plastic bags each holding about 7½ lb., frozen on trays, placed on portable racks, and these are wheeled into an air-blast freezer maintained at −25°F. (−32°C.). The frozen foods are shipped to a central warehouse in Portland, Ore.

When required for serving in a cafeteria or restaurant, the foods are thawed and reheated by the "boil-in-the-bag" method in a bain marie (see Fig. 107).

### Bickfords

Another large restaurant chain that has made a success of serving precooked frozen foods is Bickfords (Anon. 1967C). The Bickford line of precooked frozen foods, served in their 250 restaurants, includes 11 soups, 20 entrées, and 12 pies. All pies are "butter treated" and frozen raw, then baked in the restaurant kitchen just before serving.

### Horn and Hardart

Horn and Hardart, the company that operates a large number of self-service restaurants called "Automats," have a new food freezing plant in Philadelphia (Anon. 1967A). Here meat and fruit pies, casseroles, dinners, cooked vegetables, and baked goods are prepared, packaged, and then frozen in air-blast tunnels.

According to Anon. (1967A) in an article in *Food Engineering*:

"Preparation, freezing, and packaging of most of these items are integrated continuous operations. Beef and chicken pies are produced on a 72-per-minute Col-

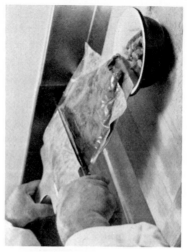

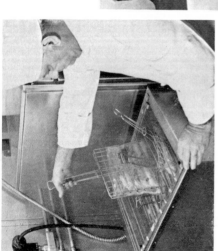

Courtesy of Cornell Hotel and Restaurant Administration Quarterly

Fig. 107. Reconstituting entrées frozen in plastic pouches. Upper, Chef Muller demonstrates the boil-in-a-bag method of reconstituting Ready Foods. A laboratory model hot water bath is shown with the food bags held immersed with long-handled holders. Final equipment will have an automatic timing device to withdraw each bag at the proper moment for a particular item, thus reducing labor and errors. In the background is a microwave oven; middle, the heated pouch can readily be held at the top when the food inside has settled to the bottom. The tool used to push food through the bag's slit bottom works like a pair of scissors with round blades. The food is easily and completely emptied from the bag; lower, food of a sticky nature is packaged in pouches with sealed corners, shown at right. The bottom of the pouch is slit, the bag laid on a shaped board and the food pushed into the small casserole with the back of a knife.

borne line complete with top-crust unit, crimper, docker, and weight classifier. In another section of the spacious preparation area, casserole items, such as macaroni and cheese, creamed spinach, and baked beans are prepared on a dual 72-per-minute line. This system employs Elgin fillers, lidders, and checkweighers."

"Thus, pie and casserole items can be produced simultaneously and conveyed to an overhead −40°F. (−40°C.) freezing tunnel built into an adjacent −10°F. holding room. This is accomplished by a Spivey elevating conveyor system with 6 to 8° slope. Conveyor sections from each of the product lines converge into a double-tier conveyor leading to the freezer. A similar double-tier discharge section conveys frozen goods back to the preparation area for cartoning and casing. Cases then go to the −10°F. (−23°C.) room for storage."

Because of a variation in weight, shape, method of packaging, etc., there is a difference in the time required for freezing, e.g., beef pies require 72 min., dinners 51 min., casseroles 85 min., and fruit pies 55 min.

## Schrafft's

Schrafft's, a restaurant chain specializing in high quality and gourmet foods, is serving a large proportion of frozen precooked entrées and other items prepared and frozen in their Winchester, Va., plant where they prepare, package, and freeze annually a grand total of 5,000,000 lb. of 70 different items. Some of the most popular of these are beef Burgundy, old-fashioned creamed chicken on flaky biscuit, lamb stew with vegetables, spaghetti with Italian meat sauce, fried Florida shrimp, fried bay scallops, with sauce tartare, fried Alaska King crab cakes with pimiento cream sauce, and chopped beefsteak parmigiana.

Prepared frozen dinners are served in the 50 restaurants of the Schrafft's chain—35 of these in the New York metropolitan area and the others ranging from Massachusetts to Florida.

The method of thawing and reheating the foods has been described as follows (Anon. 1967B):

"At the restaurant, the foods are stored in a walk-in freezer, which can hold a week's supply. From here they are fed to the reach-in freezer located near the ovens, as needed for each meal. A convection oven reconstitutes the frozen, prepared items. Portioned, they are set in serving dishes and placed in a warmer. When a waitress gets an order, she sets the portioned food in a serving dish in a microwave oven for as long as the time programmed for that product. Three minutes is the most any item needs to reach a high temperature and arrive piping hot at the guest's table."

## School Lunches

In an experimental test of the use of frozen precooked foods for school lunches (Anon. 1966B), 920 students of Brooklyn Public School No. 45 were daily given a lunch consisting principally of precooked frozen foods. The following are representative menus: (1) turkey croquettes with cran-

berry sauce, garden peas, and sliced pineapple; (2) beef and pork patty
with gravy, steamed rice, and fruit; (3) hot pizza with tomato sauce and
bologna, deep dish apple pie; (4) frankfurter, baked beans, sauerkraut,
plums; and (5) fish burger, whole kernel corn, buttered green beans, cole
slaw, lemon cream cake. Bread and butter were also served with the
lunches.

The method of reheating and serving these lunches was as follows:

"About 10 a.m. the kitchen helpers pull out the day's supply of what is needed
from the freezer. Food is heated directly from the frozen state in 20–25 min. and is
then wheeled on dollies into electrically heated holding cabinets, and is pulled out
pan by pan as needed. Disposable service including aquamarine trays and white-
paper plates with a green design is used. The trays are placed on a conveyor belt
inside the kitchen and are picked up by the students at an open window."

According to the writer (Anon. 1966C), cost comparisons made with conventional operations using the same menus showed an appreciable reduction in total cost per meal. Savings were reported in handling, preparation,
cleaning, and wastage. A 40% reduction in labor costs was indicated.

## FUTURE POSSIBILITIES

Benefits through food freezing and the use of frozen cooked foods will
become a "must" in the competitive public feeding establishment of tomorrow. These include greater output per man-hour with the concomitant
reduction of labor costs; adequate stocks of a wide variety of products
ready for prompt service, stored without fear of loss or deterioration for
normal storage periods; continuous uniformity of high quality, delectable
dishes; economy of space; perfect inventory and portion control; and more
satisfied patrons—greater sales volume—more profit.

## BIBLIOGRAPHY

Anon.   1954. Quick freezing of foods saves time, money. Am. Restaurant Maga-
zine 38, No. 9, 57.
Anon.   1956A. Frozen potatoes big hit with institutions. Quick Frozen Foods 18,
No. 10, 155.
Anon.   1956B. Let "Idaho Russ" solve your restaurant problems. Unnumbered
Brochure. J. R. Simplot Co., Caldwell, Idaho.
Anon.   1965. French chef dedicated to finest cuisine converts Pan-Am to frozen
entrées. Quick Frozen Foods 27, No. 6, 107–108.
Anon.   1966A. Ready prepared frozen foods. Volume Feeding Management 26,
No. 1, 36–37.
Anon.   1966B. Bulk frozen products end kitchens for New York school lunches.
Quick Frozen Foods 29, No. 3, 141–143.
Anon.   1966C. Frozen prepared entrées allow feeding of 800 more students with-
out extra help. Quick Frozen Foods 29, No. 4, 93–96.
Anon.   1967A. Optimizes multiproduct freezing. Food Eng. 39, No. 1, 80–81.

Anon. 1967B. Schrafft's reveal 65% of entrées have been frozen for two years. Quick Frozen Foods 29, No. 7, 133–136.

Anon. 1967C. Bickford's 250 restaurants serve 70% of all food from frozen state. Quick Frozen Foods 29, No. 8, 83–85.

Anon. 1967D. And leave the cooking to us. Cooking for Profit 36, No. 196, 43.

Anon. 1967E. Variations on a frozen entrée. Cooking for Profit 36, No. 196, 44–47.

Anon. 1967F. Universities build large capacity frozen food storage warehouses. Quick Frozen Foods 29, No. 8, 107–108.

Anon. 1967G. "Ready foods" systems to enable feeders to use frozen, researched at Cornell. Part 1. Quick Frozen Foods 29, No. 12, 107–108, 110. Part 2. Methods of utilizing frozen foods to ease mass-feeding costs, Ibid. 30, No. 1, 125–127.

Bitting, H. W. 1955. The use of frozen foods by restaurants and cafeterias. U.S. Dept. Agr., Agr. Marketing Service, Marketing Service Div. Unnumbered report dated March 16.

Christian, V. A. 1963. Why frozen meals are needed in university cafeterias. Quick Frozen Foods 26, No. 1, 117, 123.

Christian, V. A. 1965. Commercially prepared frozen entrées. Cornell Hotel and Restaurant Administration Quarterly 5, No. 3, 89, 99.

Dana, A. W. 1944. What restaurants want in frozen foods. Quick Frozen Foods 6, No. 11, 30, 38, 60, 73.

Heinen, D. 1966. Dramatic change: Customer satisfaction remains crux of continuing success. Volume Feeding Management 26, No. 1, 60–68.

Logan, P. P. 1955. Analysis of the extent of use of frozen foods by 45 restaurant companies. Nat'l. Restaurant Assoc. Unnumbered Rept. dated March 1.

Jones, P. 1966. Distinctive food programming. Volume Feeding Management 26, No. 1, 60–68.

Salmon, J. 1956. Private communication. Lyons Ltd., London, England.

Sayles, C. I., and Mac Lennan, H. A. 1965. Ready foods. Cornell Hotel and Restaurant Administration Quarterly Research Rept. 10.

Thome, W. J. 1963. Frozen prepared foods used by Holiday Inns. Cornell Hotel and Restaurant Administration Quarterly 4, No. 1, 20–21.

Wade, D. 1967. Convenience in action. Cooking for Profit 36, No. 196, 37–42.

Weber, E. S. 1965. Package for profits. Cornell Hotel and Restaurant Administration Quarterly 6, No. 1, 29–36.

# Index

strawberry recipe, 475–477
vanilla, 473
freezing, 470–471
temperature, 470–471
hardening, 471–472
ingredients, 462–464
emulsifiers, 463–464
milkfat, 462–463
stabilizers, 463–464
sweeteners, 463–464
mix, ageing, 470
composition, 464–465
homogenization, 468–469
pasteurization, 467–468
continuous method, 467–468
production, statistics, 460–461
steps, 465–472
soft serve, 473
Ice cream freezer, batch, 470
continuous, 470–471
Ice milk, definition, 483
formula, 483
Infant foods, freezing, 338–339
frozen, nutritive value, 339–340
preparation, 329–340
vegetables, 333–334
Insecticides, in foods, off-flavors from,
139–140
Interviews, personal, value in consumer
surveys, 98
Italian foods, frozen, methods of preparing,
356–358

**J**

Jam, frozen, preparation, 197–203
Jellies, frozen, preparation, 197–203
Jewish foods, frozen, 353–354
early production, 19

**K**

Kidney stew frozen, preparation, 257–258
Knishes, frozen, nature, 354
Kosher foods, *See* Jewish foods
Kreplash, frozen, nature, 353

**L**

Lamb, pot pies, frozen, regional use, 256
stew, frozen, preparation, 257
Laminated aluminum foil, containers, for
frozen foods, 120–121
Lasagne, frozen, preparation, 358
Lima beans, precooked, storage life, 232
Liver strained with vegetables, frozen
preparation for infant food, 338
Lobster, chowder, frozen, preparation, 156
Newburg, frozen, preparation, 311
thermidor, frozen, preparation, 311
Lobsters, cooking, 310
Lunches, school, use of precooked frozen
foods, 557–558

**M**

Maleic hydrazide, use, to prevent sprouting
of potatoes, 215
Mannings, Inc. food freezing operations, 555
Meals, frozen, 512–521
Air Force, U.S., 518
airlines, 517–518
menus offered, 518–519
components, gravy, 515
green vegetable, 514
ham, 514
potatoes, 514
sauces, 515
stable, 516
convenience, 513
Maxson, kinds, 512
preparation, 516, 520
problems, 513–516
reheating problems, 513–515
variety of menus packed, 516
Meat, freezing problems, 252–253
precooked, frozen, bacterial flora, 253
rancidity control, 253
precooking, destruction of bacteria, 253
for freezing, 251–267
Meat entrées, variety available, 251–252
Meat pies, definition, 10
frozen, consumer survey of use, 100–102
military specification, 253–254
preparation, 253–255
production, early, 10–11
Meat stews, frozen, distribution, 256–258
strained, frozen, preparation for infant
food, 337
Meat sticks, breaded, frozen, preparation,
264
Meats, synthetic, frozen, possibilities, 28
Mellorine, definition, 485–486
formulas, 485–486
MENA, use, to prevent sprouting of potatoes,
215
Mexican foods, frozen, early production,
19–20
preparation, 354–356
Microbial contamination, of precooked
frozen foods,
by equipment, 78–79
by facilities, 78–79
by ingredients, 78–79
by people, 78–79
by processing, 82–84
by thawing, 84–85
source of, 78–84
Microbiological examination, of precooked
frozen foods, 59–68
Microwave ovens, General Electric
"Electronic," for reheating frozen
precooked foods, 547–548
Raytheon RadaRange, for reheating frozen
precooked foods, 546–547
Milk, frozen, imitation, formula, 487